Pearson

BTEC National

Sport and Exercise Science

Student Book

Mark Adams
Dale Forsdyke
Adam Gledhill
Amy Gledhill
Chris Lydon
Chris Manley
Louise Sutton
Richard Taylor

Published by Pearson Education Limited, 80 Strand, London, WC2R 0RL.

www.pearsonschoolsandfecolleges.co.uk

Copies of official specifications for all Edexcel qualifications may be found on the website: www.edexcel.com

Edited by Rob Crane
Page design by Andy Magee
Typeset by Tech-Set Ltd
Original illustrations © Pearson Education Ltd
Illustrated by Tech-Set Ltd
Cover design by Vince Haig
Picture research by Susie Prescott
Cover photo/illustration © Oleksandr Briagin / Shutterstock.com

The rights of Mark Adams, Dale Forsdyke, Adam Gledhill, Amy Gledhill, Chris Lydon, Chris Manley, Louise Sutton and Richard Taylor to be identified as authors of this work have been asserted by them in accordance with the Copyright, Designs and Patents Act 1988.

First published 2016

24
10

British Library Cataloguing in Publication Data
A catalogue record for this book is available from the British Library

ISBN 978 1 292 13395 9

Printed and bound by CPI Group (UK) Ltd, Croydon, CR0 4YY

Acknowledgements
The publisher would like to thank the following for their kind permission to reproduce their photographs:

(Key: b-bottom; c-centre; l-left; r-right; t-top)

123RF.com: arekmalang 266tl, Marcin Ciesielski 161br, racorn 291tr; **Alamy Images:** Aflo Co., Ltd 79, Blend Images 265tr, Dave & Les Jacobs / Blend Images 160tl, dpa picture alliance archive 96br, Ian Francis 326br, Image Source 125tr, ITAR-TASS Photo Agency 221, Juice Images 169b, pa european pressphoto agency b.v. 20tr, PCN Photography 387, Radius Images 208bl, Zoonar GmbH 214tr; **Courtesy of Premier League:** 341bl; **DJO UK Ltd:** 418tl; **Food Standards Agency:** © Crown copyright 2016 366; **Fotolia.com:** Cesar Romero 143b, Dan Race 194tl, Kadmy 343tr, Kalim / Fotolia 307b, leungchopan 240tl, Monkey Business 204cl, pixelheadphoto 116tr, Sebastian Kaulitzki 39, .shock 277c, Syda Productions 250t, sylv1rob1 292tl, travelbook 345, WavebreakmediaMicro 29bl, 121, 267, Zdenka Darula 239tr; **Getty Images:** Aflo 241, AFP 33t, Bob Thomas / Popperfoto 327br, Bryn Lennon 199tl, Clive Brunskill 246bl, Dan Mullan 91tr, David Madison / Photographers Choice 134bl, Dennis Grombkowski 90cl, Franck Fife / AFP 73br, Fuse / Corbis 276cl, Gary Dineen / NBAE 110tl, Glyn Kirk / AFP 73tr, 111cr, Inti St Clair / Digital Vision 195, JEWEL SAMAD / AFP 319, Lars Baron 138cl, LIONEL BONAVENTURE / AFP 376b, Loic Venance / AFP 83t, londoneye 219tr, Media for Medical / UIG 422tl, Mike Tittel / Cultura RM 1, Paul Faith / AFP 310t, Richard Martin / AFP 324br, Science Photo Library 155, Scott Barbour 339br, Sean Garnsworthy 373t, Shaun Botterill 73cr; **Hypoxico Inc:** 31b; **Pearson Education Ltd:** Studio 8 293, 318tl, Jon Barlow 317tr, Gareth Boden 154tl; **Press Association Images:** Carlos Osorio / AP 75cl, Jae C. Hong / AP 94bl; **Prozone Sports (www.prozonesports.stats.com):** 253tl; **Shutterstock.com:** Africa Studio 356bl, Alberto Zornetta 153tr, arek_malang 287br, Dziurek 201cr, Hogan Imaging 344tl, Hurst Photo 347bl, Jaimie Duplass 193tr, Jiang Dao Hua 255bl, Juriah Mosin 427tr, Kaliva 209cr, Maxisport 246bc, michaeljung 35tr, mooinblack 101tl, Robert Kneshke 273b, Teodor Ostojic 323bl, wavebreakmedia 220tl, XiXinXing 76tr, ZouZou 428tl; **Sport England:** 330bl

All other images © Pearson Education

The authors and publisher would like to thank the following individuals and organisations for permission to reproduce their materials:

p.84: Self-determination theory. Ryan, R. and Deci, E. (2000) Intrinsic and Extrinsic Motivations: Classic Definitions and New Directions. *Contemporary Educational Psychology* 25: 54–67. Produced by Elsevier Science & Technology Journals. Reproduced by permission of Elsevier via Rightslink; **p.97:** Extract from Bandura, A. (1977) Self-efficacy: Toward a unifying theory of behavioural change. *Psychological Review*, 84(2): 191–215. Published by the American Psychological Association. Used by permission of the American Psychological Association via Rightslink; **p.106, Figure 3.8:** Extract from Chelladurai's multidimensional model of sport leadership, by Professor Chelladurai. Used with kind permission of Packianathan Chelladurai; **p.131:** From Durnin, J.V.G.A. and Womersley, J. (1974). Body fat assessed from the total body density and its estimation from skinfold thickness: measurements on 481 men and women aged from 16 to 72 years. *British Journal of Nutrition*, 32, 77–97. Published by Cambridge University Press. Reproduced with permission of Cambridge University Press via Rightslink; **p.132:** Extract from Brozek, J., Grande, F., Anderson, T. and Keys, A. (1963) Densitometric analysis of body composition: Revision of some quantitative assumptions. *Ann N Y Acad Sci* 26(110): 113–40. Published by John Wiley and Sons. Reproduced by John Wiley and Sons via Rightslink; **p.133, Figure 4.2:** Nomogram for predicting body fat in males and females. Wilmore, J. H. (1986) *Sensible Fitness*, Champaign, IL: Human Kinetics. Used by kind permission of the author's estate; **p.133:** Extract from Sloan, A., Burt A. and Blyth C. (1962) Estimating body fat in young women. *J. Appl. Physiol.* 17: 967–970. Published by The American Physiological Society. Used by permission of The American Physiological Society via Rightslink; **p.136, Figure 4.3:** Heath-Carter's (1967) anthropometric somatotype rating form. Carter, J.E.L. and Heath, B. H. (1990) *Somatotyping: Development and Applications*, Cambridge. Copyright © Cambridge University Press 1990, reproduced with permission of Cambridge University Press; **p.137:** The somatochart shows 13 somatotype categories. Carter, J.E.L. and Heath, B. H. (1990) *Somatotyping: Development and Applications*, Cambridge. Copyright © Cambridge University Press 1990, reproduced with permission; **p.138:** Heath-Carter's somatotype chart. Carter, J.E.L. and Heath, B. H. (1990) *Somatotyping: Development and Applications*, Cambridge. Copyright © Cambridge University Press 1990, reproduced with permission; **p.182:** Table of critical values for Spearman's rank order correlation. Vincent, W.J. (1999) *Statistics in Kinesiology*, 2nd edition, Champaign, IL: Human Kinetics. Used with permission of Human Kinetics; **p.272:** Extract from Karvonen, J. and Vuorimaa, T. (1988) Heart rate and exercise intensity during sports activities: Practical application. *Sports Medicine* 5(5): 303–11. Published by Springer. Reproduced with permission of Springer via Rightslink; **p.330:** Extract from This Girl Can: http://www.thisgirlcan.co.uk/. Used by courtesy of Sport England's 'This Girl Can' campaign; **p.333:** Data from: www.gov.uk/government/uploads/system/uploads/attachment_data/file/379986/National_20Governing_20Bodies_20of_20Sport_20survey_2C_20Competitive_20school_20sport.pdf. Copyright © Crown Copyright 2016; **p.349:** Prediction equations can be used to estimate basal metabolic rate. Harris, J.A. and Benedict, F.G. (1918) A Biometric Study of Human Basal Metabolism. *Proceedings of the National Academy of Sciences of the United States of America* 4(12): 370–373. Reproduced with permission of Carnegie Science; **p.349:** To predict total daily energy requirements. Harris, J.A. and Benedict, F.G. (1918) A Biometric Study of Human Basal Metabolism. *Proceedings of the National Academy of Sciences of the United States of America*

4(12): 370–373. Reproduced with permission of Carnegie Science; **p.352:** BMI classifications based on World Health Organization's International Classification of Adult Underweight, Overweight and Obesity. Copyright © WHO. Used with permission of the World Health Organization; **p.366:** Public Health England in association with the Welsh Government, Food Standards Scotland and the Food Standards Agency in Northern Ireland. Adapted from The Eatwell Guide. Copyright © Crown Copyright 2016; **p.367, Figure 13.5:** Public Health England in association with the Welsh Government, Food Standards Scotland and the Food Standards Agency in Northern Ireland. Copyright © Crown Copyright 2016; **p.371:** Extract from International Olympic Committee: Maughan, R. and Burke, L. (2012) Nutrition for Athletes: A practical guide to eating for health and performance, *Nutrition Working Group of the International Olympic Committee.* Used with permission of the International Olympic Committee; **p.399:** Stress and Injury Model. Williams, J. and Andersen, M. (1998) Psychosocial Antecedents of Sport Injury: Review and Critique of the Stress and Injury Model. *Journal of Applied Sport Psychology* 10: 5–25. Published by Taylor & Francis. Used by permission of Taylor & Francis via Rightslink; **p.400:** Reprinted with the permission of Scribner, a division of Simon & Schuster, Inc. from *On Death and Dying* by Dr. Elisabeth Kübler-Ross. Copyright © 1969 by Elisabeth Kübler-Ross; copyright renewed © 1997 by Elisabeth Kübler-Ross. All rights reserved. **p.400:** Extract from Udry, E., Gould, D., Bridges, D. and Beck, L. (1997) Down but not out: Athletic responses to season-ending ski injuries. *Journal of Sport and Exercise Psychology*, 3: 229-248. by Human Kinetics. Reproduced with permission of Human Kinetics in the format Book via Copyright Clearance Centre; **p.401:** Extract from Brewer, B. (1994) Review and critique of models of psychological adjustment to athletic injury. *Journal of Applied Sport Psychology*, 6: 87–100. Published by Taylor & Francis. Used by permission of Taylor & Francis via Rightslink; **p.401, Figure 15.4:** Cognitive Appraisal Model. Brewer, B. (1994) Review and critique of models of psychological adjustment to athletic injury. *Journal of Applied Sport Psychology*, 6: 87–100. Published by Taylor & Francis. Used by permission of Taylor & Francis via Rightslink; **p.401:** Extract from Wiese-bjornstal, D., Smith, A., Shaffer, S. and Morrey, M. (1998) An integrated model of response to sport injury: Psychological and sociological dynamics, *Journal of Applied Sport Psychology*, 10(1): 46–69. Published by Taylor & Francis. Used by permission of Taylor & Francis via Rightslink; **p.409, Figure 15.6:** Extract from Van Mechelen, W., Hlobil, H. and Kemper, H. (1992) Incidence, Severity, Aetiology and Prevention of Sports Injuries: A Review of Concepts. *Sports Medicine* 14(2): 82–99. Reproduced with permission of Springer via Rightslink.

Websites

Pearson Education Limited is not responsible for the content of any external internet sites. It is essential for tutors to preview each website before using it in class so as to ensure that the URL is still accurate, relevant and appropriate. We suggest that tutors bookmark useful websites and consider enabling students to access them through the school/college intranet.

A note from the publisher

In order to ensure that this resource offers high-quality support for the associated Pearson qualification, it has been through a review process by the awarding body. This process confirms that this resource fully covers the teaching and learning content of the specification or part of a specification at which it is aimed. It also confirms that it demonstrates an appropriate balance between the development of subject skills, knowledge and understanding, in addition to preparation for assessment.

Endorsement does not cover any guidance on assessment activities or processes (e.g. practice questions or advice on how to answer assessment questions), included in the resource nor does it prescribe any particular approach to the teaching or delivery of a related course.

While the publishers have made every attempt to ensure that advice on the qualification and its assessment is accurate, the official specification and associated assessment guidance materials are the only authoritative source of information and should always be referred to for definitive guidance.

Pearson examiners have not contributed to any sections in this resource relevant to examination papers for which they have responsibility.

Examiners will not use endorsed resources as a source of material for any assessment set by Pearson.

Endorsement of a resource does not mean that the resource is required to achieve this Pearson qualification, nor does it mean that it is the only suitable material available to support the qualification, and any resource lists produced by the awarding body shall include this and other appropriate resources.

Contents

How to use this book

Welcome to your BTEC National Sport and Exercise Science course!

A BTEC National in Sport and Exercise Science is one of the most exciting and engaging BTEC courses. It is a vocational qualification that will help prepare you for a huge range of careers. You may be thinking of pursuing a career as a coach. At present, there are around 1.2 million coaches in Britain. You may be considering a career in sports science or therapy – there are opportunities in a huge range of sports throughout the country, to support athletes and non-professionals with everything from psychological preparation, to recovering from injury. Sports science is also an industry with many opportunities to lead and participate in research projects, covering many different areas of physical and psychological well-being.

Research shows a clear link between an active lifestyle and good health. As a result, the sports industry has grown significantly over the last 10 years, and will probably continue to grow. There is a demand for exercise professionals and there are good employment opportunities, some of which you will find out more about in this book.

How your BTEC is structured

Your BTEC National is divided into **mandatory units** (the ones you must do) and **optional units** (the ones you can choose to do).

The number of mandatory and optional units will vary depending on the type of BTEC National you are doing. This book supports all the mandatory units and the most popular optional units to allow you to complete the:

- Diploma
- Extended Diploma.

Your learning experience

You are the person most responsible for your own learning experience so you must understand what you are learning, why you are learning it and why it is important both to your course and to your personal development. Your learning can be seen as a journey with four phases.

Phase 1	Phase 2	Phase 3	Phase 4
You are introduced to a topic or concept and you start to develop an awareness of what learning is required.	You explore the topic or concept through different methods (e.g. research, questioning, analysis, deep thinking, critical evaluation) and form your own understanding.	You apply your knowledge and skills to a task designed to test your understanding.	You reflect on your learning, evaluate your efforts, identify gaps in your knowledge and look for ways to improve.

During each phase, you will use different learning strategies to secure the core knowledge and skills you need. This student book has been written using similar learning principles, strategies and tools. It has been designed to support your learning journey, to give you control over your own learning, and to equip you with the knowledge, understanding and tools you need to be successful in your future studies or career.

Features of this book

This student book contains many different features. They are there to help you learn about key topics in different ways and understand them from multiple perspectives. Together, these features:

- explain what your learning is about
- help you to build your knowledge
- help you to understand how to succeed in your assessment
- help you to reflect on and evaluate your learning
- help you to link your learning to the workplace.

Each individual feature has a specific purpose, designed to support important learning strategies. For example, some features will:

- encourage you to question assumptions about what you are learning
- help you to think beyond what you are reading about
- help you to make connections between different areas of your learning
- draw comparisons between your own learning and real-world workplace environments
- help you to develop some of the important skills you will need for the workplace, including team work, effective communication and problem solving.

Features that explain what your learning is about

Getting to know your unit

This section introduces the unit and explains how you will be assessed. It gives an overview of what will be covered and will help you to understand why the content is relevant.

Getting started

This feature appears at the start of every unit and is designed to get you thinking about the unit and what it involves. It will also help you to identify what you may already know about some of the topics in the unit and act as a starting point for understanding the skills and knowledge you will need to develop to complete the unit.

Features that help you to build your knowledge

Research

This asks you to research a topic in greater depth. These features will help to expand your understanding of a topic and develop your research and investigation skills. All of this will be invaluable for your future progression, both professionally and academically.

Worked example

Worked examples show the process you need to follow to solve a problem, such as a maths or science equation. They will help you to develop your understanding and your numeracy and literacy skills.

Theory into practice

In this feature, you will be asked to consider the workplace or industry implications of a topic or concept from the unit. This will help you to understand the relevance of your current learning and the ways in which it may affect a future career in your chosen sector.

Discussion

Discussion features encourage you to talk to other students about a topic, working together to increase your understanding of the topic and to understand other people's perspectives on an issue. These features will also help to build your teamworking skills, which will be invaluable in your future professional and academic career.

Safety tip

These tips give advice about health and safety when working on the unit. They will help to build your knowledge about best practice in the workplace, as well as making sure that you stay safe.

Key terms

Concise and simple definitions are provided for key words, phrases and concepts, giving you, at a glance, a clear understanding of the key ideas in each unit.

Link

Link features show any links between content in different units or within the same unit, helping you to identify knowledge you have learned elsewhere that will help you to achieve the requirements of the unit. Remember, although your BTEC National is made up of several units, there are common themes that are explored from different perspectives across the whole of your course.

Further reading and resources

This feature lists other resources – such as books, journals, articles or websites – you can use to expand your knowledge of the unit content. This is a good opportunity for you to take responsibility for your own learning and prepare for research tasks you may need to complete academically or professionally.

Features connected to your assessment

Your course is made up of mandatory and optional units. There are two different types of mandatory unit:

- externally assessed
- internally assessed.

The features that support you in preparing for assessment are below. But first, what is the difference between these two different types of unit?

Externally assessed units

These units will give you the opportunity to demonstrate your knowledge and understanding, or your skills, in a direct way. For these units you will complete a task, set directly by Pearson, in controlled conditions. This could take the form of an exam or it could be another type of task. You may have the opportunity to prepare in advance, to research and make notes about a topic which can be used when completing the assessment.

Internally assessed units

Most of your units will be internally assessed and will involve you completing a series of assignments, set and marked by your tutor. The assignments you complete will allow you to demonstrate your learning in a number of different ways, from a written report to a presentation to a video recording and observation statements of you completing a practical task. Whatever the method, you will need to make sure you have clear evidence of what you have achieved and how you did it.

Assessment practice

These features give you the opportunity to practise some of the skills you will need during the unit assessment. They do not fully reflect the actual assessment tasks but will help you to prepare for them.

Plan – Do – Review

You will also find handy advice on how to plan, complete and evaluate your work. This is designed to get you thinking about the best way to complete your work and to build your skills and experience before doing the actual assessment. These questions will prompt you to think about the way you work and why particular tasks are relevant.

Getting ready for assessment

For internally assessed units, this is a case study of a BTEC National student, talking about how they planned and carried out their assignment work and what they would do differently if they were to do it again. It will give you advice on preparing for your internal assessments, including Think about it points for you to consider for your own development.

Getting ready for assessment

This section will help you to prepare for external assessment. It gives practical advice on preparing for and sitting exams or a set task. It provides a series of sample answers for the types of question you will need to answer in your external assessment, including guidance on the good points of these answers and ways in which they could be improved.

Features to help you reflect on and evaluate your learning

PAUSE POINT Pause Points appear regularly throughout the book and provide opportunities to review and reflect on your learning. The ability to reflect on your own performance is a key skill you will need to develop and use throughout your life, and will be essential whatever your future plans are.

Hint **Extend** These sections give you suggestions to help cement your knowledge and indicate other areas you can look at to expand it.

Features which link your learning with the workplace

Case study

Case studies throughout the book will allow you to apply the learning and knowledge from the unit to a scenario from the workplace or industry. Case studies include questions to help you consider the wider context of a topic. They show how the course content is reflected in the real world and help you to build familiarity with issues you may find in a real-world workplace.

THINK FUTURE

This is a case study in which someone working in the industry talks about their job role and the skills they need. The *Focusing your skills* section suggests ways for you to develop the employability skills and experiences you will need to be successful in a career in your chosen sector. This will help you to identify what you could do, inside and outside your BTEC National studies, to build up your employability skills.

About the authors

Mark Adams

Mark is a senior standards verifier for the QCF and NQF BTEC Sport qualifications and has worked for Pearson for over 10 years. He has taught BTEC qualifications in schools and colleges and most recently in an elite sports environment. Mark is currently Head of Education at a Premier League football club. He has contributed as a writer and series editor to a number of BTEC Sport text books at Level 2 and Level 3.

Dale Forsdyke

Dale Forsdyke has over 12 years of teaching experience and is a senior lecturer in Sports Injury Management at York St John University. He has previously written text books on sports therapy and his research has been published in practitioner- and peer-reviewed journals. Alongside teaching, Dale is a practising sports therapist (MSST) and has the role of Head of Science and Medicine in a Tier One Regional Talent Club. He has also worked in Women's Super League (WSL) football and for the Football Association.

Adam Gledhill

Adam has 15 years' experience working within further and higher education. He works within qualification development for Pearson and is a co-author of previous editions of this book. Adam has experience of providing interdisciplinary sport science support to different athlete populations; from youth and senior international football players, to youth athletes in a range of sports. Among his consultancy roles, he has worked as Head of Sport Science for an FA Women's Super League team and as Head of Psychosocial Development for a Football Association Licensed Girls' Football Centre of Excellence.

Amy Gledhill

Amy Gledhill is the course leader for Sport and Exercise Sciences at a Further Education college and has taught BTEC Sport qualifications for 6 years, following the completion of an MSc in Sport and Exercise Physiology. She has experience working with a range of athletes across football and track and field athletics, including as Head of Sport Science for a regional Cerebral Palsy Football Centre of Excellence.

Chris Lydon

Chris has worked in further and higher education for twenty years as a senior sports science lecturer specialising in anatomy and physiology and fitness training. He has also worked as an external standards verifier for Pearson and an external examiner for a number of universities. He is currently employed as an Assistant Principal at a large FE college where he is responsible for the recruitment and support of staff and students. Chris has previously written a number of books relating to BTEC sports qualifications.

Chris Manley

Chris splits his time between roles as a Postgraduate Education Tutor at Canterbury Christ Church University and as a Senior Practitioner at an FE college. Chris has been a National League basketball coach, tutor and referee and was a successful slalom canoeist. He has a Master's degree in Education and postgraduate qualifications in the sociology of sport, and works in a variety of roles related to BTEC for Pearson. Chris has published for BTEC and for teaching professionals studying teaching qualifications.

Louise Sutton

Louise is a principal lecturer in sport and exercise nutrition at Leeds Beckett University. She has a particular interest in the practical application of sport dietetics in elite environments over the past 20 years, having advised elite athletes from a range of professional sports. She has extensive experience in delivering nutrition education programmes to support junior athlete development and was recently awarded the British Dietetic Association's Roll of Honour for her contribution to the development of the Sport and Exercise Nutrition Register.

Richard Taylor

Richard is a former rower and personal trainer with several years of experience in teaching Further and Higher Education sports programmes and PE in schools. Currently a tutor for Gillingham FC's academy, Richard has worked with a number of professional football clubs, written several higher education sports programmes and contributed to previous editions of this book.

Sport and Exercise Physiology 1

Getting to know your unit

Assessment

This unit is assessed by an examination that is set and marked by Pearson.

When your body is doing little physical activity, your oxygen and energy demands are low and are easily met by shallow breathing and a low pulse rate. The blood circulating around your system delivers glucose and oxygen to your cells and takes away waste products, such as carbon dioxide.

But if you were to get up and run around a sports field, significant changes would take place. To fuel this activity, your body must adapt quickly and it does so in a variety of ways involving many processes. This unit is designed to examine these processes and their implications for sports performance.

How you will be assessed

This unit will be assessed externally using an examination set by Pearson. The paper will contain a number of short- and long-answer questions that will assess your understanding of exercise physiology in both normal conditions and in different environmental conditions.

As the guidelines for assessment can change, you should refer to the official assessment guidance on the Pearson Qualifications website for the latest definitive guidance.

Throughout this unit you will find activities that will help you work towards your assessment. Completing these activities will not mean that you have achieved a particular grade, but you will have carried out useful research or preparation that will help you later when you do your external assessment.

This unit has four Assessment Outcomes (AO) which will be included in the external examination. Certain 'command words' are associated with each assessment outcome (see Table 1.1).

- **AO1** Demonstrate knowledge and understanding of body systems and how they respond and adapt to exercise in different environments
  - Command words: identify, describe, give, state/name, explain
  - Marks: range from 1–5 marks
- **AO2** Apply knowledge and understanding of body systems and how they respond and adapt to exercise in different environments in context
  - Command words: describe, explain
  - Marks: range from 1–5 marks
- **AO3** Analyse sports performance data to interpret the body's responses and adaptations to exercise and evaluate their impact on sport and exercise performance
  - Command words: analyse, assess, evaluate, discuss
  - Marks: 10 marks
- **AO4** Make connections between how the body systems work together in response to the demands of sport and exercise and to enhance performance
  - Command words: analyse, assess, evaluate, discuss
  - Marks: 10 marks

Table 1.1: Command words used in this unit

Command word	Definition – what it is asking you to do
Analyse	Identify several relevant facts of a topic, demonstrate how they are linked and then explain the importance of each, often in relation to the other facts.
Assess	Evaluate or estimate the nature, ability, or quality of something.
Describe	Give a full account of all the information, including all the relevant details of any features, of a topic.
Discuss	Write about the topic in detail, taking into account different ideas and opinions.
Evaluate	Bring all the relevant information you have on a topic together and make a judgement on it (for example, its success or importance). Judgements should be clearly supported.
Explain	Make an idea, situation or problem clear to your reader, by describing it in detail, including any relevant data or facts.
Give	Provide examples, justifications and/or reasons to a context.
Identify	State the key fact(s) about a topic or subject. The word *outline* is similar.
State/name	Give a definition or example.

Getting started

Chris Froome is a two-time winner of the Tour de France. During a race, his muscles need a supply of fuel and oxygen while his lungs eliminate waste products such as carbon dioxide. These processes occur when you do any form of exercise. The difference is that Froome can push them much further. Why can you not ride at the same intensity as Froome?

Response of the body systems to a single sport or exercise session

Physiology is the study of your body's responses to exercise and and training. When exercising, you increase your body's energy use. This is reflected in increased oxygen consumption. Under certain conditions where the work rate is constant, the pattern of oxygen consumption shows an initial rise then levels off: once this plateau is reached, oxygen consumption remains steady over the period of the exercise.

For example, if you undertake 20 minutes of continuous same-speed jogging, a number of responses occur. Your heart and respiratory rates increase to accommodate the demands placed on the body, more ATP is produced and neuromuscular changes occur. (These changes are covered later in this unit.) After 3 or 4 minutes your body adapts to the increase in exercise intensity and your physiological demands level out. For the remaining time, you undergo 'steady-state exercise'.

Throughout this unit two key words crop up repeatedly.

- **Aerobic** means 'with oxygen' and involves the use of oxygen in energy production. In general, aerobic exercise is performed at a moderate level of intensity over a long period of time, such as long-distance running at a moderate pace. During aerobic exercise, your body uses oxygen in a number of different chemical reactions to generate energy almost as quickly as it is being used, depending on the exercise intensity. Glycogen is broken down to produce glucose, but in its absence fat metabolism is used instead.
- **Anaerobic** means 'without oxygen'. Anaerobic exercise relies on energy sources stored in the muscles and, unlike aerobic exercise, is not dependent on oxygen. Anaerobic exercise includes heavy weightlifting, sprints (running, cycling) and isometrics (in which one part of the body is used to resist the movement of another part) or any rapid burst of hard exercise.

Link

This unit links with *Unit 2: Functional Anatomy* and *Unit 7: Biomechanics in Sport and Exercise Science.*

Skeletal system responses

Long-term exercise slows the rate of skeletal ageing. People who maintain active lifestyles have greater bone mass compared to those who participate in less exercise. Weight-bearing exercises (e.g. running or walking) are particularly beneficial to the skeletal system, but this is also dependent on adequate **calcium** supply.

Bone is a dynamic tissue. It is constantly reshaped by **osteoblasts**. In return, **osteoclasts** break down the tissue to allow new growth. During midlife, osteoblast and osteoclast activity is in balance. However, as the body ages, osteoclast activity increases, breaking down bone tissue to release calcium and other minerals into the bloodstream. Research suggests weight-bearing exercise stimulates the activity of osteoblasts and suppresses osteoclast activity, maintaining a healthy bone density.

Key terms

Physiology – study of the way that the body responds to exercise and training.

Calcium – a mineral essential for bone growth and found in a wide range of foods including milk, cheese, yoghurt, nuts, broccoli and beans.

Osteoblasts – specialised bone cells that build new bone tissue.

Osteoclasts – large nucleated cells that destroy bone cells, reabsorb calcium and play a major role in bone remodelling.

Key terms

Viscosity – how thick a fluid is, affecting its resistance to flow.

Cardiac muscle – muscle tissue found only in the heart.

Maximal exercise – level of training intensity when an athlete approaches their maximal heart rate and performs exercise to an increasingly anaerobic level.

Synovial fluid is a thick, straw-coloured liquid that acts as a lubricant and is found primarily in the cavities of synovial joints. Exercise increases the amount of synovial fluid, decreasing its **viscosity**, keeping joints healthy, while stopping cartilage from drying out. Research suggests exercise also increases the range of movement at the joints as more synovial fluid is released into them.

Muscular system responses

High-intensity cardiovascular exercise can improve the strength of **cardiac muscle**, while intense strength conditioning can decrease sensitivity to muscular soreness post-workout. These short-term effects enable a performer to be more resilient to injury while improving their muscular strength and endurance in the long term.

Muscle fibre recruitment (Type I, Type IIa, Type IIx)

Recruitment of muscle fibres during exercise follows a specific pattern (see Figure 1.1). First, slow-twitch (Type I) muscle fibres are brought into action, then fast-twitch muscle fibres (first Type IIa and finally Type IIx). The level of recruitment is generally determined by the demand placed on the muscle. However, even during **maximal exercise** activity, the nervous system does not use all the muscle fibres. Generally, only a fraction of muscle fibres are recruited at any one time to avoid muscle damage and injury.

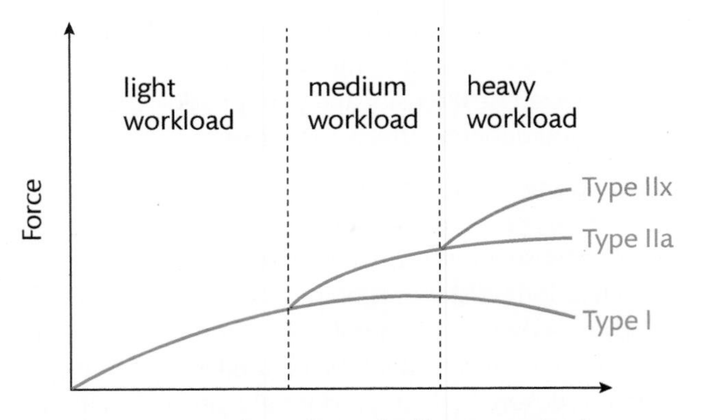

▶ **Figure 1.1:** Recruitment of muscle fibres during exercise

Muscle fibres will react to long-term exercise depending on the type of exercise they are subjected to. When training for muscular endurance events the main adaptations will occur in Type I fibres, creating within the muscle a greater ratio of Type I to Type IIa and Type IIx fibres. The result will be greater endurance capacity but a decrease in strength capacity. When training for muscular strength, Type IIa and Type IIx fibres must be recruited; the best way to achieve this is by lifting heavy weights.

Blood flow to working muscles

Cardiac output (the amount of blood the heart pumps through the circulatory system in a minute) is, at rest, approximately 5–6 litres for an adult male, but the blood flow is never evenly distributed throughout the body's organs and tissues. Instead, the body sends blood where it is needed. This redistribution of blood is achieved primarily by **vasoconstriction** (reduction in the diameter of blood vessels) and **vasodilation** (expansion in the diameter of blood vessels), which are regulated by hormones or chemicals. (For more about vasoconstriction and vasodilation, see page 8.)

At rest, approximately 20 per cent of the blood goes to muscles. Blood flow is distributed according to the need of the organs involved in the digestive process. During exercise, cardiac output can increase from 5-6 litres to 15–20 litres per minute and blood flow distribution changes dramatically, with up to 86 per cent of the blood going to the muscles.

Micro-tears

Every muscle in the body is made up of hundreds of thousands of tiny fibres. During exercise, muscle fibres will contract and relax against each other, resulting in microscopic tears to the fibres. When you rest after the activity your body heals and uses proteins to fill the gaps in the tears, resulting in extra strength and, depending on the exercise type, an increase in muscle size.

Temperature

During exercise all muscles require energy, gained from fuels such as carbohydrates and fats. One of the products is heat. As the muscles warm up, blood circulating through the muscles is also warmed resulting in a rise in the body's temperature. The amount of heat your muscles produce is related to the amount of work they perform: the more intense the exercise, the more heat they produce.

PAUSE POINT Do you think there is merit in training endurance athletes with heavy workloads requiring increased force production?

Hint Think about the types of muscle fibres endurance athletes use most often.

Extend Consider what types of gym-based exercises an endurance athlete might perform, in terms of workloads, reps and sets.

Respiratory system responses

The levels of oxygen in arterial blood change very little, even during exercise, but carbon dioxide levels vary according to the level of physical activity. The more intense the exercise, the greater the carbon dioxide concentration in the blood. To combat this, your breathing rate increases to help expel the carbon dioxide.

Control of breathing rate

Physical exercise increases the oxygen consumption of skeletal muscles. A trained athlete at rest might use 250 ml of oxygen per minute, but require 3600 ml per minute during maximal exercise. When oxygen consumption increases, the volume of carbon dioxide produced also increases. Decreased blood oxygen (the amount of oxygen in blood) and increased blood carbon dioxide concentration stimulate the respiratory centre to increase breathing rate (chemical control). A minor increase in breathing rate before exercise is known as an **anticipatory rise**. However, when exercise begins, there is an immediate and greater increase in breathing rate due to receptors in the muscles and joints (neural control).

After several minutes of aerobic exercise, breathing continues to rise at a slower rate, levelling off (while exercise intensity remains constant) until exercise ends. During maximal exercise, the breathing rate continues to rise until exhaustion. In both cases, after exercise is finished, breathing returns to normal - rapidly at first and then more slowly.

The increase in breathing rate during exercise demands an increase in blood flow to the skeletal muscles. Should respiratory or muscular systems fail to keep up with demands, you will feel out of breath. This is due to the inability of the heart and circulatory system to move enough blood between the lungs and the skeletal muscles, not necessarily an inability of the respiratory system to provide sufficient oxygen.

Key terms

Anticipatory rise – a minor increase in breathing rate prior to exercise.

Link

Information about the functioning of the respiratory muscles can be found in *Unit 2: Functional Anatomy.*

Respiratory muscles

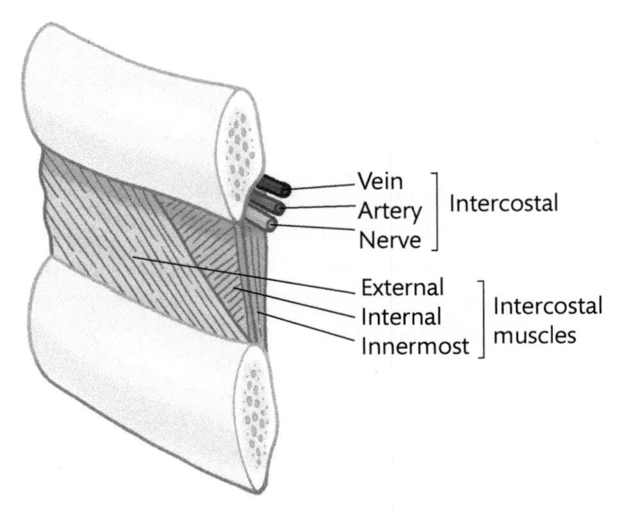

▶ **Figure 1.2:** Eleven pairs of intercostal muscles occupy the spaces between 12 pairs of ribs

During exercise, forced breathing is used. This differs from normal breathing because, during expiration, the internal intercostal muscles contract (see Figure 1.2), moving the ribs and sternum upwards and outwards forcibly. The abdominal muscles also contract, increasing the pressure of the abdominal cavity, helping the diaphragm to rise more forcibly. During exercise the muscles involved in the breathing process can use up to 10 per cent of the body's total oxygen uptake. Cramp in these muscles is thought to be the cause of a 'stitch'.

Tidal volume

Tidal volume is the amount of air ventilated in or out of the lungs in one breath. More information can be found on page 52 in *Unit 2: Functional Anatomy.* It increases dramatically during exercise due to the body's demand for more oxygen and/or the need to offload increased levels of carbon dioxide. Increases in breathing rate maintain **alveolar ventilation** during steady-state exercise. Trained athletes achieve the required alveolar ventilation by increasing tidal volume and only minimally increasing breathing rate. With deeper breathing, alveolar ventilation can increase from 70 per cent at rest to over 85 per cent of total ventilation during exercise. This increase occurs because deeper breathing causes a greater tidal volume to enter the alveoli.

Key term

Alveolar ventilation – tidal volume minus dead space (air that remains in trachea, bronchi, etc.).

Minute volume (VE)

At a low to moderate exercise intensity, tidal volume and breathing rate increase proportionally. However, at a high exercise intensity, tidal volume reaches a peak so any further increase in minute volume requires an increase in breathing rate. Minute volume is measured in litres per minute and is calculated by multiplying tidal volume by breathing rate. For example, an adult with a tidal volume at rest of 0.4l, who breathes 12 times per minute will have a minute volume of 4.8l/min.

Theory into practice

Calculate the number of breaths taken by an adult over 1 year with the following approximate criteria:

- average period of sleep per day = 8 hours during which the breathing rate is 10 breaths per minute
- remainder of time deemed to be awake and the average breathing rate is 12 breaths per minute.

Oxygen dissociation curve

The oxygen dissociation curve (see Figure 1.3) shows the relationship between the percentage of oxygen saturation of blood (a measure of oxygen dissolved or carried in blood) and the **partial pressure** of oxygen. During steady-state exercise, increased temperature and lower blood pH concentration affect the oxygen-**haemoglobin** dissociation curve so that more oxygen can be unloaded to supply the active muscle. In prolonged high-intensity exercise, large amounts of **lactate** enter the blood from the active muscle. At exhaustion, **blood pH** can approach 6.8. Only after exercise ceases does blood pH stabilise and return to 7.4.

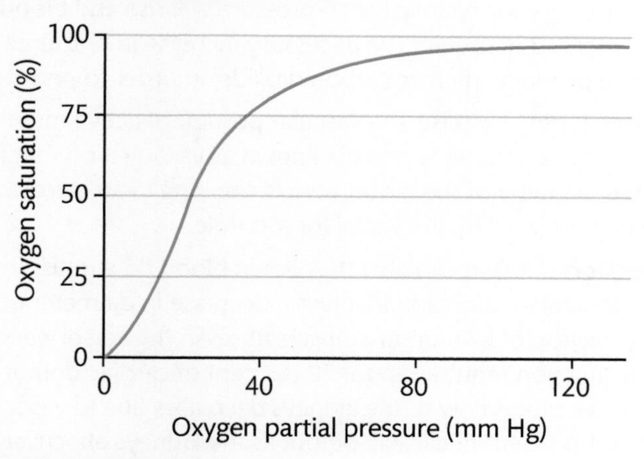

Figure 1.3: Oxygen dissociation curve

Key terms

Partial pressure – pressure applied by a single gas in a mixture of gases.

Haemoglobin – oxygen transporting component of red blood cells.

Lactate – product of lactic acid which occurs in blood.

Blood pH – measure of acidity or alkalinity of a solution.

Research

Asthma is a common condition among the general population. Find out how asthma affects the respiratory system and what problems it might present for sports participation.

Case study

Elite athletic performance

Mary Keitany is an elite distance runner who has won both London and New York marathons. She completed the London Marathon in 2012 in a time of 2 hours, 18 minutes and 37 seconds. Crossing the line, Mary was clearly tired. She took several rapid and deep breaths once she had stopped. But within a few minutes, her breathing rate had slowed enough for her to hold brief media interviews.

Check your knowledge

Why would it be virtually impossible for Mary to give an interview immediately after she had crossed the finish line? Concentrate on the physiology of the respiratory responses to exercise and why Mary needed those extra few minutes before holding a conversation.

PAUSE POINT Name the different measures of respiratory volume.

Hint Using paper, whiteboard or a tablet, list the measures of respiratory volumes and provide a brief description for each.

Extend Think about how these volumes might be improved. What types of training will have a positive effect on these volumes?

Cardiovascular system responses

When exercising, changes occur within the cardiovascular system. You must understand these changes as they affect an athlete's training and performance.

Link

More information about the cardiovascular system can be found in *Unit 2: Functional Anatomy.*

Key terms

Cardiac cycle – the sequence of events (systole – during which cardiac muscle contracts – and diastole – during which cardiac muscle relaxes) that take place during a single heartbeat.

Neurotransmitters – chemicals used to carry signals or information between neurons and cells.

Stroke volume – volume of blood pumped out of the heart's left ventricle per beat.

Cardiac cycle

When the body detects an increase in exercise intensity, the **cardiac cycle** must respond accordingly. It achieves this by speeding up to meet the demands of the exercise. As a result, heart rate will increase, the amount of blood filling your atria and ventricles will increase, your systolic blood pressure will rise and blood will be diverted to the skeletal muscles that require the necessary increase in nutrients and oxygen, and remove waste products such as carbon dioxide, in order to perform effectively.

- **Vasodilation** – during exercise, the vascular portion of active muscles increases through dilation of arterioles, a process known as vasodilation that involves an increase in the diameter of the blood vessels resulting in an increased blood flow to the muscle area supplied by the vessel (or arteriole).
- **Vasoconstriction** – vessels can also shut down blood flow to tissues. This process is known as vasoconstriction and involves a decrease in diameter of a blood vessel by contraction of involuntary muscle fibres in the vessel walls. For example, at rest kidney function requires about 20 per cent of cardiac output. During maximal exercise, blood flow to the kidneys decreases due to vasoconstriction to approximately 1 per cent of cardiac output as the kidneys effectively shut down during exercise.

Anticipatory increase in heart rate

An anticipatory increase in heart rate occurs before the start of exercise. Heart rate can be changed by **neurotransmitters** such as adrenaline and noradrenaline, released from the brain. Therefore, before exercise, the heart rate increases and the subsequent increase in blood flow has already begun to supply oxygen and nutrients to the muscle or muscles about to be worked.

Cardiac output

Cardiac output is the volume of blood pumped out of the heart in 1 minute. It is expressed as Q and is equal to heart rate multiplied by the **stroke volume**. Cardiac output may reach up to 30 litres per minute during extreme exercise.

Stroke volume

Stroke volume is the amount of blood pumped by the left ventricle in one contraction. About two-thirds of the blood in the ventricle is put out with each beat. During exercise, stroke volume increases progressively and gradually levels off at a higher level until the exercise has ended. Assuming normal stroke volume ranges between 70 and 80 ml per beat, a trained athlete's stroke volume can be 110 ml. During exercise, blood flow increases sharply, allowing for a greater oxygen supply to the skeletal muscles.

Heart rate

Heart rate changes according to the body's needs. It increases during exercise (see Figure 1.4) to deliver extra oxygen to tissues and remove carbon dioxide. At rest, a normal adult heart beats approximately 75 times per minute, peaking at around 200 beats per minute for strenuous activity, depending on age.

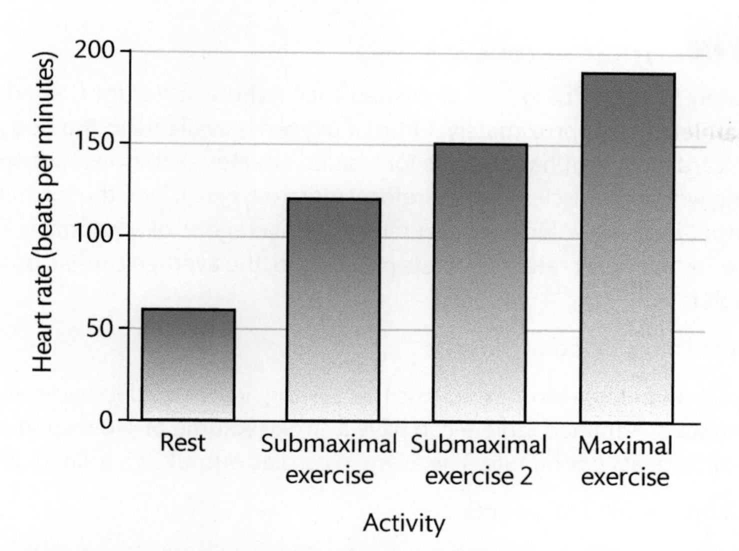

▸ **Figure 1.4:** Heart rate during exercise. 'Submaximal exercise 2' is aerobic exercise of greater intensity than 'Submaximal exercise' given the increased heart rate

Heart rate is controlled by the **sinoatrial node** (SAN). The rate goes up or down when the SAN receives information via nerves that link the SAN with the cardiovascular centre in the brain. When you exercise, information is communicated and the heart adapts accordingly. It does so in two ways:

- the **sympathetic nerve** speeds up the heart – the synapses at the end of this nerve secrete a hormone called noradrenalin
- the vagus nerve (**parasympathetic nerve**) slows down the heart – the synapses at the end of the nerve secrete a hormone called acetylcholine (see Figure 1.5).

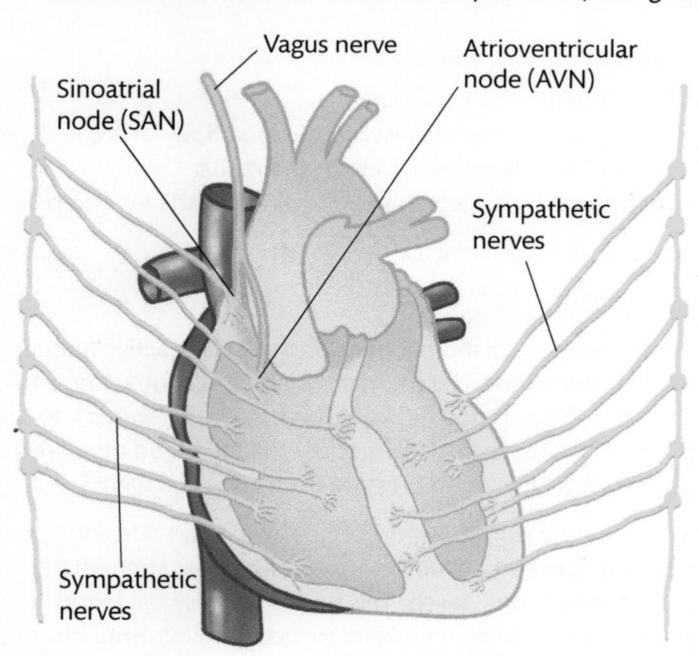

▸ **Figure 1.5:** The heart is connected via the vagus nerve and sympathetic nerves to the brain

Stroke volume reaches a peak during submaximal exercise and does not increase during maximal exercise. The greatest increase in stroke volume occurs in the transition from rest to moderate exercise. During maximal exercise, stroke volume does not increase as the left ventricle is, at this point, already full to capacity. The body tolerates maximal activity for as long as it can by increasing heart rate and maintaining stroke volume.

Changes to cardiac output

Approximately 5 litres of blood are circulated each minute at rest for trained or untrained athletes, so approximately 1 litre of oxygen is available to the body. An increase in cardiac output has benefits for trained athletes as they can transport more blood to the working muscles and, therefore, more oxygen. Given the formula for cardiac output is stroke volume × heart rate, if the average stroke volume is 70 ml and the average resting heart rate is 70 beats per minute, the average cardiac output of a healthy adult is:

70 × 70 = 4900 ml of blood per minute

A key adaptation of long-term exercise is that resting heart rate decreases while stroke volume increases. A trained athlete can have a stroke volume of 110 ml and a resting heart rate of 50 beats per minute. The average cardiac output of a trained athlete is:

110 ml × 50 bpm = 5500 ml per minute

Therefore, greater cardiac output maintained by fewer beats is an indication of increased fitness.

Starling's law

Starling's law is a theory which states that stroke volume increases in response to an increase in blood volume filling the heart. This stretches the ventricular wall, causing the cardiac muscle to contract more forcefully. The stroke volume may also increase due to stronger contractions in the cardiac muscles during exercise. Therefore, the reduced heart rate of a trained athlete allows for greater filling during the longer diastole, so the stretch of the cardiac muscle is greater. This in turn increases the stroke volume.

Blood pressure

Blood pressure is determined by two factors:

- the resistance offered by blood vessel walls to blood flow – this can depend on several factors including blood vessel length and radius
- cardiac output or blood volume pumped out of the heart's left ventricle in 1 minute.

Therefore, blood pressure is defined as:

cardiac output × resistance

During steady-state exercise, dilation of the blood vessels in active muscles increases the vascular area for blood flow. The alternate rhythmical contraction and relaxation of the skeletal muscles forces blood through the vessels and returns it to the heart. During exercise, although both cardiac output and blood pressure increase, mechanisms act to restrict the blood pressure from rising too high.

Key term

Systolic pressure – pressure exerted in the arteries when the heart contracts.

The higher the exercise intensity, the greater the rise in heart rate and, consequently, an increase in **systolic pressure** generally occurs. Muscular strength training can significantly raise blood pressure levels. This occurs because the blood has to be forced through skeletal muscle tissue subject to increased intra-muscular pressure, so the cardiovascular system has to work harder to achieve circulation requirements.

Readings

Medical staff sometimes measure blood pressure manually using the brachial artery. A blood pressure cuff is wrapped around the arm above the elbow and inflated until a brachial pulse cannot be felt or heard. The pressure is gradually released and the first sounds of forced blood through the brachial artery are listened for with a stethoscope.

This gives the systolic pressure. As cuff pressure reduces the sounds of the forced blood disappear, giving the **diastolic pressure**. Alternatively, blood pressure can be easily measured at the touch of a button using digital instruments.

At rest, normal adult systolic pressure varies between 110 and 140 mm Hg, and diastolic pressure between 70 and 80 mm Hg (see Figure 1.6). Blood pressure varies with age, gender, race and amount of physical activity carried out: remember, what is normal for one person may not be normal for another.

Blood pressure around 120/80 mm Hg is optimal for adults. Systolic pressure readings of 120 to 139 mm Hg or diastolic pressure of 80 to 89 mm Hg is considered as **prehypertension** and needs to be watched carefully. A blood pressure reading of 140/90 mm Hg or higher is considered to be hypertensive. **Hypertension** is high blood pressure and increases the risk of cardiovascular diseases or kidney failure because it adds to the workload of the heart.

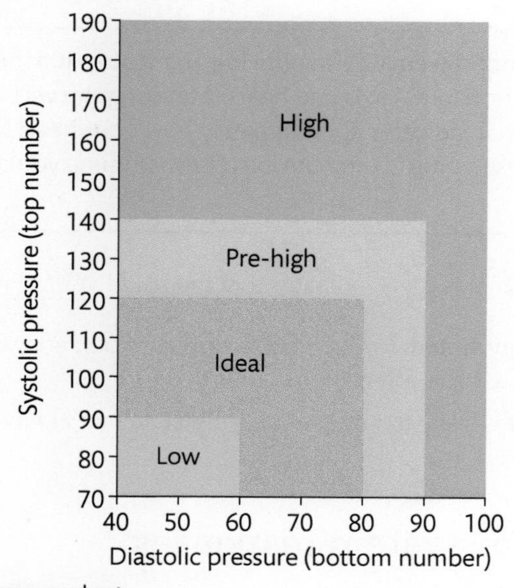

Figure 1.6: Blood pressure chart

During aerobic exercise, oxygen consumption and heart rate increase in relation to the intensity of the activity. Systolic blood pressure rises progressively, while diastolic blood pressure stays the same or decreases slightly. The pulse rate rises and blood flow to the muscles increases.

Theory into practice

Work in pairs or small groups. Use a digital blood pressure monitor to determine your own blood pressure and that of your friends. Compare your readings against the blood pressure norms identified in the main text.

Changes in blood pH

The pH of a substance refers to a measure of acidity or alkalinity. A pH value of 7 indicates neutral, a value above 7 indicates alkalinity, and below 7 indicates acidity. The pH of blood is generally between 7.2 and 7.5, indicating very weak alkalinity. However, during exercise blood pH can drop and become more acidic (i.e. below pH 7). The acidity is due to the inclusion of waste products such as carbon dioxide in the blood due to exercise intensity. During high-intensity exercise using anaerobic metabolism, lactic acid is released into the blood again as a waste product.

Key terms

Diastolic pressure – pressure exerted in the arteries when the heart relaxes and fills with blood.

Prehypertension – means someone does not have high blood pressure now but they are likely to develop it in future.

Key terms

Arterial blood – bright red in colour due to high concentrations of oxygen.

Venous blood – darker red than arterial blood due to high concentrations of carbon dioxide.

Diffusion rate

During exercise, diffusion rates increase to allow more oxygen movement from the capillaries to the working muscles, while carbon dioxide is exchanged into the blood for exhalation. The more you exercise, the more efficient this process becomes so that, with long-term aerobic training, your body becomes more efficient at allowing oxygen and carbon dioxide to diffuse.

Arteriovenous oxygen difference (a–VO2 diff)

Arteriovenous oxygen difference is the difference in the oxygen content between **arterial** and **venous blood**. Exercise leads to an increase in this difference because, as exercise intensifies, the working muscle tissue demands more oxygen from the arterial blood, so the oxygen content of venous blood decreases.

Theory into practice

Imagine you have undertaken a 20-minute jog at a steady 10 km/h. Draw a graph with time along the horizontal axis and heart rate along the vertical axis. Sketch a line on your graph that indicates approximately how your heart rate has changed throughout the course of the 20-minute exercise, assuming you did not run to exhaustion.

When you exercise, what is a key indicator that the pH of your blood has dropped?

Hint Consider which energy system lowers the pH of your blood and what type of exercise is likely to cause this effect.

Extend What type of training is likely to improve your resistance or ability to tolerate a lower blood pH?

Neuromuscular system responses

The term 'neuromuscular' refers to both the nervous system and the muscular system. There are two kinds of nerves:

- **sensory neurons** (or 'sensory nerves') which carry information from our extremities (the skin) to the central nervous system (the brain and spinal cord)
- **motor neurons** (or 'motor nerves') which carry information from our central nervous system to our muscles.

Nervous control of muscular contraction

Muscles contract when stimulated by nerves. Three basic types of contraction can occur during exercise, each with a variation of contraction pattern.

- **Isotonic contraction** – the muscle shortens as it develops tension.
- **Isometric contraction** – the muscle develops tension but does not change length.
- **Isokinetic contraction** – the muscle contracts to its maximum at a constant speed over the full range of movement.

Muscles contract and relax due to muscle filaments moving backwards and forwards across each other. What causes these backwards and forwards movements to occur is the actions of specialised nerve cells called motor units working at a neuromuscular junction.

- **Neuromuscular junction** – a neuromuscular junction is the site at which a motor neuron communicates with a muscle fibre using nerve impulses.

- **Motor unit** – a motor unit is made up of a motor neuron and all the associated muscle fibres it affects. Motor units work together to coordinate contractions of a single skeletal muscle, although the number of fibres in each unit varies based on the muscle size and role. During low-intensity exercise, Type I motor units are recruited. As the intensity is increased Type IIa motor units are recruited until the intensity is enough to recruit Type IIx motor units.

Muscle spindles and Golgi tendon organs (covered in the next sections) provide sensory information about the intensity of exercise, allowing smooth, coordinated movement patterns.

Muscle spindles

Muscle spindles (see Figure 1.7) are **proprioceptors** found in skeletal muscles, located within muscle fibres known as **intrafusal fibres**. They detect muscle stretch and initiate a reflex that resists the stretch and prevents muscle tears. When muscle is stretched, primary sensory receptors in the muscle spindle respond to the velocity and degree of stretch, then send this information to the brain via the spinal cord. Secondary sensory receptors detect and send information about the degree of stretch to the central nervous system. This information is transmitted to a motor neuron, which activates the muscle to contract, thus reducing the stretch. The more your body is used to steady-state exercise, the more efficient the muscle spindles become at transmitting this information.

Key term

Proprioceptors – sensory receptors found in muscle tissue, tendons and joints which tell the brain about the physical state and position of a muscle or joint.

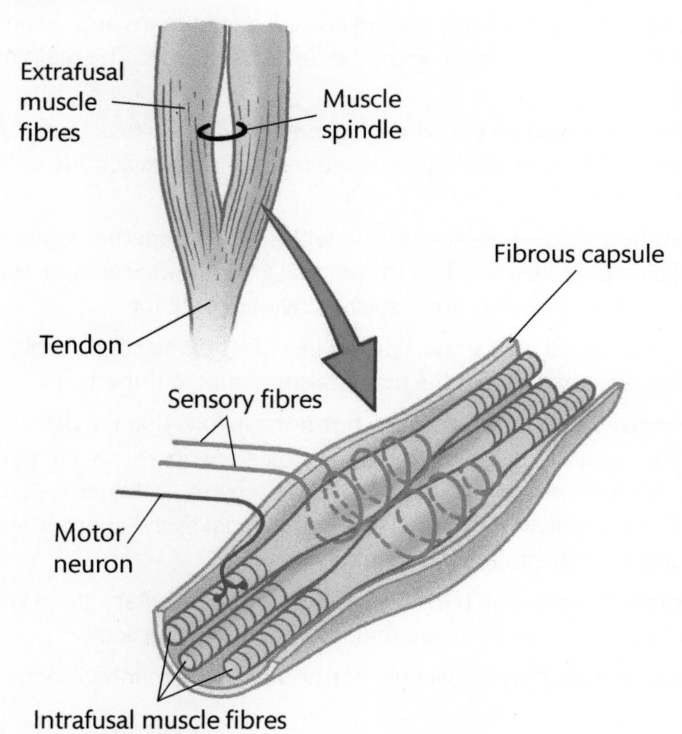

Figure 1.7: Muscle spindles provide information about any changes in length and tension of muscle fibres

Golgi tendon organs

Golgi tendon organs (GTOs) are proprioceptors located within the tendons and are sensitive to stretch. Golgi tendon organs send information to the central nervous system concerning the strength of a muscle contraction and, together with muscle spindles, facilitate smooth movement patterns.

Chemoreceptors, thermoreceptors and baroreceptors

Receptors are groups of specialised cells that detect changes in the environment (internally and externally), which send impulses to the brain that result in the body adapting to these changes.

- **Chemoreceptors** - sense chemical stimuli within the body. For example, chemoreceptors detect carbon dioxide in the blood. If, during exercise, increased levels of carbon dioxide are detected, the brain sends a signal to the respiratory system to increase the breathing rate to allow the carbon dioxide to be offloaded by exhalation.
- **Thermoreceptors** - sense changes in temperature and are key to the thermoregulation process. If a thermoreceptor senses a warm environment or increased body temperature due to exercise, the body's cooling processes are activated (see pages 32–33). Likewise, if the environment is cold the body will respond with warming actions (e.g. shivering or blood diversion).
- **Baroreceptors** - located in blood vessels and sense blood pressure. The information from baroreceptors is sent to the brain so that correct blood pressure can be maintained at all times. The information provided by baroreceptors can influence cardiac output during exercise.

Endocrine system responses

The endocrine system is the body system consisting of organs and tissues that secrete hormones in response to exercise and other external factors. The main hormones of the body are:

- **adrenaline** - secreted by the adrenal glands, it increases heart rate, breathing rate and metabolic rate and improves the force of muscle actions, delaying the onset of fatigue
- **noradrenaline** - closely related to and with similar properties to adrenaline, noradrenaline is also secreted by the adrenal glands and acts as a neurotransmitter. Low levels of noradrenaline are associated with depression
- **cortisol** - associated with stress, cortisol increases blood sugar levels, suppresses the immune system and aids the metabolism of macronutrients
- **testosterone** - the primary male sex hormone involved in the development of muscle tissue and muscular strength, testosterone increases the number of neurotransmitters, encouraging muscle tissue growth. Testosterone also increases levels of human growth hormone (HGH) which makes the appropriate type of exercise promote the building of muscle tissue
- **human growth hormone (HGH)** - secreted by the pituitary gland which stimulates general body growth and the lengthening of bones in particular
- **oestrogen** - the primary female sex hormone; known to inhibit bone resorption.

PAUSE POINT How do you think hormone effects might be exploited by athletes looking to cheat their way to success?

Hint Research high-profile cases of athletes looking to enhance their performance using steroids and HGH.

Extend Research the potential impact and negative effects of illegal ergogenic aids designed to enhance performance.

Energy systems responses

Energy sources

The body relies on three energy systems, which are outlined later in this section:

- the ATP-PC system
- the lactate system
- the aerobic system.

During exercise, the body does not switch from one energy system to another – energy is derived from all systems at all times. However, the emphasis changes depending on the intensity and duration of the activity.

Theory into practice

Energy systems do not operate in isolation; they interact to supply the energy required for muscular movement. Energy systems are like 'taps' that are never fully turned off – the energy flows continually (like water at differing pressures) according to the exercise being undertaken. Select two sports or activities and compare the likely energy system usages (as a percentage) for each.

Exercise requires the body to extract energy from food. Carbohydrate, fat and protein follow different metabolic pathways but ultimately produce **adenosine triphosphate (ATP)**, the only molecule that is able to provide energy to muscle fibres. Phosphocreatine (PC) is another high-energy compound stored in cells and can be rapidly used to help short explosive physical efforts. To sustain any physical activity, the body must constantly replenish its ATP and PC stores.

- Carbohydrates are broken down into blood glucose, the body's main energy source. Blood glucose can be used immediately as fuel, or can be sent to the liver and muscles and stored as glycogen. During exercise, muscle glycogen is converted back into glucose for use by working muscle fibres.
- Fat is the body's most concentrated source of energy, providing more than twice as much energy as carbohydrate or protein (9 calories per gram versus 4 calories each per gram). During exercise, fat (in the form of triglycerides in adipose or fat tissue) is broken down into fatty acids. These are transported through the blood to the muscles as fuel. This is a slower process than the mobilisation of carbohydrate for fuel.
- Protein is used to build, maintain and repair body tissues. Under ordinary circumstances, protein meets only approximately 5 per cent of the body's energy needs. Under more extreme circumstances, for example, when we eat too few calories or not enough carbohydrate, as well as undertaking the final stages of endurance exercise, once the glycogen reserves are depleted then skeletal muscle is broken down and used as fuel.

ATP production

Your body stores only a small quantity of ATP in its cells – enough to power only a few seconds of all-out exercise. Therefore, your body must replace or resynthesise ATP on a continual basis. ATP consists of a base (adenine) and three phosphate groups (see Figure 1.8). It is formed by a reaction between an adenosine diphosphate (ADP) molecule and a phosphate. When a molecule of ATP is used, the last phosphate group splits off and energy is released.

Training to improve ATP energy transfer capacity requires repetitive, intense, short-duration exercise. The activities chosen should engage muscles in the movement for which the athlete desires improved anaerobic power. This enhances metabolic capacity of engaged muscle tissue or fibres and improves neuromuscular adaptations to the sport-specific pattern of movement.

Discussion

Look back at the definitions of 'aerobic' and 'anaerobic' on page 3. Consider the various movements and actions undertaken by a footballer during a match (for example, heading, shooting, tackling, jogging, marking, etc.). Which rely primarily on aerobic metabolism and which rely primarily on anaerobic metabolism? As a group discuss and justify your decisions.

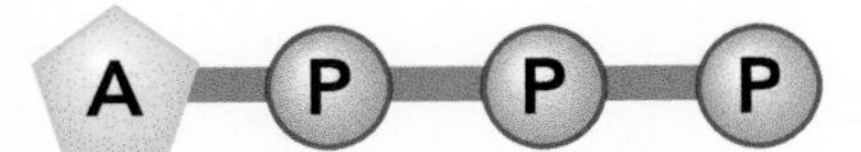

(a) ATP is formed when adenosine diphosphate (ADP) binds with a phosphate (P)

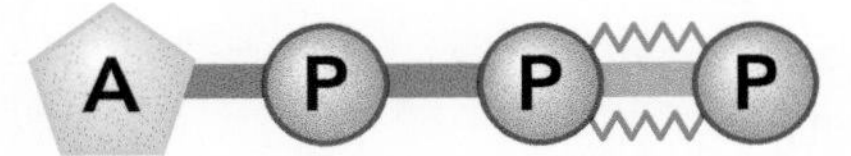

(b) Energy is stored in the bond between the second and third phosphate groups

(c) When a cell needs energy, it breaks the bond between the phosphate groups to form ADP and a free phosphate molecule

▶ **Figure 1.8:** ATP production (a) – (c)

ATP-PC system

ATP and creatine phosphate (phosphocreatine or PC) make up the ATP-PC system. PC is broken down, releasing both energy and a phosphate molecule (which is then used to rebuild ATP). The enzyme that controls the breakdown of PC is called **creatine kinase**.

The ATP-PC system can operate with or without oxygen, but because it does not rely on the presence of oxygen it is anaerobic. During the first five seconds of exercise, regardless of intensity, the ATP-PC system is relied on almost exclusively. The ATP-PC system can sustain all-out exercise for 3 to 15 seconds. If activity continues beyond this period, the body must rely on an additional energy system to resynthesise ATP.

Lactate system (anaerobic glycolysis)

Glycolysis is the term used to describe the breakdown of glucose. It consists of a series of enzymatic reactions. The end product of glycolysis is pyruvic acid which is used in a process called the **Krebs cycle** (see Figure 1.9) or converted into lactic acid.

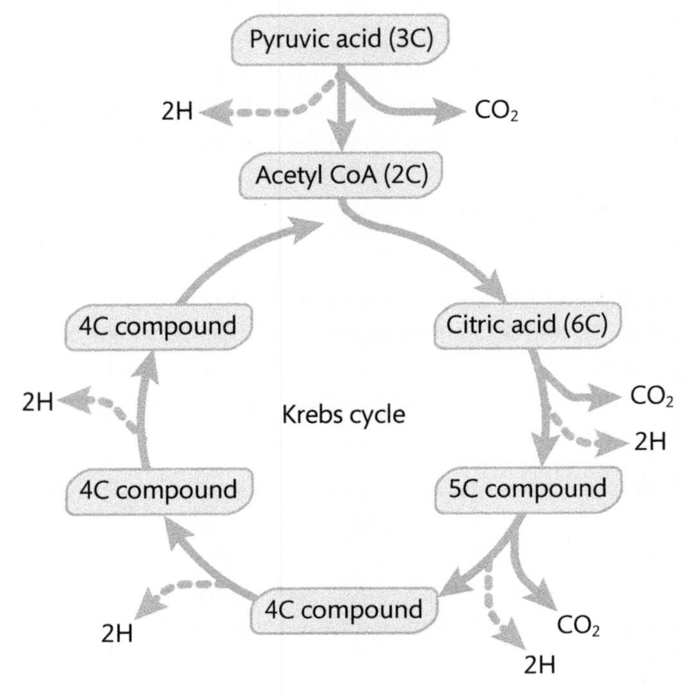

▶ **Figure 1.9:** Krebs cycle

Anaerobic glycolysis occurs at times when energy is required in the absence of oxygen. It is vital for tissues with high energy requirements or an insufficient oxygen supply. It involves the breakdown of glycogen to form ATP (for energy) plus lactate. The build-up of lactate in the muscles ends the use of this energy system after 40 to 60 seconds of maximum effort, so this system is called on by athletes whose sports demand high-energy expenditure for up to 60 seconds, such as 400 metre runners and rugby players.

Glycolysis forms pyruvic acid and hydrogen ions (H+). A build-up of hydrogen ions makes the muscle cells acidic and interferes with their operation, so carrier molecules called nicotinamide adenine dinucleotide (NAD+) remove the H+. As they do this, the NAD+ is reduced to NADH, which deposits the H+ during the **electron transport chain** to be combined with oxygen to form water.

Key term

Electron transport chain – a series of biomechanical reactions during which free energy contained within hydrogen (derived from the Krebs cycle) is released. For more information, see pages 17–18.

If there is insufficient oxygen, NADH cannot release the H+ and they build up in the cell. To prevent a rise in acidity, pyruvic acid accepts H+, forming **lactic acid** that then dissociates into lactate and H+. Some of the lactate diffuses into the bloodstream. The normal pH of the muscle cell is 7.1, but if the build-up of H+ continues and pH is reduced to around 6.5, muscle contraction is impaired.

Aerobic energy system

The aerobic energy system uses carbohydrates, fats and proteins extracted from the diet to resynthesise ATP. This system produces more ATP than the ATP-PC or the lactate system, but does so at a slower rate and is therefore less suitable for intense exercise. The aerobic system consists of three stages, each of which produce ATP.

Stage 1: Aerobic glycolysis

Aerobic glycolysis converts stored glycogen to glucose. This glucose is broken down by enzymes in the presence of oxygen. Two ATP molecules are used to fuel aerobic glycolysis and four are created, resulting in a gain of two ATP molecules for use in muscle contraction. Pyruvate is created as the end product of the breakdown of glucose and, in the presence of oxygen, the pyruvate is converted into acetyl coenzyme A. Acetyl coenzyme A can be synthesised during the second and third stages of the aerobic system to create more ATP.

This system involves prolonged work at low intensity and increases in importance as the sport's duration increases. Lack of fuel, overheating or **dehydration** will end the exercise.

Fuel for this system varies according to the duration and intensity of exercise. In prolonged aerobic exercise, the preferred fuel is free fatty acids because glycogen stores are limited compared to our plentiful fat stores.

Stage 2: Krebs cycle

Acetyl coenzyme A enters what is called the Krebs cycle (see Figure 1.9) and is broken down, producing ATP and the by-products of carbon dioxide and water.

The Krebs cycle is a series of aerobic reactions that take place in the matrix in mitochondria. Carbon dioxide is produced and hydrogen removed from carbon molecules and joins NAD to form $NADH_2$. The Krebs cycle provides a continuous supply of electrons to feed the electron transport chain. This cycle begins when the 2-carbon acetyl CoA joins with a 4-carbon compound to form a 6-carbon compound called citric acid. Citric acid (6C) is gradually converted back to the 4-carbon compound ready to start the cycle once more.

Key terms

Dehydration – depletion of fluids that can impede thermoregulation and cause a rise in core body temperature.

Mitochondria – the organelles within cells in the body where aerobic respiration takes place. Pyruvate oxidation and the Krebs cycle take place in the matrix (fluid) of the mitochondria, while the electron transport chain takes place in the inner membrane itself.

During both the Krebs cycle and aerobic glycolysis, hydrogen ions are produced which, if left unchecked, would cause cells to become too acidic. The Krebs cycle tackles this problem by transferring the hydrogen ions (acid) to the electron transport chain (third stage) where the acidity issue is dealt with while enabling the aerobic system to continue resynthesising ATP.

To summarise, the key steps of the Krebs cycle are:

1. acetyl coenzyme A enters Krebs cycle
2. acetyl coenzyme A is broken down into carbon dioxide and hydrogen ions
3. 2 ATP are synthesised and made available to fuel muscle contraction
4. hydrogen ions are transferred to the electron transport chain (Stage 3).

Stage 3: Electron transport chain

The electron transport chain (see Figure 1.10) is a series of biomechanical reactions during which free energy contained within hydrogen (derived from the Krebs cycle) is released, so that it can be used to synthesise ATP during aerobic metabolism. The electron transport chain occurs in the many cristae in **mitochondria**. Each reaction involves a specific electron-carrier molecule which has a particular attraction for hydrogen. The final link in the electron transport chain is oxygen, which combines with the hydrogen and electrons to form water. The electron transport chain produces 34 ATP for every molecule of glucose used.

The key steps of the electron transport chain are:

1. hydrogen ions from the Krebs cycle are carried to the electron transport chain by carrier molecules
2. hydrogen ions undergo a series of chemical reactions
3. a hydrogen ion gradient is created – as hydrogen ions move across this gradient adenosine diphosphate (ADP) is phosphorylated (adds another phosphate group) to form ATP
4. water is created as a by-product.

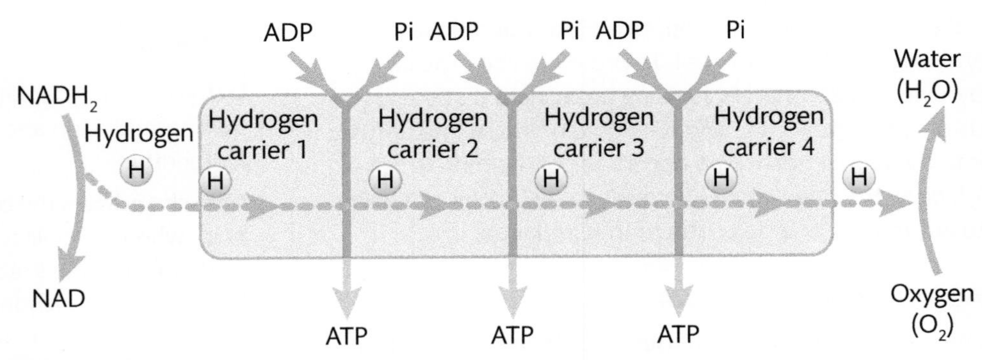

Figure 1.10: The electron transport chain

ATP yield for each system

Each energy system produces a different amount of ATP, shown in Table 1.2.

Table 1.2: ATP yield for each energy system

Energy systems	ATP yield per molecule of glucose
Aerobic glycolysis	2 ATP
Krebs cycle	2 ATP
Electron transport chain	34 ATP
Anaerobic glycolysis	2 ATP

Energy system continuum

Energy systems are viewed as a continuum. High-intensity exercise lasting 8–10 seconds requires the ATP-PC system to meet the energy demands. As the duration increases the intensity of the demand decreases and the lactate system is used. The point at which blood lactate builds up so it prevents effective muscle contraction occurs between 30 seconds and 3 minutes depending on the intensity of exercise and the fitness of the athlete. This point is known as the onset of blood lactate accumulation or OBLA (see the next section for more about this). Once the duration of exercise goes beyond 3 minutes, the majority of energy comes from the aerobic system.

However, while the energy continuum looks at the three energy systems as separately engaged entities, in reality this is not the case. Providing energy for resynthesis of ATP involves all the systems operating at once. For example, at rest the majority of the energy demands are met by the aerobic system, with the ATP-PC and lactate system playing small roles. During intense exercise the demands for energy increase dramatically and the ATP-PC and lactate systems play a more active role to supply the energy needed as anaerobic sources can supply energy at four times the rate of aerobic sources. It is therefore the duration and intensity of exercise that governs which of the energy systems resynthesise ATP at the required rate.

Table 1.3 gives some examples of the three energy systems, their duration and their uses.

Table 1.3: The three energy systems, their duration and their uses

Energy system	Fuel	Duration	Intensity	By-products	Sporting example
Phosphocreatine	Phosphocreatine (PC)	8–10 seconds	High	Free creatine	100 metres/short sprints
Lactic acid/anaerobic glycolysis	Carbohydrate	30–90 seconds	Medium	Lactic acid and associated H+	400 metres/repeated runs in football or rugby
Aerobic	Carbohydrate, fat, protein	Hours	Low	CO_2 and H_2O	10,000 metres/mountain hike

Onset of blood lactate accumulation (OBLA)

OBLA is the level above which blood lactate is produced faster than it can be used aerobically. OBLA occurs when the concentration of blood lactate reaches approximately 4 mmol/L. Continued exercise above the lactate threshold results in the accumulation of hydrogen ions in muscle tissue, causing fatigue and intramuscular pain.

Recovery time for each system

Approximate recovery times for each system are outlined in Table 1.4. However, it should be stressed that recovery rates are very much dependent on the duration and intensity of the exercise undertaken.

Reflect

Think about your own training and how your fitness levels have improved over time. Do you now understand how your body has adapted to training and why you are able to train or compete?

▶ **Table 1.4:** Energy system recovery times

Energy system	Fuel	Recovery period
Phosphocreatine	Phosphocreatine (PC)	Approximately 180 to 240 seconds to replenish phosphocreatine (PC) levels
Lactic acid/anaerobic glycolysis	Carbohydrate	2–10 minutes will allow removal of most lactic acid produced
Aerobic	Carbohydrate, fat, protein	60–180 seconds – an athlete showing signs of fatigue will require longer to recover and replenish muscle energy stores

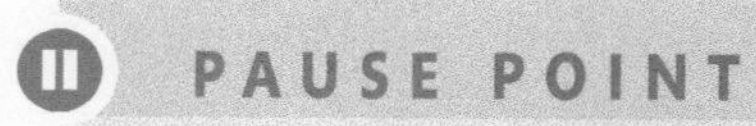

PAUSE POINT Do you know which energy system you use primarily for your chosen sport?

Hint Is your sport more aerobic or anaerobic? It could be a combination of both.

Extend Try allocating a percentage to each of the three energy systems for your chosen sport.

Assessment practice 1.1

Finlay is a club-level rugby player who has just returned to the sport as a centre after a one-year break due to a fractured right femur. He needs to improve his fitness to resume full training in eight weeks' time. He has joined a gym and has been given the following training programme to increase his fitness levels:

- Monday: 20–30 minutes continuous running
- Tuesday: weight training (lower body)
- Wednesday: rest day
- Thursday: 20–30 minutes continuous rowing
- Friday: weight training (upper body)
- Saturday: 20–30 minutes walking in morning

1. Explain how this programme will increase the strength of Finlay's bones.
2. How is the programme designed to decrease Finlay's resting heart rate?
3. Explain how Finlay's nervous system can control the force exerted by his muscles during weight training sessions.
4. Finlay underwent a series of fitness tests at the beginning and the end of his fitness training programme. His test results at the end showed an increase in his VO_2 max and tidal volume. Explain the impact of the training on Finlay's cardiovascular and respiratory systems and explain how this might affect his future rugby performances.
5. After the programme, Finlay commented that he felt much stronger and had noticed an increase in muscle size and definition. Explain how the programme caused Finlay's energy systems to adapt. What further adaptation of his endocrine system could also explain his increased muscle definition and size?

B Fatigue and how the body recovers from exercise

Exercise places demands on the body. Fatigue is the exhaustion of muscle from prolonged exertion or over-stimulation. We cannot exercise indefinitely because of neuromuscular fatigue, which occurs as a result of the different causes and systems explored in this learning aim. For example, during short-term maximal exercise, insufficient oxygen and/or increased lactate levels can bring about fatigue – reliance on anaerobic metabolism impairs energy transfer via glycolysis and inhibits the contractile mechanisms of muscle fibres.

Case study

Fatigue

It is not uncommon to hear of Tour de France riders suffering while riding its many stages, but what does this suffering actually entail? The 180 km plus stages require constant physical exertion for several hours at a time, resulting in sore or aching muscles, cramp, lack of energy and difficulty breathing. The riders must consume around 6000 calories and many additional litres of fluid per day. Despite the hours in the saddle, many of the stages end with a sprint to the finish when the riders approach speeds up to 60 km/h.

Check your knowledge

1. What visual clues might indicate a cyclist is suffering from fatigue?
2. How might a cyclist try and combat the onset of fatigue during a race?
3. What processes might coaches employ to help a cyclist recover from fatigue after a race?

Causes of fatigue

Depletion of energy sources

One of the causes of fatigue is when your body suffers from depleted energy sources, denying it the energy it needs in order to function effectively.

- Fatigue can result from a fall in the amount of **phosphagen**. Phosphagen is synthesised in the liver and transported to skeletal muscles for storage. It is used to form ATP from ADP and is particularly important for intense efforts of physical exercise. A fall in this will lead to less ATP in the bloodstream.
- Another cause is a reduction in **muscle and liver glycogen and blood glucose** during submaximal exercise. Once glycogen stores are depleted, muscles cease contracting – even during steady-state exercise – as the body is unable to use fat as the only fuel source. Marathon runners must be careful not to deplete their glycogen stores early in a race by setting off too fast, so that they can run at a pace that metabolises fats so the rate of glycogen depletion is reduced.

▶ Triathletes often suffer from fatigue as they finish an event

Accumulation of waste products

The main waste products of exercise are urea, carbon dioxide, water and lactic acid. Urea and water are filtered through the kidneys, while carbon dioxide is carried in the blood to the lungs, into the alveoli and then expelled from the body.

- **Blood lactate accumulation** – during exercise, raised levels of carbon dioxide increase blood acidity, increasing lactic acid which dissociates into lactate and hydrogen ions in blood.
- **Carbon dioxide** – in the blood, carbon dioxide combines with water producing carbonic acid.
- **Increased acidity** – carbonic acid is further broken down into bicarbonate and hydrogen ions. The hydrogen ions contribute to the blood's increased acidity.

Muscle lactate is disposed of first by oxidation to pyruvate and then by dissimilation to carbon dioxide and water. Some blood lactate is taken in by the liver which reconstructs it to glycogen. Remaining blood lactate diffuses back into the muscle to be oxidised then dismantled.

Neuromuscular fatigue

Neuromuscular fatigue is an inevitable after-effect of prolonged exercise. The physical factors employed by the central nervous system (CNS) (e.g. motor units) may, after prolonged exercise, become compromised and reduce their ability to carry out their functions effectively, resulting in a loss of performance.

- **Depletion of acetylcholine** – acetylcholine is a neurotransmitter released to stimulate skeletal muscles and the parasympathetic nervous system. Its effect is short-lived because it is destroyed by acetylcholinesterase, an enzyme released into the sarcolemma of muscle fibres to prevent continued muscle contraction in the absence of additional nervous stimulation.
- **Reduced calcium-ion release** – as part of the sliding filament theory (see page 65), calcium ions are released within the structure of muscle fibre allowing actin and myosin to couple and form actomyosin. If the store of calcium ions is reduced, the ability of the actin and myosin to couple is compromised, preventing continued muscle contraction.

Research

Explain why the mineral calcium is important to help prevent fatigue.

Recovery of energy systems

Once fatigue has set in, a number of processes have to be satisfied before the exhausted muscle can again perform to its optimum level.

Excess post-exercise oxygen consumption (EPOC)

The need for additional oxygen to replace ATP and remove lactic acid is known as 'oxygen debt' or excess post-exercise oxygen consumption (EPOC). The two major components of EPOC are:

- **fast components** (alactacid oxygen debt) – the amount of oxygen required to synthesise and restore muscle phosphagen stores (ATP and creatine phosphate)
- **slow components** (lactacid oxygen debt) – the amount of oxygen required to remove lactic acid from muscle cells and blood.

Bodily processes do not immediately return to normal after exercise. After light exercise recovery takes place quickly but with more intense steady-state exercise it takes time for the body to return to normal.

Fast components

- **Restoration of muscle phosphagen stores** – alactacid oxygen debt (without lactic acid) represents the oxygen used to synthesise and restore muscle phosphagen stores (ATP and phosphocreatine) that have been almost completely exhausted during high-intensity exercise. During the first 3 minutes of recovery, EPOC restores almost 99 per cent of ATP and phosphocreatine used during exercise (see Table 1.5).

Table 1.5: Restoration of muscle phosphagen

Recovery time (seconds)	Muscle phosphagen restored (%)
10	10
30	50
60	75
90	87
120	93
150	97
180	99
210	101
240	102

Key term

Catabolised – the breaking down of molecules into smaller units or components.

- The removal of lactic acid – lactic acid is **catabolised** into lactate and hydrogen ions, and removed, resulting in the feeling of pain or burning sensation in the muscles.

Slow components

The slow component of EPOC concerns the removal of lactic acid from the muscles and the blood. This can take several hours, depending on the intensity of the activity. Around half of lactic acid is removed after 15 minutes, and most is removed after an hour. Once exercise is over, the liver synthesises lactic acid into glycogen via a process called gluconeogenesis. This process is one of several mechanisms used by the body to maintain blood glucose levels while the remainder of the body can remove small amounts of lactic acid through respiration, perspiration and excretion.

- Myoglobin is an oxygen-storage protein found in muscle. Like haemoglobin, it combines with oxygen while the supply is plentiful, and stores it until the demand for oxygen increases. During exercise the oxygen from myoglobin is quickly used up, and after exercise additional oxygen is required to replace any oxygen that has been borrowed from myoglobin stores.
- The replenishment of muscle and liver glycogen stores depends on the type of exercise. Short-distance, high-intensity exercise may take two or three hours, whereas long endurance activities such as a marathon may take several days. Replenishment of glycogen is most rapid during the first few hours after training. Complete restoration of glycogen stores is accelerated with a high carbohydrate diet.

Nutritional strategies to help recovery

Adequate **protein intake** is essential to aid recovery, particularly for strength training when muscle tissue requires repair after training or exercise. Protein can also be metabolised for energy, so it is also useful for energy-demanding aerobic endurance sports. Protein requirements generally form 20 per cent of dietary intake, which is often enough to repair any micro-tears resulting from training or exercise.

Carbohydrate requirements are dependent on the fuel needs of an athlete's training or performance levels. As the body's carbohydrate storage is limited, athletes are encouraged to plan their carbohydrate intake around training and competition and, given the requirements as an exercise fuel, carbohydrates generally account for approximately 70 per cent of dietary intake.

Athletes should always begin exercise or training in a well **hydrated state** to prevent fatigue. Immediately after exercise, athletes should drink according to thirst and not drink too much fluid too quickly.

Research

In groups, research the commercially available dietary supplement products, such as protein shakes and carbohydrate drinks/gels, designed to help athletes recover after exercise. What do these products contain that helps athletes with the recovery process? Discuss your answers.

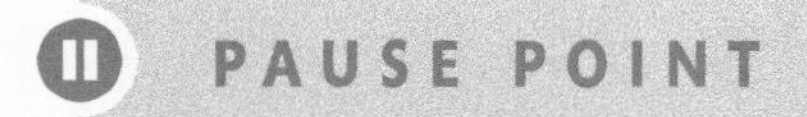

Why is it important for coaches and sport scientists to understand the impact and consequences of fatigue?

Hint Think about the potential negative effects of fatigue that may impair future training and performance.

Extend What steps can a coach or sport scientist make to counteract fatigue immediately after training or competition?

Recovery of musculoskeletal system

After exercise, the musculoskeletal system also takes a while to recover due to the number of potential fatigue factors.

- **Replacement of collagen in tendons and ligaments** – tendons and ligaments are made of collagen. When the body undergoes a period of exercise, these are placed under forces due to muscle contraction and body locomotion. When tendons and ligaments are damaged or stressed, the body produces collagen to heal them. However, tendons and ligaments have a poor blood supply, resulting in the potential for neither to heal completely. To help avoid sprains or strains of tendons or ligaments, which often require prolonged periods of recovery, it is important to perform appropriate stretching techniques before and after exercise.
- **Replacement of calcium in bones** – physical activity increases bone density throughout the body, not only in the bones being stressed during exercise. Bone hypertrophy is stimulated by the amount of loading placed on the skeletal system rather than the frequency of loading. Therefore, weightlifters will have a greater bone density than marathon runners. In both cases, exercise stimulates the release of calcium and vitamin D as part of the process of ossification, which increases bone strength and density.
- **Repair to micro-tears in muscles** – exercise places stress on muscles, leading to tiny tears in the muscle fibres. These tears will cause some pain and swelling in the muscle tissue. Protein is needed to build and repair these tears, making the muscle tissue stronger.
- **Delayed onset of muscle soreness (DOMS)** – DOMS is muscular discomfort which develops 24–48 hours after exercise. Research suggests it is caused by structural damage to muscle cells or inflammatory reactions in and around the muscle tissue. It is recommended that exercise is not resumed until the effects of the DOMS has worn off. Experienced athletes are less susceptible to the effect of DOMS unless their training programme undergoes changes.

Over-training

Link

This section links to *Unit 3: Applied Sport and Exercise Psychology* (pages 86–87).

Over-training is exercise at a level beyond normal physical tolerance limits, meaning the body is unable to recover adequately during rest periods. Over-trained athletes often complain of tiredness, lack of motivation and difficulty sleeping. Over-training can be caused by exercise addiction (a state of dependence on the feelings associated with exercise) and an imbalanced training programme concentrating on one area of training.

Physiological effects of over-training

There are three main physiological effects of over-training.

- **Imbalance in the endocrine system** – exercise requires the constant input of the endocrine system to release hormones to control important body functions. Over-training disrupts the endocrine system, resulting in the production of too much or too little of the various hormones secreted which can have knock-on effects on the digestive and nervous systems.
- **Excess adrenaline and cortisol production** – a periodised training programme allows adrenaline and cortisol levels to return to a normal state. In contrast, over-training is associated with imbalances or elevated levels of adrenaline and cortisol, leading to a suppressed immune system and reduced capacity to exercise before fatigue sets in.
- **Insufficient rest periods to repair muscular and skeletal tissues** – adaptation to training will only result in performance gains if the body is provided with adequate rest and training. In over-training there is insufficient rest and little or no adaptation in terms of muscle or bone growth.

Link

Periodised training is covered in *Unit 8: Specialised Fitness Training.*

Impact on performance and body system

Over-training has an impact on performance and body systems in the following ways.

- **Decrease in performance level** – over-training leads to performance decline, fatigue and sluggishness, prolonged recovery after competitive events, and an inconsistent level of performance.
- **Decreased immune function** – excessive training impacts the number and function of immune system cells such as white blood cells and antibodies. Inadequate rest increases the danger of infection, especially in the respiratory tract.
- **Increased susceptibility to injury** – the physiological effects associated with over-training combine with insufficient rest and recovery to increase the risk of injury. Overuse injuries can occur, such as microtrauma to muscle tissue, bone tissue or connective tissue.

- **Disruption to sleep** – over-training can lead to a hormonal imbalance (raised cortisol and adrenaline levels) which can disrupt sleep patterns. Normal sleep patterns are essential for the body to recover and repair itself.

PAUSE POINT Do you think over-training is more of an issue for athletes who train alone (without a coach)?

Hint A coach should notice the tell-tale signs of over-training and implement the required changes or rest.

Extend What strategies would you suggest to help an athlete who trains alone to check or watch for the signs of over-training?

Assessment practice 1.2

Amy took part in a cycling event that covered 300 miles. The event was made up of three stages on consecutive days.

- Stage 1 – 100-mile daytime ride across mostly flat terrain with the occasional slight incline
- Stage 2 – 100-mile daytime ride over hilly terrain (climbs and descents) for the middle 50 miles, with the 25 miles either side relatively flat. The final mile of the stage was a steep incline (10 per cent gradient)
- Stage 3 – 100-mile daytime ride across mostly flat terrain; the last 20 miles were by the coast, with strong cross winds.

Approximately two hours before each stage Amy consumed a large healthy meal with plenty of complex carbohydrates. During each stage, which lasted 5–6 hours, Amy consumed carbohydrate gels at hourly intervals.

1. Explain why Amy needed to consume a large healthy meal with plenty of carbohydrates before each stage and why she had carbohydrate gels every hour during each stage.
2. Explain why Amy's legs felt sore during the hill climbs (especially during Stage 2) compared to the flat stretches.
3. Explain why Amy had to take deep breaths throughout her slow, steady hill climbs during Stage 2, but was able to breathe relatively easily on the flat terrain.
4. The morning after completing Stage 3, Amy's legs were tired and her leg muscles were sore. Justify why the muscles in her legs were sore despite her obvious levels of physical fitness.

C Adaptations of the body systems to exercise

The body adapts to exercise with permanent changes that take place as a result of long-term exercise. If you exercise regularly, your body adapts and you get fit. This means you are able to cope with exercise that previously you might have found difficult, allowing you to cope with your chosen sport.

Link

There is more information on these body systems in *Unit 2: Functional Anatomy*.

Skeletal system adaptations

The skeletal system makes several adaptations in response to long-term exercise, shown in Table 1.6.

Table 1.6: Skeletal system adaptations to long-term exercise

Adaptation	Description
Osteoblast, osteoclast and osteocyte activity	• **Osteoblasts** migrate to the surface of the bone, making it more dense allowing the manufacture of new cells at the outer layer known as the periosteum. Weight-bearing exercise increases the width, density and strength of bones. In long bones, osteoblasts carry out **ossification**, which transforms fibrous tissue or cartilage into bone. • **Osteoclasts** are cells that destroy bone and reabsorb calcium and play a key role in **bone remodelling**, helping to regulate bone growth. Weight-bearing exercise suppresses osteoclast activity, maintaining a healthy bone density. • Exercise and an adequate diet containing sufficient calcium and vitamin D are essential for ossification.
Mineral content	Long-term exercise slows skeletal ageing. People who maintain active lifestyles have greater bone mass. Exercise of moderate intensity provides a safe and potent stimulus to maintain and increase bone mass.
Collagen and increased tendon strength	Collagen is a fibrous protein found in all connective tissue. It is the most common protein in the human body, giving bone its flexibility and helping bone resist tension (i.e. weight-bearing exercise). Weight-bearing exercise causes micro-tears to connective tissue and the body adapts by regenerating new tissues made of protein that is mostly collagen.

Muscular system adaptations

There are several different muscular system adaptations that the body makes to exercise (see Table 1.7).

Table 1.7: Muscular system adaptations to long-term exercise

Adaptation	Description
Hypertrophy	An increase in muscle size from training with greater resistance. Increases cross-sectional size of existing muscle tissue due to increases in the number of myofibrils and connective tissue (tendons and ligaments), which then become more pliable.
Increase tendon strength	As skeletal muscles become larger, stronger or more efficient, connective tendons adapt to meet increased demands to avoid injury from increased forces of contraction.
Muscle tone	An unconscious low-level contraction of muscle tissue while at rest, achieved via an effective training programme keeping muscle tissue primed. This state of constant muscle activation helps maintain balance and posture, and allows for quick reflex actions.
Muscle endurance	Endurance training improves muscular endurance by increasing the number of capillaries per area of muscle tissue, increasing oxygen supply to the muscle.
Hyperplasia	The action of splitting muscle cells contributing to muscle growth (different from hypertrophy which increases the number of individual cells). Research into hyperplasia continues, and it remains controversial and limited evidence suggests it is a recognised adaptation.
Increased mitochondria	With training, muscles increase oxidative capacity through an increase in the number of mitochondria in the muscle cells, an increased ATP supply and an increase in the quantity of the enzymes involved in respiration.
Increased myoglobin stores	With training, muscles increase their ability to store glycogen and myoglobin.
Increased storage of glycogen and triglycerides	With training (especially steady-state exercise), muscles increase the ability to store and use both triglycerides and glycogen as energy stores.
Adaptation of muscle fibres	Exercise leads to an increase in number and size of mitochondria within Type I and some Type IIa fibre cells. This improves muscle fibres' oxidation ability and their capacity to use oxygen. Strength training for Type IIx and some Type IIa muscle fibres can increase the number of contractile proteins (actin and myosin) and increase the recruitment of these fibres.
Capillarisation	Exercise enables muscle tissue to increase capillary density, supplying muscles with increased amounts of oxygen, and to remove more carbon dioxide, allowing greater exercise intensity and endurance.

PAUSE POINT What do you think happens to the skeletal or muscular adaptations of an athlete once they retire from competition?

Hint Would you expect atrophy (a decrease in bone density, muscle size and tendon elasticity) if training is not maintained?

Extend Investigate how retired athletes try to maintain some degree of fitness after retirement.

Key term

Minute ventilation – also known as minute volume = tidal volume × frequency of breaths per minute.

Respiratory system adaptations

Table 1.8 outlines the three main adaptations that the respiratory system makes to long-term exercise.

▶ **Table 1.8:** Respiratory system adaptations to long-term exercise

Adaptation	Description
Respiratory muscle efficiency	An increase in strength allows the external intercostal muscles greater contraction, while internal intercostal muscles relax during inspiration, forcing more air into the lungs. The greater the degree of contraction of the internal intercostals and relaxation of the external intercostals, the greater the volume of air inspired.
Lung volume adaptations	• Tidal volume can increase dramatically, to approximately 1 litre for an average adult and 2 litres for an elite athlete. • Vital capacity can increase allowing for deeper and more oxygen-rich breaths. Residual volume is also likely to increase in proportion to this increase. • Trained athletes' **minute ventilation** can increase by 50 per cent to 150 litres per minute.
Respiratory rate	As exercise continues, the body adapts by increasing respiratory rate (breaths per minute and depths of breath) to aid delivery of more oxygen to the working muscles. However, over time the tidal volume of athletes undertaking long-term exercise increases, so their respiratory rate can decrease for normal breathing but has the capacity to process increased amounts of oxygen at higher breathing rates.

Cardiovascular system adaptations

Table 1.9 outlines the four main areas and parts of the cardiovascular system that make adaptations to long-term exercise.

▶ **Table 1.9:** Cardiovascular system adaptations to long-term exercise

Adaptation	Description of adaptation
Cardiac cycle	• Heart size increases, particularly the chambers, allowing a greater stroke volume and a lower resting heart rate. This leads to a greater cardiac output, allowing the athlete to more easily continue working at a certain intensity. • The increased size of the left ventricle (cardiac hypertrophy) also lowers systolic blood pressure as less arterial pressure is needed to pump an increased volume of blood through the aorta. This also increases cardiac output. • Increased blood flow leads to an increase in blood volume. • Increased stoke volume and cardiac hypertrophy leads to a fall in resting heart rate. • Overall, the cardiovascular system becomes more efficient and able to deliver a greater volume of oxygen and nutrients to working muscles.
Sinoatrial node	Training causes an increase in the parasympathetic activity of the heart, decreasing the sinoatrial node's firing rate and slowing or lowering resting heart rate.
Blood composition	• Exercise raises the amount of proteins in blood plasma causing water retention and elevating blood volume. • Exercise also increases the number of red blood cells within the body. Elite athletes have a proportionally greater number of red blood cells. This enhances the ability to transport oxygen to working muscles during exercise. In trained males, blood volume equates to approximately 75 ml per kg of bodyweight, and in females it is approximately 65 ml per kg of bodyweight.
Diffusion rate	Long-term exercise can lead to the development of a capillary network to a part of the body. Aerobic training improves capillarisation of cardiac and skeletal muscles by increasing the number of capillaries and their density (the number of capillaries in a given area of muscle tissue), allowing for greater diffusion of oxygen from the blood to the tissues and greater removal of carbon dioxide.

Neuromuscular system adaptations

Table 1.10 outlines the adaptations the nervous system makes to long-term exercise.

▸ **Table 1.10:** Nervous system adaptations to long-term exercise

Adaptation	Description
Motor units	The ability of a motor unit to summate (fire a lot of impulses in target muscles all at once) is improved with strength and power training as they require maximum activation of target muscles to create the desired force.
Neural pathway transmission efficiency	Changes include **cellular adaptations**, modifications of neurotransmitters, alterations in reflex, and chemical and biochemical responses. For example, sprint training actually produces relatively small metabolic changes but has substantial effects on performance.
Nervous inhibition	Training is known to decrease nervous inhibition which itself is a response of the central nervous system to feedback sent from the muscle tissue. Nervous inhibition prevents the muscle from overworking and potentially ripping itself apart as the muscle undergoes levels of force it is not used to.

Key term

Cellular adaptations – changes within the cell structure (for example, an increase in mitochondrial size).

PAUSE POINT Can you think of a situation where a decrease in nervous inhibition leads to negative implications for an athlete?

Hint Consider what may happen during intense exercise or competition that may cause injury or trauma to an athlete.

Extend Research any high-profile sudden injury cases that resulted in unexpected muscle tears or other tissue damage.

Endocrine system adaptations

The endocrine system produces chemical messages in the form of hormones, which are carried by the bloodstream to tissues or organs throughout the body. These messages include signals for either an increase or decrease in tissue or organ activity. During exercise, adrenaline, noradrenaline and cortisol function together to synthesise fuel for the production of ATP. There are three adaptations that the endocrine system makes to long-term exercise, as shown in Table 1.11.

▸ **Table 1.11:** Endocrine system adaptations to long-term exercise

Adaptation	Description
Adrenaline and noradrenaline secretion	These enhance cardiac output by increasing heart rate, vasodilation in targeted blood vessels and increasing blood pressure. In strength and endurance training these direct blood flow to the tissues that are being exercised. Long-term exercise makes this system more efficient and increases the body's capacity to secrete both into the bloodstream.
Cortisol	Cortisol enhances muscle tissues by increasing blood glucose levels to provide quick bursts of energy. However, cortisol is 'catabolic' and interferes with anabolic functions. If the body remains in a catabolic 'breakdown' state this can lead to a decrease of muscle tissue, immunity is lowered and imbalances in blood sugar levels develop. However, strength training can lead to an increase in cortisol at rest which enables an increased supply of blood glucose for the next exercise session.
Testosterone and HGH	Testosterone and human growth hormone (HGH) are the two hormones primarily involved in strength training adaptations. Testosterone aids the release of HGH and interacts with the nervous system. Research indicates strength training increases the frequency and volume of both testosterone and HGH secretion, which, in turn, increases muscle hypertrophy. Strength training can increase the HGH at rest which enables an increase in strength capabilities for the next training session.

Discussion

Do you think it is acceptable for athletes to take legal ergogenic aids (any product that gives them a physical benefit) that might raise their testosterone levels for training and competition? What physical benefits do you think may occur as a result of taking such aids?

Energy systems adaptations

Table 1.12 outlines the adaptations the energy system makes to long-term exercise.

▶ **Table 1.12:** Energy systems adaptations to long-term exercise

Adaptation area	Description
Increased anaerobic and aerobic enzymes	Cellular adaptation, such as an increase in number and size of mitochondria, is usually accompanied by an increase in the level of aerobic system enzymes, which enhances the ability of slow-twitch muscles to generate adenosine triphosphate (ATP), allowing an athlete to sustain prolonged periods of aerobic exercise. The anaerobic system also undergoes changes, including an increase in the intramuscular levels of ATP and an increase in the enzymes (especially in fast-twitch muscles) that control the anaerobic phase of glucose breakdown.
Increased stores of phosphocreatine (PC)	An adaptation of strength training in particular is an increase in muscle cells' ability to store phosphocreatine (PC), enabling short bursts of high-intensity exercise.
Decreased stores of triglycerides	Research shows that individuals who exercise regularly have lower blood levels of triglycerides than sedentary individuals.
Increased use of fats	The use of fats as an energy source occurs during low-intensity exercise. Fat combustion powers almost all exercise at approximately 25 per cent of aerobic power. Fat oxidation increases if exercise extends to over an hour as glycogen levels deplete. Beyond an hour, fats account for approximately 75 per cent of total energy required.
Higher tolerance of lactic acid	As you get fitter, oxygen is used to break down lactate to carbon dioxide and water, preventing lactate from pouring into the blood. Low lactate threshold can be due to: • not getting enough oxygen inside your muscle cells • inefficient lactate buffering (i.e. carnosine and phosphate) • insufficient mitochondria in your muscle cells • muscles, heart and other tissues being inefficient at extracting lactate from the blood. Long-term exercise saturates muscles in lactic acid, training your body to deal with it more effectively. The accumulation of lactate in working skeletal muscles is associated with fatigue after 50–60 seconds of maximal effort. Therefore, training continuously at about 85–90 per cent of your maximum heart rate for 20–25 minutes improves the body's tolerance to lactic acid. For example, a sedentary individual's OBLA will activate around 50–60 per cent of VO_2 max, whereas a trained athlete's OBLA will activate around 70–80 per cent of VO_2 max. Given a trained athlete will have a higher VO_2 max anyway, the increase in OBLA for trained athletes can be quite significant. Long-term exercise can lead to an ability to exhale an increased level of carbon dioxide during intense exercise delaying OBLA. This process causes the respiratory exchange ratio (RER) to exceed a normal value of 1.00 (i.e. equal inhalation/exhalation ratio of oxygen/carbon dioxide).

Measurement of body systems and their contribution to sport and exercise performance

Measurement of body systems can provide an indication of current fitness levels and, if previous baseline tests have been undertaken, any increase in fitness levels (for example VO_2 max) can be determined along with an estimate of the impact of a training programme (see Table 1.13).

Link

You can read more about measuring body systems in *Unit 4: Field- and Laboratory-based Fitness Testing.*

▶ **Table 1.13:** Body systems that can be tested to measure fitness

Body system	Description
VO_2 max	This is one of the best indicators of cardiovascular fitness. Increased VO_2 max indicates a high rate of absorption and use of oxygen, giving the potential to train at higher intensities before muscle tissue demand for oxygen exceeds supply. High VO_2 max indicates a very efficient cardiovascular system, allowing for increased endurance performance and more rapid rates of recovery post-exercise. Weight-bearing exercises (e.g. running) significantly influence VO_2 max levels, while non-weight-bearing (e.g. swimming) have comparatively less influence.
Anaerobic threshold (% of VO_2 max)	Continued high volume and intensity of endurance exercise is further likely to improve an athlete's anaerobic threshold. This is when the blood concentration of lactate and hydrogen ions increase as the body's requirements become more reliant on the lactate energy system to meet the intensity demands of the exercise. Athletes with a high VO_2 max who undertake regular intensive exercise can tolerate increasingly higher levels of blood lactate than athletes with a lower VO_2 max.
Anaerobic power	This can be increased by either sprint (or speed) training or power training. Maximal sprint or power training overloads ATP-PC and lactate energy systems and can be measured using sprint tests. This enhances anaerobic metabolic capacity of the muscles being trained, allowing an athlete to train and perform at higher intensities.
Strength (1RM)	Strength training results in structural and functional adaptations to the body (muscle tissue in particular). These adaptations depend on the amount of training undertaken, but the strength, measured by 1RM, will have increased for the muscle group in question and so the 1RM can be used to measure adaptations over time.
Muscular endurance (15RM)	The level of adaptation can be measured in the ability of the muscle to contract repeatedly for 15 repetitions at a given weight or resistance.

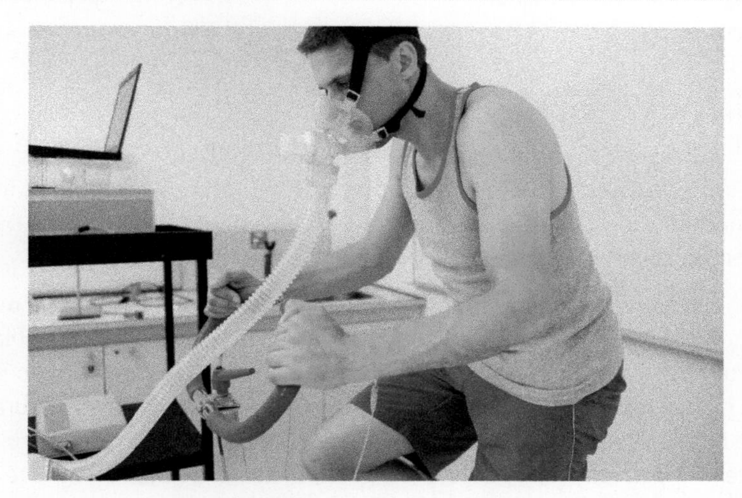

▶ VO_2 max tests can be done in a laboratory to measure cardiovascular fitness improvements

PAUSE POINT Explain how persistence with training can be measured and demonstrate an increase in fitness over time.

Hint Depending on the type of training, which measurement or test might you use to determine fitness level increases?

Extend Can training increase two or more body system measurements during the same period? Justify your answer.

Assessment practice 1.3

Finlay, the rugby player featured in Assessment practice 1.1, has now undergone three months of rugby training since he completed his initial eight-week fitness programme at the gym. The rugby training includes:

- 4 × weekly session of rugby drills
- 2 × strength and power sessions per week
- 1 × intense sprint interval session per week
- 1 × 45 minute continuous run (low intensity) per week.

1 Testing shows that Finlay's resting heart rate has dropped further. Explain how the rugby training has contributed to this.

2 Why might Finlay now be less conscious of his previously fractured femur? How might his rugby training have strengthened his bones further?

Finlay decided to attempt the one-minute press-up test. Upon completion of his fitness training programme at the gym, Finlay completed 38 press-ups. Now he can complete 63.

3 Analyse Finlay's rugby training and suggest a possible explanation for his ability to increase his press-up count to his current performance level.

D Environmental factors and sport and exercise performance

Elite athletes compete and train around the world so need to cope with numerous environmental conditions. Altitude and temperature vary greatly depending on location. For example, golfers could be in Dubai playing in 40°C heat one week and in near freezing conditions in Scotland the next. But these environmental factors can also have an effect on responses to training.

High altitude

Altitude is the measure of elevation above sea level. As altitude increases, atmospheric pressure decreases, leading to a fall in oxygen pressure. Today, it is common for athletes to not only compete but also train at altitude, enabling the body to become more efficient at absorbing oxygen. This is known as **acclimatisation**.

Decreases in oxygen pressure cause the body's chemoreceptors to become more responsive to an increase in carbon dioxide. This leads to an increase in ventilation as the brain attempts to restore gaseous exchange to a normal level. As oxygen is less available at high altitude, this results in lower than normal haemoglobin saturation levels in the blood. At 5000 metres above sea level the oxygen saturation in blood is approximately 70 per cent (compared to 98 per cent at sea level). If an athlete has not acclimatised, the lack of oxygen may seriously impair physical activity. However, most people can ascend to 2400 metres above sea level without difficulty.

Responses of body systems to high altitude

- **Hypoxia** occurs when the body is deprived of oxygen. At high altitude, the demands of the cardiovascular and respiratory systems are increased. Without acclimatisation the body's tissue may become hypoxic and deprived of adequate oxygen.
- **Increased breathing rate** (hyperventilation) involves increased ventilation of the lungs caused by impaired gaseous exchange in the lungs.

- **Increased heart rate** (possible tachycardia) - tachycardia is a resting heart rate above normal (more than 100 beats per minute). High altitude causes only a minimal reduction in resting stroke volume, but a decrease in maximal heart rate response lowers cardiac output.
- **Reduced VO_2 max** - there is an estimated reduction in VO_2 max of 2 per cent for every 300 metres above 1500 metres above sea level. This drop in VO_2 max means an athlete's oxygen uptake decreases which will (without acclimatisation) adversely affect performance, particularly during endurance events.
- **Altitude sickness** - an illness brought on by an ascent to high altitude and characterised by a shortage of oxygen leading to hyperventilation, exhaustion and nausea.

Adaptations of the body systems to high altitude

During acclimatisation, generally over a period of two or more weeks, there is an increase in red blood cell count and haemoglobin concentration. This is caused by an increase in the manufacture of red blood cells in bone marrow to carry more oxygen to muscles. Other changes also take place:

- **increased capillarisation** - to counteract the lower concentrations of oxygen in the blood, the number of small blood vessels in the body increases to ensure that all available oxygen is used efficiently
- **increased mitochondria** - altitude causes an increase in the myoglobin and mitochondria within cells
- **oxidative enzymes** - altitude causes an increase in oxidative enzymes in mitochondria. This allows Type I and Type IIa muscle fibres to process increased levels of oxygen for use with the aerobic energy system.

Acclimatisation during training may not always be possible, so there are alternative training options that promote equivalent adaptations to enhance sport and exercise performance at sea level.

- **Hypoxic (altitude) chambers** - these are used to simulate the effects of high altitude on the human body.
- **Sleep high, train low** - the body adapts to sleeping at high altitude with low oxygen levels, while training at a low altitude where the oxygen levels are much higher. This allows the body to benefit from the benefits of being at high altitude (increase in blood cell production) without interfering with a training programme.
- **Aerobic performance** - exercise performance (aerobic) is enhanced due to the red blood cells becoming more efficient at uploading oxygen to tissues.
- **Anaerobic performance** - exercise performance (anaerobic) is enhanced due to an increase in OBLA because of changes in the acid/alkali balance in the blood.

Hypoxic or altitude chambers can be used to help athletes acclimatise while training at sea level

Discussion

Do you consider altitude training to be performance enhancing? What are the differences between altitude training and blood doping?

Key term

Homeostatic response – the body's attempts to maintain a condition of balance within its internal environment, such as its temperature, even when faced with external changes or challenges.

Thermoregulation

The body's thermoregulatory system enables a **homeostatic response** to temperature changes. During exercise, the metabolic rate can increase twenty-fold and this increase in energy consumption raises body temperature significantly.

The body tackles this via the hypothalamus, the body's thermostat. The hypothalamus contains the central point within the body for temperature regulation. A group of specialised neurons at the base of the brain helps regulate body temperature within a narrow band around 37°C. The hypothalamus receives a generous blood supply allowing it to monitor body temperature and initiate a response when temperature changes.

The body loses heat through a combination of:

- **convection** – the process of water or air flowing over the skin and carrying away body heat
- **conduction** – involves heat moving from or to the body from its surrounding air. The faster cooler air moves around the body, the greater the quantity of heat conducted from the body
- **radiation** – the transfer of heat from one object to another without contact. Through radiation, an athlete radiates heat towards cooler objects. The closer the two temperatures (the athlete and the object), the less heat the athlete loses. At rest, radiation is the main method of losing body heat
- **evaporation** – water vaporisation lost through breathing or sweating transfers heat from the body to the surrounding environment – this is the body's major defence against overheating. In response to overheating, the sweat glands secrete lots of saline solution (NaCl dissolved in water) forming sweat. The cooling process occurs when sweat reaches the surface of the skin and evaporates.

Excessive heat

There are two main responses that the body makes to excessive heat during sport and exercise performance.

- **Hyperthermia** – this occurs when the body cannot lose excess heat. Early symptoms include excessive sweating, headache, nausea, dizziness and hyperventilation. Overexposure to hot and humid conditions can lead to normal heat loss processes becoming ineffective. A core temperature greater than 40°C increases metabolic rate, increasing heat production. The skin becomes hot and dry and the temperature rise risks organ damage. To combat this, cool the body in water and administer fluids.
- **Dehydration** – excessive water loss. When water output exceeds intake, the body has a negative fluid balance. A serious consequence is a lowering of blood plasma levels leading to inadequate blood volume to maintain cardiovascular function. It is avoided by drinking plenty of water. When a large amount of water is lost through perspiration, causing possible salt depletion, it is vital to maintain electrolyte balance. This can cause further symptoms including tiredness, irritability, fainting, cramps and loss of performance.

▶ Competitors in the Marathon des Sables need to avoid hyperthermia or dehydration

During sport and exercise performance, the body can respond and adapt to excessive heat in various ways, including:

- **increased sweat production** – to enable the loss of excess heat the body increases its sweat production, allowing greater evaporation. However, it is important you remain properly hydrated and that electrolyte levels remain stable
- **reduced electrolyte concentration due to sweating** – during excessive periods of sweating, electrolytes are lost and must be replaced. Failure to do so may lead to inhibited nervous function and, in extreme cases, can be fatal
- **increased blood plasma volume or earlier onset of sweating** – a benefit of heat acclimatisation is an increase in blood plasma volume. Just as altitude training stimulates the body to produce more red blood cells, training in locations with a high temperature stimulates the body to produce more plasma. The result is a greater cardiac output, and higher VO_2 max
- **reduced aerobic and anaerobic performance** – the body cools down by circulating blood through the skin. This diverts blood from the muscles, which in turn increases heart rate. If the temperature is high the body needs to circulate more blood to the skin, depriving muscles of much-needed oxygen and nutrients. This will have an impact on both aerobic and anaerobic performance.

Extreme cold

The body has several methods for reducing heat loss during sport and exercise performance in extreme cold conditions:

- **vasoconstriction** reduces the amount of convection heat transfer from the skin and concentrates the remaining heat in and around the body's core (its vital organs)
- **shivering** is a response to feeling cold. When the core body temperature drops, a shivering reflex is triggered to maintain homeostasis. Skeletal muscles will shake in small movements, creating warmth by expending kinetic energy
- **shivering thermogenesis** is the fastest thermogenic process a static body can produce and involves a series of involuntary muscle contractions producing heat in response to a cold environment. The conversion of chemical energy of ATP into **kinetic** energy causes some of this kinetic energy to be transferred as heat
- **non-shivering thermogenesis** occurs in brown adipose tissue and involves a series of complex cellular reactions which enable energy from free fatty acids to be dissipated within the body as heat.

Key term

Kinetic – relating to or resulting from motion.

The main effects of extreme cold on the body during sport and exercise performance are:

- **hypothermia** – a condition where low body temperature results from prolonged exposure to cold. Breathing, blood pressure and heart rate decrease and drowsiness sets in. If uncorrected, hypothermia can be fatal as body temperature approaches 29°C. Hypothermia develops if the rate of heat loss from your body exceeds the rate at which the body is producing heat
- **frostbite** – this is damage to skin and tissue caused by prolonged exposure to freezing temperatures. The body responds to cold temperatures by vasoconstriction and blood flow to the extremities (hands, feet, ears, nose and lips) slows down, so that blood flow to vital organs can be increased. The tissues in these extremities are deprived of oxygen and the fluid in the tissues freezes into ice crystals causing severe cellular damage. If blood flow cannot be restored quickly, the tissue will die and will need to be removed through surgery.

PAUSE POINT Why is the type of clothing worn important when training in hot or cold climates?

Hint Clothing will impact thermoregulation levels in hot and cold climates.

Extend Research the types of sports clothing and how they help thermoregulation in different climates.

Assessment practice 1.4

Consider Amy, the cyclist in Assessment practice 1.2. The climate was different on each stage of the cycling event. During Stage 1 the temperature reached 32°C with 95 per cent humidity. During Stage 3 it was much cooler and, near the coast, the temperature dropped to 10°C with an added wind chill factor.

- Analyse how thermoregulation allows Amy to maintain her core body temperature while cycling in the different conditions.

Further reading and resources

Books

Brooks, D. (2004) *The Complete Book of Personal Training*, Champaign, IL: Human Kinetics.

Coulson, M. (2013) *The Complete Guide to Personal Training*, London: Bloomsbury.

Katch, V., McArdle, W. and Katch, F. (2011) *Essentials of Exercise Physiology*, 4th edition, Philadelphia, PA: Lippincott Williams & Wilkins.

Vander, A., Sherman, J. and Luciano, D. (2014) *Human Physiology: The Mechanisms of Body Function*, 7th edition, Boston, MA: McGraw Hill.

Websites

www.eis2win.co.uk – English Institute of Sport: information about the nutritional principles used by the EIS to improve athlete performance.

www.uksca.org.uk – UK Strength and Conditioning Association: information and advice about how to become an accredited strength and conditioning coach.

www.bases.org.uk – British Association of Sport and Exercise Sciences: news and other information about sport and exercise sciences.

THINK FUTURE

Isobel Graham
Personal trainer

When I started my Level 3 BTEC Sport and Exercise Sciences course, I soon took an interest in how the body works and adapts to fitness training and programming. I knew that when I finished I wanted to be a personal trainer, so I took a Level 2 gym instructors award. The content of the BTEC course, especially the exercise physiology, helped me pass the exam. Not long after gaining my Level 2 qualification, I got a part-time job at a local health club while continuing my studies at college.

When I completed the BTEC course, I was able to enrol on a Level 3 Personal Trainer course. This took me approximately 12 months to complete and it was hard work, but I'm now a fully qualified advanced personal trainer and have a list of clients that I train at the same health club, some of whom are competition athletes.

The job is very rewarding and, in addition to all the required specialist knowledge, it's vital to have a good rapport with your clients. It's important to make people feel comfortable and good about themselves. Their health, well-being and achievements are a reflection of my efforts, so I'm very proud of my clients and all they've accomplished in the gym.

Personal training is my dream job. I realised early on in my BTEC course that this was what I wanted to do, and that focus helped me to complete the BTEC and all subsequent courses. I make a good living and I'm just about to put a deposit down on a flat. Would I change anything? Not a thing!

Focusing your skills

Fitness knowledge

Use your knowledge and expertise to the best of your ability and provide the best service you can when developing individual training programmes.

- A personal trainer needs excellent knowledge of how the body moves and functions. This specialised knowledge is based on human anatomy, physiology, psychology, nutrition and exercise programming.
- You are a mixture of coach and teacher to your clients, and must blend long-term goals and motivational techniques into a training programme.
- You will need to develop individual training programmes, all of which are different. This will require the utmost planning, coordination and organisation.

Conducting health monitoring tests

You must follow the correct protocol when undertaking health monitoring tests. These tests give a good indication of a client's level of fitness and whether your programming is having an impact.

- Treat your clients with courtesy and respect. Emphasise that your clients' results are confidential and will not be passed to anyone else without their consent.
- Conduct tests in a suitable environment and in a professional manner. Explain what you are doing and maintain an air of calm authority throughout.
- Upon completion of any test, explain the results and discuss the role they will play in developing any future training programme.
- Ensure the testing area is left exactly as you found it and all equipment is safely stowed away.

Getting ready for assessment

This section has been written to help you do your best when you take your assessment task. Read through it carefully and ask your tutor if there is anything you are still not sure about.

Worked example

Question 1

Adnan has returned to football after a three-year break. He needs to improve his general fitness so he decides to undertake a 12-week training programme at his local gym. His fitness instructor gives him the following programme.

Day	Training task(s)
Monday	20–30 mins running on a treadmill (10–12 km/h)
Tuesday	Resistance machines (upper body)
Thursday	15–20 mins rowing (24–28 strokes per minute); 15–20 mins cycling
Friday	Resistance machines (lower body)
Saturday	20–30 mins cross-country running

(a) Explain how Adnan's fitness training programme might increase his bone strength and/or density. [3]

Look carefully at how the question is set out to see how many points need to be included in your answer.

Adnan's training involves weight-bearing exercises which are known to strengthen bones. He will also use resistance machines which make bones more dense and able to support more weight. This is helped by calcium in the diet.

This answer demonstrates a basic understanding of skeletal adaptations to exercise. Although the learner has not mentioned osteoblast activity, they have shown their knowledge that weight-bearing and resistance exercises strengthen bone tissue and mentioned the role calcium plays in the process. 2 marks awarded.

Upon successful completion of the 12-week training programme, a series of health monitoring tests reveal that Adnan's resting heart rate has dropped from 88 bpm to 77 bpm, and show a significant improvement in his VO_2 max, from 35.2 ml/kg/min to 40.01 ml/kg/min.

(b) Explain why Adnan's fitness training programme has caused a reduction in his resting heart rate and a rise in his VO_2 max value. [5]

Due to the amount of cardiovascular exercise Adnan was doing over 12 weeks, this exercise would have led to cardiac hypertrophy. This means that the heart muscle tissue will have enlarged due to the exercise undertaken. This increase in heart muscle size means the stroke volume would have increased. If the cardiac output stayed the same, then the resting heart rate can reduce. This will have made Adnan fitter and he would have found the cardiovascular exercise easier by week 12.

Adnan's VO_2 max would have increased because of capillarisation. This means that the number of capillaries would have increased in his tissues (due to cardiovascular training) so his blood would be able to deliver more oxygen to the working muscles. This is why his VO_2 max increased.

This answer demonstrates a good understanding of cardiovascular and respiratory adaptation to training and the specific relevance to the client's requirements. The learner takes into account his current level of fitness and explains how the adaptations work in terms of the client's performance. 4 marks awarded.

When Adnan trained his larger muscle groups (chest, back and legs) he used weights of 25, 30, 35 and 40 kg on the resistance machines.

(c) Explain how Adnan's nervous system can control the force generated by his muscles to allow him to use the various weight levels on the resistance machines. [4]

Muscle spindles and Golgi tendon organs provide the information about the intensity of exercise, allowing Adnan to carry out strong and coordinated movement patterns.

This answer demonstrates a basic understanding of the nervous system's adaptations to exercise. Although the learner has not mentioned the process of nervous inhibition, the knowledge of how weight training involves the use of muscle spindles and Golgi tendons is described, but it could be explained in further detail. 2 marks awarded.

Question 2

Gemma is a triathlete who took part in a 1.5 km swim, 50 km cycle ride and 10 km run. Gemma consumed plenty of calories in the form of balanced meals leading up to the event. She consumed carbohydrate gels at hourly intervals during the triathlon, along with plenty of fluids.

(a) Explain why Gemma consumed carbohydrate gels during the triathlon. [3]

Gemma is using mostly the aerobic energy system to complete the triathlon which utilises carbohydrates, fats and proteins extracted from the diet for resynthesising ATP. The aerobic system produces more ATP than any other energy system but does so at a slower rate and is therefore less suitable for intense exercise but ideal for the steady state of a triathlon. The aerobic systems consist of three processes or stages, each of which produce ATP. They are aerobic glycolysis, the Krebs cycle and the electron transport chain. The carbohydrate gels keeps the aerobic energy system continually fuelled with blood glucose to allow for completion of the event and prevents fatigue.

This answer demonstrates an excellent understanding of energy systems and explains why the consumption of carbohydrate gels was important for the triathlon. 3 marks awarded.

(b) The final 5 km of the cycle component was executed on a 3 per cent gradient. Towards the end of this, Gemma's legs started to feel sore. In terms of energy systems, what accounts for this muscle soreness and why did it occur? [3]

The gradient means that Gemma had to work harder on the cycle component. If the gradient was very steep then her muscles would have needed more than the aerobic energy system, and would need to have used the lactate system which makes muscles sore.

This answer demonstrates only a basic understanding of energy systems. The learner identified that the lactate system was engaged to an increasing level at a gradient, but failed to explain what caused muscle soreness (hydrogen ions) or the fact that all energy systems operate at the same time but to differing degrees. 1 mark awarded.

After 6 km of the running stage, Gemma had to climb a steep gradient for 200 m. At the top of the hill Gemma felt breathless, had to slow her running rate significantly and needed to breathe deeply for several minutes.

(c) Explain why Gemma needed to breathe deeply despite slowing her running rate significantly. [3]

The gradient meant that Gemma was working at the limits of her aerobic energy system and probably utilising more of the lactate system. This would produce large volumes of CO_2 in the blood which needs to be expelled. If it doesn't then Gemma will have to stop. The best way to get rid of CO_2 is to breath deeper. Once the breathing rate returns to normal then the excess CO_2 has been expelled.

This answer demonstrates a good understanding of energy systems and the issues surrounding waste products in the blood. The learner understands the basic mechanics of how the body rids itself of excess carbon dioxide. 2 marks awarded.

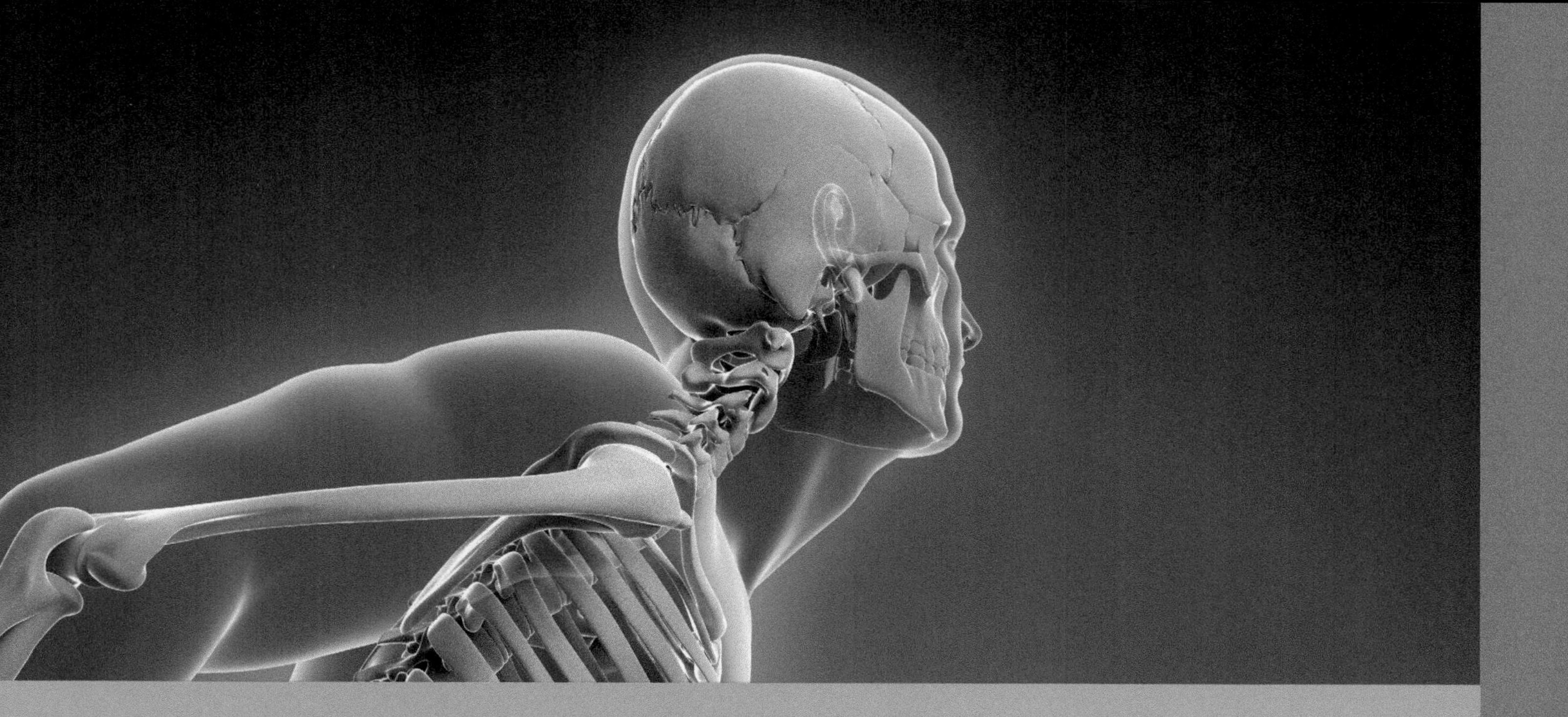

2 Functional Anatomy

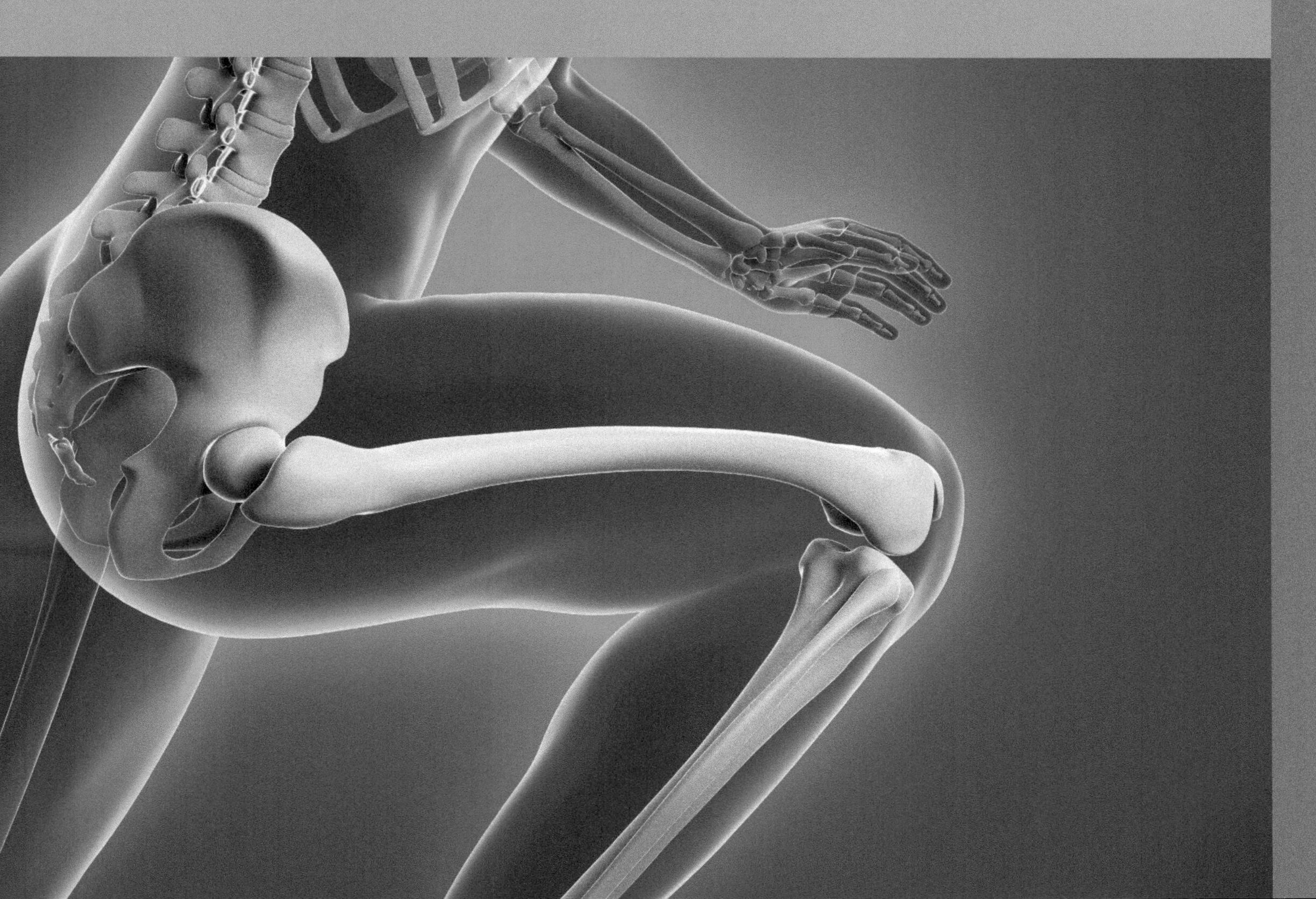

Getting to know your unit

Assessment
This unit is assessed by an examination that is set and marked by Pearson.

To understand what happens during sport and exercise, you must know about the different body systems. This unit examines the systems that make up the body, how these systems interact and work with each other, and why they are so important to sports performance. You will be introduced to the structures and functions of the four key systems and the effects that sport and exercise has on them, and how these systems work together effectively to produce movement.

How you will be assessed

This unit will be assessed by an examination set by Pearson. It will contain a number of short and long answer style questions.

As the guidelines for assessment can change, you should refer to the official assessment guidance on the Pearson Qualifications website for the latest definitive guidance.

During this examination you will need to show your knowledge and understanding of the anatomy of the cardiovascular, respiratory, skeletal and muscular systems and how they work together to produce movement.

Throughout the unit, you will find assessment practice activities to help you prepare for the exam. Completing each of these will give you an insight into the types of questions and, more importantly, how to answer them.

Unit 2 has four assessment outcomes (AO) which will be included in the external examination. Certain 'command words' are associated with each assessment outcome – see Table 2.1.

- **AO1** Demonstrate knowledge and understanding of the language, structure, characteristics and function of each anatomical system
  - Command words: describe, give, identify, name, state
  - Marks: range from 1 to 5 marks
- **AO2** Apply knowledge and understanding of the structure, characteristics and function of the anatomical systems in context
  - Command words: describe, explain
  - Marks: range from 2 to 5 marks
- **AO3** Analyse the anatomical systems' effectiveness in producing sport and exercise movements and evaluate their impact on performing movements successfully
  - Command words: analyse, assess, evaluate, discuss, to what extent
  - Marks: range from 8 to 20 marks
- **AO4** Make connections between anatomical systems and how they interrelate in order to carry out different exercises and sporting movements in context

Table 2.1: Command words used in this unit

Command word	Definition – what it is asking you to do
Analyse	Identify several relevant facts of a topic, demonstrate how they are linked and then explain the importance of each, often in relation to the other facts.
Assess	Carefully consider varied factors or events that apply to a specific situation and identify those which are the most important or relevant to arrive at a conclusion.
Describe	Give a full account of all the information, including all the relevant details of any features, of a topic.
Discuss	Identify an issue/situation/problem/argument that is being assessed and explore all aspects and investigate fully.
Evaluate	Bring all the relevant information on a topic together and make a judgement on it (for example, on its success, importance, strengths, weaknesses, alternative actions, relevant data or information). This should be clearly supported by the information you have gathered.
Explain	Make an idea, situation or problem clear to your reader by making a point/statement or by linking the point/statement with a justification/expansion.
Give	Provide examples, justifications and/or reasons to a context.
Identify	State the key fact(s) about a topic or subject. The word 'outline' is similar. You should assess factual information that may require a single-word answer, although sometimes a few words or a maximum of a single sentence are required.
State/name	Give a definition or example.
To what extent	Review information then bring it together to form a judgement or conclusion, after giving a balanced and reasoned argument.

Getting started

The human body is made up of a number of different systems that interact together, allowing you to take part in sport and exercise. Write a list of how the body changes immediately before, during and after a sport or exercise session. Consider these changes and think about the system that is affected. Why do you think these changes occur?

A Anatomical positions, terms and references

When examining the human body it is important you are able to refer to the location of different parts of the body. This is particularly important when describing movements and body locations in relation to each other.

The 'anatomical position' is a standard standing position used in most diagrams of the body (see Figure 2.1), with the body facing forward, feet pointed forward and slightly apart, and arms hanging down on each side. This is also known as the **point of reference**.

A number of specialist terms that you need to understand are described in Table 2.2.

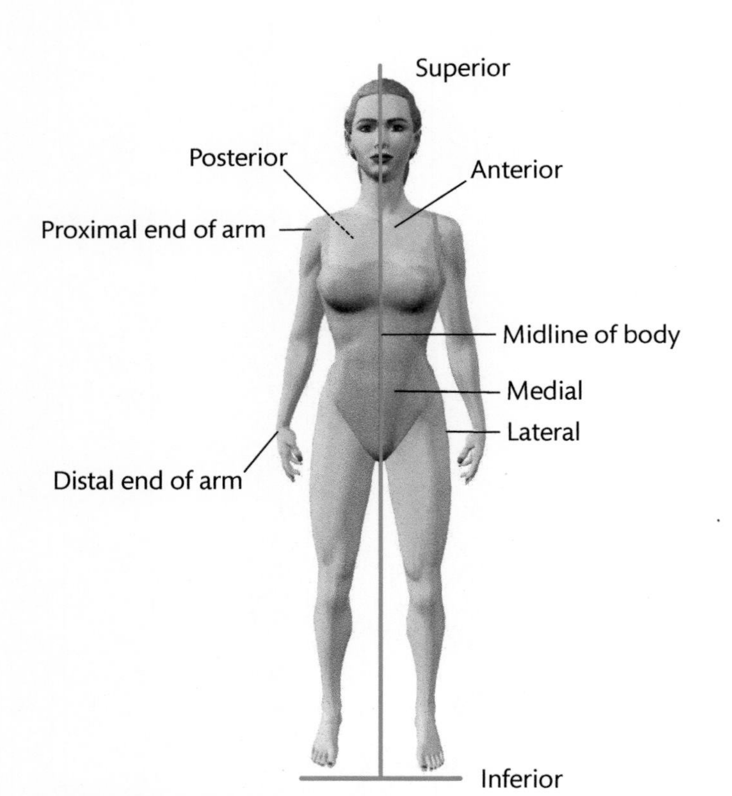

Figure 2.1: Anatomical positions

Table 2.2: Anatomical terms

Anatomical term	Definition
Anterior	To the front or in front
Posterior	To the rear or behind
Lateral	Away from the midline or axis, an imaginary line down the centre of the body
Medial	Towards the midline or axis
Proximal	Near to the root or origin (e.g. the proximal of the arm is towards the shoulder)
Distal	Away from the root or origin (e.g. the distal of the arm is towards the hand)
Superior	Above
Inferior	Below
Peripheral	Away from the centre of the body
Superficial	Near the surface of the skin
Deep	Away from the surface of the skin
Supine	Lying down with face pointing upwards
Prone	Lying down with face pointing downwards

Anatomy of the cardiovascular system

The cardiovascular system is also known as the **circulatory system**. It is the major transport system in your body, carrying food, oxygen and all other essential products to cells, and taking away waste products of respiration and other cellular processes, such as carbon dioxide.

Anatomy of the heart

The heart is a unique hollow muscle and is the pump of the cardiovascular system. It is located under the sternum (a long flat bone like a neck tie at the front of the ribcage, which provides protection) and is about the size of a closed fist. The heart drives blood into and through the arteries to the tissues and working muscles.

It is surrounded by a twin-layered sac known as the **pericardium**. The cavity between the layers is filled with pericardial fluid, which prevents friction as the heart beats. The heart wall is made up of three layers: the epicardium (the outer layer), the myocardium (the strong middle layer that forms most of the heart wall) and the endocardium (the inner layer).

The heart is actually two pumps in one: the two chambers on the right (the right atrium and the right ventricle) and the two chambers on the left (the left atrium and the left ventricle). The right side is separated from the left by a solid wall known as the **septum**. This prevents the blood on the right side coming into contact with the blood on the left side.

The specific parts of the heart, also shown in Figure 2.2, are as follows.

- **Coronary arteries** – the blood vessels supplying **oxygenated blood** to the heart muscle. There are two coronary arteries, the left and right.
- **Atria** – the upper chambers of the heart. They receive blood returning to your heart from either the body or the lungs. The right atrium receives **deoxygenated blood** via the superior and inferior vena cava (a large vein). The left atrium receives oxygenated blood from the left and right pulmonary veins.
- **Ventricles** – the pumping chambers of the heart. They have thicker walls than the atria. The right ventricle pumps blood to the pulmonary circulation for the lungs and the left ventricle pumps blood to the systemic circulation for the body including the muscles.
- **Bicuspid (mitral) valve** – one of the four valves in the heart, situated between the left atrium and the left ventricle. It allows the blood to flow in one direction only, from the left atrium to the left ventricle.
- **Tricuspid valve** – located between the right atrium and the right ventricle, it allows blood to flow from the right atrium to the right ventricle and prevents blood from flowing backwards.
- **Semilunar valves** (**aortic valve** and **pulmonary valve**) – between the left ventricle and the aorta, these prevent backflow from the aorta into the left ventricle. They are also situated between the right ventricle and the pulmonary artery.
- **Chordae tendineae** – chord-like tendons connected to the bicuspid and tricuspid valves to prevent valves turning inside out.

Key terms

Anatomy – study of the structure of the body such as the skeletal, muscular or cardiovascular systems.

Oxygenated blood – blood containing oxygen.

Deoxygenated blood – blood without oxygen (containing carbon dioxide).

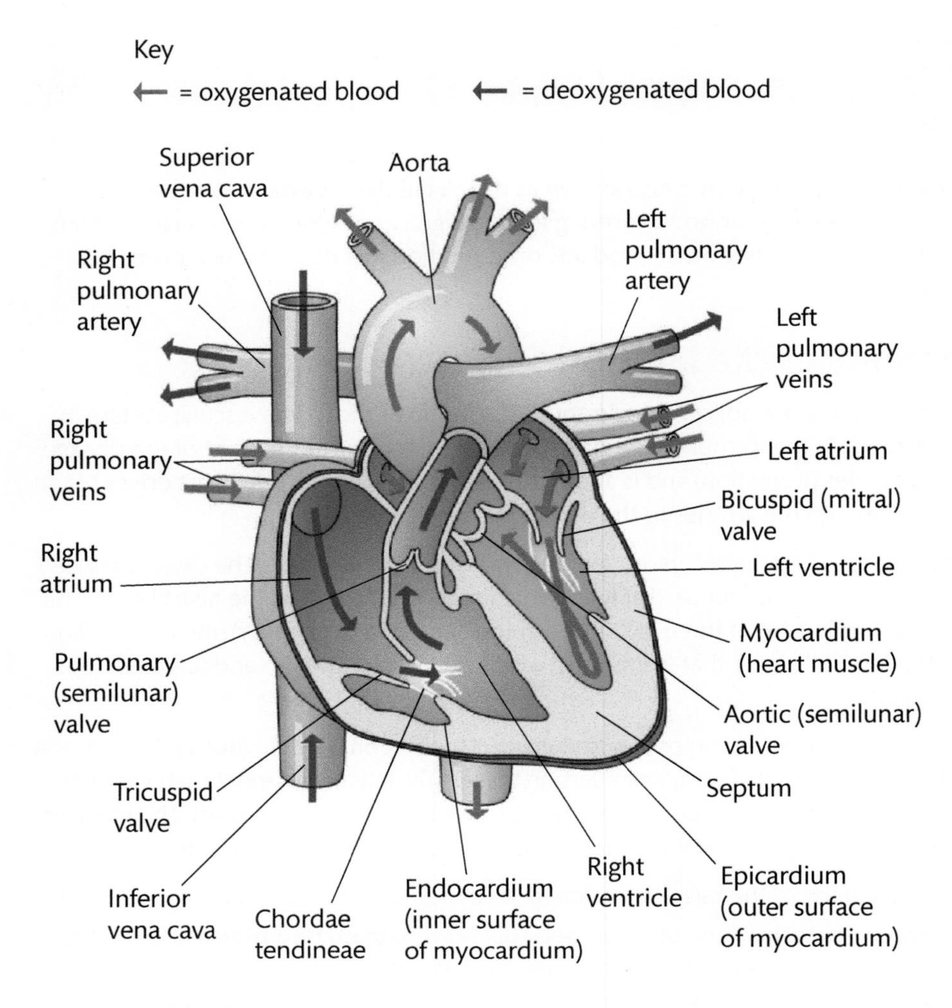

Figure 2.2: Diagram of the heart

Function of the heart

The chambers on the right of the heart supply blood at a low pressure to the lungs via blood vessels, where **gaseous exchange** (see pages 51–52) takes place: oxygen that has been breathed in through the lungs is transferred to the blood, and carbon dioxide, a waste product from the body's activities, is deposited ready to be exhaled from the body. This blood is then returned to the left side of the heart via the blood vessels (see the next section for more information about blood vessels).

When the chambers of the left side of the heart are full, it contracts at the same time as the right side. This side of the heart supplies oxygenated blood via the blood vessels to the tissues of the body such as muscle cells. Oxygen passes from the blood to the cells, and carbon dioxide (a waste product of aerobic respiration) passes into the blood from the cells. The blood then returns to the right atrium of the heart via the blood vessels.

Circulation through the heart is shown in Figure 2.3.

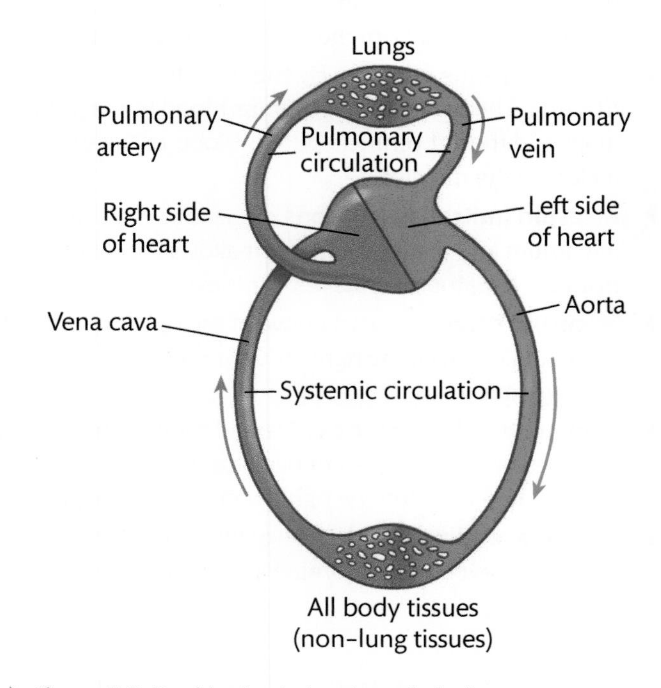

Figure 2.3: Double circulation through the heart

PAUSE POINT Describe the structure and function of the heart.

Hint Draw a basic diagram of the heart and label each part ensuring you check your spelling of anatomical terms.

Extend Label the blood flow and consider the double circulation through the heart.

Blood vessels

As the heart contracts, blood flows around the body in a complex network of vessels. There are five main blood vessels in the human body.

- **Aorta** – this is the body's main artery. It originates in the left ventricle and carries oxygenated blood to all parts of the body except the lungs.
- **Superior vena cava** – a vein that receives deoxygenated blood from the upper body to empty into the right atrium of the heart.
- **Inferior vena cava** – a vein that receives deoxygenated blood from the lower body to empty into the right atrium of the heart.
- **Pulmonary vein** – carries oxygenated blood from the lungs to the left atrium of the heart.
- **Pulmonary artery** – carries deoxygenated blood from the heart back to the lungs. It is the only artery that carries deoxygenated blood.

Structure of blood vessels

The structure of different blood vessels depends on their function and the pressure of blood within them – see Table 2.3.

Table 2.3: Types of blood vessel

Blood vessel	Anatomy and location
Arteries	• Carry blood **away** from the heart and (apart from the pulmonary artery) carry oxygenated blood. • Thick muscular walls carry blood at high speeds under high pressure. As they have high pressure, they do not need valves, except where the pulmonary artery leaves the heart. • Have two major properties: **elasticity** and **contractility** – the smooth muscle surrounding them enables their diameter to decrease and increase as needed (e.g. when the heart ejects blood into the large arteries, they expand). This contractility helps maintain blood pressure as blood flow changes. • Largely deep, except where they can be felt at a pulse point. They branch into smaller arterioles that deliver blood to the capillaries.
Arterioles	• Have thinner walls than arteries and control blood distribution by changing diameter. This adjusts blood flow to the capillaries in response to differing demands for oxygen. • For example, during exercise, muscles require increased blood flow for extra oxygen and the diameter of the arterioles leading to muscles dilates. To compensate for this increase in blood demand, other areas of the body (e.g. the gut) have their blood flow temporarily reduced, and the diameter of their arterioles is decreased.
Veins	• Allow **venous return** (the return of deoxygenated blood to the heart). • Have thinner walls than arteries and a relatively large diameter. • When blood reaches veins it is flowing slowly and under low pressure. Contracting muscles push the thin walls of the veins inwards to squeeze blood towards the heart. As muscle contractions are intermittent, a number of **pocket valves** in veins prevent any backflow when muscles relax. • Mainly close to the surface and can be seen under the skin. • They branch into venules, connected to the capillary network.
Venules	• Small vessels that connect capillaries to veins. • Take blood from the capillaries and transport this deoxygenated blood under low pressure to the veins which, in turn, lead back to the heart.
Capillaries	• Connect arteries and veins by uniting arterioles and venules. • Smallest of all blood vessels, narrow and thin. • Allow the diffusion of oxygen and nutrients required by the body's cells – their walls are one cell thick, allowing nutrients, oxygen and waste products to pass through. • The number in a muscle may increase after frequent and appropriate exercise. This means the surrounding muscles get the oxygen and nutrients to produce energy. • Pressure of blood is higher than veins, but less than arteries.

The walls of blood vessels have three layers - see Figure 2.4a and b. These surround the **lumen**, which is the blood-containing vessel.

- The inner **tunica intima** lines the lumen and creates a slick surface, minimising friction as the blood passes.
- The middle **tunica media** layer is made from smooth muscle cells and elastic tissue. Depending on the needs of the body, either **vasodilation** or **vasoconstriction** occurs.
- The outer **tunica externa** layer is made from **collagen** fibres that protect and reinforce the vessel, and keep it in place in the body's structure.

Key terms

Vasodilation - an increase in the diameter of blood vessels.

Vasoconstriction - a reduction in the diameter of blood vessels.

Collagen - a protein-based building material used in the repair of tissues. Collagen also provides strength and cushioning for body parts.

Artery

Elastic fibres

Round lumen

Muscle layer

Lining

Muscle layer

Tunica intima

Tunica externa

Tunica media

Lumen

▶ **Figure 2.4a:** Structure of an artery

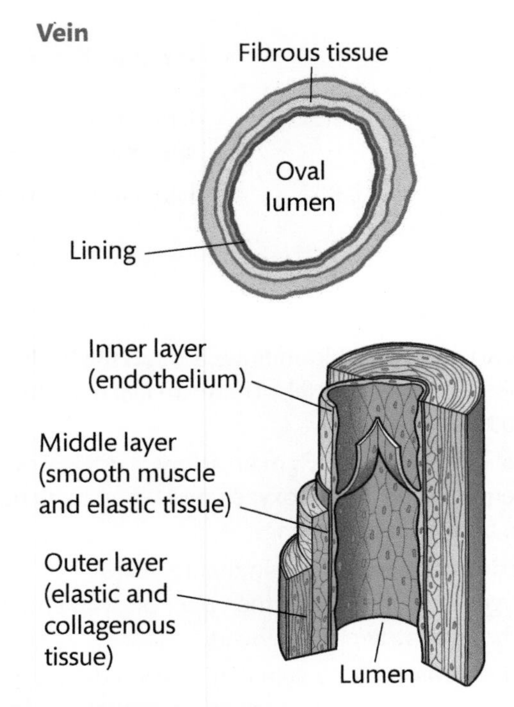

▶ **Figure 2.4b:** Structure of a vein

Composition of blood

The average adult has approximately 4–5 litres of blood. Blood is composed of:

- **red blood cells** (erythrocytes) - carry oxygen to all living tissue. They contain a protein called haemoglobin, giving blood its red colour, which when combined with oxygen forms oxyhaemoglobin. They are round, flattened discs with an indented shape giving them a large surface area and allowing them to flow easily within plasma. A drop of blood contains millions of red blood cells
- **plasma** - the straw-coloured liquid in which all blood cells are suspended. It is approximately 90 per cent water and contains electrolytes such as sodium, potassium and proteins. It also carries carbon dioxide, dissolved as carbonic acid
- **white blood cells** (leucocytes) - the components of blood that protect the body from infections, they account for less than 1 per cent of blood volume. They identify, destroy and remove from the body pathogens such as bacteria or viruses. They originate in bone marrow
- **platelets** (thrombocytes) - disc-shaped cell fragments produced in the bone marrow. Their primary function is clotting to prevent blood loss, sticking to the damaged area to form a temporary plug to seal the break.

Explain the functions of veins, venules, arteries, arterioles and capillaries.

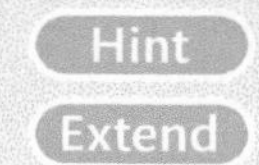

Hint: What are the main differences between the types of blood vessel?

Extend: Explain why there are structural differences between arteries and veins.

Discussion

In groups, discuss the role and importance of the cardiovascular system in sport and exercise. Consider each component of the system. You could also consider the short-term responses of exercise to these components as well as the long-term adaptations.

Lymphatic system

The lymphatic system is a drainage system and also forms part of the immune system. The system is responsible for transporting a clear watery fluid known as **lymph** which contains white blood cells, debris of other cells and bacteria. The system helps the body get rid of excess fluid and waste products through excretion of urine and faeces.

Function of the cardiovascular system

The cardiovascular system fulfils a number of important functions, particularly during sport and exercise.

- The key function is to **supply oxygen and nutrients** to the tissues of the body via the bloodstream. During exercise your body needs more of these so the cardiovascular system responds to meet these increased demands. When it can no longer meet these demands, muscle fatigue occurs and performance deteriorates.
- The circulatory system also **carries waste products** from the tissues to the kidneys and the liver, and returns carbon dioxide from the tissues to the lungs. During exercise, muscles produce more carbon dioxide and lactate and it is essential these are removed, otherwise muscle fatigue will occur.
- The cardiovascular system is responsible for the distribution and redistribution of heat within your body to maintain thermal balance during exercise. This ensures that you do not overheat during exercise.
  - **Vasodilation of blood vessels near the skin** – during exercise the part of the active muscles where gaseous exchange takes place increases through dilation of arterioles, caused by the relaxation of the involuntary muscle fibres in the walls of the blood vessels. This causes an increase in the diameter of blood vessels to decrease resistance to the flow of blood to the area supplied by the vessels. This decreases body temperature as heat within the blood is carried to the body's surface.
  - **Vasoconstriction of blood vessels near the skin** – blood vessels can temporarily shut down blood flow to tissues. This causes a decrease in the blood vessel diameter. This leads to an increase in body temperature as heat loss reduces as blood is moved away from the surface.
- Blood provides the fluid environment for cells and is the medium which carries material to and from these cells. White blood cells (leucocytes) are essential to **fight infection** and defend against viruses and bacteria. Leucocytes are constantly produced inside bone marrow and are stored in your blood. They can consume and ingest **pathogens**, produce antibodies that will also destroy pathogens and produce antitoxins which neutralise the toxins released by pathogens.
- **Blood clotting** is a complex process during which white blood cells form solid clots. A damaged blood vessel wall is covered by a fibrin clot to help repair the damaged vessel. Platelets form a plug at the site of damage. Plasma components known as coagulation factors respond to form fibrin strands which strengthen the platelet plug. This is made possible by the constant supply of blood through the cardiovascular system.

Key term

Pathogen – a bacterium, virus or other microorganism that can cause disease.

The cardiac cycle

Your heart pumps (or beats) when the atria and ventricles work together. Both the atria and the ventricles contract independently, pushing blood out of the heart's chambers. The process of the heart filling with blood followed by a contraction where the blood is pumped out is known as the **cardiac cycle**. The electrical system of your heart is the power source that makes this possible.

Blood flow through the heart

Blood pressure is the pressure of the blood against the walls of your arteries and results from two forces:

- **systolic pressure** – the pressure exerted on your artery walls when your heart contracts and forces blood out of the heart and into the body
- **diastolic pressure** – the pressure on the blood vessel walls when the heart is relaxed between beats and is filling with blood.

During exercise your systolic blood pressure increases as your heart is working harder to supply more oxygenated blood to the working muscles. Your diastolic blood pressure stays the same or decreases slightly.

When blood pressure is measured, it is written with both the systolic and the diastolic pressure noted. The top number is the systolic pressure and the bottom number is the diastolic pressure, for example: $\frac{120}{80}$ mm HG

Neural control of the cardiac cycle

Your heart's electrical system (see Figure 2.5) is made up of three main parts.

- **Sinoatrial node (SAN)** – located within the walls of the right atrium. The SAN sends an impulse or signal from the right atrium through the walls of the atria which causes the muscular walls to contract. This contraction forces the blood within the atria down into the ventricles.
- **Atrioventricular node (AVN)** – located in the centre of the heart between the atria and the ventricles, and acts as a buffer or gate that slows down the signal from the SAN. By slowing down the signal, the atria are able to contract **before** the ventricles which means the ventricles are relaxed (or open) ready to receive the blood from the atria at the top of the heart.
- **Bundle of His** and **Purkinje fibres** – specialist heart muscle cells responsible for transporting the electrical impulses from AVN, and found in the walls of the ventricles and septum. At the end of the Bundle of His are thin filaments known as Purkinje fibres which allow the ventricle to contract at regular intervals (i.e. your regular heartbeat). This causes the blood to be pushed out of the heart, either to the lungs or to the working muscles.

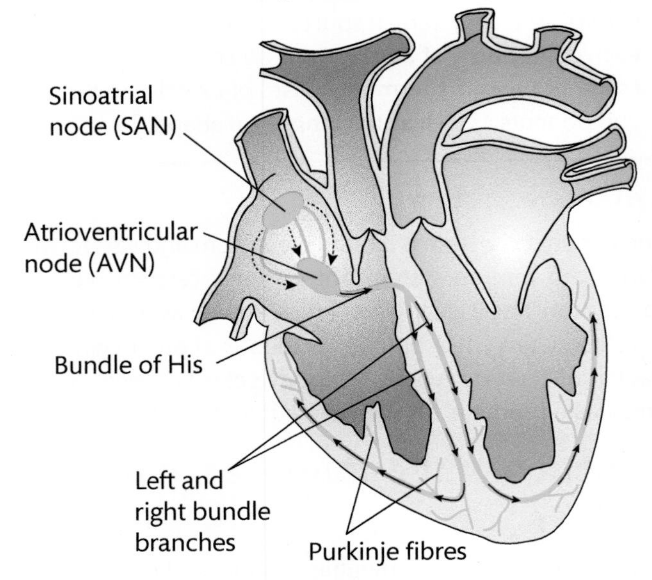

Figure 2.5: The heart's electrical system

Theory into practice

In pairs, choose a single-person sport you both enjoy. Take 8–10 minutes to perform a thorough warm-up and then take part in your chosen activity for at least 20 minutes at moderate intensity levels. At the end of the session spend approximately 5 minutes to cool down. During each part of the activity, pay close attention to the changes that are taking place in your body. Get your partner to record these for you, then swap roles.

1. During the warm-up what changes occurred to your heart rate and breathing?
2. During the main exercise what changes occurred? Think about how you felt: did you get hot? How did your body adapt to control your temperature? What do think would have happened if you had exercised at higher intensities?

Check your knowledge of the cardiovascular system by identifying and listing the key components of this system.

Hint: Describe the function of each component of the cardiovascular system.

Extend: Explain why each described component is important to sport and exercise.

Assessment practice 2.1

1. Identify the function of the sinoatrial node. (1 mark)
2. Describe the function of red blood cells. (2 marks)
3. Identify the functions of the cardiovascular system. (5 marks)
4. Describe how the cardiovascular system helps the body to thermoregulate in hot environments. (4 marks)

Plan

- Have I planned my answers based on the point I want to make?
- Have I written some notes on a blank page, including key words that should be included in my answers?

Do

- Have I answered the simpler questions first, making sure I have enough time for the more complex questions?
- Have I allowed enough time to answer all the questions and to check my answers?

Review

- Have I re-read my answers and made any necessary changes?

C Anatomy of the respiratory system

The respiratory system provides oxygen to all living tissue in your body, and removes waste products such as carbon dioxide, heat and water vapour. Your body's ability to inhale and transport oxygen while removing waste products is critical to exercise: the better your body is at this, the better you will perform in sport.

Location, anatomy and function of respiratory system components

Air is drawn into your body via the nose and mouth, and passes through a series of airways to reach the lungs. This is referred to as the **respiratory tract**. The upper respiratory tract includes the nose, nasal cavity, mouth, pharynx and larynx; the lower respiratory tract includes the trachea, bronchi and lungs. The different parts of the respiratory system are shown in Figure 2.6 and examined in more detail in Table 2.4.

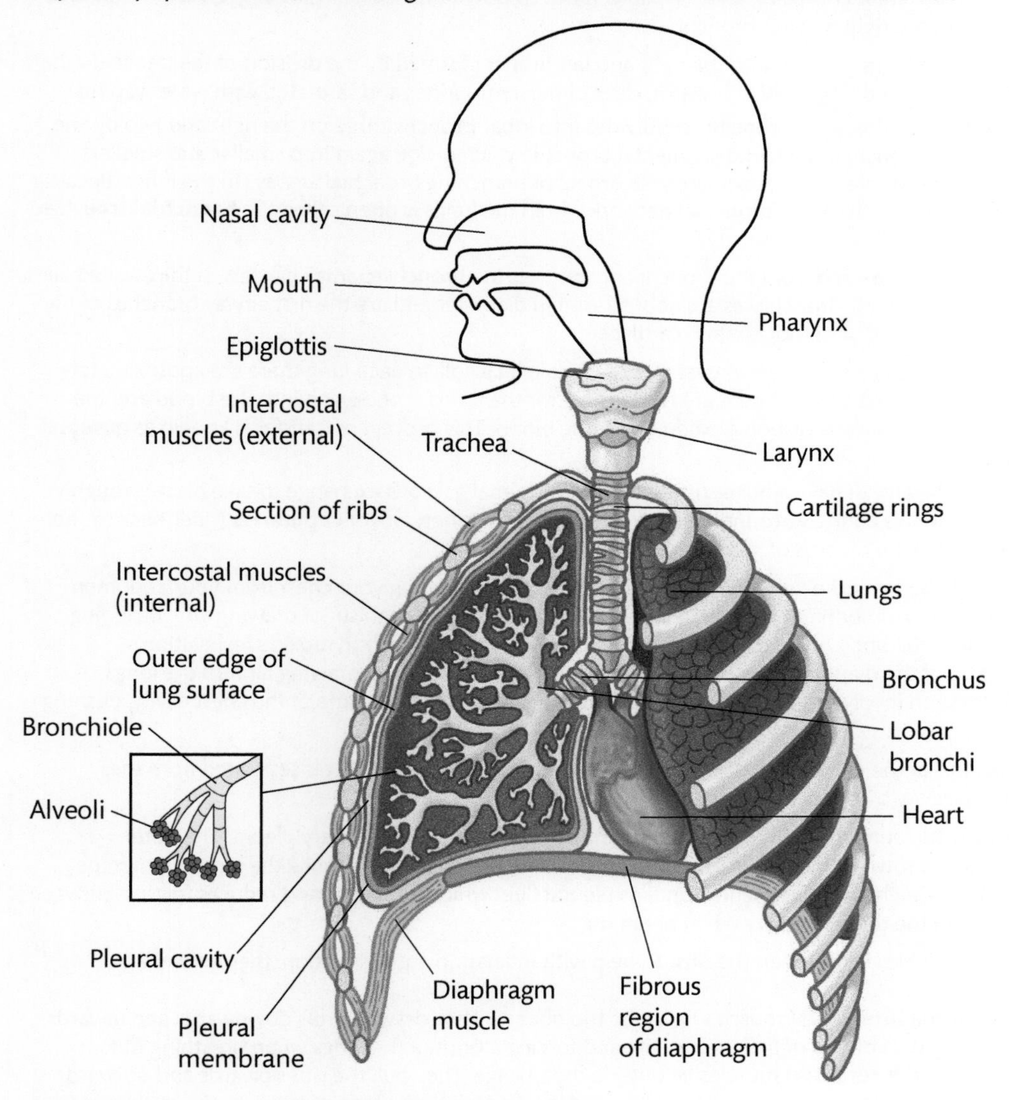

Figure 2.6: The anatomy of the respiratory system

Table 2.4: Parts of the respiratory system

Component	Description
Nasal cavity	Air enters the nasal cavity through the nostrils. Hairs filter out dust, pollen and other foreign particles before air passes into the two passages of the internal nasal cavity. Air is warmed and moistened before passing into the pharynx. A sticky mucous layer traps smaller foreign particles, which tiny hairs (cilia) transport to the pharynx to be swallowed.
Pharynx (throat)	A small tube approximately 10–13 cm from the base of the skull to the level of the sixth cervical vertebra. The funnel-shaped pharynx connects the nasal cavity and mouth to the larynx (air) and oesophagus (food) and is a passageway for food and air, so special adaptations are required to prevent choking when food or liquid is swallowed.
Epiglottis	The small flap of cartilage at the back of the tongue which closes the top of the trachea when you swallow to ensure food and drink pass into your stomach and not your lungs.
Larynx (voice box)	Has rigid walls of muscle and cartilage, contains the vocal cords and connects the pharynx to the trachea. It extends for about 5 cm from the level of the third to sixth vertebra.
Lungs (lobes)	The organs that allow oxygen to be drawn into the body. The paired right and left lungs occupy most of the thoracic cavity and extend down to the diaphragm. They hang suspended in the right and left pleural cavities straddling the heart. The left lung is smaller than the right.
Trachea (windpipe)	The start of the lower respiratory tract. It is about 12 cm long by 2 cm in diameter. It contains rings of cartilage to prevent it collapsing and is flexible. It travels down the neck in front of the oesophagus and branches into the right and left bronchi.
Bronchus	Carry air to the lungs, divided into the right and left bronchi formed by the division of the trachea. When inhaled air reaches the bronchi, it is warm, clear of most impurities and saturated with water vapour. Once inside the lungs, each bronchus subdivides into lobar bronchi: three on the right and two on the left. The lobar bronchi branch into segmental bronchi, which divide again into smaller and smaller bronchi. Overall, there are approximately 23 orders of branching bronchial airways in the lungs. Because of this branching pattern, the bronchial network within the lungs is often called the **bronchial tree**. (See Figure 2.6.)
Bronchioles	Small airways that extend from the bronchi and connect the bronchi to small clusters of thin-walled air sacs, known as alveoli. Bronchioles are about 1 mm in diameter and are the first airway branches of the respiratory system that do not contain cartilage.
Alveoli	At the end of each bronchiole is a mass of air sacs called alveoli. In each lung there are approximately 300 million gas-filled alveoli. These are responsible for the transfer of oxygen into the blood and the removal of waste such as carbon dioxide out of the blood. This process of transfer is known as **gaseous exchange**. Combined, the alveoli have a huge surface area for maximal gaseous exchange to take place – roughly the size of a tennis court. Surrounding each alveoli is a dense network of **capillaries** (refer back to Table 2.3) to facilitate the process of gaseous exchange.
Diaphragm	A flat muscle beneath the lungs within the thoracic cavity separating your chest from your abdomen. One of several components involved in breathing which is the mechanism of drawing air – including oxygen – into the body (inhalation) and removing gases including carbon dioxide (exhalation). Contraction of the diaphragm increases the volume of the chest cavity, drawing air into the lungs, while relaxation involves recoil of the diaphragm and decreases the volume of the chest cavity, pushing air out.
Thoracic cavity	The chamber of the chest that is protected by the thoracic wall (ribcage). It is separated from the abdominal cavity by the diaphragm.
Pleura (visceral and parietal)	Each lung is surrounded by a fluid-filled membrane known as the pulmonary pleura. The outer membrane is known as the parietal membrane and lines the chest cavity while the inner membrane (visceral) lines each lung. The pleura contains pleural fluid which lubricates and reduces friction between the lungs and the thoracic cavity when breathing.
Internal and external intercostal muscles	Intercostal muscles lie between the ribs. To help with inhalation and exhalation, they extend and contract. • The **internal intercostal** muscles lie inside the ribcage. They draw the ribs downwards and inwards, decreasing the volume of the chest cavity and forcing air out of the lungs when breathing out. • The **external intercostal** muscles lie outside the ribcage. They pull the ribs upwards and outwards, increasing the volume of the chest cavity and drawing air into the lungs when breathing in.

PAUSE POINT List the key components of the respiratory system and draw a diagram to show how this system works.

Hint Describe the function of each of these components.

Extend Explain the role of the diaphragm in breathing.

Function of the respiratory system

Breathing or **pulmonary ventilation** is the process by which air is transported into and out of the lungs. The thorax increases in size to take in air, followed by a decrease to allow air to be forced out. Breathing has two clear phases.

- **Inspiration** – the process of breathing air into the lungs. The intercostal muscles contract to lift the ribs upwards and outwards, while the diaphragm is forced downwards. This expansion of the thorax in all directions causes a drop in pressure within the lungs to below atmospheric pressure (the pressure of the air outside the body), which encourages air to be drawn into the lungs.
- **Expiration** – the process of breathing air out of the lungs. It occurs when the intercostal muscles relax. The diaphragm relaxes too, moving upwards, and the ribs retract. Pressure within the lungs is increased and air is pushed out of the body.

Greater amounts of oxygen are required by the body during exercise, requiring the intercostal muscles and diaphragm to work harder. This increases your breathing rate and the force of your breath.

Gaseous exchange

Gaseous exchange is the process in which one type of gas is exchanged for another. In the lungs, gaseous exchange occurs by **diffusion** between air in the alveoli and blood in the capillaries surrounding their walls. It delivers oxygen from the lungs to the bloodstream while removing carbon dioxide. Table 2.5 shows the percentage amount of carbon dioxide and oxygen inspired and expired during respiration.

You can see how much more carbon dioxide is exhaled than is inhaled as well as the amount of oxygen that the body extracts from the air (approximately 5 per cent).

Table 2.5: Percentage amount of carbon dioxide and oxygen inspired and expired during respiration

Gas	% in inhaled air	% in exhaled air
Oxygen	21	16
Carbon dioxide	0.04	4

Key term

Diffusion – the process by which a substance such as oxygen passes through a cell membrane either to get into the cell or to get out of the cell. Substances move by diffusion from an area where they are more concentrated to an area where they are less concentrated.

The alveolar and capillary walls form a **respiratory membrane** with gas on one side and blood flowing past on the other. Blood entering the capillaries from the pulmonary arteries has a lower oxygen concentration and a higher carbon dioxide concentration than the air in the alveoli. Oxygen diffuses into the blood via the surface of the alveoli, through the thin walls of the capillaries, through the red blood cell membrane and finally latches on to haemoglobin. Carbon dioxide diffuses in the opposite direction, from the blood plasma into the alveoli.

Lung volumes

Your **respiratory rate** is the amount of air you breathe in 1 minute. For a typical 18-year-old, this represents about 12 breaths per minute at rest, during which time about 6 litres of air passes through the lungs. During exercise this can increase by as much as 30–40 breaths per minute. The lung volume and capacities of a healthy adult are shown in Figure 2.7.

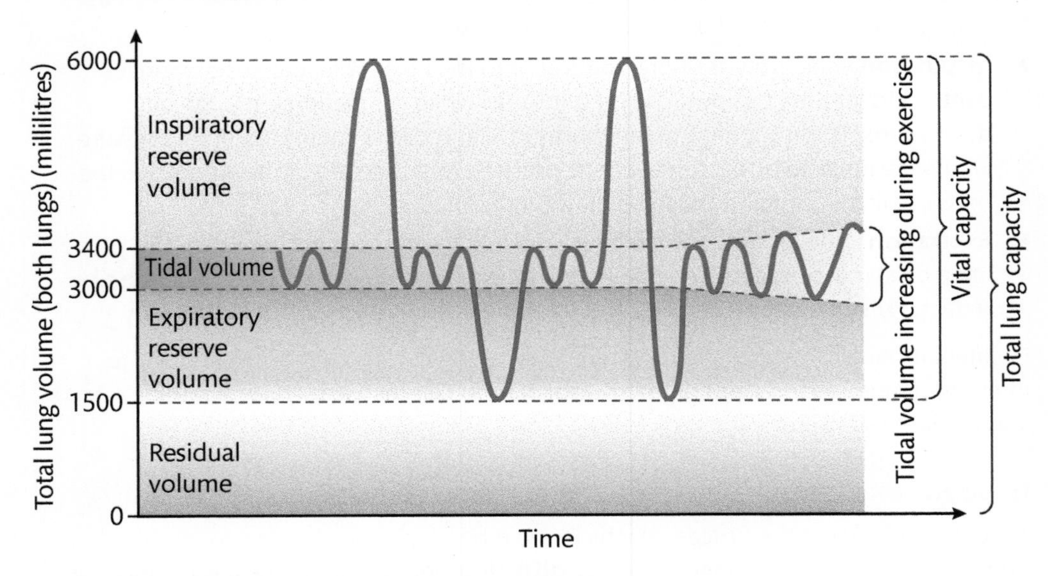

▶ **Figure 2.7:** Lung volume and capacities of a healthy adult

- **Tidal volume** is the volume of air breathed in and out with each breath. Normally this represents about 500 ml of air breathed, both inhaled and exhaled. Approximately two-thirds (350 ml) reaches the alveoli where gaseous exchange takes place. The remaining 150 ml fills the pharynx, larynx, trachea, bronchi and bronchioles and is known as dead or stationary air. During exercise, tidal volume increases to allow more air to pass through the lungs. The volume of air passing through the lungs each minute is known as **minute volume**, determined by the breathing rate and the amount of air taken in with each breath.
- The lungs usually contain about 350 ml fresh air, 150 ml dead air and 2500 ml air that has already undergone gaseous exchange with the blood.
- The lungs are never fully emptied of air, otherwise they would collapse. The air remaining in the lungs after maximal expiration (when you breathe out as hard as you can) is the **residual volume**. This volume is around 1200 ml for an average male.
- **Vital capacity** is the amount of air that can be forced out of the lungs after maximal inspiration. This volume is around 4800 ml.
- By breathing in deeply, you can take in more air than usual, so more oxygen can reach the alveoli. You can breathe in up to 3000 ml of fresh air in addition to the normal tidal volume – this is known as the **inspiratory reserve volume**.
- The **expiratory reserve volume** is the amount of additional air that can be breathed out after normal expiration. This can be up to 1500 ml. At the end of a normal breath, the lungs contain the residual volume plus the expiratory reserve volume. If you then exhale as much as possible, only the residual volume remains.
- **Total lung volume** is your total lung capacity after you have inhaled as deeply and as much as you can. It is around 6000 ml for an average male.

Research

In pairs investigate inspiratory reserve volume and expiratory reserve volume. How do these relate to the normal volume of air in the lungs? How can they be affected by breathing? What benefits can they give to sports performance? Report your findings to the rest of the group.

PAUSE POINT Identify each of the different lung volumes that make up total lung volume.

Hint Describe each of these volumes and consider how exercise affects each of them.

Extend Explain why your breathing changes during exercise and the impact this has on your lung volumes.

Control of breathing

Breathing is a complex process largely under involuntary or automatic control by the respiratory centres of your brain. Remember that inspiration is an active process as the diaphragm **actively** contracts causing air to enter the lungs; expiration is a passive process as the diaphragm **relaxes** to allow air to exit the lungs. This process is controlled by neurones, cells that conduct nerve impulses, and which are part of the brain stem.

Neurones in two areas of the **medulla oblongata** are critical in respiration. These are the dorsal respiratory group (DRG) and the ventral respiratory group (VRG). The VRG is thought to be responsible for the rhythm generation that allows rhythmic and continuous breathing.

Other factors controlling breathing are the continually changing levels of oxygen and carbon dioxide. Sensors responding to such chemical fluctuations are called **chemoreceptors**. These are found in the medulla and in the **aortic arch** and **carotid arteries**. During exercise, these chemoreceptors detect changes in blood carbon dioxide levels as well as changes in blood acidity, and send signals to the medulla that will make changes in breathing rates.

Key term

Medulla oblongata – located in the middle of your brain, it is responsible for involuntary functions such as breathing, heart rate and sneezing.

Assessment practice 2.2

Felix is football player.

1. Explain the short-term effect of taking part in football on Felix's tidal volume. (3 marks)
2. Explain the role of carbon dioxide in the chemical control of breathing during exercise. (3 marks)
3. Explain the function of visceral pleura when breathing. (2 marks)
4. Describe the process of gaseous exchange in the lungs. (5 marks)

Plan

- Have I planned my longer answers by noting the key words and identifying suitable examples?
- Have I looked at the marks available and allowed time to write a full answer?

Do

- Have I structured my answers carefully to ensure I cover all the necessary points?
- Have I given relevant examples linked to the structure and function of the body system?

Review

- Have I re-read my answers? Have I included a response to the key terms?
- Have I fully answered the question making the relevant number of points linked to the marks available?

D Anatomy of the skeletal system

Anatomy of bone

Bones contain living tissue that grows, repairs and contains vital minerals. **Long bones** are the bones found in the limbs. Their primary function is to support body mass and to create large movements. Long bones such as the femur are also crucial in producing bone marrow, essential for blood cell production. The structure of a long bone is shown in Figure 2.8 and explained in more detail in Table 2.6.

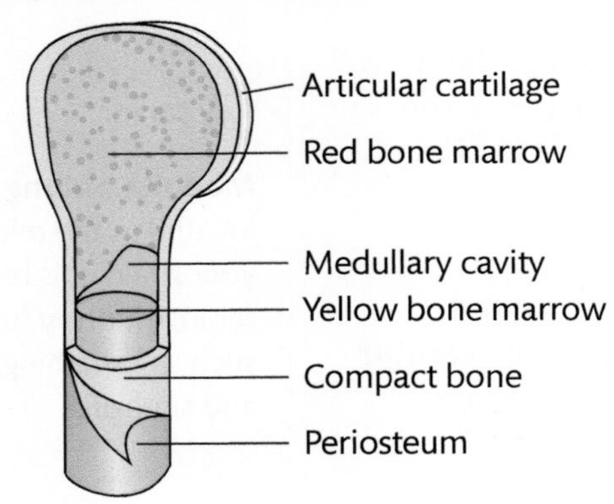

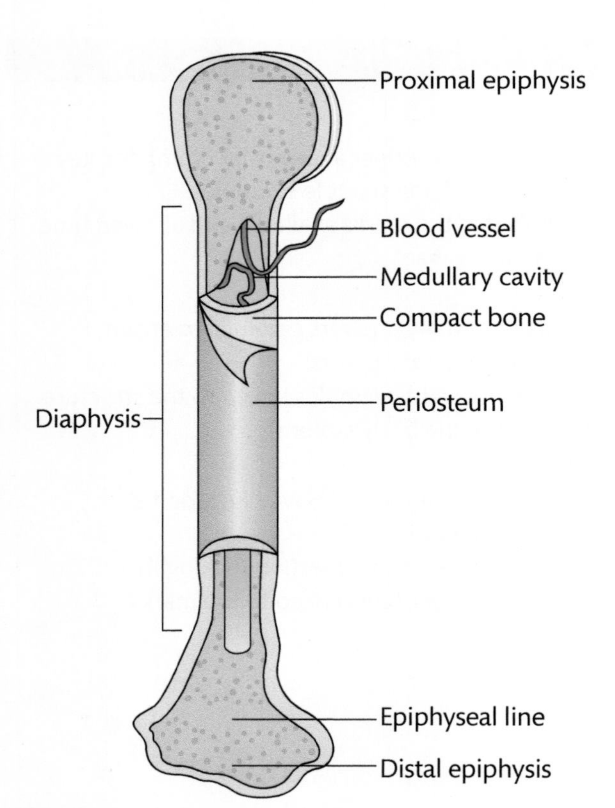

▶ **Figure 2.8:** Structure of a long bone

▶ **Table 2.6:** Parts of a long bone

Part of a long bone	Description
Periosteum	The tough outermost layer of the bone.
Bone minerals	Bone minerals such as calcium and phosphorus are stored within the bone. They are essential in bone creation and reabsorption of bone tissue.
Bone marrow	Soft and spongy tissue found within bones. There are two types of bone marrow: • red bone marrow which produces red blood cells, white blood cells and platelets • yellow bone marrow which produces fat and cartilage.
Epiphysis	The rounded end of the bone, it commonly forms an articulation or joint with another bone.
Diaphysis	The central shaft or long part of the bone.
Growth plates (or epiphyseal plate)	A disc of cartilage found at the end of each long bone of children and adolescents and responsible for the bone growth. It separates the diaphysis from the epiphysis and is the only place where an increase in bone length can take place. Once growing stops it is replaced by an epiphyseal line.
Cancellous bone	The spongy bone found within the ends (epiphysis) of long bones. The cancellous bone has a honeycomb appearance and provides space for the red bone marrow inside the bone structure.
Compact bone	The hard tissue surrounding the bone and often referred to as 'cortical bone'.
Articular cartilage	The ends of long bones are covered with articular cartilage, allowing bones to move over each other with minimum friction.
Medullary cavity	The space in a bone where marrow is stored.
Blood vessel	Provides blood to the bone.

Long bones of the body contain many distinct regions due to the way they develop. These include:

- **notches** – the V shaped depressions at the edge of a flat area
- **fossas** – shallow depressions on the surface of the bones which commonly receive another articulating bone were a joint is formed
- **condyles** – rounded bumps or large rounded prominences which usually fit into a fossa on another bone to form a joint

- **borders** – the main portion of the bone
- **processes** – raised areas or projections that can be used to attach connective tissue
- **tuberosity** – a large rounded projection that looks like a raised bump. Tuberosities are often sites for muscle attachment.

Process of bone growth and remodelling

Bone is a living organ that is continuously being **remodelled** through a process called **ossification**. Throughout this process parts of the bone are reabsorbed, so unnecessary **calcium** is removed (via cells called **osteoclasts**) while new layers of bone tissue are created.

The cells that bring calcium to your bones are known as **osteoblasts**, and are responsible for creating bone matter. Osteoblast activity increases when you exercise, so your bones will become stronger the more exercise you do. Bone calcium stores increase to cope with the demand for calcium, so exercising also reduces the risk of osteoporosis. Weight-bearing activities build stronger bones, including tennis, netball, basketball, aerobics, walking and running.

Osteocytes form from osteoblasts and make up the majority of mature bone matter.

Key terms

Bone remodelling – the ongoing replacement of old bone tissue with new bone tissue and the redistribution of bone tissue to areas where stress forces are greatest.

Calcium – a mineral essential for bone growth and found in a wide range of foods including milk, cheese, yoghurt, nuts, broccoli and beans.

Osteoporosis – a medical condition that weakens bones due to a loss of stored calcium. This makes bones fragile, brittle and more likely to break.

The end of each long bone contains growing areas – or plates – which allow the bone to grow longer. This continues throughout childhood until the child reaches full maturity. These areas are call the **epiphyseal plates** and allow the long bones to extend. Once a long bone is fully formed the head – or end of each bone – fuses with the main shaft (diaphysis) to create the **epiphyseal line**.

Use of minerals (calcium, vitamin D)

Calcium and vitamin D are essential in the formation, growth and remodelling of bone tissue. If the body removes more calcium than it replaces, bones will become weak and brittle. It is important your diet includes food containing calcium. This is particularly important in young children, adolescents and older people.

Vitamin D is needed to absorb calcium. Without vitamin D bones will become weaker as existing stores will be used to maintain bone structure and cannot be replaced by new calcium found in the diet.

PAUSE POINT What is bone remodelling?

Hint Draw a simple diagram of a long bone and label the key structures.

Extend Further explain the function of each of these structures.

Structure of the skeletal system

The human skeleton is made of 206 bones held together by connective tissue known as ligaments, while joints at the junction between bones provide mobility. The skeletal system (see Figure 2.9) is made up of bones, **cartilage** and joints.

> **Key term**
>
> **Cartilage** – a strong and flexible tissue that is commonly found in joints of the body. It is smooth in texture and acts to reduce friction at joints and stop bones from grinding together.

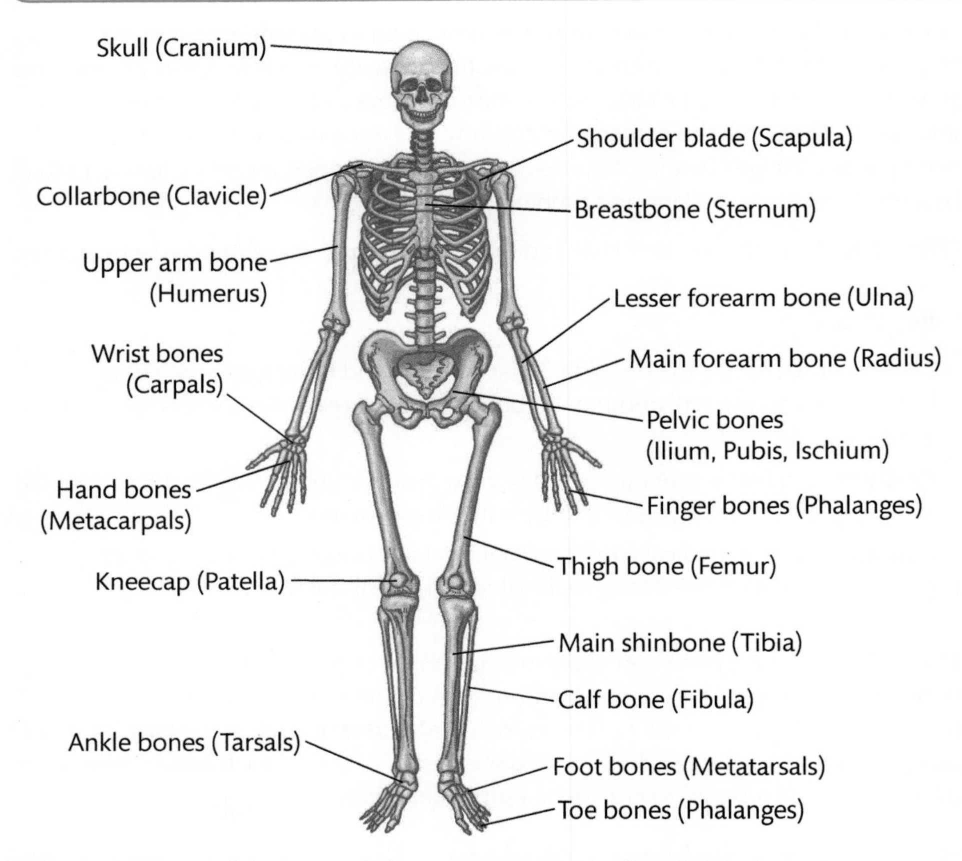

Figure 2.9: Bones of the human skeleton; Latin names are shown in brackets

Types of bone

The skeleton has five main types of bone according to their shape and size. As well as **long bones** these are:

- **short bones** – small, light, strong, cube-shaped bones consisting of cancellous bone surrounded by a thin layer of compact bone. The carpals and tarsals of the wrists and ankles (see Table 2.7) are examples of short bones
- **flat bones** – thin, flattened and slightly curved, they have a large surface area. Examples include the scapulae, sternum and cranium (see Table 2.7)
- **sesamoid bones** – these have a specialised function and are usually found within a tendon. They provide a smooth surface for the tendon to slide over. The largest sesamoid bone is the patella in the knee joint
- **irregular bones** – have complex shapes that fit none of the categories above. The bones of the spinal column are a good example.

Major bones of the skeletal system

The major bones of the skeletal system are identified in Table 2.7.

Table 2.7: Major bones of the skeletal system

Bone	Description
Cranium	Box-like cavity of interlinking segments of bone fused together. It contains and protects the brain.
Clavicles	Commonly known as the collar bones. Long, slim bones form the anterior part of the shoulder girdle. Provide a strong attachment for the arms.
Ribs	There are 12 pairs of ribs and they are part of the **thoracic cage**. The first seven pairs are 'true ribs' attached to the sternum; the remaining five are 'false ribs', i.e. not attached to the sternum. Ribs are long, flat bones.
Sternum (breastbone)	The elongated, flat bone running down the centre of the chest and forming the front of the thoracic cage. Seven pairs of ribs are attached to the sternum, providing protection and muscular attachment.
Scapula	Or shoulder bone. Large, triangular, flat bone forms the posterior part of the shoulder girdle.
Humerus	The long bone of the upper arm and the largest bone of the upper limbs. The head of the humerus articulates (joins) with the scapula to form the shoulder joint. The distal end articulates with the radius and ulna to form the elbow joint.
Radius and ulna	The ulna is the longer of the two forearm bones. The ulna and radius articulate distally with the carpals.
Carpals	Eight small bones that make up the wrist. Irregular, small bones arranged in two rows of four. They fit closely together and are kept in place by ligaments.
Metacarpals	Five long bones in the palm of the hand, one corresponding to each digit (finger). These run from the carpal bones of the wrist to the base of each digit in the hand.
Phalanges	Bones that make up the thumbs, fingers and toes. Most fingers and toes have three phalanges, but the thumbs and big toes have two.
Pelvis	Made up of two hip bones of three sections: **ilium**, **ischium** and **pubis** which fuse together during puberty. The ilium structure provides the socket for the ball and socket joint of the femur, allowing the legs to be attached to the main skeleton. The **iliac crest** is the curved superior border of the ilium.
Femur	The longest and strongest bone in the body, sometimes referred to as the **thigh bone**. The head fits into the socket of the pelvis to form the hip joint; the lower end joins the tibia to form the knee joint.
Patella	The large, triangular sesamoid bone found in the quadriceps femoris **tendon**. It protects the knee joint.
Tibia and fibula	The long bones forming the lower leg. The tibia is the inner and thicker bone, known as the **shin bone**. The upper end of the tibia joins the femur to form the knee joint, while the lower end forms part of the ankle joint. The fibula is the outer, thinner bone of the lower leg; it does not reach the knee, but its lower end does form part of the ankle joint.
Tarsals	Along with the tibia and fibula, seven bones known as tarsals form the ankle joint. The calcaneus, or heel bone, is the largest tarsal bone. It helps support the weight of the body and provides attachment for the calf muscles via the Achilles tendon. The tarsals are short and irregular bones.
Calcaneus (heel bone)	A large bone that forms the foundation of the rear part of the foot.
Metatarsals	There are five metatarsals in each foot, located between the tarsals and the phalanges (toes). Each metatarsal has a similar structure, with a distal and proximal head joined by a thin shaft (body). Responsible for bearing a great deal of weight and balancing pressure through the balls of the feet. A common site of fracture in sport.

Key term

Tendon – strong fibrous tissue that attaches muscle to a bone.

The bones that make up the wrist, hand and foot are shown in detail in Figures 2.10 and 2.11.

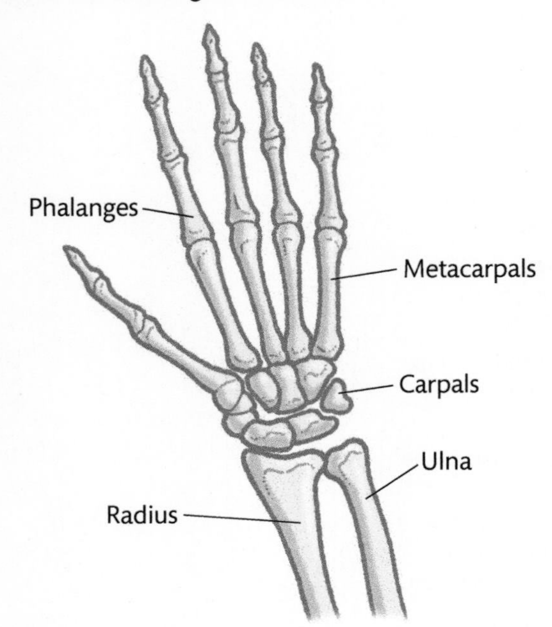

▶ **Figure 2.10:** The bones of the wrist and hand

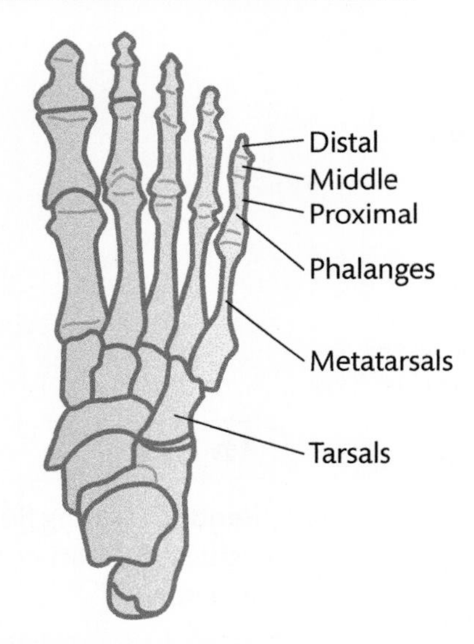

▶ **Figure 2.11:** The bones of the foot

Areas of the skeleton

The skeleton can be divided into two groups: 80 bones form your **axial skeleton** (the long **axis** of your body) and the other 126 bones form your **appendicular skeleton** (the bones that are attached to this axis).

Key term

Axis - a centre line through any body or object. The body or object to either side of the line should be symmetrical (a mirror image).

Axial skeleton

The axial skeleton (see Figure 2.12) is the main core or axis of your skeleton and consists of the skull, the thoracic cage and the vertebral column.

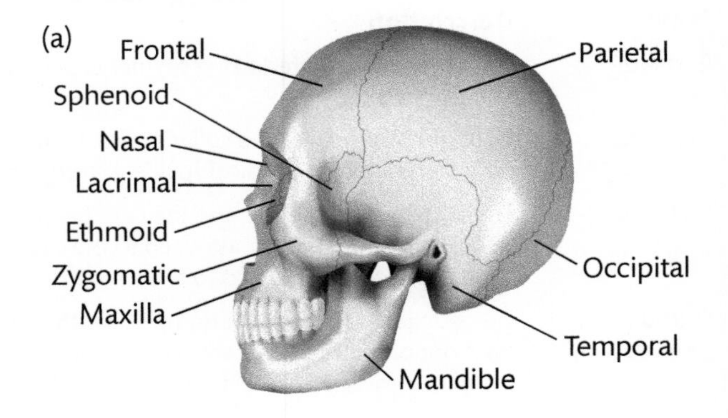

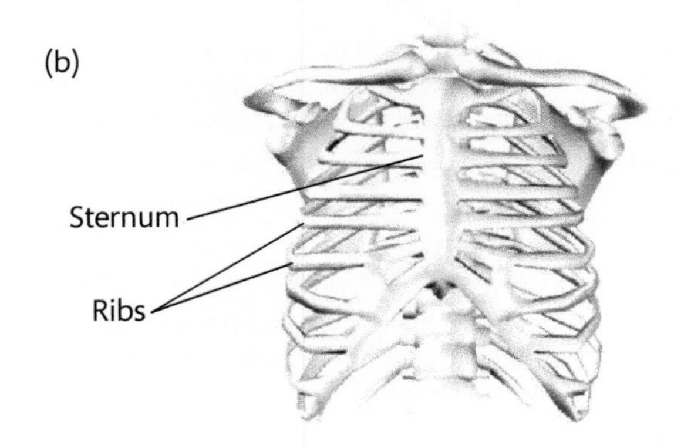

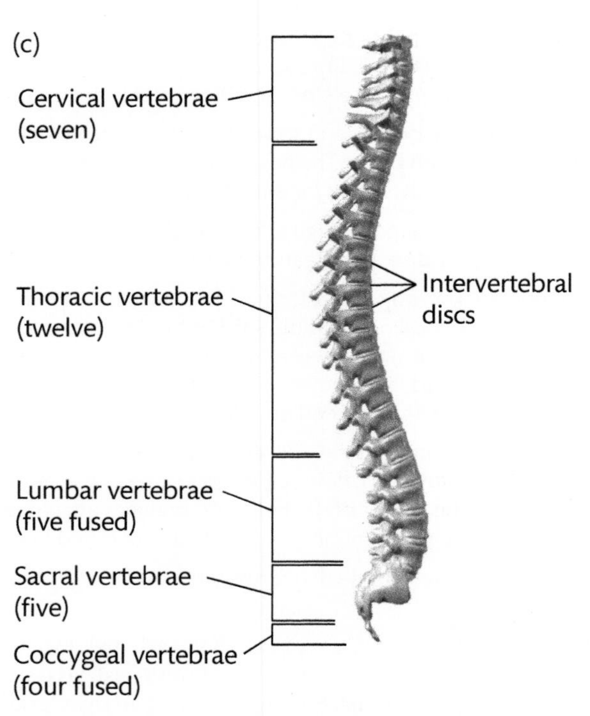

▶ **Figure 2.12:** The axial skeleton: (a) the skull, (b) the thorax and (c) the vertebral column

Appendicular skeleton

The appendicular skeleton (see Figure 2.13) consists of the bones that are attached to the axial skeleton. It consists of the following parts.

- **The upper limbs** consist of 60 bones (30 in each arm) including the humerus, radius, ulna, carpals, metacarpals and phalanges.
- **The lower limbs** consist of 60 bones (30 in each leg) including the femur, patella, tibia, fibula, tarsals, metatarsals and phalanges.
- **The shoulder girdle** consists of four bones - two clavicles and two scapulae - which connect the limbs of the upper body to the thorax.
- **The pelvic girdle** is made of three bones: the ilium, pubis and ischium. These fuse together with age and are known as the innominate bone. Its main function is to provide a solid base for transmitting the weight of the upper body. It also provides attachment for the powerful muscles of the lower back and legs, and protects the digestive and reproductive organs.

The spine or vertebral column

The vertebral column is commonly known as the spine or backbone and extends from the base of the cranium to the pelvis, providing a central axis for the body. It is made up of 33 irregular bones called **vertebrae**. The vertebrae are held together by powerful **ligaments**. These allow little movement between adjacent vertebrae but a considerable degree of flexibility along the spine as a whole.

Key terms

Ligaments - short bands of tough and fibrous flexible tissue that hold bones together.

Concave - having an outline or surface that curves inwards.

The vertebral column can be classified into five sections or regions (see Figure 2.12(c)):

- **cervical vertebrae** - the seven vertebrae of the neck. The first two are known as the atlas (C1) and the axis (C2). They form a pivot joint that allows the head and neck to move freely
- **thoracic vertebrae** - the 12 vertebrae of the mid-spine, which articulate with the ribs. They lie in the thorax, a dome-shaped structure that protects the heart and lungs
- **lumbar vertebrae** - the five largest of the movable vertebrae, situated in the lower back. They support more weight than other vertebrae and provide attachment for many of the muscles of the back. The discs between these vertebrae produce a **concave** curve in the back

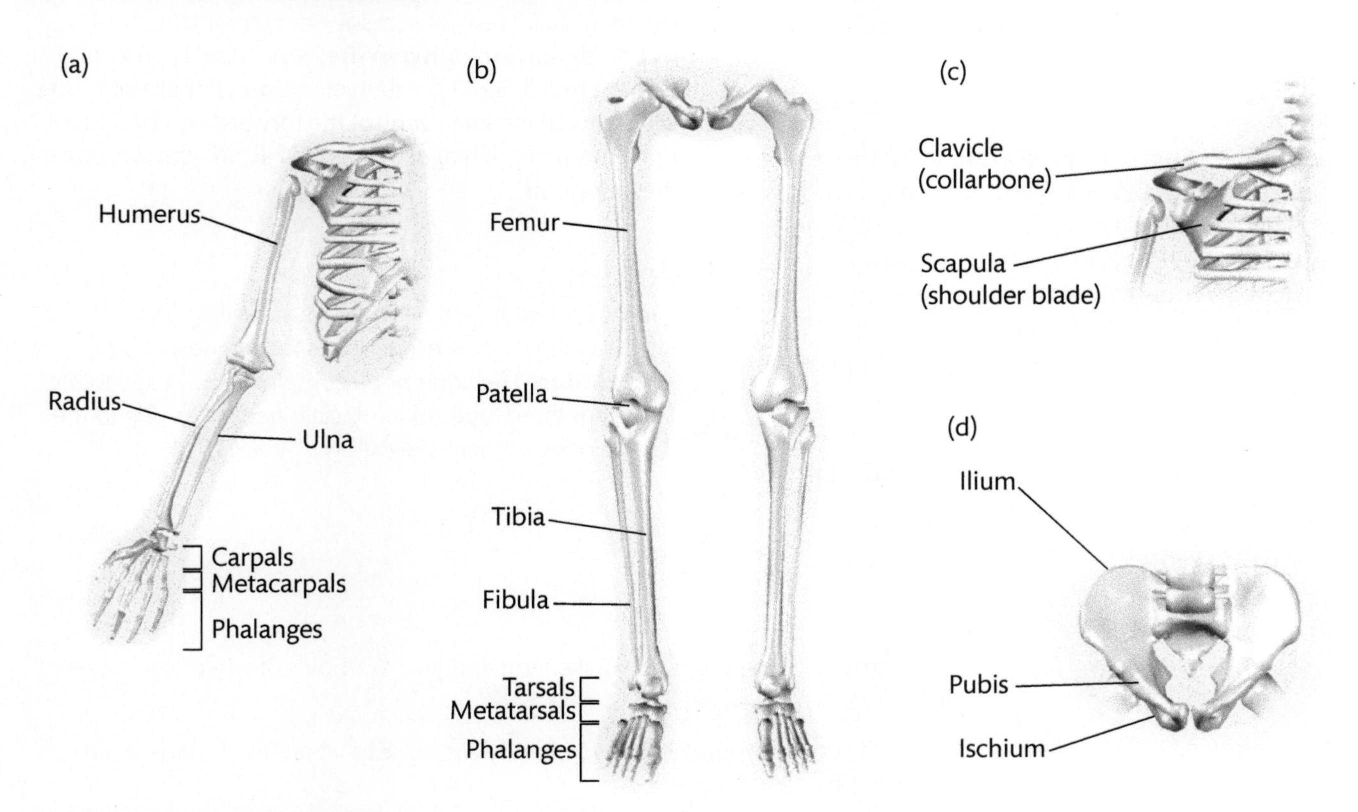

Figure 2.13: The appendicular skeleton: (a) the upper limbs, (b) the lower limbs, (c) the shoulder girdle and (d) the pelvic girdle

- **sacral vertebrae** - the five sacral vertebrae are fused together to form the **sacrum**, a triangular bone located below the lumbar vertebrae. It forms the back wall of the pelvic girdle, sitting between the two hip bones. The upper part connects with the last lumbar vertebra and the bottom part with the coccyx
- **coccygeal vertebrae** - at the bottom of the vertebral column there are four coccygeal vertebrae, which are fused together to form the **coccyx** or tail bone.

The vertebral column protects the spinal cord and supports the ribcage. The larger vertebrae of the lumbar region support a large amount of body weight. The flatter thoracic vertebrae offer attachment for the large muscles of the back and the four curves of the spine. These, along with the **intervertebral discs**, receive and distribute impact associated with sporting performance, reducing shock.

Key terms

Intervertebral discs - fibrocartilaginous cushions that act as the spine's shock-absorbing system which prevent injury to the vertebrae and brain.

Hyper-extension - a movement of a joint beyond its normal limits, normally beyond 180°.

Hyper-flexion - the flexion of a joint beyond its normal limits or range.

Articulation - where two or more bones meet.

Curves of the spine

The 33 vertebrae of the spine have a distinctive shape when stacked on top of one another. The normal shape consists of a curve in the cervical (neck), thoracic (mid back), lumbar (lower back) and sacral (bottom of spine) regions when viewing laterally. A **neutral spine** refers to a good posture with the correct position of the four natural curves. When viewing the spine from the front (anterior), it should be completely vertical.

Function of the skeletal system

The main functions of the skeletal system when performing sport or exercise are:

- **support and weight bearing** - your bones give the body shape and provide a supporting framework for the body. Bones also support the weight of your tissue
- **protection** - bones surround and protect vital tissues and organs
- **attachment for skeletal muscle** - parts of your skeleton provide a surface for your skeletal muscles to attach to, allowing you to move. Tendons attach muscles to bone, providing leverage
- **source of blood cell production** - blood vessels feed the centre of your bones and store blood marrow which continually produces red and white blood cells
- **store of minerals** - bone is a reservoir for minerals such as calcium and phosphorus, essential for bone growth and the maintenance of bone health
- **leverage** - the bones provide a lever system against which muscles can pull and movement can occur.

Ligaments

Ligaments are short bands of tough and fibrous flexible tissue holding bones together. Their primary function is to maintain joint structure and stability by holding the bones of a joint in place. However, they are also slightly elastic so the bones of the joint can move correctly. Generally the more ligaments a joint has, the stronger and more stable it is.

Ligaments also restrict excessive movements such as **hyper-extension** or **hyper-flexion**. Some ligaments also prevent movement in certain directions. For example, the ligaments of the knee control the forward and backward movement of the hinge joint as well as prevent twisting of the knee joint.

Joints

For movement to occur, bones must be linked. A joint is where two or more bones meet, known as an **articulation**. The adult body contains around 350 joints. There are three types of joint, classified according to the degree of movement they allow.

PAUSE POINT Name the main bone types of the skeleton and give examples of where each type of bone is located.

Hint Consider a sport of your choice and identify the bones that are used in the main actions involved in that sport.

Extend How could understanding how these bones work affect your performance in sport?

- **Fixed (fibrous or immoveable) joints** do not move. They form when bones interlock and overlap during early childhood. Held together by bands of tough, fibrous tissue, they are strong with no movement between the bones. An example is the bone plates in your cranium, fixed together to protect your brain.
- **Cartilaginous joints** allow slight movement and are therefore also known as **slightly moveable joints**. The ends of the bone are covered in a smooth, shiny covering known as articular or hyaline cartilage, reducing friction between the bones. The bones are separated by pads of white fibrocartilage (a tough cartilage which absorbs considerable loads). Slight movement is made possible because the pads of cartilage compress.
- **Synovial joints**, or **freely moveable joints**, offer the highest level of mobility at a joint and are vital to all sporting movements (see Figure 2.14). They make up most of the joints of your limbs. They include the following features:
  - a **joint capsule** to help to hold the bones in place and protect the joint
  - a **bursa,** a small fluid-filled sac providing a cushion between the tendons of the muscles and the bones, preventing friction. Bursae are filled with synovial fluid
  - **articular cartilage** on the ends of the bones, to provide a smooth and slippery covering to stop the bones rubbing or grinding together
  - a **synovial membrane** is the capsule lining that releases synovial fluid
  - **synovial fluid** which lubricates the joint and reduces the friction. It also provides nutrients to the articular cartilage
  - **ligaments** to support the joint.

Research

1. What are the main ligaments of the knee and what are their functions?
2. Why are knee injuries in football relatively common?
3. Why does a ligament injury take so long to heal?

Key term

Convex – curving outwards.

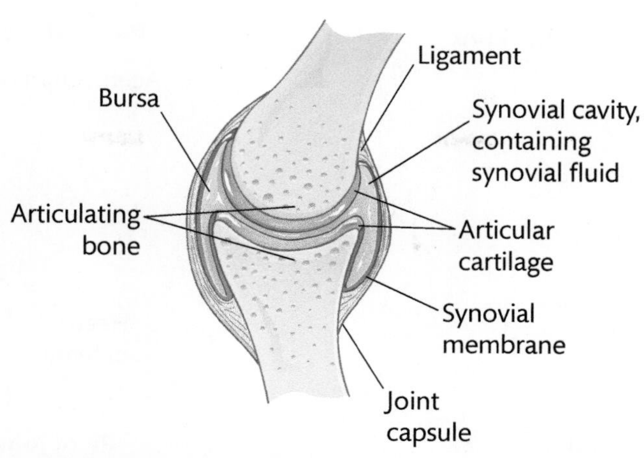

Figure 2.14: A synovial joint

Types of synovial joints

There are six types of synovial joint (see Table 2.8 and Figure 2.15) and each is categorised according to its structure and the movements it allows. These joints will permit specific movements and combined will allow you to perform complex techniques such as a somersault or a tennis serve.

Table 2.8: Types of synovial joint

Synovial joints	Description
Hinge	Allow movement in one direction only (like a door hinge), for example, elbow and knee joints which only allow movements forwards or backwards.
Ball and socket	Round end of one bone fits into a cup-shaped socket in the other bone, allowing movement in all directions. Examples include hip and shoulder joints.
Condyloid	Also known as **ellipsoidal joints**. Similar to a ball and socket joint, in which a bump (condyle) on one bone sits in the hollow formed by another. Movement is backwards and forwards and from side to side. Ligaments often prevent rotation.
Gliding	Allow movement over a flat surface in all directions, restricted by ligaments or a bony prominence, for example, in the carpals and tarsals of wrists and ankles.
Pivot	A circular bone fits over a peg of another, allowing controlled rotational movement, such as the joint of the atlas and axis in the neck, which allows you to move your head from side to side.
Saddle	Similar to condyloid joints but the surfaces are **concave** and **convex**. The joint is shaped like a saddle with the other bone resting on it. Movement occurs backwards and forwards and from side to side, like that at the base of the thumb.

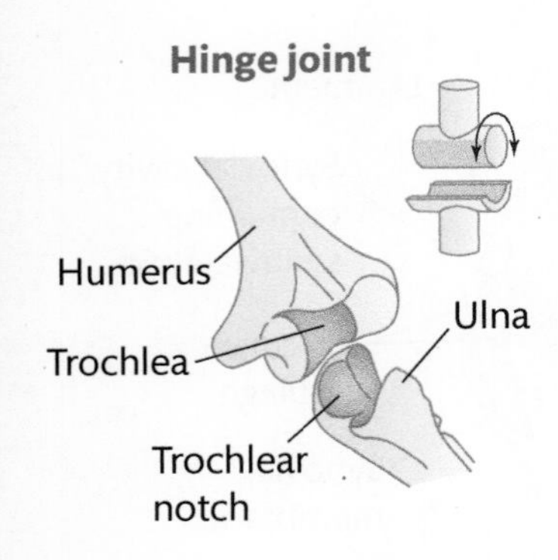

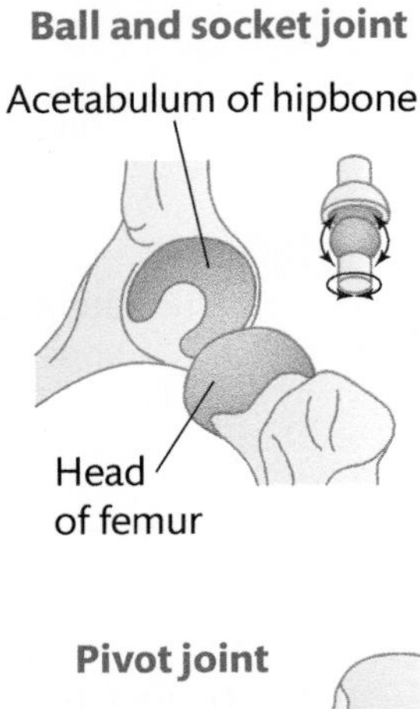

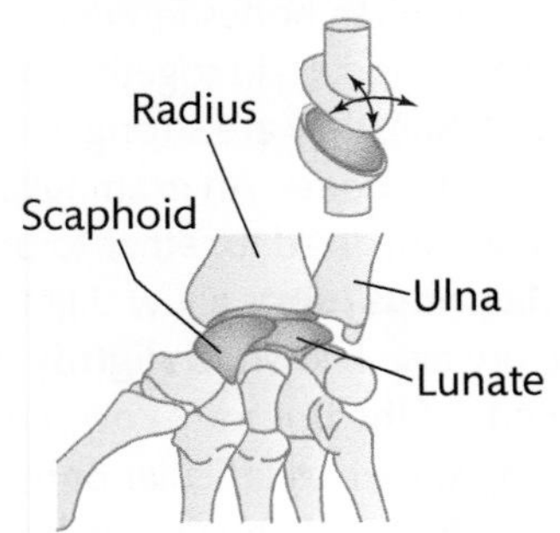

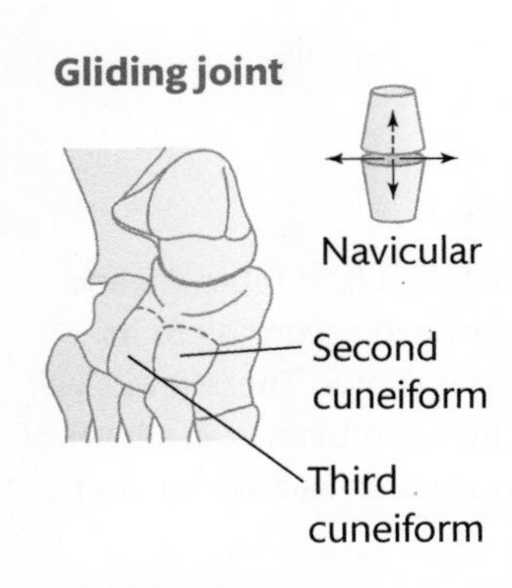

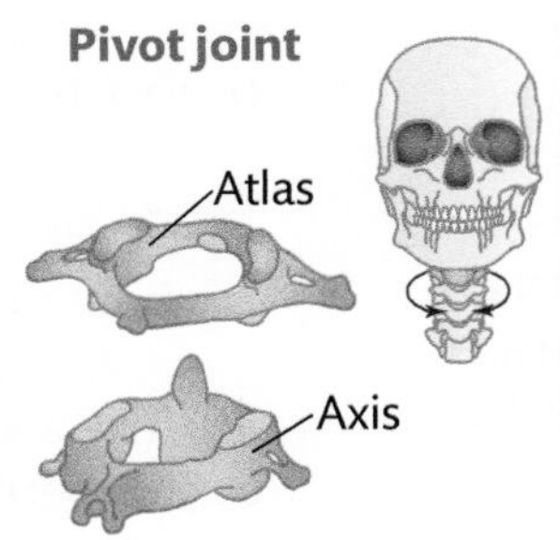

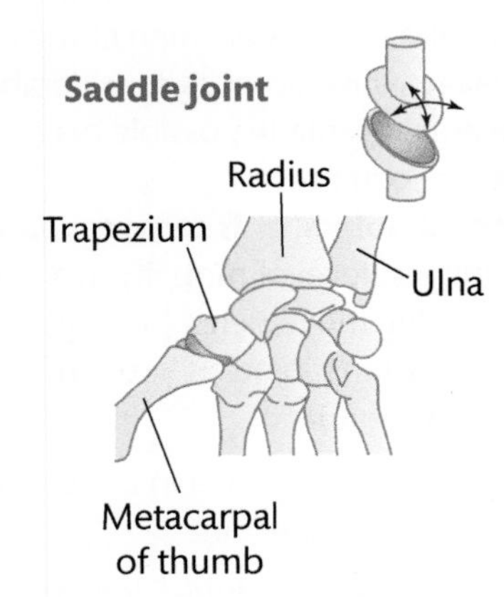

▶ **Figure 2.15:** Types of synovial joint

Research

In groups, analyse a sporting movement such as a throw in cricket, a serve in tennis or a free throw in basketball. Identify the main bones being used as well as the function of those bones. You should also identify and analyse the main synovial joints that are used and how they combine to produce the overall action.

Movements at synovial joints

The types of movements that each synovial joint allows is determined by its structure and shape. Sporting techniques usually use a combination of different joints to allow a wide range of movement or technique. For example, when bowling, a cricketer will use joints in the fingers (phalanges), wrist, elbow and shoulder. They will also use the joints of the foot, ankle, knee and hip when running.

It is important that you are able to break down these techniques and identify the specific movements at each joint.

The range of motion at a joint is often referred to as joint **flexibility**. Flexibility will also depend on a number of factors including age, the tension of the supporting connective tissue (tendons) and muscles that surround the joint, and the amount of **soft tissue** surrounding the joint.

Key terms

Flexibility – the range of movement around a joint or group of joints.

Soft tissue – the tissue that connects, supports and surrounds structures such as joints or organs. It includes tendons, ligaments, skin, fat and muscles.

PAUSE POINT What are the different types of joint? Identify the locations of each type of joint.

Hint Draw a synovial joint, labelling the main structural features.

Extend Explain the functions of the main structural features of your labelled synovial joint.

Assessment practice 2.3

1. Explain how the bones of the skeleton are used in movement for sport. (2 marks)
2. Describe the process of bone remodelling. (3 marks)
3. Identify the six types of synovial joint and give an example of where each one is located. (6 marks)
4. Explain the function of the axial and appendicular skeleton. (4 marks)

Plan

- What is the question asking me to do? Do I need to give sporting examples?
- What are the key words that I will need to include relating to the skeletal system?

Do

- Have I identified the key terms that need to be included in each answer?
- Have I given sufficient examples relating to the number of marks available?

Review

- Have I checked my answer? Is it clear? Did I give suitable examples?

Anatomy of the muscular system

Muscle types

There are over 640 named muscles in the human body making up approximately 40 per cent of your body mass. There are three main types of muscle.

- **Skeletal muscle** – also known as striated or striped muscle because of its striped appearance when viewed under a microscope, this type of muscle is voluntary (under your conscious control). These muscles are critical to sport and exercise as they are connected to the skeletal system via tendons and are primarily responsible for movement. Skeletal muscles contract and as a result pull on your bones resulting in an action. They can get fatigued during exercise.
- **Cardiac muscle** – this type of muscle tissue is only found in the wall of your heart. It works continuously. It is involuntary (not under conscious control). It is composed of a specialised type of striated tissue with its own blood supply. Its contractions help force blood through your blood vessels to all parts of your body. The cardiac muscle does not fatigue which means that it does not get tired during exercise.
- **Smooth muscle** – an involuntary muscle, under the control of your nervous system, it is located in the walls of your digestive system and blood vessels and helps regulate digestion and blood pressure.

Key terms

Mitochondria – the organelles within cells in the body where aerobic respiration takes place.

Aerobic respiration – the process of producing energy using oxygen where energy is released from glucose.

Fibre types

All skeletal muscles are made up from muscle fibres. The mix of fibres varies from individual to individual, but training can influence the efficiency of these different fibre types. There are three main types.

- **Type I (slow-twitch) fibres** – contract slowly and with less force. They are slow to fatigue and suited to longer duration aerobic activities. They have a rich blood supply and contain many **mitochondria** to sustain aerobic metabolism. They have a high capacity for **aerobic respiration**.
- **Type IIa fibres (fast-twitch or fast-oxidative fibres)** – fast-contracting, able to produce a great force and resistant to fatigue. They are less reliant on oxygen for energy supplied by the blood and fatigue faster than slow-twitch fibres.

- **Type IIx fibres (fast-twitch or fast-glycolytic fibres)** - contract rapidly and have the capacity to produce large amounts of force, but fatigue faster so are better suited to **anaerobic activity**. They depend almost entirely on **anaerobic respiration** and are recruited for higher-intensity, shorter-duration activities.

Key terms

Anaerobic activity - activity where your body uses energy **without** oxygen; that is, activity that results in muscle cells using anaerobic respiration.

Anaerobic respiration - the process of breaking down glucose without oxygen to produce energy.

Central nervous system - the brain and spinal cord responsible for transferring electrical impulses.

Discussion

Sometimes you can override a reflex or learn to ignore it. People wearing contact lenses have to overcome the blinking reflex. Can you think of any other examples of overriding a reflex?

Link

You can read more about the body's energy systems in *Unit 1: Sport and Exercise Physiology*.

Anatomy of the skeletal muscle

Skeletal muscles contain thousands of individual muscle fibres or strands (see Figure 2.16). These are combined into bundles known as fasciculi (or **fascicle** if referring to just one bundle). Each fascicle is held together by a connective tissue known as **perimysium**. Each fascicle contains between 10 and 100 muscle fibres, depending on the muscle. For example, a large muscle required to produce big powerful movements would have a large number of fibres in each fascicle. All muscle fibres (e.g. all fasciculi) are held in place by a muscle sheath known as **epimysium** which also protects the muscle from friction against other muscles and bones.

When examining an individual muscle fibre you will see these are covered in a fibrous connective tissue which acts as an insulator. This is known as the **endomysium**.

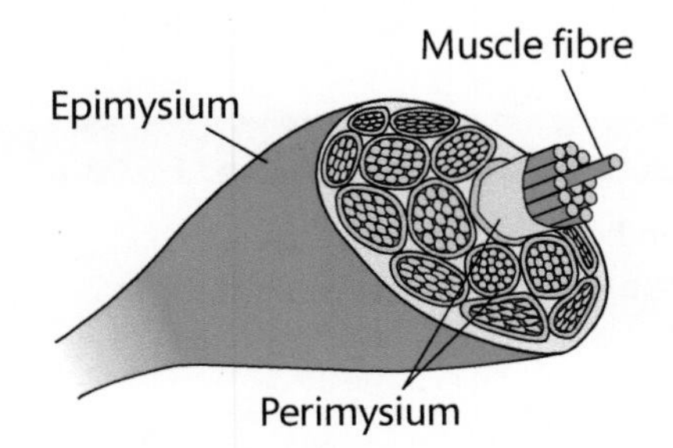

Figure 2.16: The structure of a skeletal muscle

Neuromuscular process of muscle contraction

The term 'neuromuscular' refers to both the nervous system and the muscular system. There are two kinds of nerves:

- **sensory neurons** (or nerves) which carry information **from** our extremities (the skin) to the central nervous system (the brain and spinal cord)
- **motor neurons** (or nerves) which carry information from our central nervous system **to** our muscles.

Muscles only contract when a nerve ending is stimulated by electrical impulses from the **central nervous system** (CNS).

A muscular contraction occurs when the CNS sends a signal or **nerve impulse** to the muscle. This is received by a motor neurone contained within the muscle fibres and converts the impulse into a muscular contraction. The site where this occurs is known as the **neuromuscular junction** or **synapses**. When the impulse is received the motor neuron releases a chemical (**acetylcholine**) which transmits the signal into a muscle fibre resulting in a contraction. The release of acetylcholine occurs at the **neurotransmitter**.

When a motor neuron is not conducting an impulse it has a resting potential. This changes when a stimulus reaches a resting neuron. The motor neuron transmits the signal known as the action potential.

PAUSE POINT Explain how different muscle fibre types affect sport.

Hint List three sports and the types of muscle fibres required for each.

Extend Explain why your chosen sports require these fibres and how an athlete can use them to improve performance.

Sliding filament theory

Sliding filament theory explains how muscles contract (see Figure 2.17). Muscles are comprised of thin muscle fibres know as **myofibrils** each containing **myosin** and **actin** filaments in series (one after the other). During contraction, myosin filaments attach to actin filaments forming chemical bonds called **crossbridges**. This basic unit of a muscle cell is known as a **sarcomere**. Sarcomeres give skeletal muscle tissue its striped or striated appearance. Each sarcomere is divided into different areas as follows:

- **H zone** – the centre of the A band of each sarcomere. Here there are only thick filaments, no thin filaments
- **Z line** – the area at each end of separate sarcomeres where the actin filaments are attached
- **A band** – the active area where contraction takes place between the actin filaments and the myosin filaments. It is the relatively dark area of the sarcomere and contains the thick filaments
- **I band** – the region between adjacent A bands, in which there are only thin filaments and no thick filaments. Each I band extends across two adjacent sarcomeres.

Myosin molecules act like a ratchet, while actin molecules form passive filaments transmitting the force generated by the myosin to the ends of the muscle tissue. The myosin progresses along an actin filament, constantly binding, ratcheting and then letting go. This process allows muscles to contract. When the muscle does not need to contract, thin strands of a further protein (**tropomyosin**) are wrapped around the actin filaments to stop the myosin from binding. As a muscle undergoes contraction:

- molecules called **troponin** attach to tropomyosin
- **calcium ions** are introduced into the muscle cell and bind with troponin
- calcium binding changes the shape of troponin, causing tropomyosin to move, exposing actin
- myosin is now free to bind with actin and the muscle contracts.

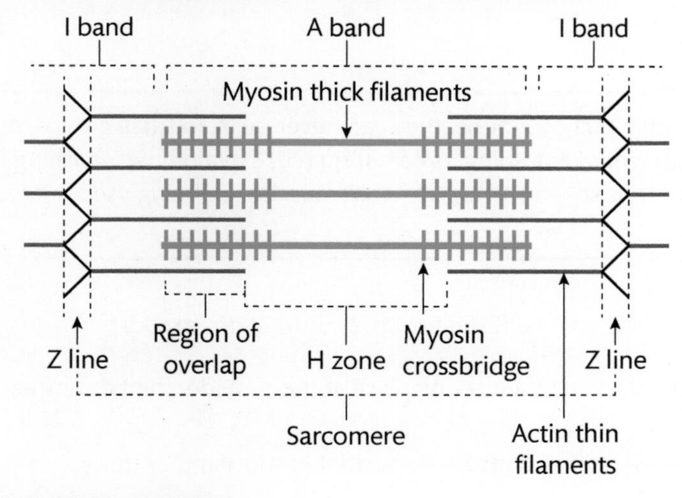

Figure 2.17: Sliding filament theory

Troponin and tropomyosin are proteins that form part of the thin or actin filament. Tropomyosin is a rod-shaped protein that spirals about the actin core to stiffen it. Troponin binds to the tropomyosin and helps it bind to the actin. The skeleton is the major mineral storage site for calcium and releases calcium ions into the bloodstream under controlled conditions. Circulating calcium is either ionised or bound to blood proteins such as troponin. The ions are stored in the **sarcoplasmic reticulum** of muscle cells.

Key term

Sarcoplasmic reticulum – regulates the calcium ion concentration in the muscle cells.

Link

You can read more about ATP, ADP, phosphate and reversible reaction in *Unit 1: Sport and Exercise Physiology.*

ATPase is an enzyme that catalyses (speeds up) the following reversible reaction enabling a quick supply of energy for muscle contraction:

$$ATP + H_2O \Leftrightarrow ADP + phosphate$$

Types of skeletal muscle contraction

There are three different types of muscle contraction.

- **Concentric** - when you make any movement such as a bicep curl, your muscle will shorten as the muscle fibres contract. In the bicep curl, the brachialis and bicep shorten, bringing your forearm towards your upper arm. They are sometimes known as the **positive phase** of muscle contraction.
- **Eccentric** - when a muscle returns to its normal length after shortening against resistance. In a bicep curl this is the controlled lowering of your arm to its starting position. At this point your muscles work against gravity and act like a brake. This can be easier to perform but does produce muscle soreness. Eccentric contraction can be a significant factor in the stimulus that promotes gains in muscle strength and size. Eccentric contractions are sometimes known as the **negative phase** of muscle contraction.
- **Isometric** - the length of a muscle does not change and the joint angle does not alter. However, the muscle is actively engaged in holding a static position, for example, during the abdominal plank. This work is easy to undertake but rapidly causes fatigue. It can cause sharp increases in blood pressure as blood flow is reduced.

Key term

Motor unit - a motor neuron and all the associated fibres it affects. Motor units work together to coordinate contractions of a single skeletal muscle.

All or none law

For a muscle to contract it must receive a nerve impulse and this stimulus must be sufficient to activate at least one **motor unit** which contains the motor neuron (nerve cell) and the attached muscle fibres. Once activated, **all** the muscle fibres within the motor unit will contract and produce a muscle twitch. This is known as the 'all or none' law as muscle fibres either respond completely (all) or not at all (none). For more intense exercises, more motor units will be recruited or used and therefore more fibres will contract.

Discussion

Muscles can only pull on a bone, they can never push. In small groups, discuss a rugby scrum where a pushing force is required. Explain how a pushing force is created when muscles can only pull. What muscles are being used to create this movement?

PAUSE POINT Explain the importance of different muscle contractions in sport.

Hint What types of contraction are taking place at the shoulder joint during each phase of a press-up?

Extend Explain why these contractions are important in sport and exercise.

Major skeletal muscles of the muscular system

Skeletal muscles are voluntary muscles, meaning you must send a conscious signal from your brain to your muscles to perform any sporting action. Skeletal muscles are attached to your skeleton by tendons which pull on specific bones when a muscle contracts. Skeletal muscles provide you with movement, strength and power and are also responsible for maintaining posture and body temperature. Figure 2.18 and Table 2.9 will help you locate the main ones which are important to sport and exercise.

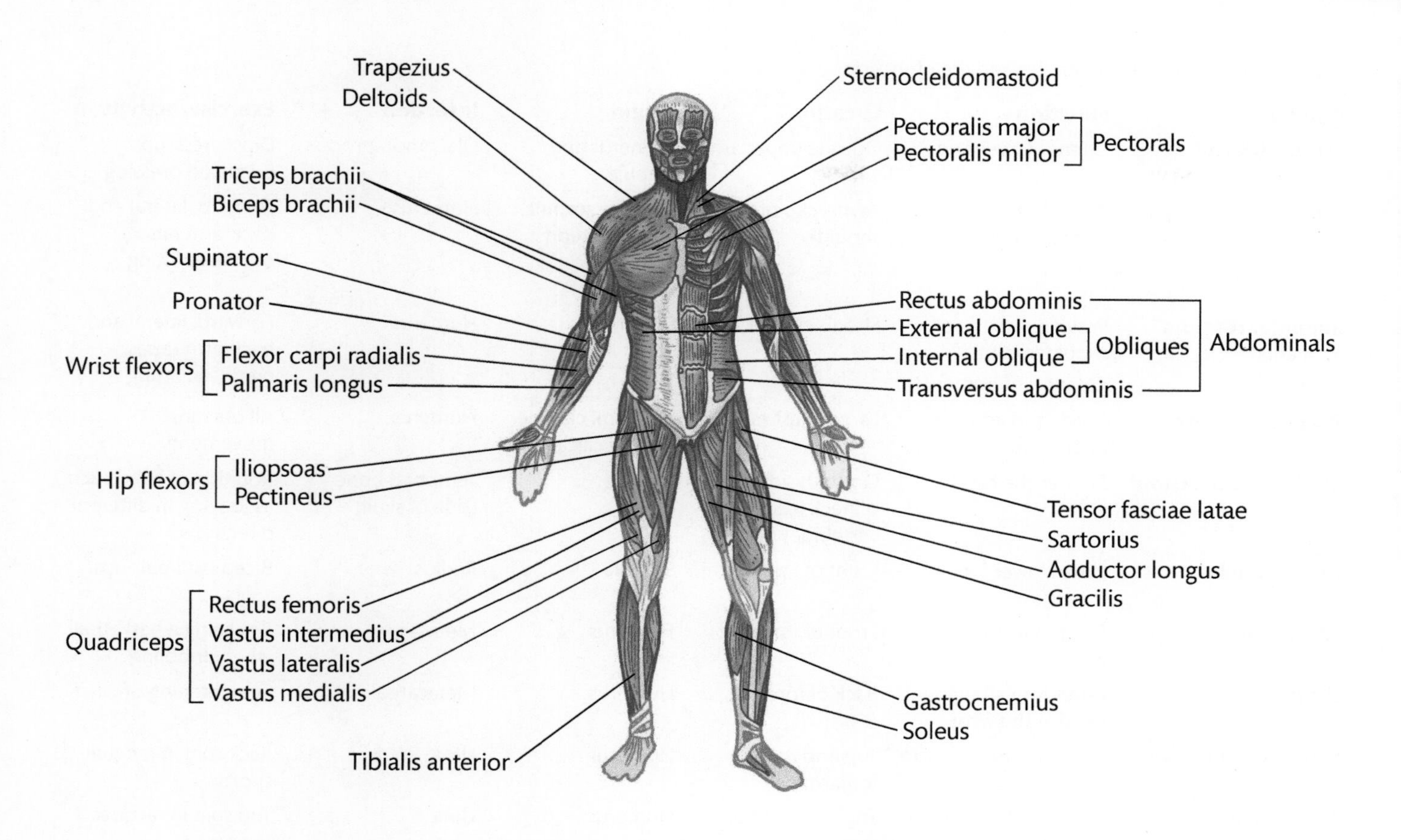

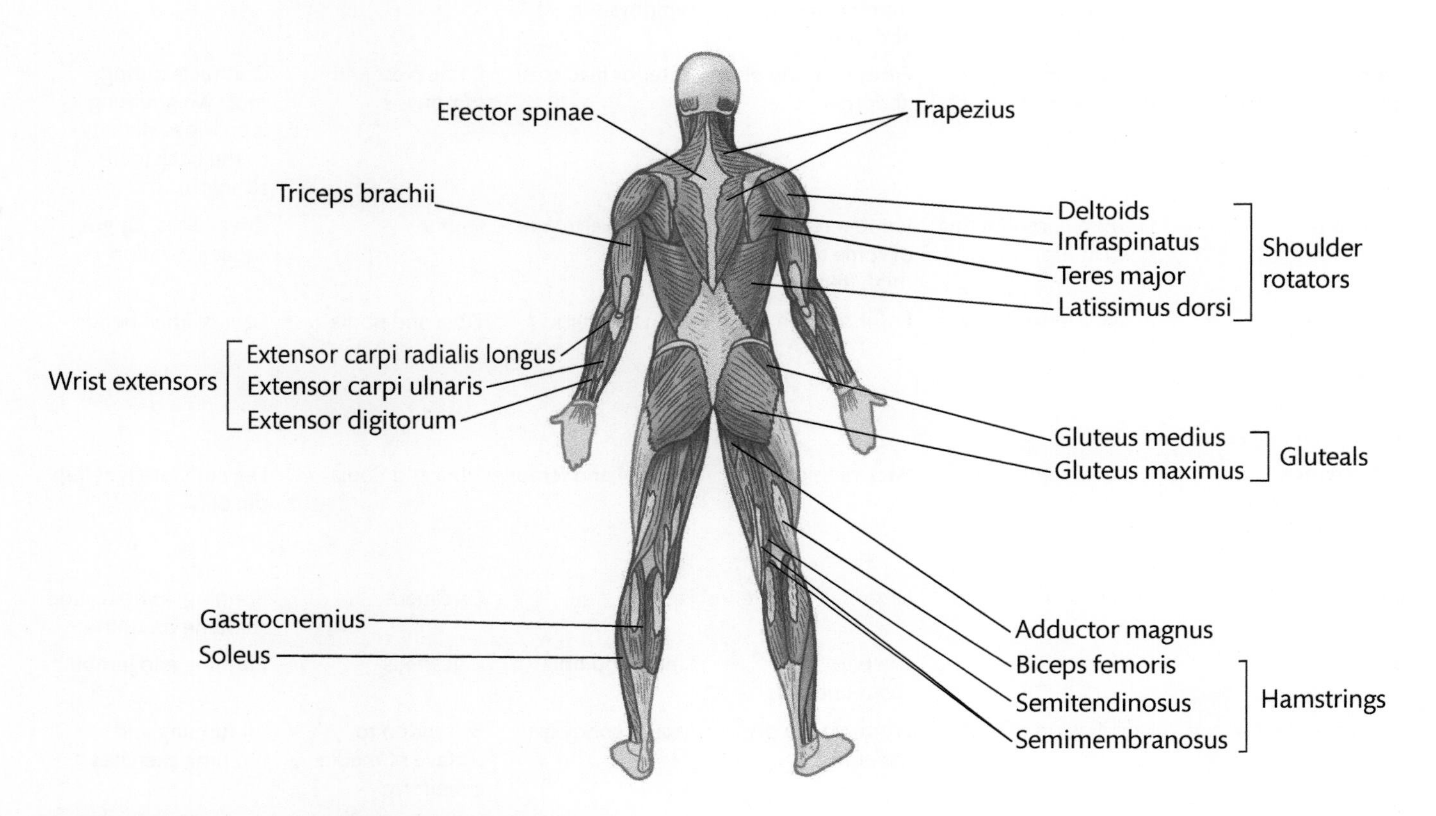

Figure 2.18: Major skeletal muscles and their location

Table 2.9: Major skeletal muscles and their function

Muscle	Function	Location	Origin	Insertion	Exercise/activity
Triceps brachii	Extends lower arm	Outside upper arm	Humerus and scapula	Olecranon process	Dips, press-ups, overhead pressing
Deltoids • posterior • anterior • medial	Abducts, flexes and extends upper arm	Forms cap of shoulder	Clavicle, scapula and acromion	Humerus	Forward, lateral and back-arm raises, overhead lifting
Shoulder rotators • medial • lateral	Provide stability of shoulder joint Rotation of humerus	Shoulder joint	Scapula	Humerus	Forward, lateral and back-arm raises, overhead lifting
Pectoralis major	Flexes and adducts upper arm	Large chest muscle	Sternum, clavicle and rib cartilage	Humerus	All pressing movements
Sternocleidomastoid	Rotates the head	On both sides of neck (cervical vertebrae)	Clavicle	Temporal bone (side of skull)	Rotation of head such as looking in different directions
Biceps brachii	Flexes lower arm at the elbow	Front of upper arm	Scapula	Radius	Bicep curl, pull-ups
Wrist flexors	Flexes hand at the wrist	Front of forearm	Humerus	Metacarpal	Bouncing a basketball when dribbling
Wrist extensors	Extends or straightens hand at the wrist	Back of forearm	Humerus	Metacarpal	Straightening of wrist
Forearm supinator	Supinates the forearm	Top and rear of forearm	Humerus	Ulna	Back spin in racquet sports
Forearm pronator	Pronates the forearm	Top and front of forearm	Humerus	Ulna	Top spin in racquet sports
Rectus abdominis	Flexes and rotates lumbar region of vertebral column	'Six-pack' muscle running down abdomen	Pubic crest and symphysis	Xiphoid process	Sit-ups
Transverse abdominis (TVA)	Provides stability of the spine and pelvis Maintains posture	Front and side of abdomen	Anterior iliac crest	Pubic crest and symphysis	Contracts during most weightlifting as it provides stability to the back (core strength)
Iliopsoas	Flexes hip joint (lifting thigh at hip)	Lumbar region of spine to top of thigh (femur)	Lumbar vertebrae	Femur	Knee raises, lunges, squat activation
Quadriceps • rectus femoris • vastus intermedius • vastus lateralis • vastus medialis	Extends lower leg and flexes thigh	Front of thigh	Ilium and femur	Tibia and fibula	Squats, knee bends
Hamstrings • biceps femoris • semitendinosus • semimembranosus	Flexes lower leg and extends thigh	Back of thigh	Ischium and femur	Tibia and fibula	Leg curls, straight leg deadlift
Gastrocnemius	Plantarflexion, flexes knee	Large calf muscle	Femur	Calcaneus	Running, jumping and standing on tiptoe
Soleus	Plantarflexion	Deep to gastrocnemius	Fibula and tibia	Calcaneus	Running and jumping
Tibialis anterior	Dorsiflexion of foot	Front of tibia on lower leg	Lateral condyle	By tendon to surface of medial cuneiform	All running and jumping exercises

Table 2.9: Major skeletal muscles and their function - *continued*

Erector spinae	Extends spine	Long muscle running either side of spine	Cervical, thoracic and lumbar vertebrae	Cervical, thoracic and lumbar vertebrae	Prime mover of back extension
Rhomboids (not shown in Figure 2.18)	Retract the scapula toward the vertebral column; hold the scapula against thoracic cage	Upper back between the scapula and the vertebral column	Thoracic vertebra	Scapula	Shoulder raise
Trapezius	Elevates and depresses scapula	Large triangular muscle at top of back	Continuous insertion along acromion	Occipital bone and all thoracic vertebrae	Shrugging and overhead lifting
Latissimus dorsi	Extends and adducts lower arm	Large muscle covering back of lower ribs	Vertebrae and iliac crest	Humerus	Pull-ups, rowing movements
Obliques	Flexes trunk laterally	Waist	Pubic crest and iliac crest	Fleshy strips to lower eight ribs	Oblique curls
Gluteals • Gluteus maximus • Gluteus medius • Gluteus minimus (not shown in Figure 2.18)	Extends thigh	Large muscle on buttocks	Ilium, sacrum and coccyx	Femur	Knee-bending movements, cycling, squatting

Antagonistic muscle pairs

When a muscle contracts, it exerts a pulling force on the bones it is attached to, causing movement at a joint. Muscles must cross the joints that they move - without this no movement can occur.

Muscle fibres work on an 'all or nothing' basis - either contracting completely or not at all. At the point of contraction your muscles shorten and pull on the bones they are attached to. When a muscle contracts, one end normally remains stationary while the other is drawn towards it. The end that remains stationary is known as the **origin**, and the moving end is called the **insertion**.

Key terms

Origin - the fixed end of the muscle that remains stationary.

Insertion - the end of the muscle that moves. The insertion usually crosses over a joint to allow movement when the muscle shortens.

Muscles are assembled in groups and work together to bring about movement. They act only by contracting and pulling. They do not push, but can contract without shortening and hold a joint fixed in a certain position. When the contraction ends, the muscles become soft but do not lengthen until stretched by the contraction of the opposing muscles. This is known as **antagonistic pairs** of muscles. Figure 2.19 shows how the bicep and tricep work together to perform a bicep curl.

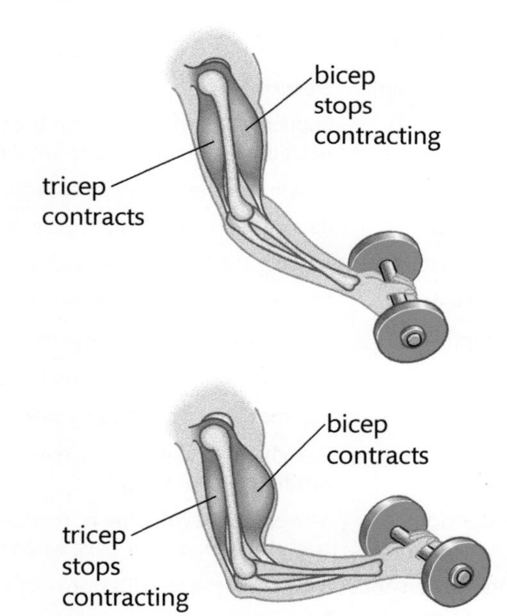

Figure 2.19: Bicep and tricep muscles work together during a bicep curl

Reflect

Consider the main muscle contracting and the opposite relaxing during a movement. What happens when the opposite movement occurs?

- The muscle that shortens to move a joint is called the **agonist** or prime mover. This is the muscle principally responsible for the movement taking place - the contracting muscle.

- The muscle that relaxes in opposition to the agonist is called the **antagonist**. If it did not relax, movement could not take place. Antagonists exert a 'braking' control over the movement.
- **Synergists** are muscles that enable the agonists to operate more effectively. They work with the agonists to control and direct movement by modifying or altering the direction of pull to the best position.
- **Fixator** muscles stop any unwanted movement by fixing or stabilising the joint or joints involved. Fixator muscles stabilise the origin so that the agonist can achieve maximum and effective contraction.

PAUSE POINT Name the main skeletal muscles and state where they are located.

Hint Consider a sport and describe the role of the specific muscles used in this sport.

Extend Think of a sporting movement and list the pairs of muscles being used for each phase of the movement.

Types of movement

Muscles can combine to achieve the movements shown in Table 2.10, all of which are common across a wide range of sports.

Table 2.10: Types of movement

Type of movement	Description
Flexion	Reducing the angle between the bones of a limb at a joint: muscles contract, moving the joint into a bent position. Examples include bending the knee when preparing to kick a football
Hip flexion	Moving the femur forwards reducing the angle between the thigh and the anterior torso
Shoulder flexion	Raising the arm at the shoulder joint
Hip extension	Moving the femur backwards increasing the angle between the thigh and the anterior torso
Shoulder extension	Lowering the arm at the shoulder joint
Dorsiflexion	An upward movement, e.g. moving the foot to pull the toes towards the knee in walking
Plantarflexion	A movement that points the toes downwards by straightening the ankle, e.g. jumping to defend in netball
Lateral flexion	The movement of bending sideways, for example, at the waist
Extension	Straightening a limb to increase the angle at the joint, e.g. straightening your arm to return to your starting position in a bicep curl
Hyper-extension	Movement beyond the normal anatomical position in a direction opposite to flexion, e.g. at the spine when a cricketer arches their back when bowling
Horizontal flexion and horizontal extension	Bending the elbow (flexion) while the arm is in front of your body; straightening the arm at the elbow is extension
Abduction	Movement away from the body's vertical midline, e.g. at the hip in a side-step in gymnastics
Adduction	Movement towards the body's vertical midline, e.g. pulling on the oars while rowing
Horizontal abduction and adduction	Movement of bringing your arm across your body (flexion) and then back again (extension)
Rotation	Circular movement of a limb. Rotation occurs at the shoulder joint during a tennis serve. Rotation can also occur at the hip and a movement where the thigh moves outwards is known as lateral rotation whereas the movement where the thigh moves inwards is known as medial rotation
Circumduction	A circular movement that results in a conical action
Pronation	A rotational movement where the hand and upper arm are turned inwards. Also where the foot is turned outwards at the ankle
Supination	Where the forearm or palm are rotated outwards. Also where the foot is turned inwards at the ankle
Elevation	An upwards movement (superior), e.g. shrugging where the scapula is raised

▶ **Table 2.10:** Types of movement – *continued*

Type of movement	Description
Depression	The opposite of elevation and involves a downwards or inferior action
Protraction	A forward movement away from the frontal plane of motion, e.g. the shoulder joint moving forward during the reaching phase of a rowing action
Retraction	A backwards movement towards the frontal plane of motion, e.g. the shoulder joint moving backwards during the pulling phase of a rowing action

Planes of movement

Sporting movements are based on planes and axes of movement. There are three planes.

- **Sagittal plane** – splits the body into imaginary left and right halves. Movements in the sagittal plane are related to flexion and extension (side to side). Running and cycling will take place in the sagittal plane.
- **Frontal plane** – separates the body into imaginary front to back halves. Movements in the frontal plane are related to abduction and adduction (front to back). Raising your arms to the side will take place in the frontal plane.
- **Transverse plane** – splits the body into imaginary top to bottom halves. Movements in the transverse plan are related to rotation (up and down). Twisting movements such as turning your head will take place in the transverse plane.

Link

Axes of movement are covered in Unit 7, on page 237.

Assessment practice 2.4

1. Explain the different muscle fibre types, giving an example of a sport that would predominantly use each one. (3 marks)
2. Describe the three types of muscular contraction and give an example of an exercise for each that would use each one. (3 marks)
3. Explain sliding filament theory in relation to muscular contraction. (6 marks)
4. Giving a sporting example, describe each of the following actions: extension, rotation, supination, circumduction, protraction. (5 marks)

Plan

- What are the key terms and words being used in the question?
- Do I need to include specific examples, such as different types of movement?

Do

- Have I written down the key words and explained them?
- Have I contextualised my answers by giving relevant examples?

Review

- Have I given sufficient examples linked to the marks available?
- Have I broken down any movements into key phases and explained all the key terms used?

F Analysis of the skeletal and muscular systems and how they produce movements in sport and exercise

Phases of sport and exercise movement

All sport and exercise movements require interaction and coordination of the skeletal and muscular systems. The muscular system allows the athlete to maintain posture, holding joints in place and providing muscular contractions that pull on the bones of the skeletal system, resulting in movement. There are three phases in these movements.

- **Preparation** – where the athlete is preparing to undertake an action or exercise, they will be both physically and psychologically preparing themselves. During this phase the athlete may consider what they wish to achieve, for example, where they wish to place the football when taking a penalty.
- **Execution** – immediately following the preparation phase, the athlete will perform the planned action. This will involve the interaction of the muscular and skeletal systems to produce the chosen movement or technique.
- **Follow through** – this is the action the body undertakes following the execution of a movement or **technique**. This may involve slowing down a body part using the muscular system or a change in direction.

Key term

Technique – a series of basic movements that combine to result in a recognised sporting or exercise movement.

Case study

Sporting movements

Many sporting movements look complex but in reality they can be viewed and analysed as separate, smaller movements. It is commonplace for modern coaches to use video equipment to film specific techniques so that the series of movements can be analysed and discussed with the athlete.

Consider the action of throwing a ball. You will use a number of different joints including the ball and socket joint of the shoulder, the hinge joint of the elbow and the gliding joints of the wrist (carpals). In combination with the skeletal muscles, you will be able to use the long bones as levers to produce a large powerful movement in order to throw the ball.

Check your knowledge

1. Can you think of any other sporting techniques that are similar to throwing a ball?
2. What sports share the same movements?
3. How would a coach benefit from being able to identify different and identical sporting movements?

Interrelationship of muscular and skeletal systems in movement analysis

When examining the three phases of a sporting movement, it is useful to examine the different body sections separately so a detailed analysis can be conducted. The three broad body sections that can be analysed are:

- the upper trunk including the shoulders and arms
- the trunk (main torso)
- the lower body.

Being able to break movement down into smaller body parts will make it easier for you to analyse the chosen sporting or exercise movement during the three phases.

For each of the phases and body areas you should consider:

- the bones being used (including their type)
- the muscles being used, the role or function they are playing in the movement and the types of contraction taking place
- the type of joint being moved
- the type of action occurring, such as flexion
- the planes of movement that are involved.

Remember it is easier to break down complex actions such as a rugby place kick into smaller stages so a clear analysis can be made – and many sports and exercise techniques share the same basic movements, such as running, jumping and throwing. Having an understanding of each of these will allow you to transfer your knowledge to a wider range of sporting movements.

Worked example: the rugby place kick

- The action of kicking takes place in a sagittal plane about a frontal axis and involves the hip, knee and ankle joints.
- The hip bones involved are the femur and pelvic girdle which form a ball and socket joint.
- The knee bones involved are the femur and tibia which form a hinge joint.
- The ankle bones involved are the tibia and calcaneus.
- Kicking comprises three phases: the preparatory phase, execution phase and the follow through phase.

The three phases can be summarised as shown in Tables 2.11, 2.12 and 2.13.

▶ **Table 2.11:** The preparation phase of a rugby place kick

Joint	Joint type	Joint movement	Agonist	Type of contraction of agonist	Antagonist
Left shoulder	Ball and socket	Abduction	Middle deltoid	Concentric	Latissimus dorsi
Right hip	Ball and socket	Extension	Gluteus maximus	Concentric	Iliopsoas
Right knee	Hip	Flexion	Biceps femoris, semitendinosus, semimembranosus	Concentric	Rectus femoris, vastus lateralis, vastus medialis, vastus intermedius

▶ The preparation phase of a rugby place kick

▶ **Table 2.12:** The execution phase of a rugby place kick

Joint	Joint type	Joint movement	Agonist	Type of contraction of agonist	Antagonist
Left shoulder	Ball and socket	Horizontal flexion	Pectoralis major	Concentric	Trapezius
Spine	Cartilaginous Pivot Gliding	Rotation	External obliques	Concentric	Internal obliques
Right hip	Ball and socket	Flexion	Iliopsoas	Concentric	Gluteus maximus
Right knee	Hinge	Extension	Rectus femoris, vastus lateralis, vastus medialis, vastus intermedius	Concentric	Biceps femoris, semitendinosus, semimembranosus
Right ankle	Hinge	Dorsiflexion	Tibialis anterior	Concentric	Gastrocnemius

▶ The execution phase of a rugby place kick

▶ **Table 2.13:** The follow through phase of a rugby place kick

Joint	Joint type	Joint movement	Agonist	Type of contraction of agonist	Antagonist
Left shoulder	Ball and socket	Horizontal extension	Trapezius	Concentric	Pectoralis major
Spine	Cartilaginous Pivot Gliding	Rotation	Internal obliques	Concentric	External obliques
Right hip	Ball and socket	Extension	Gluteus maximus	Concentric	Iliopsoas
Right knee	Hinge	Flexion	Biceps femoris, semitendinosus, semimembranosus	Concentric	Rectus femoris, vastus lateralis, vastus medialis, vastus intermedius
Right ankle	Hinge	Dorsiflexion	Gastrocnemius	Concentric	Tibialis anterior

▶ The follow through phase of a rugby place kick

Movement efficiency

Link

This section links with *Unit 7: Biomechanics in Sport and Exercise Science.*

Sport and exercise can be very strenuous on the body, with large internal and external forces applied to the skeletal and muscular systems. It is essential when undertaking a sporting technique that you only use the body parts required for the movement. This will prevent wasted energy and limit unwanted movement that may have a negative effect on your technique and performance.

- **Static and dynamic balance** are basic skills needed in practically every sport activity. Ensuring your joints are stable will provide you with a platform to perform complicated sporting movements. Your muscular system will help by using fixator muscles to ensure specific joint actions only occur when required.
- A **kinetic chain** is a series of joint movements contributing to an overall complex movement. For example, a basketball free throw can be broken down into movement at the ankles, knee, hip, shoulder, elbow and wrist. Each of these joint movements will affect the overall action or technique.
- Most actions occur **across different body segments**, for example, a bowler in cricket uses the lower body to run and create speed and this supports the action of the upper body in generating the power and technique to deliver the ball. Each separate action will have an effect on the other parts of the body within the overall action.
- To ensure your body can cope with the demands placed on it while maintaining performance, your skeletal and muscular system will **transfer the forces** so that one specific area is not overloaded. This transfer of loads also helps maintain movement efficiency as one particular area will not become overworked.
- When one muscle is stronger than its opposing muscle, you do not have **muscle balance**. For instance, if you do push-ups or bench presses daily, but never do rows, pull-ups, or other upper body pulling movements, there is a chance your chest will become stronger than your back, and you have a strength imbalance where one particular muscle group may dominate. It is important when you train to consider all parts of the muscular system so that muscles remain balanced.
- The more efficiently you move, with the least amount of effort expended, the longer you will be able to perform. This is known as **mechanical efficiency**. This is particularly important in sports that put high demands on the body such as rowing, marathon running or swimming.

Assessment practice 2.5

Otis is practising his basketball free throw. There are three phases to the movement:

- preparation
- execution
- follow through

Joint	Type of joint	Bones	Joint movement	Plane of movement	Muscles	Muscle contraction
Elbow					Agonist –	
					Antagonist –	
Shoulder					Agonist –	
					Antagonist –	
Wrist					Agonist –	
					Antagonist –	

Copy and complete the table three times, once for each phase of the movement. (20 marks)

Plan

- What are the key phases of movement being used?
- What main joints of the upper body are being used and what movements occur for each phase?

Do

- Have I written down the joints, muscles and movements and explained them all?
- Have I identified the plane of movement in which each action is taking place?

Review

- Have I given sufficient examples linked to the marks available?
- Have I broken down the movements into each key phase and explained all the key terms used?

Further reading and resources

Books

Bartlett, R. (2014) *Introduction to Sports Biomechanics*, Oxford: Routledge.

Howley, E. T. and Franks, B. D. (2003) *Health Fitness Instructor's Handbook*, Champaign, IL: Human Kinetics.

Marieb, E. N. and Hoehn, K. (2015) *Human Anatomy*, Oxford: Pearson.

Palastanga, N. and Soames, R. (2012) *Anatomy and Human Movement: Structure and Function*, London: Churchill Livingstone.

Sharkey, B. J. and Gaskill, S. E. (2013) *Fitness & Health*, Champaign, IL: Human Kinetics.

Tortora, G. J. and Derrickson, B. H. (2008) *Principles of Anatomy and Physiology*, London: John Wiley and Sons.

Websites

www.humankinetics.com – Human Kinetics: a range of books, journals and articles focused on fitness, anatomy and physiology.

www.sportscoachuk.org – sports coach UK: extensive information on sports coaching and sports education.

www.topendsports.com – Top End Sports: a wide range of information about sport, sports science, fitness and nutrition.

www.brianmac.co.uk – Brian Mac Sports Coach: a wide range of information related to fitness and training.

THINK ▶FUTURE

Grace Vosper

Sports coach

I have been working as a sports coach for six years and over this time I have worked with a wide range of people in a variety of places. On any given day I will work with people of different ages and different abilities. For example, I may work with children helping them develop the basic core skills such as throwing and catching for a variety of sports or I may work with an experienced athlete who is trying to improve their personal performance in readiness for a competition.

Having a detailed knowledge of anatomy and physiology is essential to my job as I have to understand how each body system works and how the body will be affected by exercise. I also have to understand how each system interacts with others and how this can affect performance.

Often I will be working with athletes who are looking to improve a specific aspect of their performance. This requires to me to analyse their fitness and technique and make recommendations based on my findings. Often I will make suggestions based on fitness, and a knowledge of functional anatomy allows me to set targets and goals that will help that individual.

When setting goals or giving advice it is essential that these are set at the correct level so that injury does not occur. I have to ensure that each of my clients can train safely and use the correct techniques so that they do not harm themselves.

One of the most important skills that you need to be a successful sports coach is the ability to motivate people. Being able to get an athlete to reach their goal when they are tired or returning from injury is challenging but also one of the most rewarding parts of my job. Seeing individuals and teams achieve their long-term goals and knowing that you were key to their success is hugely satisfying.

Focusing your skills

Think about the role of a sports coach. Consider the following:

- What types of people will you work with and how will you support them?
- What role will you play in helping them achieve their goals?
- What types of training goals will you need to help people with? Will you work with elite athletes or children that are new to sport?
- What different types of exercise activities will you recommend and how will these affect each of the body's systems?
- What skills do you currently have? What skills do you think may need further development?

Getting ready for assessment

This section has been written to help you to do your best when you take the assessment test. Read through it carefully and ask your tutor if there is anything you are still not sure about.

About the test

The assessment test will ask a range of short answer questions as well as some longer answer questions.

- Short answer questions will be worth 1–2 marks.
- A longer answer question will be worth up to 8 marks.

Remember all the questions are compulsory and you should attempt to answer each one. Consider the question fully and remember to use the key words to describe, explain and analyse. For longer questions you will be required to include a number of explanations in your response.

As the guidelines for assessment can change, you should refer to the official assessment guidance on the Pearson Qualifications website for the latest definitive guidance.

Remember to plan your answer and write in detail.

Sample answers

For some questions you will be given some background information on which the questions are based. Look at the sample questions which follow and the tips on how to answer these.

Answering short answer questions

- Read the question carefully.
- Highlight or underline key words.
- Note the number of marks available.
- Make additional notes that you can include in your answer.
- Make sure you make the same number of statements as there are marks available. For example, a two mark question needs two statements.

Worked example

Look carefully at how the question is set out to see how many points need to be included in your answer.

The table below shows Jack's tidal volume as he takes part in a game of rugby.

Tidal volume before taking part in rugby	Tidal volume after 40 minutes of playing rugby
500ml	650ml

Explain why Jack's tidal volume has changed after 40 minutes of exercise. **[4]**

Answer: Tidal volume is the amount of air in one breath. Tidal volume increases during exercise because during exercise a person has to take in (inhale) more air. More air is required as it contains oxygen which is needed to provide energy for the working muscles so that they can contract. The body also needs to remove waste products such as carbon dioxide during exercise.

This answer gives a brief description of what tidal volume is (1 mark) and what happens to tidal volume during exercise (1 mark) plus an explanation of how (1 mark) and why this increases (1 mark).

Answering extended answer questions

Example:

Nancy is a marathon runner and Grace is a 100-metre sprinter. They recruit different skeletal muscle fibre types to compete in their sport.

Explain why different muscle fibre types would be recruited when taking part in the marathon and 100-metre events. [6]

For a question using the word 'explain', you must do more than just describe. You might need to talk about the structure and function of the different fibre types and then highlight why these are suited to different sports.

Answer: Grace would need powerful movements for the 100-metre sprint and would therefore use fast-twitch fibres [1] as these contract at speed and with a high amount of force [1] without using oxygen [1]. Nancy would need her muscles to produce steady movement over a longer period of time without fatiguing [1]. These would be slow-twitch fibres [1] which produce less powerful movements, do not fatigue easily and use the aerobic energy system [1].

This answer describes the different fibre types in relation to the two different athletics events and explains the types of contraction that these produce. The answer further explains why these types of fibres are suited to the selected sports.

It is possible that you will write a considerably longer section when answering an extended answer question, perhaps even multiple paragraphs. Before you start to answer the question, remember to make notes, writing down all the key words that could be included in your answer. Ensure that you plan all aspects of your longer answer to cover the number of marks available.

Applied Sport and Exercise Psychology 3

Getting to know your unit

Assessment
You will be assessed by a written task that is set and marked by Pearson.

Sports psychology is increasingly prominent in modern sport. An individual's psychological approach is often the key factor in successful sport performance and finding sport enjoyable. Understanding the different psychological factors that can affect sports participation and performance, as well as how to develop these qualities, is important for those working in the sports industry, such as athletes, tutors and coaches.

How you will be assessed

You will be assessed by a written task that is set and marked by Pearson. Your assessment will take place under supervised conditions.

A set period of time ahead of the supervised period you will be given a case study to base your written answer around. The case study could be based on an individual or a team that requires guidance on psychological interventions in response to psychological factors that are affecting their performance. You independently research the case study and make notes.

When you are preparing for your case study, consider the following questions.

- What are the key psychological factors that are affecting performance?
- Are these factors positive or negative?
- Which psychological intervention(s) would benefit this individual or team?
- Why would these intervention(s) benefit this individual or team?
- Can you find any theory/theories, or other forms of evidence, that can support the use of these intervention(s)?

The supervised assessment period must be taken within a short period that will be specified by Pearson. You should be told by your school or college when this will be but it is likely to be sometime in May or June. You are expected to complete the set task during the assessment period. The set task will assess your ability to interpret psychological factors, suggest psychological interventions and apply psychological theories.

As the guidelines for assessment can change, you should refer to the official assessment guidance on the Pearson Qualifications website for the latest definitive guidance.

The assessment outcomes for this unit are shown in Table 3.1.

Table 3.1: Unit 3 assessment outcomes

AO1	Demonstrate knowledge and understanding of psychological factors, concepts, interventions and theories in sport and exercise activities
AO2	Apply knowledge and understanding of psychological factors, concepts, interventions and theories, and their influence in sport and exercise activities on real-life sporting contexts
AO3	Analyse and evaluate information related to individuals or teams to determine appropriate psychological interventions
AO4	Be able to recommend psychological interventions underpinned by theory and in context with appropriate justification

There are several key command words you will need to understand as part of your assessment (see Table 3.2). These will help you understand what a question is asking you to do.

Table 3.2: Command words used in Unit 3

Command word	Definition
Analyse	Give reasons or evidence to support an opinion or a decision **or** to prove something is right or reasonable.
Evaluate	Use information, themes or concepts to consider wider issues such as: strengths or weaknesses, advantages or disadvantages, alternative actions, relevance or significance. This should lead to a clearly supported judgement with a conclusion.
Interpretation	Understand and describe the meaning, purpose or qualities of something.
Intervention	An action performed to create a change in people or in teams.
Justification/rationalisation	Give a reason or evidence to support an opinion or a decision and prove something right or reasonable.
Psychological factors	Examples include motivation, anxiety, arousal, stress, self-confidence, mindset and aggression.
Relevance	Important to the matter you are discussing.
Recommend	Put forward something (or someone) as being suitable for a particular purpose or role.

Getting started

In 2015 the England women's football team finished third in the FIFA Women's World Cup. This was their best ever finish. Along the way they experienced challenges, difficulties and successes. Produce a mind map of all of the ways you think sport psychology could have helped the team to success.

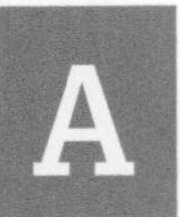

A Motivation for sports and exercise

Link

This unit links to *Unit 6: Coaching for Performance and Fitness* and *Unit 8: Specialised Fitness Training.*

Types of motivation

Motivation level is one of the most important qualities for any athlete. Too high and you may run the risk of injury, too low and you may not be able rise to the sporting occasion.

Often motivation is defined as the direction and intensity of effort. This definition encompasses what the athlete is motivated towards as well as how motivated they are. Other common definitions of motivation define it as being determined by internal and external factors, which arouse and direct behaviour.

Intrinsic motivation

Intrinsic motivation refers to someone participating in an activity without an external reward and/or without the primary reason being the achievement of an external reward. This is motivation that 'comes from within'. Fun is the most common form of intrinsic motivation. Three key elements can affect our intrinsic motivation:

- **accomplishments** – when athletes wish to increase their level of skill to get a sense of accomplishment
- **stimulation** – seeking an 'adrenaline rush' or some form of excitement
- **knowledge** – being curious about performance; wanting to know more about it and how to develop new techniques or skills that benefit performance.

Extrinsic motivation

Extrinsic motivation is when someone's behaviour is influenced by an external factor. Common forms of extrinsic motivation are tangible and intangible rewards. **Tangible rewards** are physical rewards, like money and medals, whereas **intangible rewards** are non-physical rewards such as praise or encouragement.

For extrinsic motivation to be effective, rewards must be effective. If a reward is given frequently, it will be of less value to the athlete and may lose its impact on performance. Equally, if an athlete places too much emphasis on the reward and it is subsequently removed, their motivation levels might decrease. A coach needs to have an in-depth knowledge of their athletes to maximise the effectiveness of extrinsic rewards.

What are the key differences between intrinsic and extrinsic motivation?

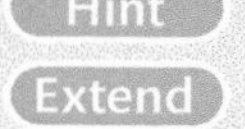

Hint: Produce a table that provides examples of intrinsic and extrinsic motivation.

Extend: How do you think intrinsic and extrinsic motivation can interact to influence sport performance, both positively and negatively?

▶ Olympic medals are one form of tangible reward

Amotivation

Amotivation is absence of motivation. It can be caused by a lack of perceived competence or autonomy, a negative self-perception, or the athlete not valuing the activity they are going to take part in.

Theories of motivation

Need achievement theory

Athletes can be grouped into two categories: those who **need to achieve** ('Nach') and those who **need to avoid failure** ('Naf'). Nach athletes tend to strive for success, keep trying when things go wrong, and feel a sense of pride in accomplishments. There is less focus on comparing skill, ability or performance against other athletes, with a greater emphasis on realistic and challenging personal goals.

High achiever Nach athletes typically set themselves challenging goals, prefer competition against worthy opponents and perform well when being evaluated. Naf athletes tend to avoid these scenarios. For example, an athlete with low achievement motivation will prefer playing against a weaker opponent where success is virtually guaranteed, or against an opponent who is so good that they are guaranteed to fail.

Everyone has aspects of both Nach and Naf, but the balance of the two determines a person's achievement motivation.

Achievement goal theory

Achievement goal theory (AGT) suggests that three factors - achievement goals, perceived ability and achievement behaviours - interact to produce an athlete's levels of motivation.

According to AGT, to understand motivation we first need to understand what success and failure mean to an athlete. We need to consider achievement goals to understand this. Achievement goals can be:

- **outcome-orientated goals** (sometimes referred to competitive goals) that use external references - such as comparing performance with others, focusing on beating opponents and placing emphasis on winning prizes. These are also known as 'ego orientated' goals
- **task-orientated goals** (sometimes referred to as mastery goals) that focus on comparing own performance to previous performance and emphasise personal improvement - these can help motivation as the athlete is more in control of whether they achieve the goal or not.

There is some debate over whether outcome- or task-orientated goals are better for motivation. Traditionally, task-orientated goals have been shown to increase levels of effort and persistence, reduce levels of disappointment or frustration and reduce fear of failure, because the athlete is more in control of goal achievement.

Outcome-orientated goals have been shown to result in lower levels of perceived competence, effort and persistence, as well as athletes attributing failure to more unstable, external sources. This could be a result of the athlete feeling less in control over the goal.

The debate over these two contrasting viewpoints centres on the simplicity of the arguments. For example, if an individual places a great deal of meaning on an event's outcome then they may be more likely to persist in trying to achieve, even if they are at first unsuccessful. Equally, an athlete constantly using task-orientated goals who is unsuccessful in improving may see their motivation to improve decrease.

Discussion

Some situations result in people demonstrating both task- and outcome-orientation. How can this be?

Theory into practice

Jamal is a competitive power lifter. He trains hard because he wants to see his personal best improve: his major competition is against himself, and he sets challenging goals related to self-improvement. However, in competitions Jamal always focuses on beating his opponents. If he does not win, he usually has a lull in his training regime and tells himself that he is not good enough. How do Jamal's goals, and his reaction to them, change according to his situation?

Self-determination theory

This is a **meta theory** originally designed by two respected psychologists, Edward Deci and Richard Ryan. It has helped sport psychologists understand exercise adherence, sport dropout rates and psychological well-being in coaches and athletes. The most popular of the sub-theories is the basic psychological needs theory (BPNT), which argues that we have three basic needs which must be satisfied to be motivated. These are:

- **competence** – our perception that we can successfully complete a task to the required/desired quality
- **autonomy** – our perception that we have choice or control over events happening in our lives
- **relatedness** – our perception of connectedness or belonging to others.

If these three psychological needs are met, people are more likely to be intrinsically motivated towards a particular activity. This means they are more likely to try hard, keep going if things go wrong and appreciate the experience of psychological growth from taking part in sport and exercise.

Key term

Meta theory – a theory that is made up of several smaller theories to provide an understanding of a topic.

Reflect

Think about a time when you either felt you were not very good at an activity, or that you constantly felt you were being told what to do with no choice in activities, or times when you felt isolated from the rest of a group. Did you want to carry on with your activity?

Research

Visit www.selfdeterminationtheory.org and produce a table that summarises each of the six sub-theories of the self-determination theory.

Weiner's attribution theory

In sport, attribution theory looks at how people explain success or failure. Attributions provide explanations for successes or failures and fall into one of the following categories.

- **Stability** – is the reason stable or unstable?
- **Causality** – does the reason come from an external or an internal factor?
- **Control** – is the reason under the participant's control or not?

Table 3.3 provides examples of each attribution. These can help you understand key factors such as motivation behind behaviour and expectations of future success and failure. For example, a boxer who attributes their points victory to stable, internal and controllable factors is more likely to feel confident and motivated to carry on with boxing in the future because they will feel it is likely their successful performance will happen again.

Reflect

Think about the last time you won and the last time you lost in sport. What reasons did you give to explain both events? What types of attribution would you class these reasons as?

Table 3.3: Types of attribution with examples from boxing

Type of attribution	Winning example	Losing example
Stability	• 'I was more able than my opponent' (stable) • 'I was lucky' (unstable)	• 'I was less able than my opponent' (stable) • 'I didn't have that bit of luck I needed today' (unstable)
Causality	• 'I tried really hard' (internal) • 'My opponent was easy to beat' (external)	• 'I didn't try hard enough' (internal) • 'My opponent was impossible to beat' (external)
Control	• 'I trained really hard for this fight' (under control) • 'He wasn't as fit as I was' (not under control)	• 'I didn't train hard enough for this fight' (under control) • 'He was fitter than I was' (not under control)

Motivational environment and its influence on sports performance

Sport psychologists accept motivation comes from more than just the individual. There are many environmental factors than can also affect motivation.

Influence of coach, teacher or instructor

Coaches, teachers and instructors can have a significant effect on motivation as they play a key role in creating the motivational climate. A mastery climate is often preferred, particularly when working with young athletes.

Mastery climate

A mastery climate (sometimes called a **task-orientated climate**) is a motivational climate focused on mastery of tasks (i.e. athletes receive positive reinforcement and there is greater emphasis on teamwork, cooperation and mutual support). It helps develop motivation through improving attitude, effort and learning techniques.

There are many benefits to mastery-orientated climates, including increased intrinsic motivation, increased information processing, decreased stress and anxiety and an increase in overall psychological well-being. Collectively, these factors are likely to enhance performance.

To develop an effective motivational climate, use the TARGET technique (see Unit 15):

- **Tasks** – a range of tasks requiring the athlete to actively participate in learning and decision making.
- **Authority** – athletes have authority over monitoring and evaluating their learning and decision making.
- **Reward** – using rewards focused on individual improvement rather than comparison to other athletes.
- **Grouping** – giving athletes the opportunity to work in groups to develop skills in a group-based environment.
- **Evaluation** – focusing on an individual's effort and improvement.
- **Timing** – timing activities effectively so that all of the above conditions can interact effectively.

Competitive climate

A **competitive climate** or outcome-orientated climate is one in which there is a lot of focus on the outcome. Competition is strongly encouraged and only those with the highest ability receive attention, and athletes may feel they will be punished for mistakes. This often leads to less effort and persistence from athletes, and failure is often attributed to lack of ability.

Influence of family and peers

Parents

Parents can affect motivation by helping support coach-athlete relationships, providing social support, and having conversations with athletes about what and how they are learning and developing through their sport. Often (particularly with young athletes) parent feedback can be the most influential factor affecting motivation, so it is important that parents are aware of this.

Peers

Peers can influence an athlete's motivation in the following ways.

- **Competitive** – peers can influence an athlete's motivation positively or negatively by being competitive. If the competition is constantly trying to belittle somebody, this can often negatively impact motivation. However, if competition is healthy and tries to help athletes improve, it will often enhance motivation.
- **Collaborative** – peers can affect motivation by agreeing to meet up for extra practice, training or recreational play.
- **Evaluative comments** – peers can provide feedback that evaluates performance and, because they are friends, athletes can sometimes be happier to discuss these comments with them further. If these comments are made with the intention of helping the athlete develop, they are likely to enhance motivation.
- **Social relationships** – these are important as they create a support network for athletes. This can be particularly important during difficult times, such as during injury periods.

Discussion

How can the theories of motivation be used to explain how peers can positively and negatively influence motivation?

Influence of personality

Traits

The trait-centred view of motivation suggests someone is motivated because they have certain personality traits. Some highly motivated people do have attributes making them more likely to be successful in sport. However, personality factors alone cannot account for motivation. For example, one athlete may display different levels of motivation when two different coaches work with them. Most sport psychologists see the trait-centred view as too simplistic and that the environment must be taken into account to understand motivation.

Social learning

Bandura's social learning theory suggests personality is not a stable characteristic, but constantly changing as a result of experiences of different social situations. It states individuals learn in sporting situations through two processes – modelling and reinforcement – which can affect their motivation.

- **Modelling** occurs when individuals try to emulate the behaviour of other athletes (who they use as a model).
- **Reinforcement** is important because, if an individual's behaviour is reinforced or rewarded, it is likely that an athlete will repeat it.

Four main stages of observational learning have been identified, demonstrating how modelling influences personality and behaviour.

1. **Attention** – to learn through observation, you must have respect and admiration for the model you are observing. The amount of respect depends on the model's status. If the model is successful and dominant, they will hold your attention.
2. **Retention** – for modelling to be effective, you must retain the observed skill or behaviour in your memory, to be recalled when needed.
3. **Motor reproduction** – you must be physically able to perform the task you are observing. You need time to practise the skill and learn how it should be performed.
4. **Motivational response** – unless you are motivated, you will not go through the first three stages of modelling. Motivation is dependent on reinforcement (for example, praise, feedback, sense of pride or achievement), the perceived status of the model and task importance.

Reflect

Think about a time when you did not want to go to your sport because of things like the weather, not liking the people around you or not getting on with your coach. Why did you still go? What does this tell you about the relationship between personality traits, the situation you find yourself in and how they affect motivation?

Influence of the physical environment

Think about when you arrive at a sports venue. Usually you will prefer it to be clean and tidy, and with working equipment. There is evidence to suggest that the quality of facilities and equipment in sporting environments can enhance motivation. This may be more important for younger, developing athletes than senior athletes, and the equipment provided is likely to be affected by the level that you perform at (i.e. elite athletes are more likely to be provided with state-of-the-art equipment). However, there is also **anecdotal evidence** that suggests some athletes prefer plain environments with minimal equipment (e.g. using ropes and tyres for strength and conditioning) in order to be motivated to train.

Key term

Anecdotal evidence – evidence that is drawn mainly from people's experiences rather than formal research.

Reflect

Think about the last time you felt really motivated in a particular environment. Why did that environment motivate you so much?

Over-motivation

Motivation is usually beneficial for sport and exercise performance. There are, however, instances when motivation levels can be detrimental for an individual's health. We call this over-motivation.

Signs of over-motivation

Sport psychologists must be able to identity the signs of over-motivation. One of the key challenges is that motivation levels are individual-specific, so vary from one person to the next. The signs are outlined below.

- **Over-training** – when the training load exceeds capacity to recover. It often results in a plateau or decrease in performance. Athletes may experience decreases in strength, endurance or other fitness components, as well as becoming more irritable.

PAUSE POINT Explain the social learning theory.

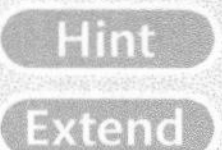

Hint: Close this book and list the main points of the social learning theory.

Extend: Explain each point and describe how it can affect motivation.

Over-training can lead to training addiction in an effort to regain performance improvements.

- **Training addiction** – a preoccupation with training at the expense of other aspects of your life, to the detriment of health. It is associated with disordered eating or eating disorders in athletes and can also lead to other mental health concerns such as depression. People with training addiction may report a sense that they do not need to sleep, rest or eat and see this as healthy behaviour.
- **Social withdrawal** – withdrawing from some, most or all normal social situations (such as stopping seeing friends outside sport). Athletes struggling with over-training or training addiction often prioritise training over any social relationships.

Safety tip

If you are ever worried that you or one of your friends is becoming addicted to their training, you should tell somebody who can help (such as a tutor or coach).

Effects of over-motivation

- **Over-confidence** – the exact relationship between over-motivation and over-confidence is unclear, but athletes may think increased training will increase performance level. Unfortunately, the opposite is often true. Over-confidence often leads to complacency, leading athletes to perform at a lower level.
- **Decrement in performance** – over-motivation is likely to lead to decreases in performance. Without intervention to help regulate motivation levels, it is unlikely performance levels will increase again.
- **Burnout** – this is a chronic physical and mental state that shows a reduced sense of accomplishment, a devaluing of or resentment towards the sport, and physical and emotional exhaustion. Over-motivated and over-trained athletes are at a high risk of burnout. Burnout can also increase stress levels, another danger as increased stress levels are associated with injury.
- **Injury** – higher than normal levels of training can increase the risk of injury. If an athlete is already injured, over-motivation could lead to the athlete doing more than the prescribed rehabilitation activities which then increases the risk of re-injury.

PAUSE POINT Why do you think an athlete might become over-motivated?

Hint Produce a mind map of the reasons why an athlete may become over-motivated.

Extend Explain why each of these factors may make an athlete over-motivated, using sporting examples, and consider the possible implications of over-motivation in different situations.

B Competitive pressure in sport

The World Cup Final. The Olympic 100-metre final. Your first game for a new team. Your first game back after a lengthy period of injury. These are all examples of scenarios where you might feel a great deal of pressure. A key challenge for sport psychologists is helping athletes to maintain and enhance attentional focus under pressure.

Arousal is a state of alertness and anticipation that prepares the body for action. It involves both physiological activation (increased heart rate, sweating rate or respiratory rate) and psychological activity (increased attention). Arousal can be seen as a **continuum**, with deep sleep at one extreme and excitement at the other.

Key term

Continuum – a continuous, gradual sequence from one extreme to another but along which there are no clearly marked distinctions.

Theories of arousal-performance relationship

A number of theories have tried to explain the arousal-performance relationship.

Drive theory

Drive theory views the arousal-performance relationship as linear. This means that as arousal increases, so does performance. The more 'learned' a skill is, the more likely it is that a high level of arousal will lead to a better performance (see Figure 3.1). However, there is little research support for this theory as there is evidence to suggest that athletic performance is benefited by arousal only up to a point.

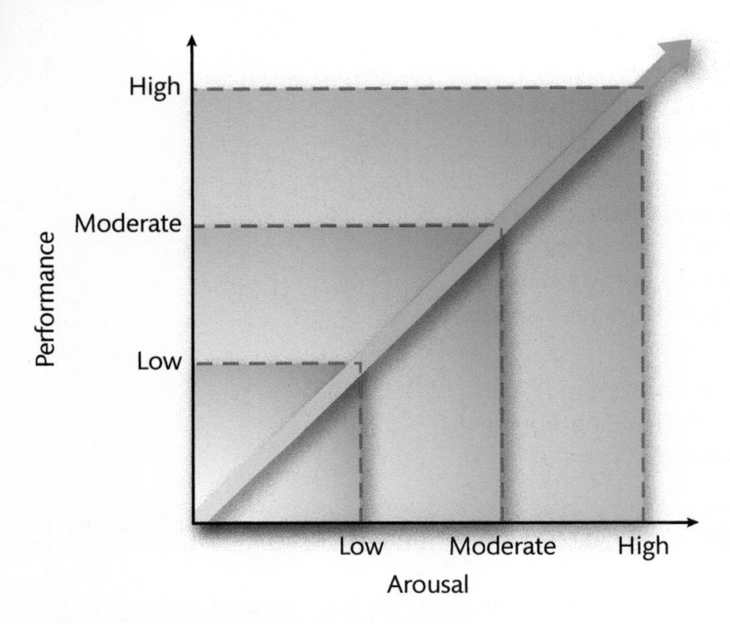

▶ **Figure 3.1:** According to the drive theory, what is the arousal-performance relationship?

Inverted U hypothesis

The inverted U hypothesis was born out of the limitations of drive theory. It states that performance levels will be at their highest at optimal arousal levels (usually a moderate level of arousal) but that when arousal is too low or too high, performance levels will be lower (see Figure 3.2). This theory argues that performance levels are lower when arousal is too low or too high because the athlete is neither physiologically nor psychologically ready (for example, heart rate and concentration levels may be too low/too high). The final key argument is that the decrease in performance after the optimal arousal level will be gradual.

The inverted U hypothesis is more widely accepted than drive theory because most athletes and coaches can report personal experiences of under-arousal (boredom), over-arousal (excitement to the point of lack of concentration) and optimum arousal (focusing on nothing but sport performance). However, there are questions over the type of curve demonstrated.

- Is the optimal arousal always a single point or do some athletes experience optimal arousal for longer?
- Is the decrease in performance always a steady decline or can it be more dramatic?

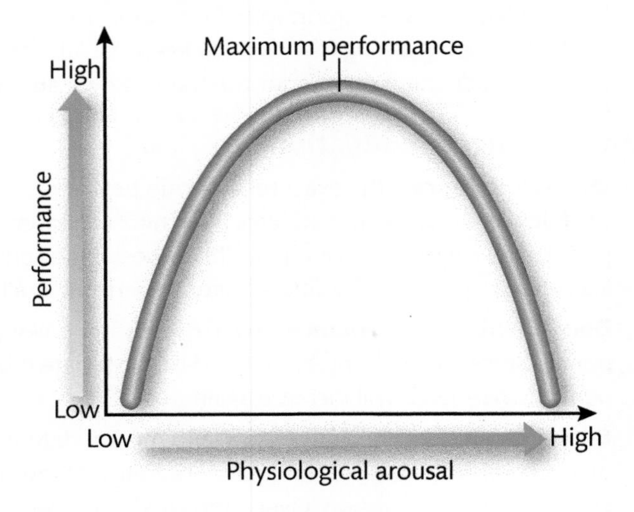

▶ **Figure 3.2:** According to the inverted U hypothesis, what is the arousal-performance relationship?

Catastrophe theory

The catastrophe theory expands on the inverted U hypothesis by suggesting performance is affected by arousal in an inverted U fashion only when the individual has low levels of **cognitive anxiety** (see Figure 3.3a). If the athlete is experiencing higher levels of cognitive anxiety, and arousal levels increase up to the athlete's threshold, the player experiences a dramatic (or catastrophic) drop in performance levels (see Figure 3.3b). The key difference between catastrophe theory and the inverted U hypothesis is that the drop in performance does not have to be a steady decline when arousal levels become too high.

Catastrophe theory does not argue that cognitive anxiety is completely negative. It suggests you will perform at a higher level if you have a degree of cognitive anxiety because attention and concentration levels increase; performance levels only decrease dramatically when levels of cognitive anxiety are combined with hyper-elevated levels of arousal. This theory has been questioned by some, over claims that everybody's optimal arousal is the same single, moderate point.

Key term

Cognitive anxiety – the thought component of anxiety that most people refer to as 'worrying about something'.

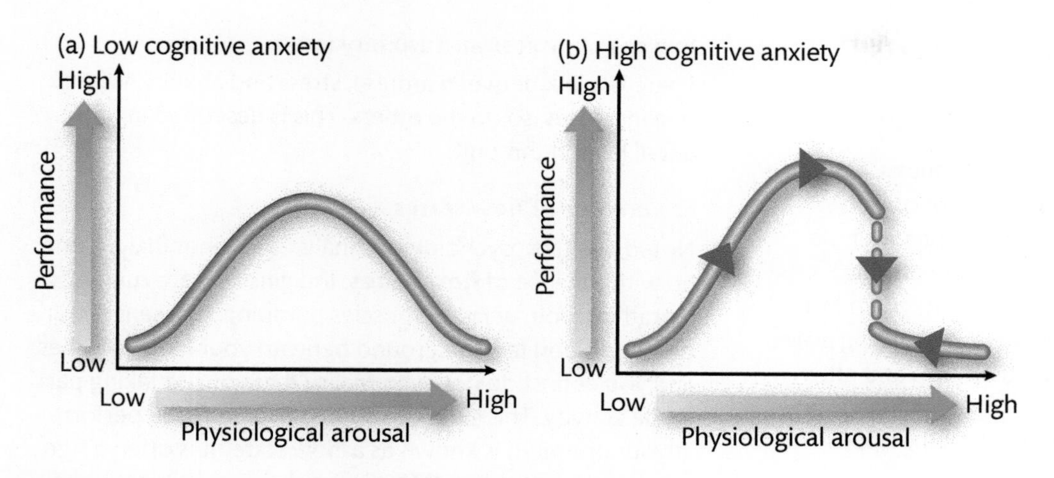

▶ **Figure 3.3:** According to the catastrophe theory, what is the arousal-performance relationship?

Individual zones of optimal functioning (IZOF)

This expands on previous theories by arguing that everyone (e.g. different personalities, participating in different sports) has different optimal levels of arousal and can remain in that zone of arousal for a period of time (see Figure 3.4), meaning athletes can perform at a higher level of performance for a longer period of time. The main differences between the inverted U hypothesis and IZOF are:

- where the inverted U hypothesis sees arousal at an optimal point, IZOF sees optimal arousal as bandwidth
- where the inverted U hypothesis sees every athlete's optimal point at a mid-point on the curve, IZOF says the optimal point varies from person to person.

IZOF and the inverted U hypothesis both suggest that, after the optimal point of arousal, performance decreases gradually.

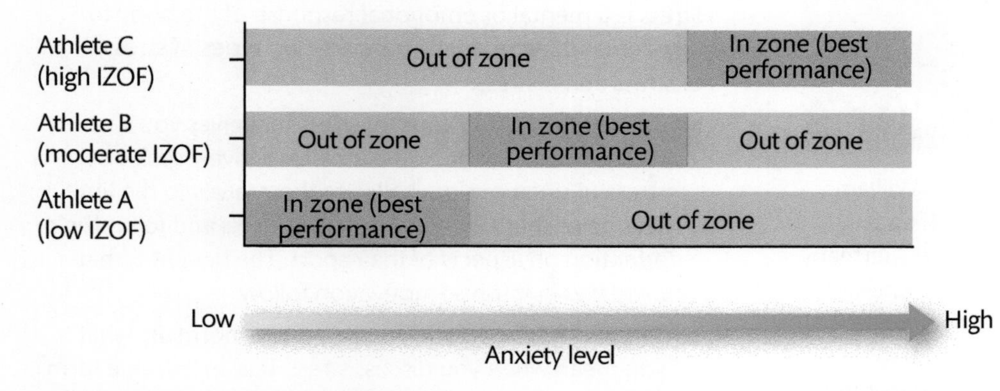

▶ **Figure 3.4:** According to the IZOF theory, what is the arousal-performance relationship?

PAUSE POINT Explain the different arousal-performance theories.

Hint Using only the diagram of each theory, explain to a friend how the theory explains the arousal-performance relationship.

Extend Considering their strengths and limitations, which theory do you think best explains the arousal-performance relationship?

Effects of changes in arousal on sports performance

Changes in attentional focus

During heightened states of arousal the attentional field, which focuses attention and concentration, becomes narrowed. The more aroused you become, the lower the number of relevant cues you can concentrate on. For example, at optimal states of arousal, the point guard in a basketball game will be able to focus on the opposing player in possession of the ball as well as on their own and other players' positions on the court. But during heightened states of arousal they may only be able to focus on the opposition player, disregarding other important cues.

Just as a heightened state of arousal can narrow the player's attention, it can also broaden it to the point where performance is decreased. In this scenario, the point guard player would be concentrating on irrelevant information like crowd noise as well as the relevant game cues.

Case study

Fara's World Cup penalty

In the 2015 FIFA Women's World Cup, Fara Williams scored a penalty in the third-place play-off against Germany to give England their first win over Germany in a competitive fixture in over 30 years. The penalty occurred in the 108th minute of the game (in the second half of extra time) with the score at 0–0. This fixture came after England women had lost the World Cup semi-final 2–1 to Japan. Fara was England women's most capped player.

Check your knowledge

1 What different attentional cues will Fara have concentrated on?
2 What type(s) of attentional focus will Fara have used while preparing and executing the penalty kick?
3 What do you think Fara's attentional strategies will have been?

Increase in stress and anxiety levels

There is a link between arousal, stress and anxiety. When one increases, so do the others. This is described in more detail later in this unit.

Experience of flow states

Noted positive psychologist Mihály Csíkszentmihályi came up with the idea of **flow states**. Imagine you are running a marathon. You feel your muscles pumping, you sense your breathing, you feel the ground beneath your feet; time flies and you almost do not even realise that you are taking part in the activity. This state of immersion where you perform at your optimum is known as a 'flow state'. It is often a sign you are at your optimal arousal level.

Choking

'Choking' can be used to describe a reduction in performance during high-pressure situations, such as when a golfer misses an easy putt required to win the Open. Choking also includes the process leading up to the decreased performance. It is an extreme form of nervousness, largely based on the subjective importance of the event (i.e. what the event means to the individual athlete). Choking can be more apparent in the presence of significant others (e.g. parents, peers) or large audiences.

Stress and anxiety

Stress

Stress is a mental or emotional response of the body to any demand made on it. There are two types of stress: eustress and distress.

- **Eustress** is a 'good' form of stress that gives you a feeling of fulfilment. Some athletes actively seek out stressful situations to challenge themselves to the limit. This helps them increase their skill levels and focus their attention on aspects of their sport. The benefit is that increases in intrinsic motivation follow.
- **Distress** is a 'bad' form of stress and is normally what you mean when you discuss stress. It is an extreme form of anxiety, nervousness, apprehension or worry as a result of a perceived inability to meet demands. It can lead to an excessive increase in arousal and a potential decrease in performance levels.

A four-stage stress process is used to explain the effects of stress on performance (see Figure 3.5).

1 Some form of environmental, physical or psychological demand is placed on the athlete in a particular situation (Stage 1). This could be taking the last penalty in a penalty shoot-out to win the UEFA Champions League.

2 The athlete perceives this demand positively or negatively (Stage 2). A positive demand is more likely to be seen as a positive challenge. However, a negative demand can be seen as a negative threat, causing a negative mental state, lack of self-confidence and lack of concentration. If the demand is seen as too great, the athlete will feel unable to meet it (negative mental state and loss of self-confidence). As a result, they will find it difficult to concentrate on what they must do to meet the demand.

3 This perception increases the arousal levels of the performer and initiates a stress response (Stage 3). During this stage they experience heightened arousal, higher levels of **cognitive** and **somatic** anxiety, and changes in their attention and concentration levels. If at Stage 2 they perceived the demand more positively, they are more likely to experience eustress with an increase in motivation and energy. If they perceived the demand negatively, they are more likely to experience hyper-elevated worry and distress.

Snooker players often face psychological pressure

Key terms

Cognitive – the degree to which you worry or have negative thoughts.

Somatic – the perception of changes in physiological activation.

4 Stage 3 determines the behavioural consequences which can affect the performance outcome (Stage 4). If the performer experiences eustress, they are more likely to have an increase in performance, while distress is more likely to lead to a decrease in performance. The outcome of performance will likely affect the athlete's perception of a similar demand the next time they experience a similar situation.

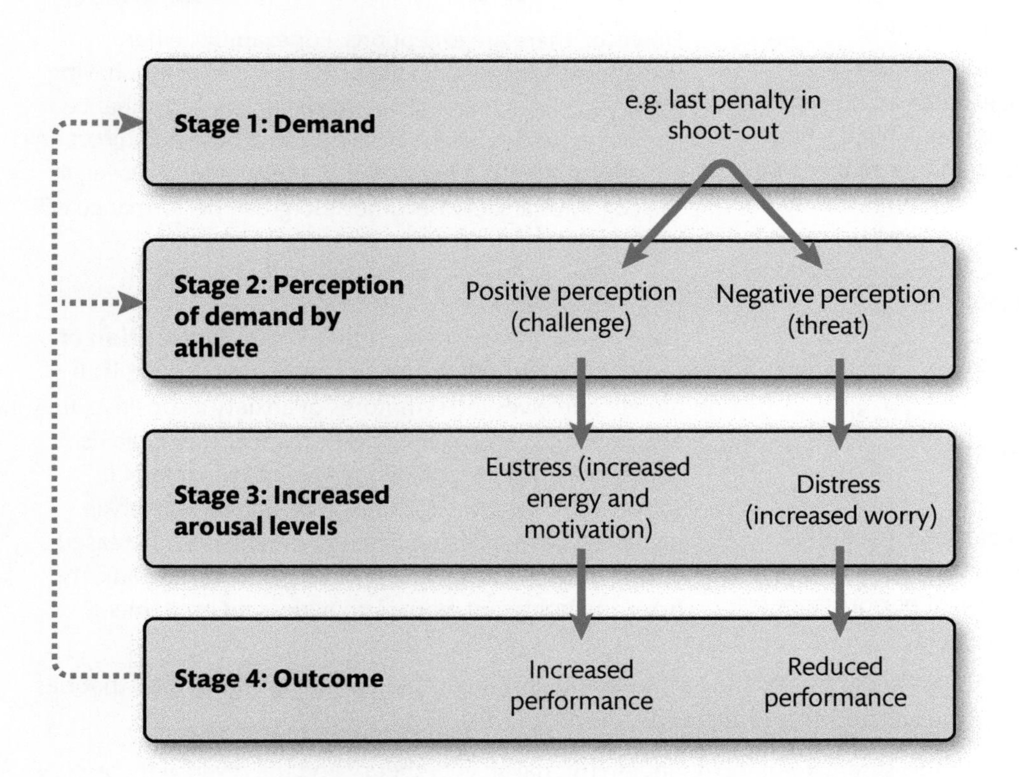

Figure 3.5: How does the stress process explain the relationship between stress, arousal, anxiety and performance?

Anxiety

Anxiety is a negative emotional state associated with feelings of nervousness, apprehension or worry.

- **Trait anxiety** is an aspect of personality and part of an individual's pattern of behaviour. Someone with a high level of trait anxiety is likely to become worried in a variety of situations, even non-threatening situations. Athletes with high levels of trait anxiety are usually more state-anxious (see next bullet point) in high pressured, highly competitive situations where there is a great deal of evaluation.
- **State anxiety** is a temporary, ever-changing mood state that is an emotional response to any situation considered threatening. For example, at the start of an Olympic 400-metre event, the runner may have higher levels of state anxiety that drop once the event begins. State anxiety levels may increase again when coming up to the final bend and be at their highest level when coming towards the finish line when they are neck-and-neck with their strongest rival.

In addition to the different types of anxiety, it is also important to know about the symptoms of anxiety.

- **Cognitive anxiety** refers to negative thoughts, nervousness or worry experienced in certain situations. Symptoms of cognitive anxiety include concentration problems, fear and bad decision-making.
- **Somatic anxiety** relates to the awareness and perception of physiological changes (such as increases in heart rate, sweating and increased body heat) when you start to play sport. For example, an athlete could be concerned because they sense an increased heart rate if they have gone into a game less prepared than usual. This increase in heart rate is necessary for performance, but is seen as negative by the athlete.
- **Behavioural** anxiety refers to how nerves affect our behaviours. Signs and symptoms of this type of anxiety include 'playing safe', changes in posture, fidgeting, rapid speech and avoiding eye contact.

Competitive anxiety

Competitive anxiety is where an athlete feels tense and inadequate in response to a competitive situation. It is usually caused by some form of fear (e.g. of performance failure, negative social evaluation or physical harm), or by changes to an established routine (e.g. last-minute change to a tactic) or some form of confusion or ambiguity (e.g. not knowing if you are going to be selected for the team until shortly before an event).

Theory into practice

Marianne is a competitive rower who is part of an Olympic development programme. Prior to competition, she gets really nervous and her heart starts to race. She always sees herself performing badly and worries about getting out of rhythm with her team mates. When she thinks about this, she starts to sweat and struggles to concentrate. Generally she is a happy person and does not tend to worry about anything other than her sport. What does this information tell you about Marianne's stress and anxiety?

Multidimensional anxiety theory

The multidimensional anxiety theory suggests somatic and cognitive anxiety can affect performance in different ways and will change in the build-up to an event. Generally, cognitive anxiety is thought to decrease performance, while somatic anxiety is thought to enhance performance (to a certain point).

However, there are exceptions. For example, where somatic anxiety is low in the build-up to an event, having slightly elevated levels of cognitive anxiety can enhance performance. This slight increase can arouse and direct an athlete's attention towards the performance; however, if the cognitive anxiety becomes too great, performance will be reduced.

Reversal theory

The reversal theory suggests that it is the **perception** of anxiety that can effect performance. For example, if an athlete perceives the symptoms of anxiety as positive, they are more likely to enhance performance. This explains why some sport psychologists highlight the role of some of the signs and symptoms of somatic anxiety (e.g. increased heart rate, increased breathing rate, increased temperature) in successful performance, turning anxiety from an unpleasant worry into a pleasant excitement.

What do the theories about stress and anxiety tell us? What impact do these theories have on sports performance?

Hint Write a summary of the multidimensional anxiety theory and the reversal theory.

Extend Discuss which theory you think best explains the relationship between anxiety and performance, justifying your answer.

Signs and symptoms of stress and anxiety

There are a number of signs and symptoms of stress. There are many ways these can be effectively managed, including through the use of psychological skills training and through effective **social support**.

- The main biological consideration is the increases in cortisol and adrenalin levels mobilising the body for the **fight or flight response**. While this is a natural response, it can be detrimental in circumstances such as injury because cortisol is a catabolic hormone reducing the rate of tissue repair, slowing down recovery.
- Cognitive considerations are the increased feelings of worry and an inability to concentrate, both of which will likely decrease performance levels as well as reducing an athlete's state of well-being.
- Common somatic considerations are an increase in pulse rate and blood pressure, as well as an increase in muscle tension. If not controlled, this increase in muscle tension can increase the risk of injury and lead to a condition known as **freezing**.
- Finally, **behavioural** signs and symptoms include rushing, talking quickly and fidgeting. These can also decrease performance as they can reduce the quality of communication between athletes and can mean that certain technical components of performance (e.g. the timing of runs) are reduced in quality.

Key terms

Social support – the presence of a support network that can help an athlete cope with stress through the exchange of resources between one person and another.

Fight or flight response – a physiological response that occurs in the body in an attempt to cope with a threat that is posed.

Freezing – hyper-elevated muscle tension that reduces movement quality or prevents an athlete from moving.

Behavioural – moment-to-moment changes in behaviour when anxious.

Cortisol – a hormone that is released in high levels during stressful situations.

Catabolic – breaks down tissue, such as muscle, making the tissue weaker.

Aggression – intentional behaviour (physical or verbal) with a goal of harming (physically or psychologically) another being.

Sources of stress and anxiety

It is common to have lots of athletes in similar situations yet with entirely different individual levels of stress and anxiety in response to those situations. Some of the main causes are highlighted below.

- **Internal** sources can include illnesses/infections, psychological factors such as cognitive anxiety, not having enough sleep, or being overly self-critical or being a perfectionist.
- **External** causes of stress include environment (e.g. too noisy, too quiet), negative social interactions (e.g. somebody being rude), major life events (e.g. a death in the family) or day-to-day hassles (e.g. travelling to and from games, training schedules).

Consequences of stress and anxiety

We have already looked at some of the positive consequences of stress and anxiety, including increases in self-confidence, energy, motivation and focus, a positive mental state, and an improvement in performance. But there are also some negative consequences of stress and anxiety, shown in Table 3.4.

Table 3.4: Negative consequences of stress and anxiety

Consequence	Description
Negative mental state	• Characterised by worry and apprehension. • If it becomes too great (i.e. performer worries too much), performance will suffer.
Loss of self-confidence	• Worrying about event can make athlete think they are not good enough to succeed. • Decreases expectations of success. • Negative impact on performance.
Decrement in performance	• Negative mental state and loss of self-confidence heighten cognitive anxiety – increased nervousness, apprehension and worry. • Athletes respond by focusing on negative feelings leading to hyper-elevated muscle tension and lack of movement coordination. • Negative impact on performance likely.
Possible injury	• Heightened levels of stress and anxiety prompt body to release higher levels of **cortisol** hormone. This has a **catabolic** effect on the body, contributing to tissue weakness and increasing risk of muscle injury. • Stress and anxiety can also make it difficult to focus on competition and increase likelihood of a mistake (e.g. mistimed tackle or poor technique – and therefore injury).
Aggression	• Can cause and be an effect of stress. • Changes in hormone levels affect behaviour.

Aggression as a response to competitive pressure

Within applied sport psychology, it is important to understand how aggression can be both positive and negative, in addition to understanding the different causes of aggression. There are four different types of behaviour that broadly come under the heading of aggression. While they are not all types of aggression, they help us to understand aggression more thoroughly.

- **Assertive behaviour** differs from aggressive behaviour because the individual is playing with emotion and within the rules of the game. Assertive behaviour demonstrates four main criteria.
  - It is goal-directed.
  - It is not intended to harm or injure.
  - It uses only legitimate force, even if this amount of force could be classed as aggression in a non-sporting or non-game setting.
  - It does not break any of the rules of the game.

  For example, you might be playing American football and tackle somebody very hard so that you can stop an opposition team's play, which carries a risk of harming or injuring the opponent. However, if you had no intention to harm them, did not break any rules of the game, and used only the necessary force to achieve the goal, this would not be classed as aggressive behaviour.
- **Instrumental aggression** (or channelled aggression) displays aggressive behaviour in the pursuit of a non-aggressive goal. Most aggression in sport falls into this category, which often occurs in contact sports. For example, in mixed-martial arts, a competitor will always intend to hurt their opponent through powerful strikes or submission holds (displaying aggressive behaviour), but they do this because it is a necessary part of winning their fight (it is in pursuit of a non-aggressive goal).

▶ Ronda Rousey is often required to be aggressive in her UFC fights

- **Hostile aggression** is aggressive behaviour with the sole intention of harming or injuring an opponent. It is not used to reach a non-aggressive goal and is never within the rules of the sport. People might display this type of aggression in reaction to an incident (reactive aggression) and it is often accompanied by anger. One of the most famous examples of hostile aggression occurred when former World Heavyweight Champion boxer, Mike Tyson, bit off part of Evander Holyfield's ear during a fight.
- **Relational aggression** is a non-physical form of aggression usually aimed at causing psychological or emotional harm. The most common forms are spreading rumours, forming social cliques to exclude certain team members, or refusing to befriend a new team member. With social media, relational aggression has become more prominent - mainly among adolescent athletes - which is why a lot of attention is paid to the moral development of athletes. Relational aggression has a number of negative consequences including decreased psychological well-being and poor levels of team cohesion.

Theories of aggression

- The **instinct theory** suggests we have an instinct to be aggressive that builds up until we can release it. This aggression can be released towards another being or through socially acceptable means such as sport. This is known as **catharsis**. However, there is little research-based evidence to support this theory so it is rarely used to explain causes of aggression.
- **Social learning theory** says aggression is a behaviour learned by observing others and experiencing reinforcement for such behaviours. For example, if a child was watching a game on television with their parents and saw a favourite player foul an opponent, not get punished, and their parents cheered, he or she is likely to imitate that behaviour when playing.
- **Frustration-aggression theory** says aggression comes from being frustrated by not achieving goals or having progress blocked. It does not have a lot of support because you can control that frustration. A revised version (known as the adapted frustration-aggression theory and now widely accepted) combines elements of the original theory with elements of social learning theory, stating that aggression occurs in situations where you become frustrated as you then experience anger and arousal. If you cannot control these feelings you are more likely to become aggressive. This theory states you are only more likely to become aggressive if the aggressive acts are supported or condoned, for instance, by a manager, coach or parent.

Discussion

Which theory of aggression do you think best explains the causes of aggression in sport?

PAUSE POINT What are the different types of aggression?

Hint Define aggression, list the criteria for aggression and identify the different types of aggressive behaviour.

Extend Provide sporting examples of each type of aggression and justify why you have classified each one as that type.

C Effects of self-confidence, self-efficacy and self-esteem on sport and exercise performance

Research

Research the England FA's 'DNA philosophy'. Why do you think confidence is included as part of the player DNA?

Self-confidence

Self-confidence is a psychological state empowered by the athletes' belief in their ability to perform and achieve specific outcomes. An individual's level of self-confidence can be influenced by their experiences in training and games, so it is important you know how to enhance the opportunities for people to build their confidence in your sessions. Think of confidence as an impenetrable brick wall – your job is to help athletes build their wall, brick-by-brick.

Reflect

Think about a time when a coach told you that you needed to be more confident. How did you behave during that event and how would you change your behaviour in future to show your increased confidence?

Vealey's multidimensional model of sport confidence

Vealey and colleagues' multidimensional model of sport confidence has four main components.

Constructs of sport confidence

The term 'constructs' means all the things that make up sport confidence. In Vealey and colleagues' model, these include decision-making skills, physical skills, anticipatory skills and the capacity to learn and develop.

Sources of sport confidence

There are a number of sources of sport confidence. Male athletes may report outperforming their competitors as a source of confidence, while female athletes report self-development and improvement as a source of confidence. Previously experiencing success can help increase levels of self-confidence for future events as the athlete will have a greater belief that they can repeat previous results. Believing they are more talented than opponents can also build confidence, partly because this contributes to feelings of having a competitive advantage over an opponent. Weinberg and Gould (2014) outlined nine sources of sport confidence.

- Mastery: developing and improving skills
- Demonstration of ability: showing ability by winning and outperforming opponents
- Physical and mental preparation: staying focused on goals and being prepared to give your all
- Physical self-presentation: feeling good about yourself (e.g. physical appearance, body weight)
- Social support: getting support from peers, family and coaches
- Coaches' leadership: feeling that you can trust the coaches' decisions and having a belief in their ability
- Vicarious experiences: seeing others do well
- Environmental comfort: feeling comfortable in the environment where you will perform
- Situational favourableness: feeling that everything is going well and that you are getting the bit of luck that you need to succeed

Consequences of sport confidence

The consequences of sport confidence are linked to 'ABCs' - affect, behaviour and cognition. If the athlete has higher levels of confidence, they are more likely to have a more positive effect (or emotion), they are likely to try harder (behaviours) and they are likely to pay closer attention to their sport to keep improving (cognitions).

Factors influencing sport confidence

Factors linked to personality, demographics and organisational structure will influence levels of sport confidence. Personality factors such as the athlete's level of optimism will increase or decrease their confidence as those with a more positive outlook (i.e. those who are more optimistic) tend to be more confident. Evidence suggests that demographic characteristics such as gender can also influence confidence levels, but there are many conflicting findings surrounding this. Finally, the organisational structure such as coach behaviours, level of competition and the motivational climate can all affect levels of self-confidence too.

Impact of self-confidence

Self-confidence can arouse positive emotions, facilitate concentration, increase effort and influence game strategy. For example, an athlete with a high level of self-confidence may want to take responsibility for set pieces in football (influencing game strategy) because the player feels they have paid attention to positions and behaviours of team mates (facilitating concentration), which they feel increase the chances of success.

Optimal levels of self-confidence can help enhance and maintain an enhanced level of performance. If an athlete has lower levels of confidence, or is over-confident, there is a strong chance performance can decrease, affecting overall psychological well-being and increasing injury risk. If an athlete lacks confidence or is over-confident, they may begin to miss relevant information because they are paying less attention.

▶ Many sprinters display supreme self-confidence before a race

Research

Research the negative consequences of over-confidence. For each one that you find, provide an example of how it may negatively affect sport performance or an athlete's well-being.

Influence of expectations on sport and exercise performance

The expectations an athlete has of themselves and the expectations others have of them can affect their behaviour. High expectations are often based on a perception of competence (a feeling that they are good at something); therefore, such expectations may enhance levels of confidence. If confidence is enhanced in this way, the athlete is likely to demonstrate more intent and effort towards achieving their goals.

Self-efficacy

Self-efficacy is an athlete's belief in their ability to successfully complete a set task.

Bandura's self-efficacy theory

Bandura, a famous sport psychologist, produced the self-**efficacy** theory, detailing how self-efficacy and, as a result, self-confidence and sporting performance can be developed. It is important to understand the principles of building self-confidence into your everyday sessions. The self-efficacy theory tells us that performance accomplishments, vicarious experiences, verbal persuasion and emotional arousal will create efficacy expectations, which will increase the chances of heightened athletic performance (see Figure 3.6).

Key term

Efficacy – the ability to produce a desired or intended result.

Performance accomplishments

Think about when you recently performed well in your sport. How did you feel afterwards? You probably enjoyed it and could not wait to play again. Recent performance accomplishments are the strongest source of self-confidence so it is important, particularly with children and young people or those returning to sport after a lengthy absence, to structure practices to allow for achievement of challenges and for athletes to receive feedback on these accomplishments.

A key consideration for coaches and sports leaders is to give specific examples of accomplishments and to praise/reinforce the effort that it has taken to reach the accomplishment. For example, if a young basketball player successfully performs their first three-point jump shot, do not just praise the outcome of the event (i.e. scoring the three points), make sure you also praise the effort they have put in (e.g. the time they have spent practising).

Vicarious experiences

The second strongest source of self-confidence is vicarious experience – this occurs when an athlete sees somebody who is similar to them (e.g. age, performance level) perform a skill successfully. Seeing somebody similar successfully complete a task can enhance your self-belief in being able to do the same. Referring back to Bandura's social learning theory (see page 86), this can have a modelling effect which is enhanced if the athlete observed is somebody significant to them (e.g. close friend, talented team mate).

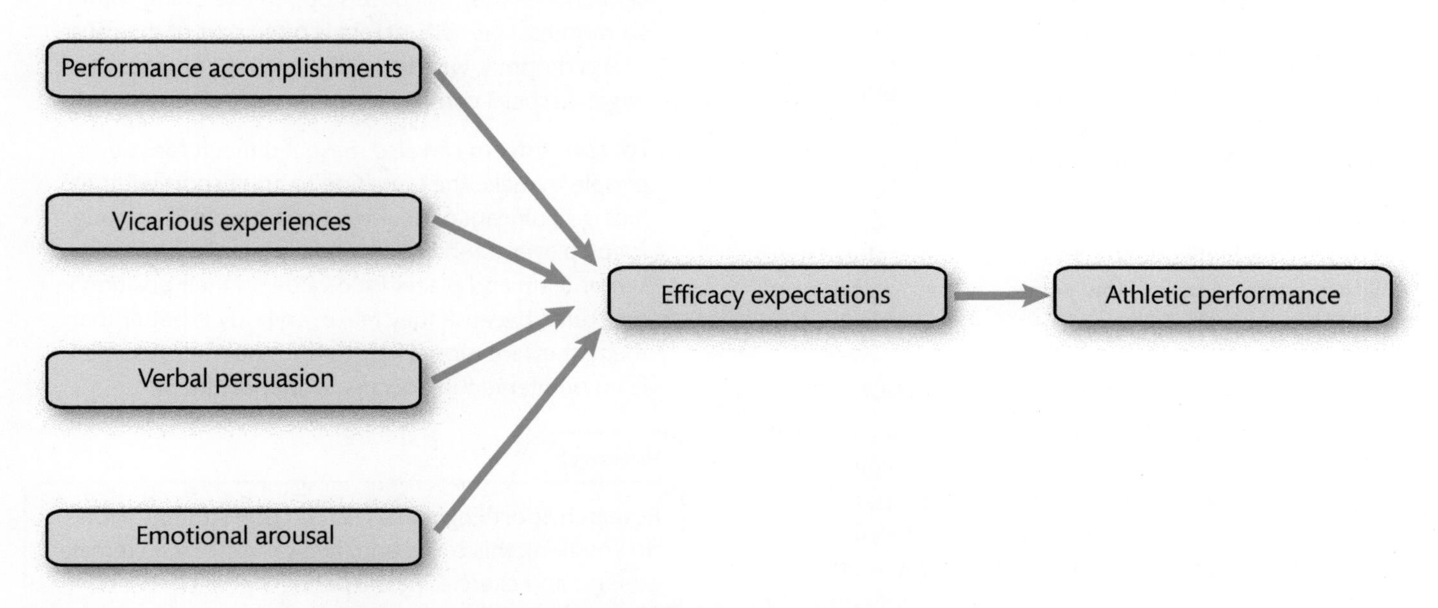

Figure 3.6: How can you apply Bandura's self-efficacy theory to your favourite sport?

To enhance the modelling effect, some coaches also use video footage of elite athletes performing a task as this can give athletes something to aspire to, without creating any negative social comparisons between team mates. This is important as recent research in football has shown that negative social comparisons between team mates can reduce a player's chances of reaching an elite level in football, due to the effects it can have on their confidence (Gledhill and Harwood, 2015).

Verbal persuasion

This is a useful way to enhance self-confidence and occurs when somebody who is important to the player (e.g. coach, team captain) tells the player they believe in them and that they are able to perform well. This is a similar idea to positive motivational self-talk but it comes from an external source, persuading the athlete that they are good enough. For coaches, it is important to model this behaviour for two main reasons.

- As a coach, you are likely to be the most influential person in a young athlete's sporting life, closely followed by their team mates and parents, so the message from you is likely to have the most impact.
- If as a coach you model the behaviour of verbal persuasion, you are more likely to have the athletes you work with model that behaviour too. This will help create a climate of confidence-building in your athletes and is more likely to create social support networks within the team. These networks are really important during setbacks, such as slumps in performance or serious injury, as athletes will feel more empowered and able to cope with these situations, and have a greater sense of team cohesion (see pages 103–105).

Emotional arousal

This is the least impactful factor affecting self-efficacy. If the athlete is sad or upset prior to a competition, this may make them think that their confidence is low.

Efficacy expectations

These are an athlete's beliefs and expectations about their ability to perform tasks. How persistent they are can play a role in how successful they are.

Impact of self-esteem on performance

Self-esteem refers to how much you like or value yourself. Sport psychologists think of self-esteem as having academic, social, emotional and physical (competence, strength, endurance and appearance) related elements. Generally, higher self-esteem is associated with better mental health, and lower self-esteem with worse mental health. This is quite a simplistic view and it is important to think about this in more detail.

Link

This content links to *Unit 10: Physical Activity for Individual and Group-based Exercise* as well as *Unit 6: Coaching for Performance and Fitness* and *Unit 8: Specialised Fitness Training.*

- **High self-esteem** has been associated with higher levels of leadership, independence and resilience, which are all important qualities for athletes who progress to senior, professional or elite levels in their sport. It is also associated with higher levels of adaptability which means athletes are more able to deal with a variety of situations and problems that may arise in sport.

  Higher levels of self-esteem make you more likely to approach challenges. If you approach these challenges then you are more likely to feel a sense of accomplishment and pride, even if you do not achieve every part of the challenge. This is part of the reason people tend to stick with exercise programmes, maintain regular physical activity and become more successful in sport.

- **Low self-esteem** is linked with higher levels of anxiety, depression and different fears. It has also been linked to decreased total mood state and more maladaptive health behaviours (such as exercise avoidance). Once people start an exercise programme, there is a 50 per cent chance they will have stopped exercising within six months. Low self-esteem is often part of the cause of this dropout, with low self-esteem often a result of negative social comparisons.

  Low self-esteem can also make it difficult for young people to make the transition to adult sport without facing significant difficulties. For example, if a young rugby player doubts themselves when they join the senior team and places little value on their position in the squad because they feel everybody is better than them, they are more likely to drop out unless some form of intervention occurs to support them.

Research

Research Sport England's *This Girl Can* strategy. How do you think this could enhance self-esteem in female athletes and exercise participants?

PAUSE POINT How does self-efficacy theory explain performance?

Hint Describe each of the sections of self-efficacy theory.

Extend Provide a sport-based example of self-efficacy theory.

D Mindset in sport and exercise performance

Growth mindset versus fixed mindset

Dweck's theory

Carol Dweck proposed the theory of 'fixed' and 'growth' mindsets. By helping people develop a growth mindset, you can help them increase a number of important qualities, such as their motivation, self-efficacy and, ultimately, their productivity. Although her theory was originally born out of work in education, it has recently started to gain wider prominence in sport environments.

Fixed vs growth mindsets

Some athletes believe their personal qualities - such as intelligence - are set in stone. They have a fear of failure, seeing it as a permanent mark against them. These athletes have a **fixed mindset**. Athletes with a fixed mindset tend to feel the need to prove themselves over and over again. They can often be preoccupied with what other people think of them, whether they win or lose, and how good they look in front of other people. The environment around athletes often fosters a fixed mindset; the behaviours of teachers, parents and coaches at a young age are often key.

In contrast, an athlete with a **growth mindset** will see failure and challenge as opportunities for self-development. An athlete with a fixed mindset might surround themselves with people who tell them how good they are to boost their self-esteem; athletes with a growth mindset will associate with people who challenge their ideas and thoughts. Where a fixed mindset athlete would try to hide their weaknesses from everybody, a growth mindset would openly discuss weaknesses and examine why things have not gone as they had planned.

A growth mindset allows athletes to thrive during times of challenge or adversity (e.g. performance slumps, personal difficulties in non-sporting life or injury periods), while a fixed mindset is likely to lead to increased catastrophising and a higher stress response during the same situations.

As a result of all of these factors, athletes with a fixed mindset tend to have lower levels of performance, can plateau earlier and achieve less in their career. Athletes with a growth mindset tend to have higher levels of achievement and a better overall sense of psychological well-being.

- **Talent versus effort** - athletes with a fixed mindset think their talent is static and there is no need for a great deal of effort. Athletes with a growth mindset place great emphasis on learning and development, seeing their athletic journey as a process towards self-improvement.
- **10,000 hours practice** - the notion of 10,000 hours practice being necessary to reach an elite level in sport is now largely discredited. While most people in sport support the idea that sport-specific practice is important for developing as an athlete, there is little evidence to suggest the figure of 10,000 hours is valid. For example, in a study of elite youth football players from many places including the UK, Europe and South America, none of the players reported a figure close to the 10,000-hour 'rule'.
- **Learned helplessness** - the idea of 'learned helplessness' in sport suggests that once athletes have failed, they feel a situation is out of their control. In Dweck's research, children categorised with learned helplessness had performance levels that reduced as they were less likely to solve problems after experiencing a failure, even when the problems were identical to those solved before the failure.

  It is suggested that athletes with learned helplessness who belittle their own ability when they come up against failure, may overestimate the number of problems they cannot cope with or manage successfully, and express large amounts of self-doubt. This pattern is usually based on the athlete's experience of negative feelings such as anxiety or sadness, and will almost certainly lead to a decreased level of performance.

What are the two key mindsets in sport and exercise performance?

Create a bullet-pointed list of key points about both mindsets.

Extend Explain how you think the mindsets can affect an athlete's sport performance and well-being.

Resilience

Resilience determines how well you can deal with difficult circumstances.

Importance of resilience in sport

Resilience is important in sport because it helps athletes overcome adversity, cope with difficult situations and minimise negative influences on performance. Situations where having higher levels of resilience is important include injury, burnout, during slumps in form and during career transitions.

Injury

During injury, particularly long-term injuries, resilience is important as it helps you stay positive and engage in behaviours which make the injury period more beneficial. For example, injury research has suggested people with resilient qualities may have better 'injury experiences'. Specifically, people are more likely to have a successful rehabilitation outcome if they view their injury as a learning experience that can be positive for their development, engage more with social support, and are more motivated to take part in rehabilitation activities.

Burnout

Burnout is a chronic physical and mental state that shows a reduced sense of accomplishment, a devaluing of, or resentment towards sport, coupled with physical and emotional exhaustion. If athletes have lower levels of resilience, they are less likely to cope with burnout effectively and may take longer to recover from it.

Slump in form

Performance slumps are a key concern for competitive athletes. This is where they experience a long-term drop in performance and struggle to find a way out of it. If an athlete has lower levels of resilience, they are more likely to struggle to cope with slumps in form. Less resilient athletes are likely to take longer to come through a performance slump. Quite often, players who experience a slump in form may be dropped from the team so they can have time to reflect. Higher levels of resilience are important as it helps an athlete to remain confident and positive and encourages them to see being dropped as an opportunity to learn and develop.

Transitions

Career transitions, particularly junior-to-senior career transitions present many challenges for athletes. For example, a young athlete will usually get promoted to an adult team because they have been a standout player in a junior or academy setup. Quite often, being the standout player has given them a social status which they enjoy and provides them with the opportunity to receive praise. However, when they progress to a senior team, the athlete often feels the need to 'prove' themselves all over again and they no longer see themselves as the best or most influential player. This can be a difficult challenge for athletes and resilience appears to be a quality that helps them to remain positive through these difficult challenges.

Case study

Adnan Januzaj

After a successful 'breakout' season under David Moyes at Manchester United, footballer Adnan Januzaj suffered a more difficult time under Moyes' replacement Louis van Gaal. In 2015 he was loaned to Borussia Dortmund where he made fewer appearances than expected, before having his loan agreement terminated by mutual consent.

Publicly, Januzaj talks about everything that he has been through since progressing to the first team as valuable learning experiences and talks about being prepared to keep fighting for his place.

Check your knowledge

1 What do you think are some of the key career transition issues faced in this case study?
2 Which of the resilience qualities do you think are important to manage this type of situation?
3 How do you think having high levels of resilience would help young players facing this type of situation?

Perfectionism

Perfectionists set extremely high performance standards for themselves. They will often be eager to please and will see the hard work and dedication required in training as the price they have to pay to achieve success. Sometimes athletes who are perfectionists are highly critical of others – this is because perfectionists may see others as not living up to their standards, which can have a negative impact on group dynamics and team cohesion.

There are two types of perfectionism:

- **Functional perfectionism** – sometimes called adaptive perfectionism, this is a **positive form** of perfectionism, usually possessed by highly motivated athletes who achieve high levels in sport or exercise. Functional perfectionism usually allows athletes to gain pleasure from pursuing challenging goals and to strive to achieve perfection without it impacting on their self-esteem.
- **Dysfunctional perfectionism** – sometimes called maladaptive perfectionism, this is a **negative form** of perfectionism that often means athletes will try to achieve the unachievable. When maladaptive perfectionists are unable to achieve the impossible standards they set for themselves, they can start to suffer mental health problems such as depression.

Impact of perfectionism on performance and behaviours

There are mixed opinions over the impact of perfectionism on performance in sport. Some believe adaptive perfectionism is associated with task orientation, while maladaptive perfectionism is associated more with ego orientation. As perfectionists can be preoccupied with not making mistakes, it can actually lead to decreases in performance. Equally, as perfectionists tend to put off doing things they find difficult, they can reduce their chances of enhancing performance.

Perfectionist tendencies can also motivate people to work hard and demonstrate commitment levels that ultimately end up improving performance. Some perfectionists are also thought to be **risk averse**. As a result of this, their levels of creativity and innovation are often reduced. This limits their potential to succeed as they might not try new things, due to a fear of failure.

In general, adaptive perfectionism is thought to enhance performance whereas maladaptive perfectionism is thought to decrease performance and lead to negative lifestyle behaviours.

Key term

Risk averse – reluctant to take risks.

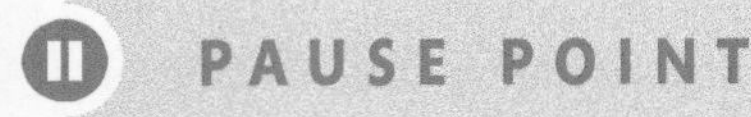

What is perfectionism?

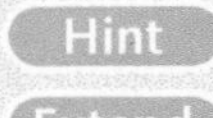

Define perfectionism and write a summary of the different types of perfectionism.

Extend Discuss how perfectionism can positively and negatively affect performance, using examples to illuminate your answer.

Group dynamics in sport

Group processes

Tuckman's stages of group development

For a group of people to become a team, they must go through four developmental stages: forming, storming, norming and performing. All groups go through these stages, but the time spent at each stage is not fixed and some teams can revert back to previous stages.

1 **Forming** – group members familiarise themselves with each other, trying to decide if they belong. Group members assess the strengths and weaknesses of each other, and test their relationships with others. Individuals get to know their roles within the group and make decisions about whether or not they feel they can fulfil (or want to fulfil) their role. Formal leaders (e.g. managers or coaches) in the group tend to be directive.
2 **Storming** – conflict begins to develop between individuals in the group. Individuals or cliques start to question the position and authority of the leader, and resist the control of the group. Often, conflicts develop because demands are placed on the group members and some individuals try to acquire more important roles. The formal leader in the group takes on more of a guidance role with decision-making and helps the team move towards what is expected in terms of professional behaviour.
3 **Norming** – conflict is replaced by cooperation. Members of the group start to work towards common goals rather than focusing on individual agendas, and group cohesion develops, increasing group satisfaction (due to satisfaction from achieving tasks) and levels of respect for others in the group. The formal leader expects group members to become more involved in the decision-making process, and the players to take more responsibility for their professional behaviour.
4 **Performing** – the team progress and function effectively as a unit. The group works without conflict towards the achievement of shared goals and objectives and there is little need for external supervision as the group is more motivated. The group makes its own decisions and takes responsibility for them.

Research

Research lifecycle and pendular perspectives on group development. How do they differ from Tuckman's linear view and how might this extend our understanding of group development?

Interactive and coactive groups and teams

There are two key types of sports team:

- **interactive teams** – team members interact and coordinate with each other in order to achieve a successful performance. Sports such as hockey are typical examples of this type of team

- **coactive teams** – there is no direct interaction between team members during the performance. Members are required to achieve success in their individual games, events or performances to achieve overall team success. An example of a coactive team is a gymnastics team, where each member takes their individual turn on the different apparatus but their individual performance scores points for the team.

The Ringelmann effect

The Ringelmann effect is a phenomenon where, as the group size increases, the individual productivity of the people in the group decreases. The Ringelmann effect is caused more by motivation faults or losses than coordination losses and occurs when people are not accountable for their own performance (as the group gets larger, athletes can hide behind other athletes and not get noticed).

Social loafing

Social loafing is when group members do not put in maximum effort when they are in a group or team. The losses in motivation causing social loafing are evident when the individual contributions of group members are not identified or are dispensable. It occurs when some players appear to be working harder than others.

Individuals who display social loafing lack confidence, are afraid of failure and tend to be highly anxious. Athletes who display social loafing do not feel they can make a useful contribution to overall team performance, which can be why they do not want to participate.

Case study

The faltering American football team

You are on a work placement with an American football team. You notice there are a few players who do not seem to be trying very much. When feeding the ball to the quarterback on set plays, they seem to be very slow on the snap.

You also notice that some of the players do not seem to be 'on the same page'. For example, the wide receiver seems to be misjudging the quarterback's passes on a regular basis and there does not seem to be a great deal of intent when players are supposed to be blocking. The other players on the team appear to be working harder to try to make up for this. However, despite their efforts, there is little interaction between blockers and runners.

Check your knowledge

1. What evidence can you see in the case study of the Ringlemann effect and social loafing?
2. If you were the coach, how could you improve these faults?

PAUSE POINT What are the two different types of team?

Hint Produce a table that shows the different types of team, describes the different types and provides an example of each.

Extend Discuss how you think a sport psychologist may work differently with the different types of team to enhance their performance.

Cohesion

A sports team is a unique type of group. Members may spend a lot of time living, training and competing together and, because of this, levels of cohesion can have a significant effect on their performance.

Carron's conceptual model of cohesion

Carron's conceptual model of cohesion (1982) explains four factors which it claims affect team cohesion (see Figure 3.7).

- **Environmental factors** – groups that are closer to each other (in terms of location), and which are smaller, are more cohesive because members have greater opportunities to interact and form relationships.
- **Personal factors** – the individual characteristics of group members are important in group cohesion. If players are motivated to achieve the group's aims and objectives, are from similar backgrounds, have similar attitudes and opinions, and have similar levels of commitment, there will be more satisfaction among group members and the group is more likely to be cohesive.
- **Leadership factors** – leadership styles, behaviours, communication styles and the compatibility of the coach's and athletes' personalities are key factors that affect cohesion.
- **Team factors** – if the team stays together for a long time, experiences successes and failures together and can be involved in the decision-making process, the group is more likely to be productive and cohesive.

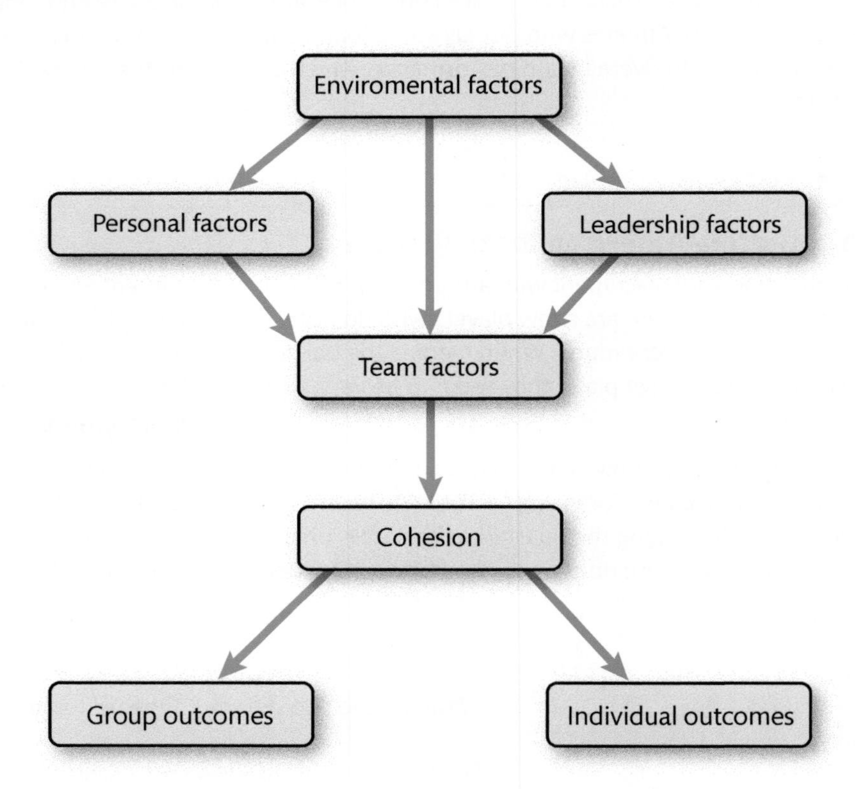

Figure 3.7: How does Carron's (1982) conceptual model of cohesion explain factors affecting cohesion?

Discussion

In a small group, discuss how you think each factor affects cohesion. Try to consider both positive and negative effects.

Task and social cohesion

Cohesion is a dynamic process reflected in the tendency for a group to stick together and remain united in the pursuit of its goals and objectives.

- **Task cohesion** – this is how well team members work together to achieve common goals and objectives. It can help create an effective team climate, as high levels of task cohesion are usually associated with higher levels of team role acceptance and task interdependence, which can increase team performance.
- **Social cohesion** – this is how much team members tend to like each other's company and how much they like each other. It can enhance the team climate as more socially cohesive teams tend to provide greater levels of social support, ascribe to more positive social norms, have a stronger sense of team identity, and are more comfortable with structured and clear communication. Collectively, these contribute to increased team performance and can increase athletes' well-being.

Research

Research the 1990s Chicago Bulls teams, including newspaper stories about relationships within the team. Which type of cohesion do you think they most often displayed? How would you describe their team climate?

Relationship between cohesion and performance

It is easy to say that the greater the level of cohesion, the higher the performance level. Interactive sports like football and volleyball require direct interaction and coordination between players so cohesion (especially task cohesion) is important. Coactive sports like golf and archery require little, if any, direct interaction or coordination. Cohesion has a greater influence on performance in interactive sports than on coactive sports.

If you think about the relationship between cohesion and performance, one question you could ask is: what is the direction of the relationship? It is plausible that cohesion affects performance and performance affects cohesion. It is understandable that a team that wins on a regular basis may get along better, but equally understandable that a team that gets on better is more likely to be successful. Many people now accept that the cohesion–performance relationship is circular: an increase in performance leads to an increase in cohesion, which leads to further increases in performance, and so on.

Leadership

Leaders need passion and they need to inspire people. Being a leader is difficult, but it is an important aspect of creating effective teams. Leaders are either prescribed or emergent.

- **Prescribed leaders** are appointed by some form of higher authority. For example, Mark Sampson was appointed the England women's football team manager by the English Football Association.
- **Emergent leaders** achieve leadership status by gaining the respect and support of the group. These leaders achieve their status through showing specific leadership skills or being skilful at their sport. For example, Wayne Rooney emerged within the Manchester United team and became an informal leader of the team before eventually being appointed club captain. He emerged because of his impressive performances, gaining the respect of others. In some situations, emergent leaders can be more effective than prescribed leaders as they already have the respect of existing group members.

Discussion

Think about situations when one of a team's senior players is promoted to become the new manager of their team. What effect might this have on the relationships they have with their former team mates who they are now managing? How might this affect the team as a whole?

Leaders can be autocratic or democratic in their approach.

- **Autocratic leaders** have firm views about how and when things should be done. They are inflexible with their approach to the group. They dictate who does what tasks and when, and often how the task should be done. They use phrases like 'do this', or 'do it the way I told you to'. The leader does not seek the views of people within the group, and rarely gets involved on a personal level with group members.
- **Democratic leaders** make decisions only after consulting group members. They encourage group involvement, adopt an informal and relaxed approach to leadership, and listen to ideas relating to the prioritisation and completion of goals. They use questions like 'How do you think we can do this?'. This shows they value the group's input, yet still maintain their position as leader by making final decisions.

Reflect

Think about times when you have been the leader of a group. Were you more autocratic or more democratic? Why did you act in that way and how would you change it if you were in the same situation again?

Theories of leadership: Chelladurai's multidimensional model of sport leadership

This theory of sport leadership says the team's performance and satisfaction with the leader will be highest if the leader's required behaviours, preferred behaviours and actual behaviours all agree. Figure 3.8 shows Chelladurai's model.

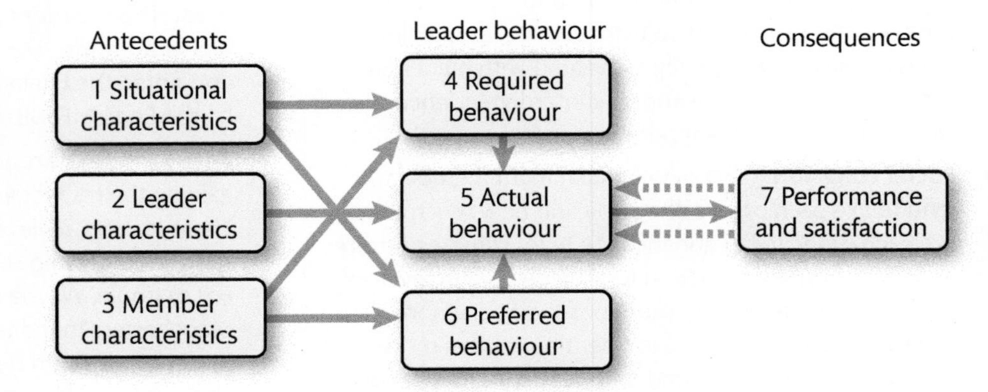

▶ **Figure 3.8:** How does this model help us to understand the factors that can create high performance and satisfaction?

- **Required behaviours** are generally determined by the situation the leader is in (e.g. the sporting organisation) and the expectation that the leader conforms to expected norms. For example, how many times have you seen a football manager punished for criticising a referee after a game? The established norm is that leaders should not criticise match officials, so that is the behaviour expected of the leader.
- **Preferred behaviour** is determined by the people within the group or team. Their preferences are related to factors including personality, experience and skill of the athletes; and non-sport-related aspects like age and gender. For example, a senior elite athlete might expect that their coach behaves differently towards them than towards a youth-level athlete just starting their career.
- **Actual behaviour** is directly determined by the characteristics of the leader, and indirectly by situational factors and the preferences of the group. For example, a grass roots sports coach might adopt more relationship-orientated behaviours as their primary goal would be to enhance enjoyment and maintain young people's sport participation, while a coach in a World Championship final might display more task-orientated leadership to try to maintain the team's focus on winning.

The antecedents (the things that lead to these types of behaviours) of these types of leader behaviour are the situation, the leader and the team members. The consequences (the things that occur as a result of these leader behaviours) are the athletes' performances and satisfaction.

Application to performance of sports groups and teams

An effective leader can help to enhance attentional focus of athletes. This can be achieved by giving clear instructions and providing a rationale for different activities. This helps athletes to understand how these activities will help them to improve their performance. Allowing the athlete to have an input in the decision-making process shows that you value their opinion. Collectively, these points can improve commitment and determination.

Case study

Leadership for sports sessions

You have been asked to take over running some sports sessions for a group of young people from an inner city. When you are provided with some information prior to running the sessions, you find out that there are usually around 30 children that attend the sessions, aged 8–13. You are also made aware that many of the children have behavioural difficulties; they are often in trouble at school and some of them have been taken into care due to their family backgrounds.

The organisation that has asked you to run these sessions is trying to use sport as a way of developing personal and social responsibility skills in young people.

You have a range of abilities in the sessions and the children play a selection of sports including football, cricket, rugby, and track and field athletics.

Check your knowledge

1. What are the key pieces of information in this case study that might determine how you work with the children and young people?
2. How can you use the information that you know about autocratic and democratic leaders to decide how you might lead the group?
3. How can you use information from the multidimensional model of sport leadership to decide how you might lead the group?

PAUSE POINT How do we understand effective leadership?

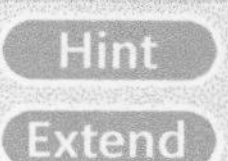

Hint: Write a summary of Chelladurai's multidimensional model of leadership.

Extend: Discuss how the theory could be used to help you enhance performance and group dynamics within a team.

Psychological interventions for sports performance and exercise

To perform at their peak, athletes need high levels of motivation and self-confidence, to self-regulate their arousal levels and to maintain positive thoughts even in the face of setbacks. These are all things that psychological skills can help with.

Performance profiling

Understanding the psychological demands of the sport an athlete takes part in is an important aspect of designing an effective psychological intervention, as it will help you to understand the athlete in more depth, and from the athlete's own perspective. Performance profiling is a technique used to identify strengths and areas for improvement. It can also enhance communication between the coach and athlete about their perceptions of these strengths and areas for improvement.

Applications of performance profiling

Performance profiling has a number of potential applications that can benefit athletes and coaches. These include the following, all of which link in with monitoring and evaluating performance.

- **Identifying psychological strengths and weaknesses** and **providing a basis for goal setting** – a central use of performance profiling is to help identify psychological strengths and weaknesses, on an objective level or a subjective level. Performance profiling can help to prioritise these strengths and weaknesses, which then forms the basis of goal setting.

- **High motivation** – reviewing the athlete's performance over time allows the athlete to see where they have improved. If they associate this improvement with efforts they have made, they will be motivated to improve further. Performance profiling also gives the athlete a voice and encourages others to consider things from the athlete's perspective. This makes the athlete feel more valued and more in control of their future planning.
- **Develop the athlete's self-awareness** – by encouraging the athlete to consider their strengths and weaknesses, you will help them to develop their self-awareness. Recent research in sports has shown self-awareness to be an important psychological quality for those who progress to an elite level. Athletes with a higher level of self-awareness are more likely to identify their strengths and areas for improvement independently and to devise strategies for improvement. They are also more likely to approach coaches and other staff to discuss their views and ways they can improve.
- **Monitor and evaluate progress** – using performance profiling on repeated occasions over a long period provides the athlete and their coach with an opportunity to monitor and evaluate their performance. This is done by comparing present assessments of strengths and areas for improvement with previous assessments, to plan for future developments.

Discussion

How can you use self-determination theory (refer back to page 84) to explain the benefits of performance profiling for athlete motivation and positive behaviour maintenance (e.g. increased practice) in sport?

Step by step: performance profiling

5 Steps

1 Identify and define key qualities for performance. Introduce the idea by asking the athlete what attributes they think are important for top performance; the athlete could also be asked to think of an elite performer and write down their qualities. Table 3.5 highlights some prompts that can be used with different athletes.
It will be useful for the athlete to record and define the qualities necessary for performance in a table format. This helps you and the athlete to develop a shared understanding of what the terms mean. To avoid misunderstanding, you must make sure the definitions used are those devised by the athlete. Some people suggest aiming for 20 qualities; however, this will vary from athlete to athlete and sport to sport. Tell them that there are no right or wrong answers.

2 Profile your perceptions of the athlete's levels and profile the athlete's perceptions of their levels. This is an assessment by you and the athlete of the current level of performance. You and the athlete write the key qualities in each of the blank spaces around the outside of the circular grid. Each quality is given a rating from 0 to 10 (see Figure 3.9).

3 Discuss your and the athlete's profiles and identify perceived areas of strength and areas for improvement. When looking at the two profiles (shown in Figure 3.9), if there are large differences between levels (a 'large' difference is classed as two points or more), this should lead to a discussion between you and the athlete about why the different levels have been given.

4 Agree on goals (benchmark for each quality) to be achieved through the Psychological Skills Training (PST) programme and discuss how they will be achieved. Normally, each of the desired benchmarks will be at level 10 – any target level below this on the athlete's behalf would suggest that there is some form of resistance to achieving the ultimate level of performance.

5 Repeat the profiling to monitor progress. Performance profiling can be repeated on a number of occasions to assess the athlete's progress. The aim is that the athlete will gradually progress further towards the outside of the scale (closer to the rating of 10). If the athlete does not make the desired progress, you and the athlete need to discuss why this is. Usually this will be because the training programme did not take into account a quality (errors in the design of the programme), you have different views on the importance of a quality (errors in communication and understanding) or the athlete has not put in the effort to achieve the improvements in performance.

Table 3.5: Examples of the demands of sport. Can you think of the five most technical demands of your sport?

Psychological	Physical	Attitudinal/character	Technical*
Confidence	Strength	Weight control	
Concentration	Stamina	Discipline	
Reflection	Endurance	Determination	
Commitment	Flexibility	Will to win	
Resourcefulness	Power	Positive outlook	
Control	Speed		
Creativity	Balance		
Resilience	Reaction time		
*Technical requirements will vary between different sports			

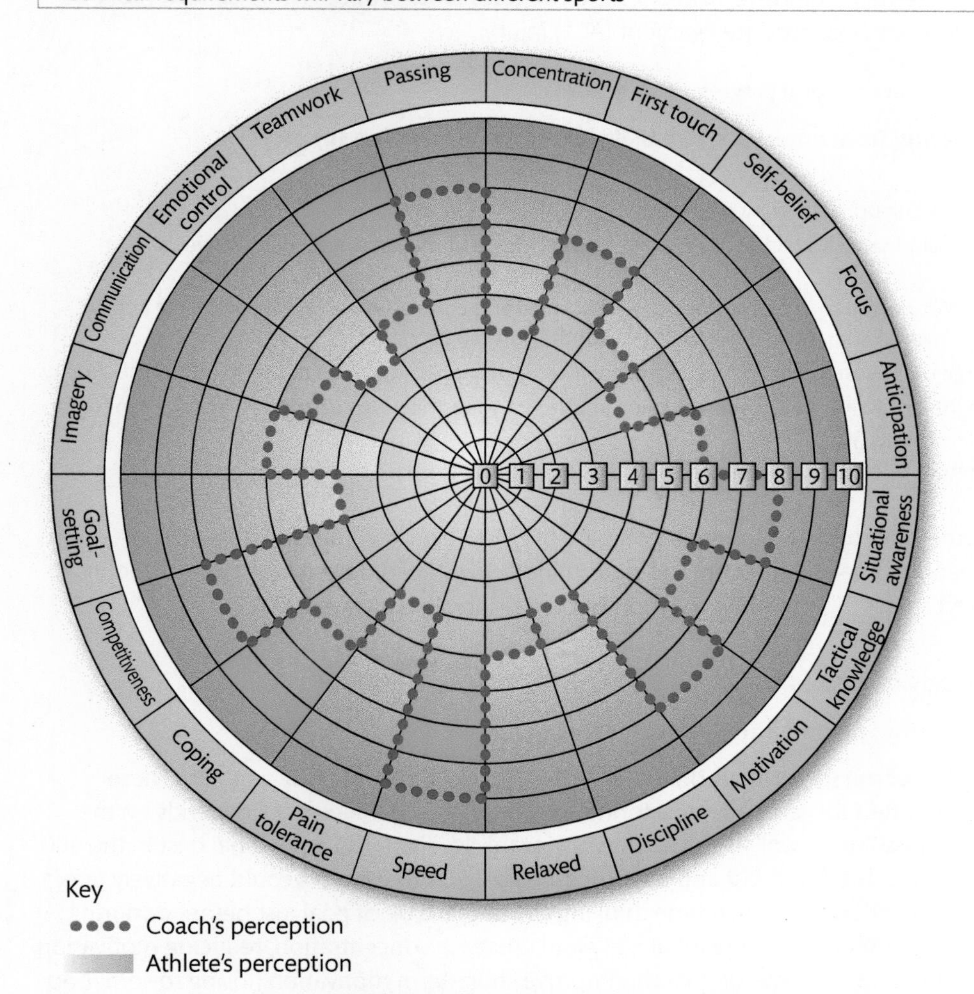

Figure 3.9: How can performance profiling benefit both the coach and the athlete?

PAUSE POINT What is performance profiling?

Hint Produce a flow diagram showing the stages of performance profiling.

Extend Discuss each stage of performance profiling and how you think this can help to enhance an athlete's performance.

Goal setting

▶ How can goal setting be useful for enhancing motivation in injured athletes?

Many factors can affect motivation. Athletes may experience performance setbacks or injuries, they may be struggling to manage the demands of sport and education, or they may have a number of competitions coming up and feel they do not know how they will manage them. In all of these situations, motivation can be improved through effective goal setting.

Goals should be set in a coherent, progressive and linked manner. You should use a combination of short-term, medium-term and long-term goals. Having a series of short-term and medium-term goals can make progress towards the long-term goals seem more realistic, and provide a continuing sense of achievement.

Avoid being too prescriptive with timescales for some goals and allow flexibility for them to be revised if the athlete is struggling to achieve them all. Table 3.6 shows short-term, medium-term and long-term goals for an athlete who has suffered a serious anterior cruciate ligament (ACL) injury.

▶ **Table 3.6:** Why do you think it is important to have a logical progression of goals?

Goal setting for an athlete who is recovering from anterior cruciate ligament reconstruction surgery	
Duration of goal	**Example**
Short-term	Progress to standing up, full weight bearing within 72 hours of surgery
Short-term	Have swelling eliminated and approximately up to 100° range of movement within two weeks post-surgery
Short-term to medium-term	Be able to perform a full squat, have unrestricted balance and control when walking and have approx. 130° of knee flexion within two weeks to three months post-surgery
Medium-term	Have full range of motion, full strength and straight line running ability by three to five months post-surgery
Medium-term to long-term	Be able to perform change of direction running and return to restricted sport-specific drills within four to six months post-surgery
Long-term	Have a full return to competitive sport within six to twelve months post-surgery

Remember to make sure that goals are SMARTS (specific, measureable, action-orientated, realistic, timed, self-determined). (Slightly different words are sometimes used to describe this abbreviation but the principle is always the same.)

Reflect

Think about the last time you set goals for yourself. Did you set goals of different types and with different timescales? Did you follow the principles of effective goal setting? How would you improve the goals that you set for yourself in future?

Types of goals

Outcome, performance and process goals

- **Outcome goals** focus on the result of the event, like winning a match. These are often the least effective for motivation as goal achievement depends on the opposition as well as the athlete. For example, if you run a personal best in the 400 metres but finish last and the outcome goal was to win, this could negatively affect motivation. Too much time thinking about this type of goal just before or during competition can increase anxiety and decrease concentration, reducing motivation. However, this type of goal can improve short-term motivation (losing to somebody can spur you on to train harder so you beat them next time).

- **Performance goals** focus on your performance and comparing your current performance to previous performances, so are independent of other athletes and give you a greater sense of control over the goal. Having greater control over goal achievement is very beneficial for motivating an athlete.
- **Process goals** are based on what the athlete has to do to improve their performance. An example would be a basketball player wanting to improve their jump shot accuracy by making sure they release the ball at the height of the jump. This type of goal is useful for improving motivation as it gives a specific element of performance to focus on, which facilitates learning and development.

Rather than using just one type of goal, try to incorporate all types when completing goal setting with athletes. When used correctly, they will complement each other and are more likely to enhance motivation.

Mastery and competitive goals

- **Mastery goals** (sometimes referred to as task or learning goals) focus on self-challenge and improvement, or at least not doing any worse than a previous performance. You do not make any comparisons between your athlete and other competitors – you focus only on setting goals that relate to your athlete surpassing their previous performance. Some sport psychologists argue these goals are best for enhancing motivation as they help an athlete strive for greater competence and because the athlete is more in control of whether these goals are achieved. There are two types of this goal.
  - MAp goals focus on performing a task well and outperforming previous personal achievements (e.g. setting new personal best times, learning a new skill). These goals tend to create the greatest levels of intrinsic motivation in athletes and can have positive effects on performance.
  - MAv goals focus on not making mistakes or not letting your performance decrease from previous levels. These goals can have negative effects on an athlete's well-being but do not always decrease performance.
- **Competitive goals** focus on demonstrating superiority over another athlete, or not being out-performed. While some people think these goals are bad for motivation because whether they are achieved is not fully in control of the athlete, they can be good for motivation if the athlete setting the goals has a high perception of competence. There are two types of this goal.
  - PAp goals can have a beneficial effect on motivation, especially when an athlete feels more competent, and have been shown to enhance performance in competitive situations.
  - PAv goals are widely recognised as the worst type of goal as they focus heavily on negative aspects of sport and can create higher levels of stress and anxiety and lower levels of motivation as a result.

Case study

Goal setting

In the 2015 Rugby World Cup, England lost 25–28 to Wales despite England leading 22–12 at one stage in the second half. Some critics felt that England had played as though they were simply trying to avoid defeat, rather than as though they really wanted to win. This could be seen as a negative approach.

Check your knowledge

1. If a team sets out to avoid losing, which type of goals are they using?
2. In a knockout tournament setting, why do you think a team might set up with the aim of avoiding losing after they have won their first match?

Reflect

Think about a time when you played sport and things did not go as well as you wanted them to – maybe you made some mistakes or you lost a game that you really wanted to win. Which of the psychological skills would you use if you were in the same situation again and how do you think they would benefit you?

Imagery

Imagery is creating or recreating images in your mind, rather than physically practising a sports skill or technique. It should involve as many senses as possible, and try to recreate emotions associated with the activity as well. The most effective imagery uses **visual**, **auditory** and **kinaesthetic** senses.

Key terms

Visual - you concentrate on the different things that you can see during the movement. This can be an internal perspective (from your own viewpoint) or an external perspective (as if watching yourself on a video).

Auditory - you concentrate on the different sounds that you associate with a sporting movement.

Kinaesthetic - you concentrate on the feel of the movement.

Cue words - single words that are a form of self-talk and used to trigger a desired response by an athlete. Common cue words include 'believe', 'relax', 'focus' and 'strong'.

Imagery can be used for:

- **reducing anxiety and stress** - imagining emotions associated with relaxation can help an athlete to control anxiety, arousal and stress levels, especially when used along with other techniques such as breathing exercises
- **influencing self-confidence** - through imagery, the athlete can experience feelings of success and come up with strategies for being successful in performance. As the performer sees that they can complete the performance successfully (even if only in their mind), their levels of self-confidence will increase
- **imagining goals** - imagery can be used to create a mental experience of you achieving your set goals (e.g. winning a medal or surpassing a personal best)
- **mental rehearsal** and **pre-performance routines** - imagery can be used as part of all types of pre-performance routine as it helps the athlete to mentally rehearse the action before performing it physically.

Self-talk

Have you ever played in a match and said something to yourself like 'Come on!' or 'Focus, keep your eye on the ball'? This is self-talk and is something most athletes do, sometimes without even doing it for any specific purpose. Self-talk is a psychological skill used to enhance learning and increase performance and motivation. The two main categories of self-talk are positive and negative self-talk.

- **Positive self-talk** is often used for motivation, aiming to increase energy levels and produce a more positive attitude in athletes. It usually involves statements such as 'Keep going!' or 'I can do this!' rather than task specific instructions. Sometimes athletes use **cue words** instead of phrases; some athletes even write cue words on their hands or wrists, or sew them into sports kit. Historically sport psychologists believed positive self-talk was beneficial for all sporting activities. However, more recent research has suggested that positive, motivational self-talk may not be as effective for sports requiring fine movements.
- **Negative self-talk** is a self-critical process which some sport psychologists have argued hinders an athlete from achieving goals and fosters self-doubt. Common self-talk statements include 'That was a stupid mistake to make' and 'I can't believe how bad I was'. However, more recently some researchers have argued negative self-talk does not always impede performance.

PAUSE POINT Think of some situations when you might use self-talk.

Hint Write a description of each type of self-talk.

Extend Using sporting examples, discuss how you think the different types of self-talk positively and negatively affect performance.

There are several uses for self-talk.

- **Self-confidence** – self-talk can give the athlete a sense of belief in what they are doing. Positive self-talk can direct the athlete's attention away from negative thoughts or things that have gone wrong, which then increases the athlete's level of self-confidence.
- **Arousal control** – cue words or positive phrases can be used to direct the athlete's attention away from negative aspects of performance that are the cause of higher levels of arousal.
- **Pre-performance routines** – athletes can use positive self-talk and another form of self-talk – **instructional self-talk** – as part of pre-performance routines. Positive self-talk helps to motivate athletes as part of pre-performance routines, whereas instructional self-talk can be used to provide sport-specific instructions for the athlete to concentrate on during games.

Reflect

Virtually everybody uses some form of self-talk. Think about a time when you used self-talk during sport or exercise. Was it positive or negative? Why did you use it? How did it impact on the activity you were taking part in at the time?

Key term

Instructional self-talk – a task-specific form of self-talk that involves the athlete giving instructions to themselves about different aspects of performance (e.g. technical or tactical elements).

Arousal control techniques

Arousal in sport runs on a continuum from deep sleep to hyperactivity. At times, you may need to help athletes regulate their arousal levels so they can perform at their best. If you need to help athletes reduce their arousal levels, you will use relaxation techniques. However, if your athlete needs to increase their arousal levels, you will need to use energising techniques.

Relaxation techniques

There are three common relaxation techniques used by sport psychologists.

Relaxation imagery

Relaxation imagery is an example of a mind to muscle technique that is used to reduce levels of arousal, stress and anxiety. It is often used to help athletes who are struggling to manage performance pressures or with athletes who have long-term injuries. Relaxation imagery can be supported by either imagery scripts (such as the one shown in the box), images or videos. Knowing about different scenarios that can help relax athletes is important – a commonly used scenario is relaxing on a beach.

Imagine that you are on a hot beach. You can feel the warm sun beating down on you. You can see the golden sands and can see where they meet the clear blue waters. You can see the blue sky that is clear with the exception of a couple of white fluffy clouds. You are now walking towards the water and you can feel the sand between your toes as you walk. You can hear the waves roll in as you get closer to the water's edge. The water starts to splash against you and you can feel its cooling effect on your skin. You are now stepping into the water. As you walk in deeper you feel the cool sensation on your feet, your ankles and then on your legs. You dive into the water and enjoy the cooling sensation. Everything is peaceful here. You are completely at peace, calm, warm and relaxed.

Progressive muscular relaxation

An easy-to-use technique that helps to reduce muscle tension. It is a useful technique because it raises your awareness of levels of muscle tension and, through the relaxation phase, helps to distinguish between what is a state of tension and relaxation. The technique involves tensing and relaxing groups of muscles in turn over the whole body. The process involves tensing a muscle group for five seconds, releasing the tension for five seconds, taking a deep breath and repeating. It is called progressive muscular relaxation because an athlete progresses from one muscle group to the next until all muscles have been tensed and relaxed.

Breathing control

This is a slow and deliberate inhalation-exhalation process. It is best used during breaks in play and is useful when athletes are getting anxious. A simple method is to work on a 1:2 ratio of breathing in to breathing out, with people most commonly taught to breathe in for four seconds and then breathe out for eight seconds. Physiological benefits include oxygen transport, carbon dioxide removal, reduced muscle fatigue and reduced chances of injuries such as cramp.

The psychological benefits are also important. One of the biggest problems with over-arousal is the reduced concentration levels that accompany it. For example, focusing on negative aspects, such as muscle tension, increased heart rate and (in some cases) nausea can be symptoms of over-arousal. Breathing control techniques can reduce arousal in two ways.

- They can reduce the physiological symptoms of arousal and anxiety.
- They can focus an athlete's attention away from the negative aspects, because they have to concentrate on getting the breathing techniques correct.

This leads to increased concentration, confidence, control and well-being. The best time to use breathing control in a competitive situation is when there is a break in the play, because it gives an athlete the chance to be slow and deliberate in their breathing technique. This helps them regain their composure.

Safety tip

Before starting any breathing control techniques with an athlete, you should find out if they have any respiratory conditions - such as asthma - that could affect their ability to breathe in deeply.

Discussion

Do you think there are any sports or athlete groups that would be resistant to these types of relaxation techniques?

Energising techniques

Common energising techniques are outlined below.

- **Pep talk** - this is a short talk that is designed to instil enthusiasm in athletes and increase their determination to succeed. Pep talks are usually quite informal but will be passionate. In team situations, pep talks are usually delivered by a leader in the group (e.g. coach or captain), but can be delivered by anybody in different situations.
- **Listening to music** - this can narrow a performer's attention and divert it from tiredness. Exciting music can increase body temperature, heart rate and breathing rate, all of which can improve sport performance. Music is also helpful for avoiding negative thoughts.
- **Positive statements** - these can be used alone or alongside other arousal-increasing techniques to increase arousal levels. When using positive statements, you should consider the following:
  - Phrase statements should be personal and address the athlete, saying 'I', 'me' or their first name, so they are personal to them. Make them in the present tense, e.g. 'I am confident of achieving the best result'.
  - Make statements as positive as possible - avoid the use of 'no', 'don't', and 'not', because if you ask the athlete not to think about something, they are more likely to think about it.
  - Make statements short, clear and simple. Long statements are difficult to remember and process, so shorter and simpler statements are better.
  - Make statements emotional - use phrases that make the athlete feel happy, empowered and self-assured, such as 'It makes me happy when I know I've tried my best'.
- **Use of energising imagery** - this can be achieved through the use of high-energy images of competition (e.g. a hard tackle in rugby), playing well (e.g. crossing the finish line first in a race) and high levels of effort (e.g. being able to lift a new weight in the gym).
- **Increasing breathing rate** - just as you can consciously control your breathing to relax, you can also increase your breathing rate to increase your arousal levels.

What are the energising techniques?

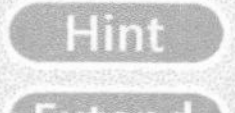

Hint: Create a list of all the energising techniques and their benefits.

Extend: Explain times when you think it would be inappropriate to use different energising techniques, and why.

Assessment practice 3.1

Elijah is an 18-year-old basketball player who has experienced a sudden drop in his free-throw performance. It has dropped from 88 per cent to 53 per cent in the space of one month and Elijah is worried about this. His coach has suggested that he might want to work on his psychological approach but Elijah does not know anything about it. Elijah has emailed you asking for help.

- Reply to Elijah explaining the impact of psychological factors in sport and exercise activities.
- Outline some psychological interventions that might help Elijah address his current situation, explaining why they might help.

Plan

- What am I being asked to do?
- What resources do I need to complete this task?

Do

- Have I made connections between my reading or research and the task, and considered the context in which I need to apply the information?
- Am I confident that I know what I am doing and understand what I am aiming to achieve?

Review

- Can I explain how I approached the task and why I completed it in this way?
- Can I explain how my applied knowledge of sport and exercise psychology has changed or developed through completing this task?

Further reading and resources

Books

Burton, D. and Raedeke, T. D. (2008) *Sport Psychology for Coaches*, Champaign, IL: Human Kinetics.

Bush, A., Brierley, J., Carr, S., Gledhill, A., Mackay, N., Manley, A., Morgan, H., Roberts, W. and Willsmer, N. (2012) *Foundations in Sports Coaching*, Harlow, Essex: Pearson Education.

Bush, A., Garrard, M., Gledhill, A., Mackay, N. and Sutton, L. (2012) *Foundations in Sports Science*, Harlow, Essex: Pearson Education.

Dweck, C. S. (2012) *Mindset: How you can Fulfil your Potential*, London: Little, Brown Book Group.

Harwood, C. and Anderson, R. (2015) *Coaching Psychological Skills in Youth Football*, Oakamoor: Bennion Kearny.

Hemmings, B. and Holder, T. (2009) *Applied Sport Psychology: A Case-based Approach*, Chichester, West Sussex: Wiley-Blackwell.

Karageorghis, C. and Terry, P. (2010) *Inside Sport Psychology*, Champaign, IL: Human Kinetics.

Kornspan, A. S. (2009) *Fundamentals of Sport and Exercise Psychology*, Champaign, IL: Human Kinetics.

Weinberg, R. S. and Gould, D. (2014) *Foundations of Sport and Exercise Psychology*, 6th edition, Champaign, IL: Human Kinetics.

Websites

www.mindsetonline.com – Mindset: this website looks at the different mindsets and will help you to think about their applications in different environments.

www.psychologytoday.com/topics/sport-and-competition – *Psychology Today*: the sport and competition section of *Psychology Today*, which contains articles and blogs associated with different sport-related topics.

www.selfdeterminationtheory.org – Self-Determination Theory: a website devoted to self-determination theory that includes descriptions of each theory and discusses research underpinned by this theory.

Journals

Forsdyke, D. and Gledhill, A. (2014) Reaching out for a helping hand: The role of social support in sports injury rehabilitation, *sportEx Medicine*, 61, 8–12.

Gledhill, A. and Forsdyke, D. (2015) The challenges of youth: psychosocial response to sports injury and rehabilitation in youth athletes, *sportEx Medicine*, 63, 12–17.

Keegan, R. J., Harwood, C. G., Spray, C. M. and Lavallee, D. (2014) A qualitative investigation of the motivational climate in elite sport, *Psychology of Sport and Exercise*, 15, 97–107.

THINK ▶FUTURE

Jefferson Richards

Sport Psychologist

I've been working as a sport psychologist in track and field athletics for five years. During this time I have encountered so many different track and field athletes who've been helped by sport psychology. After I completed my BTEC Level 3 in Sport and Exercise Science, I went to university and completed a BPS approved degree in psychology as I needed this to be able to use the title 'psychologist'. This complemented my existing athletics coaching qualifications and my previous experience as a sprinter, so I'm happy that I have the subject-specific knowledge as well as an understanding of the sport.

Having an understanding of the sport you work in is essential to work effectively as a sport psychologist. So is the ability to develop and maintain effective working relationships with different people. In doing so, you are more likely to be able to get to know your athletes, which is really useful when it comes to designing psychological skills training programmes. This is important as there is no such thing as a universal psychological skills training programme and you always have to tailor your work to the needs of your athlete.

Focusing on your skills

Designing effective psychological interventions

It is important to be able to design effective psychological interventions for athletes. Here are some tips to help you.

- Before completing any work with an athlete, make sure you have their consent.
- Conduct an appropriate needs analysis with the athlete and discuss your findings with them.
- Find out if the athlete has any previous experience of using psychological skills training programmes – they may have a preference for certain psychological skills.
- Make sure you are able to provide a clear rationale for the psychological skills that you adopt. You can usually do this by linking the needs of the athlete to the benefits of the techniques and then supporting your suggestions with appropriate evidence.
- Review your athlete's progress at scheduled interviews – this is key for monitoring their progress. This can really help their motivation levels and can also help you to alter your programme design as and when required.
- Always work within your limitations of practice. If there is anything that you are unsure of, speak to another professional or refer your athlete to them.

Getting ready for assessment

This section has been written to help you do your best when you take your assessment task. Read through it carefully and ask your tutor if there is anything you are still not sure about.

In your externally set assessment, you will have some extended answer questions. The extended answer questions will be phrased to allow you to highlight key pieces of information and start to think about how you can plan your answer. Completing the preparatory work before the externally set assessment is vital in getting to know the topic area in the context of the set question. When approaching the question, think about the following.

- Make sure that you read the question carefully.
- Identify the key words in the question.
- Focus on the words that tell you what you need to write about.
- Read the case information and highlight key parts that will help you answer the question.

An important part of the extended answer questions is that you are assessed against qualitative improvements in your answer. This means the number of marks you get will not necessarily be based on the number of points that you make, but the **quality** of the points that you make.

- Avoid simply repeating information included in the case studies. Make sure you use the information in the context of the set question, to demonstrate how psychological factors affect the athlete's or team's performance.
- Provide an answer that relates to all of the key parts of the question.
- If there is more than one perspective on a topic, ensure that you produce a balanced answer.
- Make a link between the needs of the client, appropriate theory and the psychological skills training activities selected.

Example task

Thomas is 17 years old and a very talented rugby league player. As well as playing for his school he also plays for his regional side and spends most of his time either playing, watching or talking about rugby. He is a standout player and always wants to look better than his opponents. He wants to be a professional player and his dad has told him that the best way to look good on the pitch is by making other people look bad.

It is the day of a game. He feels very excited and positive that he is going to play well, until he sees a player – Jack – who outperformed him in the last game. Jack also plays in the regional squad and has recently been offered a contract by a Super League club. As Thomas warms up for the game, all he can concentrate on is Jack. He starts to sweat when he thinks about the last game, feels a bit ill and becomes very agitated; he is worried about looking bad during the game and worried that Jack is going to outperform him. Thomas's dad is in the crowd.

Assess the impact of psychological factors on Thomas.

Thomas appears to have more of a need to avoid failure and seems to be more ego-orientated. This is because he places a lot of emphasis on comparing himself to opponents and is worried he might look bad against a better player. Part of this reason might be because of his dad who says the best way to look good is making other people look bad. This creates a situation where Thomas is more ego-orientated; and, because Jack outperformed him in the last game and Thomas' dad is at the game watching, he might be worried about letting his dad down. Thomas might be worried about letting his dad down because research suggests that parents are an important source of feedback and play a key role in creating values in players.

An important part of highlighting Thomas' need to avoid failure and his ego-orientation is that these types of people can often start to experience lower levels of psychological well-being and higher levels of stress and anxiety. It would seem Thomas is demonstrating levels of distress, higher levels of arousal and competitive anxiety because he has started to sweat; he feels ill, and is agitated. This means he is showing somatic and behavioural symptoms of anxiety. This last part about being agitated is a concern because Thomas is about to play rugby, which requires high levels of assertion to be successful, but also provides lots of aggressive cues. If Thomas is unable to control his arousal levels and Jack starts to outperform him during the game, this could increase his arousal levels further and result in Thomas becoming aggressive. This will decrease his performance further as well as increase the risk of him or one of the opponents getting injured. Because Thomas' dad is watching, this is probably going to increase Thomas' arousal levels when playing against Jack because Thomas' dad wants him to make people look bad. These are both examples of external sources of stress.

As Thomas is distressed before the game, it is likely to have a negative effect on his performance. The negative effects on performance include a negative mental state, a loss of self-confidence, possible injury, and aggression.

Try to plan out your answers more clearly. This answer contains instances of repetition that disrupt the overall flow of the answer.

This section demonstrates where you can link the different psychological factors and suggest how they can affect performance. Using supporting evidence would be beneficial here.

Concrete examples of these effects in the context of the answer would add depth.

From the case study it also looks like Thomas might have a fixed mindset rather than a growth mindset. This is because he seems to think that he can't beat Jack and he is preoccupied with what Jack is doing before the game. As this is because Jack was better than him last time, this might mean that Thomas also has some learned helplessness.

This point identifies a viable consideration but should be illuminated using specific details from the case study in combination with specific communication of the meaning of learned helplessness.

Which psychological interventions would be beneficial for Thomas?

I think that there are two ways of thinking about this. The first is there may be a long-term issue that needs taking care of in that Thomas' dad is creating the wrong type of motivation and a fixed mindset in Thomas which is making him worse. This might mean that there needs to be some TARGET work with Thomas and maybe his dad that works on developing a need to achieve or mastery-orientated motivation. However, this is a long-term solution to a problem and would be difficult to do before a game during the warm-up. So I would say that this should be done over the course of the season.

This answer identifies an appropriate long-term suggestion but does not go into specific detail about what the acronym 'TARGET' stands for, nor does it use any specific case details to demonstrate why it would be effective.

This has identified a reason to use the TARGET strategy but has not gone into depth about why these are important. This answer could be related back to specific details, such as adolescent athletes, growth and development, or psychological well-being.

The second is that this is something that is happening before the game so we need to do something about it in the short-term. As a result, I would suggest using some arousal regulation techniques. Because Rugby is a game that requires a lot of assertive behaviour to be successful, such as hard tackles to dominate your opponent, it is important to not relax Thomas too much as this might mean that he isn't as assertive as he should be. In order to relax Thomas, I would suggest using breathing control. I would suggest using this as it reduces the physiological symptoms of arousal and anxiety and it will focus Thomas' attention away from Jack. This is because Thomas will have to concentrate on getting the breathing techniques correct.

There should be continuity in an answer. This suggests the learner will go on to talk about more than one arousal reduction technique, but they have only talked about one in-depth. In only talking about one technique, the learner has not demonstrated consideration of other techniques that could have been used.

Breathing control is a slow and deliberate inhalation–exhalation process. Research says it is best used during breaks in play and is useful when athletes are getting anxious. This means it could be used in breaks in the warm-up or during the break between the warm-up and the game starting. I think using it at a break in the warm-up would be good so that it takes Thomas' attention away from Jack and puts it back on himself. I would also use it again between the warm-up and the game so that will allow Thomas to fully regain his composure before the game. This will increase his chances of being able to concentrate properly.

This section offers a clear suggestion of a psychological intervention as well as when it should be used.

Because Thomas is young, a simple method of breathing control might be better and easier to follow for him. One method of breathing control that I would use is a 1:2 ratio of breathing in to breathing out, for example, breathing in for four seconds and then out for eight. This method has physiological benefits such as: oxygen transport, carbon dioxide removal, reduced muscle fatigue and reduced chances of injuries such as cramp. This can reduce Thomas' chance of getting injured and can help to increase performance. The psychological benefits will probably be more important. As Thomas is anxious and over-aroused, one of his biggest problems is his reduced concentration levels. For example, he is focusing on negative aspects, such as when he got outperformed by Jack. This has increased his heart rate and he doesn't feel very well.

This section adds depth to the answer because it gives concrete examples of how the technique would be beneficial for the client.

4 Field- and Laboratory-based Fitness Testing

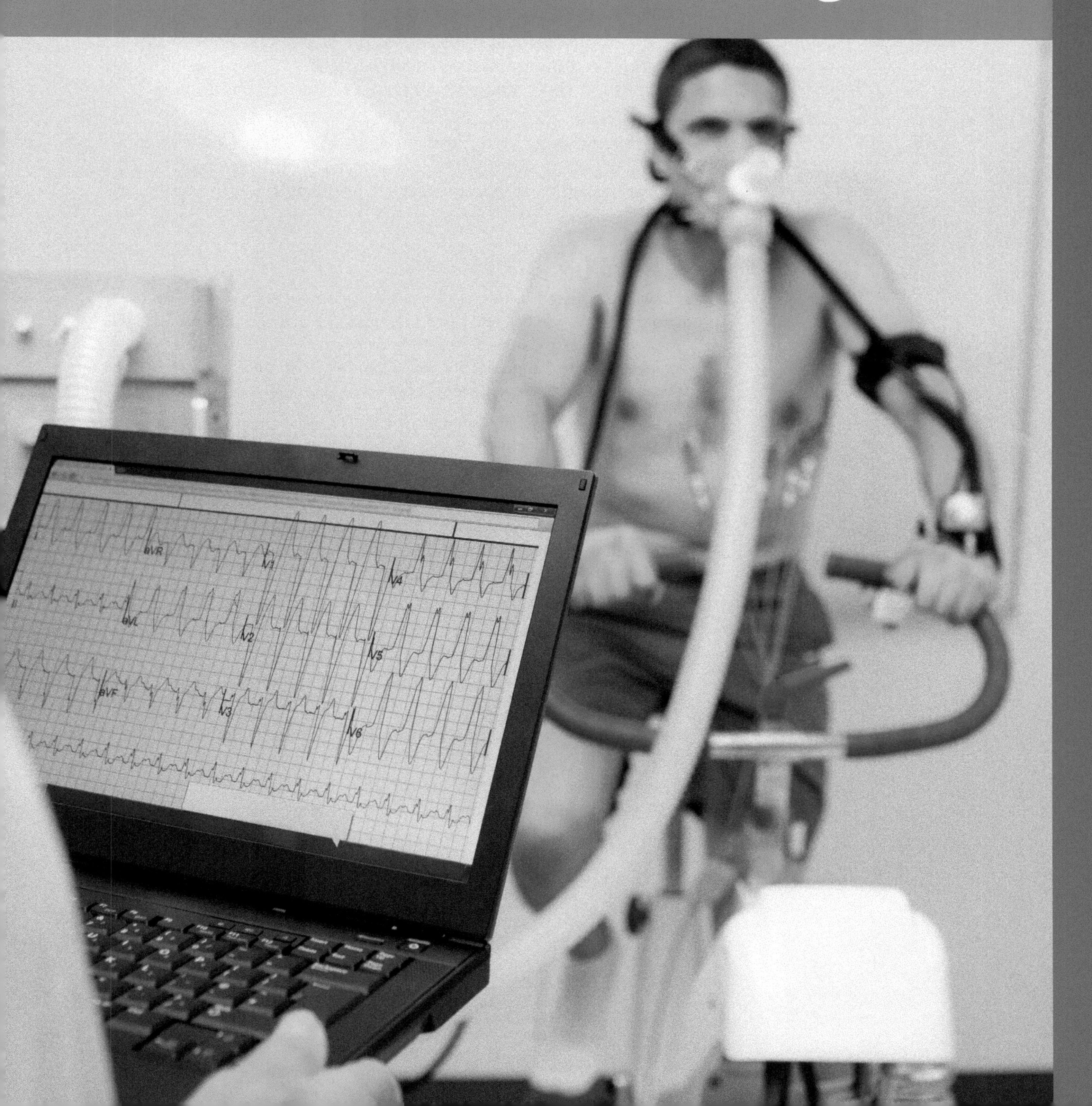

Getting to know your unit

Assessment
This unit is assessed by a series of assignments set by your tutor.

Sports scientists and health practitioners play a large role in monitoring and evaluating an individual's sport and exercise performance. To do this, they use a range of different testing protocols in both laboratories and 'in the field', in situations very close to those the individual will encounter during sport and exercise.

This unit introduces some of these protocols and will help you to understand the different stages involved in planning, administering and interpreting their outcome, as well as designing your own testing protocols.

It will allow you to develop practical skills and learn about the testing procedures and how to replicate them under scientific conditions, using the data you produce to profile a sports performer.

How you will be assessed

This unit will be assessed by a series of internally assessed tasks set by your tutor. Throughout this unit you will find assessment practice activities that will help you work towards your assessment. Completing these activities will not mean that you have achieved a particular grade, but you will have carried out useful research or preparation that will be relevant when it comes to your final assignment.

In order for you to successfully complete the tasks in your assignments, it is important to check that you have met all of the Pass grading criteria. You can do this as you work your way through the assignment.

If you are hoping to gain a Merit or Distinction, you should also make sure that you present the information in your assignment in the style that is required by the relevant assessment criterion. For example, Merit criteria often require you to analyse whereas the Distinction criteria require you to evaluate.

The assignments set by your tutor will consist of a number of tasks designed to meet the criteria in the table. This is likely to consist of a mixture of written and practical assignments and include activities such as:

- examining the health, safety, risk and ethical considerations and assessment variables of fitness testing
- evaluating the use of testing protocols and recorded data in predicting sports performance
- evaluating the use and outcomes of field- and laboratory-based testing and formal research design, and the effectiveness of client profiles created using these protocols.

Assessment criteria

This table shows what you must do in order to achieve a **Pass**, **Merit** or **Distinction** grade, and where you can find activities to help you.

Pass	Merit	Distinction
Learning aim A Examine the preparation required prior to sport and exercise field- and laboratory-based testing		
A.P1 Explain the procedures that should be completed prior to laboratory testing. **Assessment practice 4.1**	**A.M1** Recommend pre-test procedures that can be used to ensure testing is conducted in a safe, valid, reliable and ethical way. **Assessment practice 4.1**	**A.D1** Evaluate pre-test procedures that can be used to ensure testing is conducted in a safe, valid, reliable and ethical way, justifying their choices. **Assessment practice 4.1**
A.P2 Explain how validity, reliability and ethical considerations impact on field and laboratory testing. **Assessment practice 4.1**		
Learning aim B Undertake anthropometry and somatotype testing procedures in sport		
B.P3 Explain how anthropometric assessment and somatotype testing protocols are used in laboratory-based testing. **Assessment practice 4.2**	**B.M2** Assess the suitability of anthropometric assessment and somatotype testing protocols that are used in laboratory-based testing. **Assessment practice 4.2**	**B.D2** Evaluate the use of anthropometric assessment and somatotype testing protocols, justifying how their own results could predict sport and exercise performance. **Assessment practice 4.2**
B.P4 Perform three contrasting anthropometric assessment protocols and a somatotype assessment protocol following the correct procedures, recording the results in an appropriate format. **Assessment practice 4.2**	**B.M3** Perform three contrasting anthropometric assessment protocols and a somatotype assessment protocol, calculating the test results with accuracy. **Assessment practice 4.2**	
Learning aim C Explore the use of field- and laboratory-based protocols in sport and exercise sciences		
C.P5 Conduct six field- and laboratory-based testing protocols following the correct procedures and record the results in an appropriate format. **Assessment practice 4.3**	**C.M4** Conduct six field- and laboratory-based testing protocols, ensuring the test results are calculated with accuracy. **Assessment practice 4.3**	**C.D3** Evaluate the data produced from six field- and laboratory-based testing protocols using statistical calculations, justifying the protocols used with reference to the prediction of sport and exercise performance. **Assessment practice 4.3**
Learning aim D Explore profiling of a sports performer following a practical research design using field- and laboratory-based testing		
D.P6 Create a profile for a selected sports performer following the implementation of a practical research design using appropriate laboratory- and field-based protocols. **Assessment practice 4.3**	**D.M5** Analyse the practical research design followed when creating the profile, making recommendations for future testing. **Assessment practice 4.3**	**D.D4** Evaluate the effectiveness of creating performer profiles from anthropometric assessment, somatotype testing and field- and laboratory-based testing protocols in the prediction of sport and exercise performance. **Assessment practice 4.3**

Getting started

Coaches need to be aware of the fitness levels of their athletes at all times and will adapt training programmes according to these, so that the athletes' goals are constantly being met. For example, before pre-season training footballers undergo a series of body weight measurements and tests. The results of these tests will determine training programmes. How can fitness testing and results/data help you to improve your sports performance?

A Examine the preparation required prior to sport and exercise field- and laboratory-based testing

Health and safety in a sport and exercise laboratory

In all laboratory and experimental methods, you need to be aware of and follow health and safety procedures and work to prevent any physical, psychological and/or social harm/injury to participants. As the tester, it is your responsibility to ensure this and to reduce or prevent risks and hazards throughout the whole process, from when you are preparing **protocols** through to carrying them out and after their completion.

The location where you are doing your testing will have a series of safety and emergency guidelines that you will need to be familiar with and follow. During testing you will need to make the participant aware of each of these (for example, fire alarm procedures). Factors affecting health and safety include:

- **risk assessment** – you will need to conduct a thorough risk assessment before carrying out any testing. Risk assessments are designed to reduce or remove the risk of harm or injury to participants. They require you to examine all equipment and facilities and identify and eliminate any hazards. If a risk cannot be eliminated and is considered medium or high risk, the test should not go ahead
- **accident forms** – if there are any accidents during the test you will need to complete an accident form. The Health and Safety Executive (HSE) requires all accidents to be formally recorded and reported. This is so the causes of the accident can be reviewed and acted on to prevent the accident occurring again
- **emergency and first aid procedures** – you should be aware of all emergency and first aid procedures in any location you are working in. This is to protect the health and safety of both your subjects and yourself. Make sure you know the first aid processes and that you have access to qualified first-aiders and a first aid box.

Key term

Protocol – a step-by-step process for conducting a specific test that can be followed every time it is carried out to ensure accurate and consistent results.

Safety tip

You must monitor subjects throughout the test to ensure their health and safety. If they report any pain or discomfort the test should be terminated immediately. Key indications for terminating a test include:

- chest pain and/or severe breathing difficulties
- signs of poor circulation (for example, pale, clammy skin)
- signs of poor coordination, confusion and/or dizziness.

Testing environment

When setting up your environment there are two key factors you must consider:

- hygiene – this is important for ensuring the participant's health, so take care of the condition of any surfaces you are using. All work surfaces must be cleaned thoroughly before use and after testing each participant. This will prevent both cross-contamination (any infections being passed from one participant to another) and test results being affected by anything left behind by the previous participant
- stable conditions – it is important to have a constant temperature in the room, and that the room is kept relatively quiet and that it is somewhere you are unlikely to be disturbed. This is because variations in temperature and noise will have an impact on your test results.

Equipment preparation and safety

All equipment must be checked to make sure it is operating correctly, is in good condition (with regular maintenance checks) and has undergone thorough cleaning to ensure it is hygienic.

Make sure all equipment is correctly calibrated. Incorrect calibration of equipment will lead to inaccurate, and therefore invalid, results. Carefully check (and if necessary adjust) any equipment to ensure its accuracy. Compare readings against a recognised standard, such as the manual provided by the manufacturer.

Any equipment used must be fit for purpose (in other words, suitable for testing what you are aiming to test).

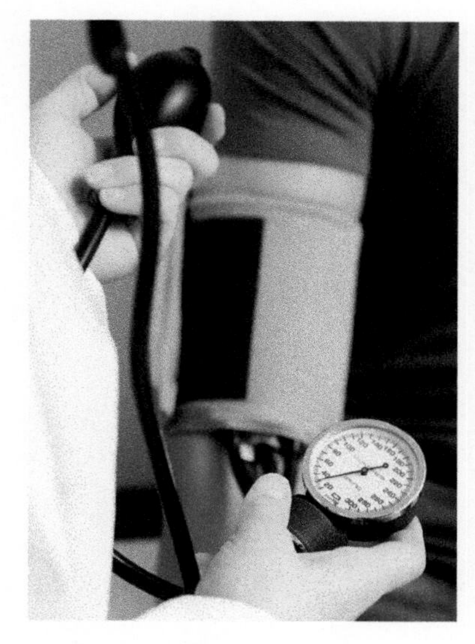

▸ Taking the participant's blood pressure is part of the pre-test procedure

Testing questionnaires

Before starting testing, it is important to collect appropriate information about your client through an efficient screening process. The information should include lifestyle information, their medical history and their physical activity history. Gathering this information allows you to check the participant can take part without putting themselves at risk and assess their suitability for testing. If there is any doubt about the participant's ability to take part, the tests should not go ahead.

Subject preparation

When preparing subjects for testing you should carry out some essential pre-test health-check measures. These measures include recording the participant's height and weight, blood pressure, heart rate, body mass index (BMI) and waist-to-hip ratio.

The subject should also be asked to change into clothing appropriate for the tests.

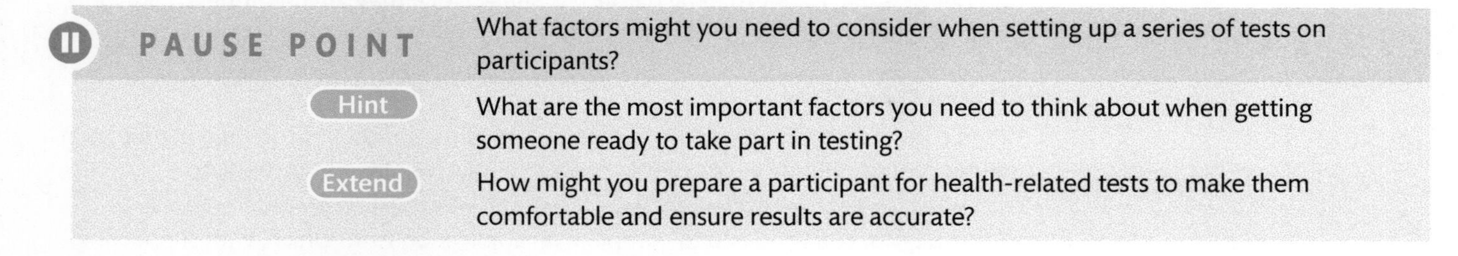

PAUSE POINT What factors might you need to consider when setting up a series of tests on participants?

Hint What are the most important factors you need to think about when getting someone ready to take part in testing?

Extend How might you prepare a participant for health-related tests to make them comfortable and ensure results are accurate?

Ethical considerations when conducting sport and exercise testing

When working with participants, you must ensure the highest standards of ethical conduct are maintained at all times. Gaining informed consent from your participants is just the first key part of establishing good ethical practice early in your testing.

Informed consent

Before beginning any testing you need to gain the participant's permission to take part. All subjects must complete clear documentary evidence of their informed consent: this requires all participants to have a clear understanding of what the test will involve and what is being asked of them before signing. You will need to ensure that the consent form shows that participants understand:

- the test methodology and any risks associated with the test protocols
- they can ask questions at any time

- their confidentiality will be respected and maintained at all times
- they can withdraw their consent at any point, terminating the test(s).

Any form should end with a final statement of consent, signed by the subject (or a parent or guardian if the participant is a minor). This confirms that they are fully aware of the nature of the tests, their rights, any risks and benefits of the test, and that they have freely given their consent to participation. This should contain a subject disclaimer which indicates that the information they have provided is true and accurate to the best of their knowledge.

Discussion

Why is informed consent so important when participants take part in tests? Discuss in a group the possible consequences of not giving people all the information about the test in advance. What implications could this have for the participants, for you and for your test results?

Data security, storage and confidentiality

Many test results produce data that is private and sensitive to individuals. You need to guarantee that this data is safely stored and cannot be lost or mislaid. The Data Protection Act (1998) legally requires you to keep all personal data secure (in a locked filing cabinet or password protected database), and that only relevant data is kept. The participant must also be told in advance what data will be collected.

Data should be collected anonymously. This means that the name or identity of the person is not connected to the individual results that are stored, helping to maintain confidentiality. Participants should be referred to as 'Subject' (or similar) followed by a number or letter, rather than by name, e.g. *Subject 15* if they are the fifteenth person tested as part of a series.

Ethical clearance

When conducting research using human participants, particularly on higher education courses, you should be aware of protocols that may require you to apply to a committee to get ethical clearance for the study. This must be granted before any testing begins. You will need to complete an application form which, with supporting documentation, is sent for review by a panel of scientists. The forms should be detailed enough to help the board make a clear judgement, giving sufficient information so that they can evaluate any risks connected with the research.

Ethical clearance forms usually include:

- a full description of the study, including its title, purpose, proposed subjects (age, number, etc.) and the methodologies to be used
- details of how you will gain informed consent and how subjects can withdraw this at any time
- details of how confidentiality will be maintained.

After reviewing the application, the committee may:

- grant ethical clearance – you will need comply with all policies and procedures
- grant ethical clearance subject to minor amendments
- grant ethical clearance subject to major amendments – you may need to resubmit to the committee
- not grant ethical clearance – especially if any risks are high for a small benefit.

To meet ethical best practice for your test(s), you must complete an ethics form with the participants before you start testing. Explain the completion stages and all ethical policies to the participant beforehand. This ensures you and the participant are undertaking the test(s) according to appropriate guidelines and protocols and that this is guaranteed to be the case throughout the testing process.

Subject welfare

As we have already seen, subjects must be closely observed and monitored during the testing. Responsibility for ensuring the subject's welfare starts from first contact with them. Throughout the testing you are responsible for their safety and protection. Every participant will have their own individual needs and your testing protocols should be flexible enough to meet these, for example, to accommodate subject availability when timetabling tests. However, remember that different groups like the ones outlined below may need additional considerations to maintain their welfare.

- Children and young people – when working with children you will need to have had an enhanced **Disclosure and Barring Service (DBS)** check to confirm that you are cleared to work with children. You will then need to follow your setting's child protection policies to guarantee the child's well-being and safety throughout the test.
- Disability considerations – ensure that the testing protocols are inclusive and do not prevent anyone with a disability from taking part (where possible).
- Age group considerations – when working with older adults you may need to consider their general fitness level, including any mobility issues that may affect the extent to which they can take part in tests.

Key term

Disclosure and Barring Service (DBS) – an organisation that helps employers make safer recruitment decisions and prevents unsuitable people from working with vulnerable groups, including children.

Remember that any testing results you produce are confidential and subject to all non-disclosure legislation. If there is a specific health and safety issue you are unsure about, you can discuss the results with colleagues but you should maintain confidentiality.

Theory into practice

A fitness coach was asked to attend a training evening for a local athletics club to perform a series of health tests on the athletes aged 14–18 years. The tests included height and weight measurements, BMI, resting heart rate and blood pressure. Thirty athletes were tested in total, three of whom were under 16 years old.

- What questions should the coach have asked regarding subject welfare for the three under-16s prior to carrying out these tests?
- What certification should you have and present before working with any children?

Validity and reliability of testing protocols

When designing testing protocols, you should ensure you take into account validity and reliability. To help ensure validity and reliability:

- always follow the pre-test preparation procedures described earlier in this unit
- always use suitable equipment that has been correctly calibrated
- be familiar with its operation and the data it will produce
- accurately follow the set protocol for the test.

When conducting any test there will be variations in the data produced. There will be an acceptable range for these variations, and you will need to be familiar with these. Any results outside this acceptable range could indicate an incorrect test procedure or issues connected to the participant, such as lack of comfort or anxiety. This will reflect on the validity or reliability of the test.

Link

More information about validity and reliability can be found in *Unit 5: Applied Research Methods in Sport and Exercise Science*, pages 160–162.

Research

Where might you find out the acceptable ranges of variation for the testing procedures you may be required to undertake as a sports scientist? Select one test and research its acceptable ranges of variation.

Validity

The first important consideration is validity. Definitions of validity vary depending on the context.

- From a data collection perspective, validity is whether you are measuring what you intended to measure.
- From a data analysis perspective, it is the soundness of the interpretations of results of tests.
- Validity also means ensuring any conclusions drawn from data are correct.

For all tests and equipment you should understand the correct protocol to follow when carrying out your test(s) in order to make sure that your test results are valid.

Reliability

Reliability refers to the consistency or repeatability of a measure or test, or of its results. It is important to remember that reliability can be achieved without validity: you could set up a test incorrectly and get a consistent series of results. In this case, your work is reliable because the results were consistent and repeatable, but they were not valid as you did not set up the test correctly.

Certain factors can affect reliability. For example:

- errors can happen if researchers do not know how to use the equipment correctly
- if the equipment is poorly maintained or the wrong type of equipment is selected.

Test-retest reliability relates to doing the same test on different occasions and getting the same (or similar) results. An example of a test-retest reliability issue is the measurement of heart rate. Heart rate can be affected by different factors, such as temperature, time of day, diet, sleep patterns, physical activity levels and alcohol consumption. If you measured heart rate at the same time but on different days, you could get different measurements.

If you are using the same equipment, calibrated to the same consistency, in the same conditions, for carrying out an identical test with different participants, your results will be reliable and consistently accurate.

Key term

Testing variables - factors outside the testing protocol design that may change or influence testing data, for example, a high temperature could affect a participant's ability to perform in a test.

Testing variables

When carrying out tests there will be a number of **testing variables** you need to consider. You need to control these variables as much as possible to avoid affecting the validity and reliability of your results.

- Environmental conditions - you will need a constant temperature and relative quiet.
- Performer motivation and behaviour - participants must be relaxed and comfortable throughout the tests.
- Pre-test physical condition - ensure all participants arrive in plenty of time and are properly hydrated, have not consumed too much caffeine and no alcohol, and have not eaten within at least two hours.
- Protocol suitability - make sure the tests you are carrying out are relevant to the area being investigated.
- Growth and maturation - if you are testing children and young adults over a long period of time (months or even years), you will need to take into account changes and developments in their body over this time.

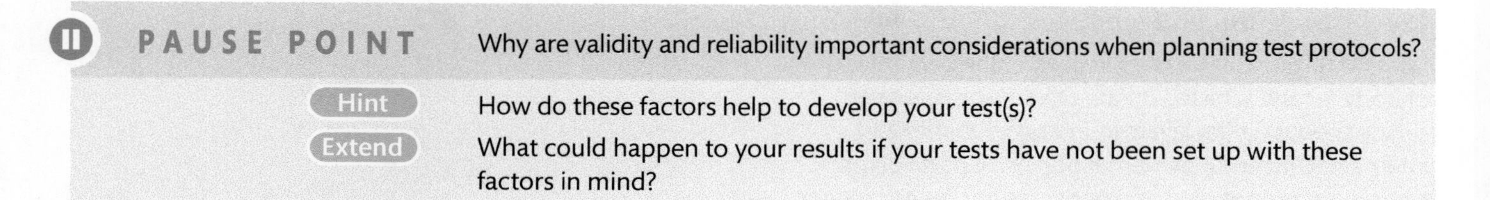

PAUSE POINT Why are validity and reliability important considerations when planning test protocols?

Hint How do these factors help to develop your test(s)?

Extend What could happen to your results if your tests have not been set up with these factors in mind?

Assessment practice 4.1

A.P1 A.P2 A.M1 A.D1

You are employed as a fitness instructor at a local gym. The gym manager has asked you to review the health and safety, risk and ethical considerations around fitness testing for participants at the gym. The manager has asked for a short written report which they can share with the rest of the team to help them plan their fitness testing in the gym's fitness testing suite. You will also need to think about the different testing variables and how they could affect results or influence the participant.

Your report should recommend and evaluate safe, ethical, valid and reliable pre-test procedures.

Plan

- What is the task? What is my report being asked to address? How can I address these issues?
- Do I understand the different stages of pre-test procedures?

Do

- Do I know how to judge best practice when following pre-test procedures?
- Do I understand safety and ethical issues involved in testing, and can I explain why they are important?

Review

- Can I explain my recommendations and justify my decisions?
- Can I explain what changes I would make if producing another similar report?

B Undertake anthropometry and somatotype testing procedures in sport

Once you have established the testing guidelines and pre-test procedures and established the health and safety of your clients and their ethical rights, you are in a position to undertake your tests. This learning aim looks at some common testing procedures that you may use.

Anthropometric assessment methods

Anthropometry is the scientific study of physical dimensions, proportions and composition of the human body, and the related variables that affect them. Anthropometric tests measure the height, weight and size of the parts of the human body to study and compare these proportions. Test results indicate the participant's level of health. For example, a high height to weight ratio indicates the participant may be overweight and may contribute towards possible health issues, as well as affecting their sports and exercise performance.

Certain body proportions are suitable for certain sports. You need to be aware of this when reviewing test results to ensure any analysis or advice you give is suitable for the participant's chosen sport. Body fat analysis in particular can have a significant impact upon the type and intensity of a participant's training programme, not forgetting the diet which will underpin this programme. For example, long-distance runners have a lower height to weight ratio so their somatotype and body fat measurements will be important when considering their training. Rugby players, however, can tolerate a higher proportion of height to weight ratio so their body fat levels are less important than their ability to move explosively.

Methods of measurement

Skinfold testing can be used to predict the percentage of body fat and is based on the relationship between subcutaneous fat (fat layers found beneath the skin), internal fat (fat around internal organs, in particular the heart, liver and kidneys) and body density (an estimate of body fat by measuring body mass ÷ body volume). There are several ways of carrying out this test.

Durnin and Womersley (1974) skinfold method

For males and females, skinfold measurements are taken on the following four sites (see Figure 4.1):

- **biceps** – a vertical fold on the anterior surface of the biceps muscle midway between the anterior axillary fold and the antecubital fossa
- **triceps** – a vertical fold on the back midline of the upper arm, over the triceps muscle, halfway between the acromion process (the bony process on the top of the shoulder) and the olecranon process (the bony process on the elbow). The arm should be held freely by the side of the body
- **subscapular** – a diagonal fold taken at a 45° angle 1–2 cm below the inferior angle of the scapulae (point of the shoulder blade)
- **suprailiac** – a diagonal fold above the crest of the ilium, taken in the anterior axillary line above the iliac crest (just above and 2–3 cm forward of the hip bone).

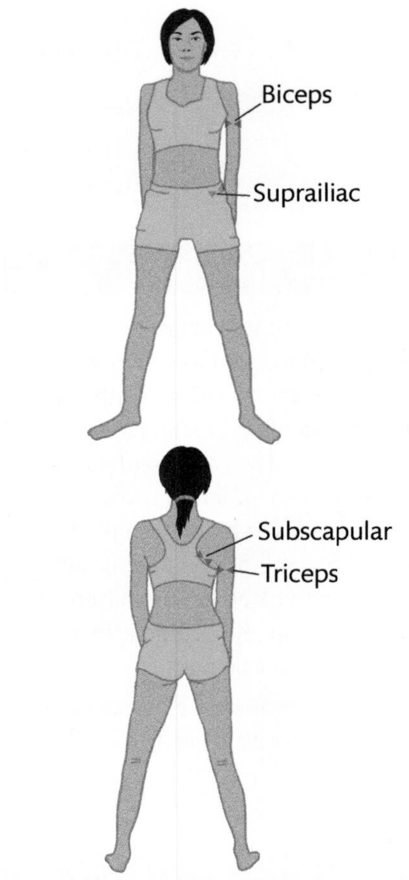

Figure 4.1: Skinfold testing: biceps, triceps, subscapular and suprailiac

Step by step: Durnin and Womersley (1974) skinfold method

9 Steps

Following a standard method like this will help ensure results are valid.

1. Measurements should be taken on dry skin on the right side of the body, unless the participant has a tattoo or deformity on the site location. Muscles should be kept relaxed during the test.
2. Mark each skinfold site with a pen and use a tape measure to find the midpoints.
3. Grasp the skinfold firmly between your thumb and index finger and gently pull away from the body. The skinfold should be grasped about 1 cm away from the site marked.
4. Place the skinfold callipers perpendicular to the fold, on the site marked, with the dial facing upwards.
5. Maintaining your grasp, place the callipers midway between the base and tip of the skinfold and allow the callipers to be fully released so that full tension is placed on the skinfold.
6. Read the dial of the skinfold callipers to the nearest 0.5 mm, 2 seconds after you have released the callipers. Make sure you continue to grasp the skinfold throughout testing.
7. Take a minimum of two measurements at each site. If repeated tests vary by more than 1 mm, repeat the measurement. Record each measurement as you take it.

8 If consecutive measurements become smaller, this means the fat is being compressed, leading to inaccurate results. If this happens, go to another site and return to the site to be tested later.

9 The final value is the average of the two readings (mm).

Using the Durnin and Womersley (1974) skinfold method

1 Add up the results for the four skinfolds (mm).
2 Calculate the body density according to gender using the following formulae:
   males (16–19 years)
   body density (d) = 1.162 – [(0.063) (∑ log of four skinfolds)]
   females (16–19 years)
   body density (d) = 1.1549 – [(0.0678) (∑ log of four skinfolds)]
3 Next, complete the following calculation for the prediction of percentage of body fat:
   $\left[\frac{4.57}{d} - 4.142\right] \times 100$ % body fat
4 Interpret the result against the norms shown in Table 4.1.

Table 4.1: Interpretation of percentage of body fat results

Rating	Males % body fat (16–29 years)	Females % body fat (16–29 years)
Very low fat	<7	<13
Slim	7–12	13–20
Acceptable	13–17	21–25
Overweight	18–28	26–32
Obese	28+	32+

Jackson and Pollock's (1978) three-site skinfold method for males

Male participants need skinfold results (mm) for the following three sites:

- **chest** – a diagonal fold, one half of the distance between the anterior auxiliary line and the nipple. (The anterior axillary line is the crease where the top of your arm, when hanging down, meets the chest.)
- **abdomen** – a vertical fold, 2 cm to the right side of the umbilicus (belly button)
- **thigh** – a vertical fold, on the front of the thigh, halfway between the hip joint and the middle of the knee cap. The leg needs to be straight and relaxed.

Jackson and Pollock's (1980) three-site skinfold method for females

Female participants will need skinfold results (mm) for the following three sites:

- **triceps** – a vertical fold on the back midline of the upper arm, over the triceps muscle, halfway between the acromion process (bony process on the top of the shoulder) and olecranon process (bony process on the elbow). The arm should be held freely by the side of the body
- **suprailiac** – a diagonal fold just above and 2–3 cm forward of the hip bone
- **thigh** – a vertical fold, on the front of the thigh, halfway between the hip joint and the middle of the knee cap. The leg needs to be straight and relaxed.

Using Jackson and Pollock's (1978, 1980) three-site skinfold method

1. Calculate body density (BD) using the Jackson and Pollock equation. This equation varies according to gender so use the internet to find the appropriate version for yourself.
2. Then predict percent body fat using the equation by Brozek *et al* (1963).

$$\left[\frac{4.57}{d} - 4.142\right] \times 100\% \text{ body fat}$$

Theory into practice

When taking skinfold measurements, the subject being measured should be standing up. With a partner, practise using both the Durnin and Womersley skinfold method and the Jackson and Pollock three-site skinfold method. How similar are the results? Did you find one method easier to calculate than the other?

Methods of interpreting body fat

Nomograms

You can use a nomogram (Wilmore, 1988) to predict per cent body fat (see Figure 4.2). In this method, circumferences are taken using a tape measure while the subject stands with feet slightly apart. Apply the tape measure direct to the skin, with no air space, placed horizontally all around the circumference. Read the measurement to the nearest 0.25 inch and repeat for reliability.

- Males need to measure lower abdominal circumference: take a horizontal measure at the level of the umbilicus (belly button).
- Females need to measure hip circumference: take a horizontal measure at the maximum circumference of the gluteal muscles (buttocks).

For males:

1. plot weight in lbs on the left-hand line
2. plot your lower abdominal circumference (girth) in inches on the right-hand line
3. using a sharpened pencil and ruler, join the two plots, which will cross over the per cent fat line to give a prediction of your percentage of body fat.

For females:

1. plot hip circumference in inches on the left-hand line
2. plot your height in inches on the right-hand line
3. using a sharpened pencil and ruler, join the two plots, which will cross over the per cent fat line to give a prediction of your percentage of body fat.

Siri equation

The Siri equation states that the body is made up of two components:

- fat mass (the total body fat of an individual): density = 0.9 g per cm^3
- fat-free mass (bone, water, muscle tissue, etc.): density = 1.1 g per cm^3

Density is calculated using the the following equation:.

density = (fat mass + fat-free mass) / volume.

The higher the level of fat-free mass, the more weight the participant is likely to have.

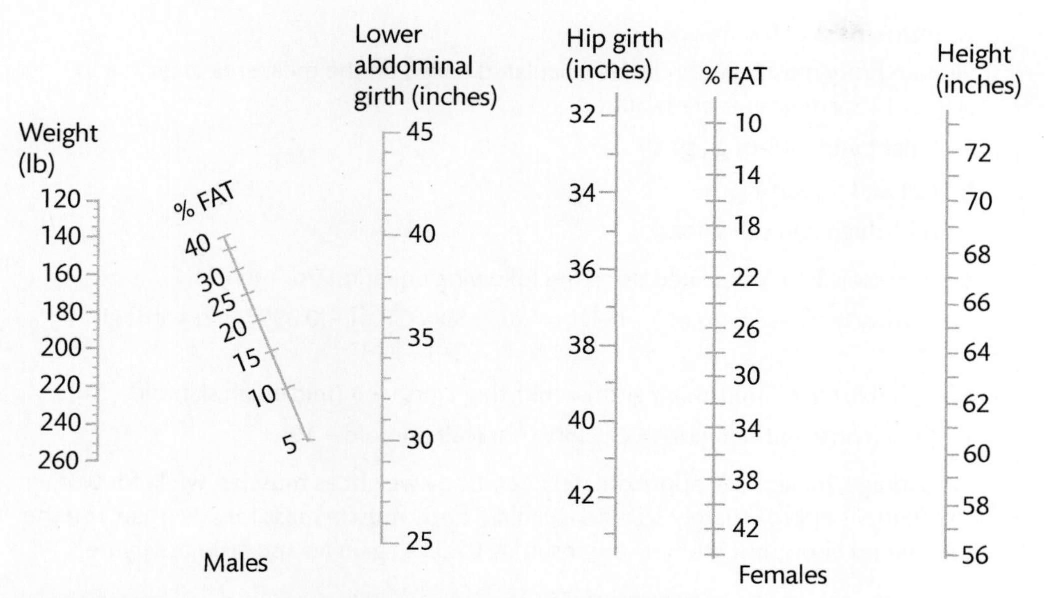

Figure 4.2: Nomogram for predicting body fat in males and females

Sloan equation

The Sloan equation gives a value for body density from skinfold test results:

- For males:

  body density = 1.1043 – (0.001327 × thigh skinfold in mm) – (0.00131 × subscapular skinfold in mm)

- For females:

  body density = 1.0764 – (0.0008 × iliac crest skinfold in mm) – (0.00088 × triceps skinfold in mm)

Body mass measures

Body mass index (BMI)

BMI is a measure of body composition in kg/m^2 and can help determine whether someone is underweight, optimal weight or overweight. As it does not take into account frame size or muscle mass, it is only an estimate. Research shows there is a significant relationship between high BMI and cardiovascular disease and diabetes.

Measure the individual's body weight (kg) and height in metres, and calculate the BMI as kg/m^2.

- For women, a desirable BMI is 21–23 kg/m^2.
- For men, a desirable BMI is 22–24 kg/m^2.

Risk of cardiovascular disease increases sharply at a BMI of 27.8 kg/m^2 for men and 27.3 kg/m^2 for women.

Ponderal index

This is a measure of a person's leanness, based on the relationship between mass and height.

$$PI = \frac{\text{mass (kg)}}{\text{height}^3\text{ (m)}}$$

The ponderal index is similar to the body mass index, except the height is cubed rather than squared.

Muscle-mass calculations

Human body muscle mass can be calculated based on the measures of girth and skinfolds. Six measures are required:

- height and mid-thigh **girth**
- calf and forearm girth
- mid-thigh and calf skinfold.

Key term

Girth – the measurement around the middle of a limb or muscle area.

Body mass is then calculated using the following equation (for men):

$$\text{muscle mass (in grams)} = \text{height} \times ([0.0553 \times CTG^2] + [0.0987 \times \text{forearm girth}^2] + [0.0331 \times CCG^2]) - 2445$$

- CTG (corrected mid-thigh girth) = mid-thigh girth – π (mid-thigh skinfold ÷ 10)
- CCG (corrected calf girth) = calf girth – π (calf skinfold ÷ 10)

On average, males have approximately 42% body weight as muscles, while for women this figure is approximately 35%. To calculate body muscle mass for a woman, use the calculation above but multiply the result by 0.833 to gain an approximate figure.

Bioelectrical impedance analysis (BIA)

Bioelectrical impedance analysis (BIA) predicts the percentage of body fat using a small electrical current. It is based on the fact that fat-free mass conducts electricity, while fat mass does not. The higher the body's resistance to a weak electrical current (bioelectrical impedance), the higher the percentage of body fat.

Hydration levels can affect validity of test results, so the subject should not:

- exercise for 12 hours prior to the test
- drink or eat within 4 hours of the test
- urinate 15 to 30 minutes before conducting the test.

1. The subject should lie down. Place the electrodes on the right side wrist, hand, ankle and foot.
2. Attach the cable leads (crocodile clips) to the exposed tabs on the electrodes.
3. Enter data into the BIA machine (for example, age, gender, height, weight and activity level). The subject should lie still as the current passes through their body.

Hydrodensitometry

Hydrodensitometry or underwater weighing is the benchmark for predicting percentage of body fat, carried out in an underwater weighing tank. Body volume is measured via the underwater weight of the body, based on the principle that weight under water is directly proportional to the volume of water displaced by body volume.

1. The subject must urinate and eliminate as much gas and faeces as possible before testing.
2. Water temperature in the tank should be 34°C to 36°C.
3. The subject sits on the chair in the tank (a belt can be placed around the waist to keep position).
4. Once submerged under water, the subject must exhale as fully as possible. Repeat the test three times for reliability.
5. Net underwater weight is calculated by subtracting the weight of the chair and any equipment and clothing from the gross underwater weight. It is corrected for residual volume of air trapped in the lungs and in the gastrointestinal tract (approximately 100 ml).
6. Body density is calculated by dividing body weight by body volume, and converted to per cent body fat by using an appropriate equation, (e.g. Brozek *et al*, 1963).

▶ Hydrodensitometry tests are one way of calculating body fat

Waist-to-hip ratio

The waist-to-hip ratio can determine levels of obesity and those at risk of heart disease. Use a tape measure placed firmly against the individual's skin to measure the waist circumference in centimetres at the narrowest level of the torso. Next, measure the hips by placing the tape measure at the maximum circumference of the buttocks. Make sure the tape measure is level when taking measurements. Divide the waist measurement (cm) by the hip measurement (cm) to obtain the waist-to-hip ratio.

PAUSE POINT How could a participant's diet or hydration levels influence anthropometric testing data?

Hint Remember both muscle and fat mass are composed of water and nutrients.

Extend How might dehydration influence anthropometric testing data?

Somatotype profiling

Somatotyping is a method used to describe human physique and to classify an individual's body type. It is described using three components:

- **endomorphy** – 'fatness' component. These individuals have a predominance of the abdomen over the thorax, high square shoulders and a short neck
- **mesomorphy** – a body that is heavily muscled. These individuals have a large thorax, a relatively slender waist and broad shoulders with well-toned abdominal muscles
- **ectomorphy** – 'leanness' component. These individuals have small bones and poor muscle development, possibly with drooping shoulders. Their abdomen and lumbar curve are flat, they have narrow shoulders and a lack of muscle bulk.

Each of these components is represented as a number. This number describes the value of a particular component of physique. The components are always recorded in the order above.

A person's body weight depends on their body type, gender and age along with their height, bone structure and muscle size. When considering somatotyping it is also wise to consult ideal height and weight norms for both males and females. A combination of these factors will influence their participation and performance in sport.

Heath-Carter anthropometric somatotype

A person's somatotype can be measured using Heath-Carter's (1967) anthropometric somatotype rating form. The three-component rating is plotted on a two-dimensional somatochart, and results interpreted according to the somatotype categories. Complete the personal data section at the top of the somatotype rating form (see Figure 4.3).

Determining endomorphy (first component)

1. Use skinfold callipers to measure the triceps, subscapular and suprailiac (supraspinale) skinfolds (mm).
2. Add up the total skinfolds (mm) and enter in the 'sum 3 skinfolds' box on the rating form. Correct this value for height by multiplying this sum by 170.18/height (cm).
3. Circle the closest value to this on the rating form and the endomorphy rating (first component).
4. You will also need to measure the calf skinfold (mm), for the second component. While the participant is seated, take a vertical fold at the maximum circumference of the calf muscle, closest to the midline.

Heath-Carter Somatotype rating form

Name... Age............... Sex: M / F No.............

Occupation... Ethnic group................. Date...........

Project.. Measured by ....

Skinfolds (mm)		Sum 3 skinfolds (mm)																							
Triceps = ☐	Upper limit	10.9	14.9	18.9	22.9	26.9	31.2	35.8	40.7	46.2	52.2	58.7	65.7	73.2	81.2	89.7	98.9	108.9	119.7	131.2	143.7	157.2	171.9	187.9	204.0
Subscapular = ☐	Mid-point	9.0	13.0	17.0	21.0	25.0	29.0	33.5	38.0	43.5	49.0	55.5	62.0	69.5	77.0	85.5	94.0	104.0	114.0	125.5	137.0	150.5	164.0	180.0	196.0
Supraspinale = ☐	Lower limit	7.0	11.0	15.0	19.0	23.0	27.0	31.3	35.9	40.8	46.3	52.3	58.8	65.8	73.3	81.3	89.8	99.0	109.0	119.8	131.3	143.8	157.3	172.0	188.0

Sum 3 skinfolds = ☐ × (170.18/ht) = mm (height corrected skinfolds)

Calf =

Endomorphy	1	1 ½	2	2 ½	3	3 ½	4	4 ½	5	5 ½	6	6 ½	7	7 ½	8	8 ½	9	9 ½	10	10 ½	11	11 ½	12

	Values																							
Height (cm) ☐	139.7	143.5	147.3	151.1	154.9	158.8	162.6	166.4	170.2	174.0	177.8	181.6	185.4	189.2	193.0	196.9	200.3	204.5	208.3	212.1	215.9	219.7	223.5	227.3
Humerus width (cm) ☐	5.19	5.34	5.49	5.64	5.78	5.93	6.07	6.22	6.37	6.51	6.65	6.80	6.95	7.09	7.24	7.38	7.53	7.67	7.82	7.97	8.11	8.25	8.40	8.55
Femur width (cm) ☐	7.41	7.62	7.83	8.04	8.24	8.45	8.66	8.87	9.08	9.28	9.49	9.70	9.91	10.12	10.33	10.53	10.74	10.95	11.16	11.36	11.57	11.78	11.99	12.21
Biceps girth ☐ – T* ☐	23.7	24.4	25.0	25.7	26.3	27.0	27.7	28.3	29.0	29.7	30.3	31.0	31.6	32.2	33.0	33.6	34.3	35.0	35.6	36.3	37.0	37.6	38.3	39.0
Calf girth ☐ – C⁺ ☐	27.7	28.5	29.3	30.1	30.8	31.6	32.4	33.2	33.9	34.7	35.5	36.3	37.1	37.8	38.6	39.4	40.2	41.0	41.7	42.5	43.3	44.1	44.9	45.6

Mesomorphy	½	1	1 ½	2	2 ½	3	3 ½	4	4 ½	5	5 ½	6	6 ½	7	7 ½	8	8 ½	9

Weight (kg) = ☐

$\frac{\text{Height}}{3\sqrt{\text{Weight}}}$ = ☐

Upper limit	39.65	40.74	41.43	42.13	42.82	43.48	44.18	44.18	45.53	46.23	46.92	47.58	48.25	48.94	49.63	50.33	50.99	51.68
Mid-point	and	40.20	41.09	41.79	42.48	43.14	43.84	44.50	45.19	45.89	46.32	47.24	47.94	48.60	49.29	49.99	50.68	51.34
Lower limit	below	39.66	40.75	41.44	42.14	42.83	43.49	44.19	44.85	45.54	46.24	46.93	47.59	48.26	48.95	49.64	50.34	51.00
Ectomorphy	½	1	1 ½	2	2 ½	3	3 ½	4	4 ½	5	5 ½	6	6 ½	7	7 ½	8	8 ½	9

	Endomorphy	Mesomorphy	Ectomorphy	By:...
Anthropometric somatotype				Rater:..

* Biceps girth in cm corrected for fat by subtracting triceps skinfold value expressed in cm
⁺Calf girth in cm corrected for fat by subtracting radial calf skinfold value expressed in cm

Figure 4.3: Heath-Carter's (1967) anthropometric somatotype rating form

Determining mesomorphy (second component)

1. Record height in cm. Place an arrow above the column containing the closest value to the individual's height.
2. Use bone diameter callipers to measure the width of the humerus and femur (cm) and circle the closest values to these in the relevant rows on the rating form.
   - Humerus width: the width between the lateral and medial epicondyles of the humerus, measured with the elbow bent.
   - Femur width: the width between the lateral and medial condyle of the femur, measured with the individual seated.
3. Measure the biceps circumference (girth) and calf circumference (girth) (cm).
   - Biceps circumference: with the arm to the side of the body, take a horizontal measure midway between the acromion and olecranon processes.
   - Calf circumference: with the individual standing, feet 20 cm apart, take a horizontal measure at the maximum circumference of the calf muscle between the knee and the ankle.
4. Convert the triceps skinfold to cm and subtract this from the biceps circumference. Circle the closest value to this corrected measurement on the rating form.
5. Convert the calf skinfold to cm and subtract this from the calf circumference. Circle the closest value to this corrected measurement on the rating form.
6. Using the height column as the starting point (see point 1), count the number of column deviations from the height column. Each deviation to the right on the rating form counts as +0.5, each deviation to the left counts as −0.5. Values circled directly next to the height column count as 0 deviations. Sum the deviations and divide this figure by 4, which gives the average deviation from the height column.
7. Add 4 to the average deviation from the height column, and circle the closest value to this on the rating form. This is the mesomorphy rating (second component).

Determining ectomorphy (third component) result

1. Use this calculation to work out the ponderal index:

$$\frac{\text{height}}{\sqrt[3]{\text{weight}}}$$

2. Circle the closest value to this on the rating form, which gives the ectomorphy rating (third component).

Somatotype profiling

You can use your results from the test to plot a somatotype rating on the somatochart (see Figure 4.4) and interpret the results.

The somatochart on page 138 shows 13 somatotype categories.

1. **Central type:** no component differs by more than one unit from the other two.
2. **Balanced endomorph:** endomorphy is dominant and mesomorphy and ectomorphy are equal (or do not differ by more than one-half unit).
3. **Mesomorphic endomorph:** endomorphy is dominant and mesomorphy is greater than ectomorphy.
4. **Mesomorph–endomorph:** endomorphy and mesomorphy are equal (or do not differ by more than one half-unit), and ectomorphy is smaller.
5. **Endomorphic mesomorph:** mesomorphy is dominant and endomorphy is greater than ectomorphy.
6. **Balanced mesomorph:** mesomorphy is dominant and endomorphy and ectomorphy are equal (or do not differ by more than one-half unit).
7. **Ectomorphic mesomorph:** mesomorphy is dominant and ectomorphy is greater than endomorphy.
8. **Mesomorph–ectomorph:** mesomorphy and ectomorphy are equal (or do not differ by more than one-half unit), and endomorphy is smaller.
9. **Mesomorphic ectomorph:** ectomorphy is dominant and mesomorphy is greater than endomorphy.
10. **Balanced ectomorph:** ectomorphy is dominant and endomorphy and mesomorphy are equal (or do not differ by more than one-half unit).
11. **Endomorphic ectomorph:** ectomorphy is dominant and endomorphy is greater than mesomorphy.
12. **Endomorph–ectomorph:** endomorphy and ectomorphy are equal (or do not differ by more than one-half unit) and mesomorphy is lower.
13. **Ectomorphic endomorph:** endomorphy is dominant and ectomorphy is greater than mesomorphy.

When reviewing results for medical and health implications, remember endomorphs are more vulnerable to diabetes, heart conditions and blood pressure conditions, due to the comparative weight differential, than mesomorphs and ectomorphs.

Theory into practice

Work out your own somatotype profile. Considering the sports you take part in, how useful and accurate do you think it is?

Performer profiling

Physique is a major determinant of athletic performance, but physique in turn is mainly determined by genetics – the skeleton's shape and size are fixed. Performance variables such as aerobic and anaerobic capacity are also influenced by physique. A person can modify their body fat and muscle mass, but only within their genetic limits.

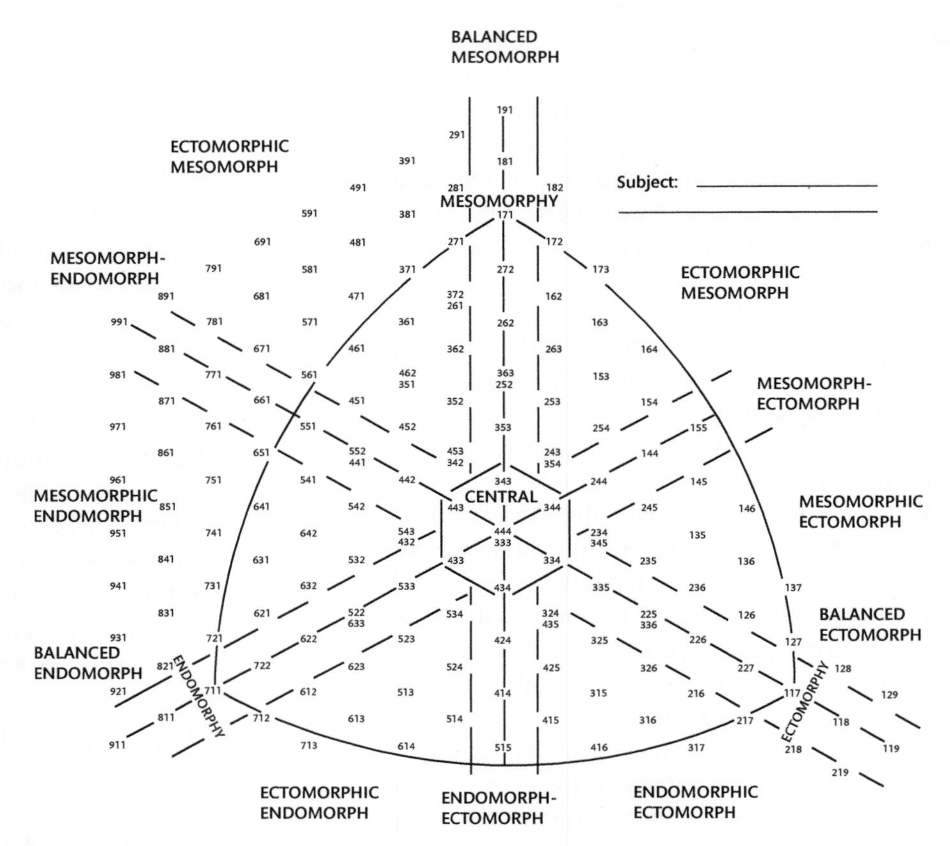

Figure 4.4: Heath-Carter's somatotype chart

Footballers Cristiano Ronaldo (pictured) and Lionel Messi have very different somatotype profiles but both are very successful

Compared to the normal population, elite sports performers actually have a limited range of physiques. For example, sprinters, shot putters and javelin throwers have more massive musculature (mesomorphy), while long-distance runners are mostly leaner body types (ectomorphy).

Using results to advise on sporting improvements

Review each component individually, highlighting strengths and areas where the individual could improve. For example, results might show the individual needs to reduce their skinfolds - training to do this could be suggested. Areas for improvement will depend on individual personal goals, their sport or experience, etc.

Plot the individual's three-figure somatotype rating on a somatochart, comparing this to published somatotyping data. You can use this to guide any recommendations. For example, a male county-level basketball player, with a mesomorphy rating of 2, could aim to increase mesomorphy rating to 4.

Justify strengths and areas for improvement through research, as this will help you to evaluate the information you have gained and to form conclusions. There must be a strong rationale for all your suggested improvements.

PAUSE POINT Are somatotypes blueprints for perfect models in a given sport?

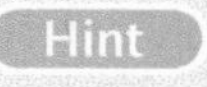

Hint Is body shape a key driver for sporting success?

Extend Lionel Messi is short and has a slight build. His rival Cristiano Ronaldo is tall and muscular. What do these very successful football players with very different body types tell us about somatotyping?

Assessment practice 4.2

B.P3 B.P4 B.M2 B.M3 B.D2

In your capacity as a fitness instructor, your gym manager has asked you to design your own anthropometric and somatotype testing programme for clients. This should include a series of anthropometric tests assessing:

- height and weight
- body mass and body fat.

Your testing programme should address the correct protocols and recording of data which will then be used to inform the participant of their likely future training needs. You should also construct a somatotype profile for the participant with additional feedback about future training needs.

Your report on this should evaluate the protocols used and data collected, and be supported by observation or video evidence of the fitness tests being administered.

Plan

- Do I understand what the aims and objectives of my testing programme will be?
- Do I know what pre-test preparation I need to undertake to ensure my results will be reliable and valid?

Do

- Am I using the best methods to record my data and analyse my results?
- Have I considered all health and safety issues when designing my testing protocols?

Review

- Do my conclusions explain and evaluate the testing protocols used?
- Have I reviewed my results and testing process and identified improvements for the future?

C Explore the use of field- and laboratory-based protocols in sport and exercise sciences

Most athletes undergo laboratory- or field-based fitness tests such as the ones outlined in the following section as a regular part of their sporting career. These tests will monitor quantitative performance levels of individual athletes and help identify areas for improvement and aid coaches with long-term planning and goal-setting.

Remember to follow all the usual pre-testing steps. Some of these fitness tests may not be suitable for all age groups, for example children or older adults. Always review the testing protocols to ensure any test is appropriate for the age group you are working with. For team sports, every team member would undertake the same tests in order to collect valid and reliable data and allow comparisons.

Laboratory-based testing protocols

Astrand-Rhyming cycle ergometer test

The Astrand-Rhyming test is a sub-maximal aerobic fitness test. It measures a participant's aerobic capacity (VO_2 max). Wearing a heart rate monitor, participants peddle on the cycle ergometer at a constant workload for 7 minutes. During this time heart rate is measured every minute.

The workload is measured in kilograms per minute. The equations for calculating VO_2max are:

females: $$VO_2 \text{ max} = \frac{0.00193 \times (\text{workload (W)} + 0.326)}{(0.769 \times [\text{heart rate of steady state} - 56.1]) \times 100}$$

males: $$VO_2 \text{ max} = \frac{0.00212 \times (\text{workload (W)} + 0.299)}{(0.769 \times [\text{heart rate of steady state} - 48.5]) \times 100}$$

'Heart rate of steady state' is the steady state heart rate after 6 minutes of exercise. After this, and cycling at a constant workload, the heart rate should level out.

30-second Wingate cycle test

The Wingate cycle test predicts the anaerobic power of the quadriceps muscle groups using a 30 second all-out maximal sprint on a mechanically-braked cycle ergometer.

1 Measure the participant's body weight in kg. To calculate the weight to add to the cycle ergometer basket, use this formula:

   weight to add to basket = body weight × 0.075 minus 1 kg for the basket weight

2 The participant wears a heart rate monitor for the warm-up and cycles between 2–4 minutes at an intensity to cause the heart to beat at 150–160 bpm. Include two or three all-out bursts of cycling for 4–8 seconds each, then rest for approximately 3–5 minutes while stretching major muscle groups.
3 On command from the timer, the participant pedals as fast as possible to overcome the flywheel inertia. The weight will then be lowered onto the basket.
4 When the final load has been added to the basket, timing should commence. The participant should pedal as fast as possible for 30 seconds (motivation may be required here).
5 Note the revolutions per minute (RPM) achieved for each 5 second period.
6 As a cool-down, the participant should continue cycling with no load, for 2–3 minutes after the test. Participants should be helped to get off the bike and then assume the recovery position.

Safety tip

This is an extremely arduous test, requiring an all-out maximal effort. Be aware that such effort may cause participants to faint or be sick following the test. Ensure that procedures are in place should this happen.

Vertical jump test

This is a test of the anaerobic power of the quadriceps muscle group using a standard vertical jump board.

1 The participant should stand with their dominant side against the board, feet together, and reach up as high as possible to record their standing reach height.
2 With only one dip of the arms and knees permitted, they should make the jump while simultaneously touching the vertical jump board at the peak of their jump.
3 Perform three times, recording the height of each jump.

Results of the test can be interpreted using Table 4.2.

Table 4.2: Interpretation of vertical jump test results for men and women aged 16 to 19

Gender	Excellent	Above average	Average	Below average	Poor
Male	>65 cm	50–65 cm	40–49 cm	30–39 cm	<30 cm
Female	>58 cm	47–58 cm	36–46 cm	26–35 cm	<26 cm

1RM test

This tests the dynamic strength of the bench pressing pectoral muscles of the chest.

1 After a warm-up, determine a comfortable weight to start to press.
2 The participant should breathe out on exertion, as holding breath will increase blood pressure.
3 Allow a 2 minute rest between trials before increasing the weight by 2.5–5 kg, until a maximum weight is successfully lifted. This is recorded as the participant's 1RM.
4 Divide the 1RM result (kg) by the participant's body weight in kg. Results of the test can be interpreted using Table 4.3.

▶ **Table 4.3:** Interpreting the results of the bench press 1RM test

Rating	Males (1RM kg/kg body weight)	Females (1RM kg/kg body weight)
Excellent	>1.26	>0.78
Good	1.17–1.25	0.72–0.77
Average	0.97–1.16	0.59–0.71
Fair	0.88–0.96	0.53–0.58
Poor	<0.87	<0.52

Back dynamometer test

This measures the static strength of the lower back muscles. A back dynamometer is a spring device attached to a long chain and dual handgrip. As force is applied, the spring is compressed and this moves the dynamometer needle, indicating the result.

1. The participant should stand with their feet shoulder width apart on top of the dynamometer, holding the grip handle so the chain is taught.
2. They should pull as hard as they can on the handle for 5 seconds, keeping their back straight.
3. Carry out three trials with 1 minute rest between trials, recording the best result.

Grip dynamometer test

This measures the static strength of the power grip-squeezing muscles, using the whole hand as a vice. As force is applied to the dynamometer, the spring is compressed, moving the needle.

1. The participant should stand with their arms by the side of their body, holding the dynamometer parallel to the side of their body with the dial/display facing away from them.
2. They should squeeze as hard as possible for 5 seconds, without moving their arm.
3. Carry out three trials on each hand, with a 1 minute rest between trials and record their best result. Use Table 4.4 to interpret the results.

Theory into practice

Experiment with the grip dynamometer test by carrying the test out on your dominant hand and your non-dominant hand. Compare the results to find out how great the difference might be.

▶ **Table 4.4:** Interpreting the results of the grip dynamometer test

Rating	Males aged 15–19 (kg)	Females aged 15–19 (kg)
Excellent	52+	32+
Good	47–51	28–31
Average	44–46	25–27
Below average	39–43	20–24
Poor	<39	<20

One-minute press-up test

This test is used to assess the endurance of the muscles of the upper body.

1. The participant positions themself in press-up position, with hands shoulder width apart, arms fully extended and straight legs supported on toes. The body is lowered until the elbows are at 90° away from the torso.
2. Return to the starting position, with arms fully extended. This action should be continuous with no rests.
3. The total number of press-ups is recorded for 1 minute. Use Table 4.5 to interpret the results.

Table 4.5: Interpretation of results from the one-minute press-up test

Rating	Males	Females
Excellent	45+	34+
Good	35–44	17–33
Average	20–34	6–16
Poor	<19	<5

One-minute sit-up test

This test assesses the endurance and development of the abdominal muscles.

1. The participant lies on a mat with knees bent and feet flat on the floor, arms folded across the body.
2. The participant raises themselves up to a 90° position and then returns to the floor.
3. The total number of sit-ups is recorded for 1 minute. Use Table 4.6 to interpret the results.

Table 4.6: Interpretation of results from the one-minute sit-up test

Rating	Males	Females
Excellent	49–59	42–54
Good	43–48	36–41
Above average	39–42	32–35
Average	35–38	28–31
Below average	31–34	24–27
Poor	25–30	18–23
Very poor	11–24	3–17

Static flexibility testing

There are a large number of static flexibility tests for different major joints in the body. This shoulder flexibility test assesses the range of motion in the upper arm. You will need a rope and tape measure.

1. The participant should grasp the rope with their hands 10 cm apart.
2. They then extend both arms in front of their chest. Next, rotate the arms overhead and down behind the neck.
3. As they meet resistance they should allow the hands to slide along the rope, moving further apart. They should stop when the rope touches the back.
4. Return the arms to the starting position, not allowing the hands to move on the rope.
5. Measure the distance between the two thumbs on the rope, to the nearest centimetre.
6. Measure shoulder width from deltoid to deltoid. Subtract the shoulder measurement from the rope measurement. Use Table 4.7 to interpret the results.

Table 4.7: Interpretation of results from the shoulder flexibility test

Rating	Males	Females
Excellent	Less than 12 cm	Less than 10 cm
Good	12–20 cm	10–18 cm
Average	21–30 cm	19–26 cm
Fair	31–40 cm	27–35 cm
Poor	More than 40 cm	More than 35 cm

Sit-and-reach test

This test is an indirect measure of static flexibility. It measures trunk forward flexion, hamstring, hip and lower back range of motion. A standard sit and reach box is used.

1. The participant sits with heels placed against the edge of the sit and reach box, legs flat on the floor.
2. They should place one hand on top of the other and reach forward slowly. Their fingertips should be in contact with the measuring portion of the sit and reach box. As participants reach forward, they should drop their head between their arms and breathe out as they push forward.
3. The best of three trials should be recorded. Use Table 4.8 to interpret the results.

Table 4.8: Interpreting the results of the sit-and-reach test

Rating	Males (cm)	Females (cm)
Excellent	>25	>20
Very good	17–25	17–20
Good	15–16	16
Average	14	15
Poor	9–13	10–14
Very poor	<9	<10

Research

There are many other types of static flexibility test, in addition to the shoulder flexibility test, for every major joint in the body, for example, ankle, hip, etc. Research these different types of test in small groups, each researching a different test, prepare a short report on your test to share with the rest of the group.

Goniometer testing

A goniometer is used to measure the range of motion of various joints in the body. It can be used for measuring flexibility of joints and is often used by physiotherapists and sports scientists. It is essentially two rulers on a fulcrum that can be used to measure a joint.

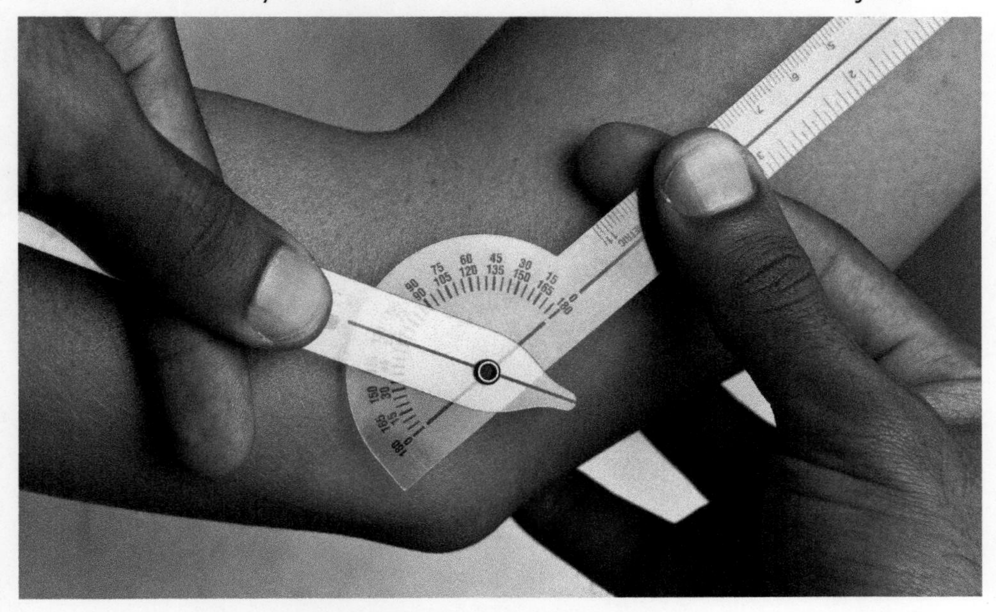

Goniometers can be used to measure the range of motion at a joint

Field-based testing protocols

Multi-stage fitness test

This test is used to predict aerobic fitness level and is often performed to pre-recorded audio in a sports hall, using two lines or cones 20 metres apart.

1. After a short warm-up, the participants line up on the start line and run to the other line after the triple bleep. They must reach the opposite line before the single bleep that determines each shuttle run. Participants should make sure they do not get ahead of the bleep.
2. The bleeps get closer and closer together, meaning participants need to increase their pace throughout.
3. A spotter checks that each line is reached in time. Participants continue running until physically exhausted and they fail to reach the line in time.
4. Use Table 4.9 to predict maximum oxygen uptake (ml/kg/min) and Table 4.10 to interpret the maximum oxygen update result.

Table 4.9: Predicted maximum oxygen uptake values for the multi-stage fitness test (ml/kg/min)

Level	Shuttle	VO_2 max	Level	Shuttle	VO_2 max	Level	Shuttle	VO_2 max	Level	Shuttle	VO_2 max
4	2	26.8	10	2	47.4	15	2	64.6	19	2	78.3
4	4	27.6	10	4	48.0	15	4	65.1	19	4	78.8
4	6	28.3	10	6	48.7	15	6	65.6	19	6	79.2
4	9	29.5	10	8	49.3	15	8	66.2	19	8	79.7
5	2	30.2	10	11	50.2	15	10	66.7	19	10	80.2
5	4	31.0	11	2	50.8	15	13	67.5	19	12	80.6
5	6	31.8	11	4	51.4	16	2	68.0	19	15	81.3
5	9	32.9	11	6	51.9	16	4	68.5	20	2	81.8
6	2	33.6	11	8	52.5	16	6	69.0	20	4	82.2
6	4	34.3	11	10	53.1	16	8	69.5	20	6	82.6
6	6	35.0	11	12	53.7	16	10	69.9	20	8	83.0
6	8	35.7	12	2	54.3	16	12	70.5	20	10	83.5
6	10	36.4	12	4	54.8	16	14	70.9	20	12	83.9
7	2	37.1	12	6	55.4	17	2	71.4	20	14	84.3
7	4	37.8	12	8	56.0	17	4	71.9	20	16	84.8
7	6	38.5	12	10	56.5	17	6	72.4	21	2	85.2
7	8	39.2	12	12	57.1	17	8	72.9	21	4	85.6
7	10	39.9	13	2	57.6	17	10	73.4	21	6	86.1
8	2	40.5	13	4	58.2	17	12	73.9	21	8	86.5
8	4	41.1	13	6	58.7	17	14	74.4	21	10	86.9
8	6	41.8	13	8	59.3	18	2	74.8	21	12	87.4
8	8	42.4	13	10	59.8	18	4	75.3	21	14	87.8
8	11	43.3	13	13	60.6	18	6	75.8	21	16	88.2
9	2	43.9	14	2	61.1	18	8	76.2			
9	4	44.5	14	4	61.7	18	10	76.7			
9	6	45.2	14	6	62.2	18	12	77.2			
9	8	45.8	14	8	62.7	18	15	77.9			
9	11	46.8	14	10	63.2						
			14	13	64.0						

Table 4.10: Interpreting maximum oxygen uptake results (VO_2 max, ml/kg/min)

Rating	Males (aged 15–19)	Females (aged 15–19)
Excellent	60+	54+
Good	48–59	43–53
Average	39–47	35–42
Below average	30–38	28–34
Poor	<30	<28

Cooper 12-minute run test

The aim of this test is to run as far as possible in 12 minutes to determine predicted VO_2 max. The test is maximal and is usually conducted on an athletics track. Markers should be placed at 50-metre intervals around the track to help measure distance.

1. When instructed, participants start running. Walking is allowed, although they should push as hard as possible to maximise the distance covered.
2. After 12 minutes the participants stop and the distance covered is measured and recorded. Use Table 4.11 to interpret the results.

Table 4.11: Interpreting 12-minute Cooper run test

	Excellent		Above average		Average		Below average		Poor	
Age	Men	Women	Men	Women	Men	Women	Men	Women	Men	Women
20–29	>2800 m	>2700 m	2400–2800 m	2200–2700 m	2200–2399 m	1800–2199 m	1600–2199 m	1500–1799 m	<1600 m	<1500 m
30–39	>2700 m	>2500 m	2300–2700 m	2000–2500 m	1900–2299 m	1700–1999 m	1500–1999 m	1400–1699 m	<1500 m	<1400 m
40–49	>2500 m	>2300 m	2100–2500 m	1900–2300 m	1700–2099 m	1500–1899 m	1400–1699 m	1200–1499 m	<1400 m	<1200 m
50+	>2400 m	>2200 m	2000–2400 m	1700–2200 m	1600–1999 m	1400–1699 m	1300–1599 m	1100–1399 m	<1300 m	<1100 m

Flying 30-metre sprint

Sprint or speed tests can be performed over a variety of different distances, with the distance used (20 metres, 30 metres, 40 metres, 50 metres or 60 metres) relating to the demands of a specific sport. The test involves running a single maximum sprint with the best time recorded.

When the test starts, participants should sprint in a straight line with maximal effort. Record the time taken from the start to the moment the finish line is crossed. Three attempts can be allowed and the fastest time used to assess performance.

Running-based anaerobic sprint test (RAST)

The running-based anaerobic sprint test (RAST) tests a runner's anaerobic performance, providing measurements of power. A participant is required to undertake six 35-metre timed sprints with 10 seconds of recovery between each set.

The power output for each sprint is calculated using the following equations:

velocity (m s^{-1}) = displacement (m) ÷ time (secs)

acceleration (m s^{-2}) = velocity (m s^{-1}) ÷ time (secs)

force (N) = participant weight (N) [= mass (kg) × acceleration of gravity (g)] × acceleration (m s^{-2})

power (Watts) = force (N) × velocity (m s^{-1})

For the six times calculate the power value for each run and then calculate:

- maximum power (highest value)
- minimum power (lowest value)
- average power (sum of all six times ÷ 6).

Illinois agility test

The Illinois agility run is used to measure agility. The test requires the subject to run through a marked course as quickly as possible. The course should be measured as 10 metres long by 5 metres wide and cones should be set out as illustrated in Figure 4.5.

To conduct the test, the subject must lie flat on their front with their head behind the start line. When the test starts, they must get up and run as quickly as possible around the marked course without knocking over the cones. They should be timed completing the course. Use Table 4.12 to interpret the results.

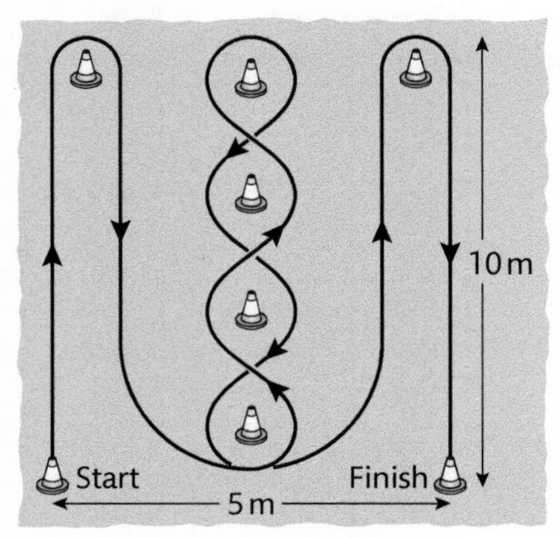

Figure 4.5: Layout of the Illinois agility run test

Table 4.12: Interpretation of Illinois agility run test results for men and women aged 16 to 19

Rating	Males (seconds)	Females (seconds)
Excellent	<15.2	<17.0
Good	15.2–16.1	17.0–17.9
Average	16.2–18.1	18.0–21.7
Fair	18.2–19.3	21.8–23.0
Poor	>19.3	>23.0

T-drill test

Similar to the Illinois agility test, the T-drill test requires a subject to run between cones in the fastest time possible (see Figure 4.6). The subject sprints to cone B and touches the base of the cone with their right hand. They then turn left and sidestep to cone C and touch its base, this time with their left hand. Then sideways to the right to cone D and touch the base with their right hand. Then sidestep back to cone B touching it with their left hand, and run backwards to cone A. The subject must not cross one foot in front of the other when sidestepping or fail to face forwards throughout the test. Use Table 4.13 to interpret the results.

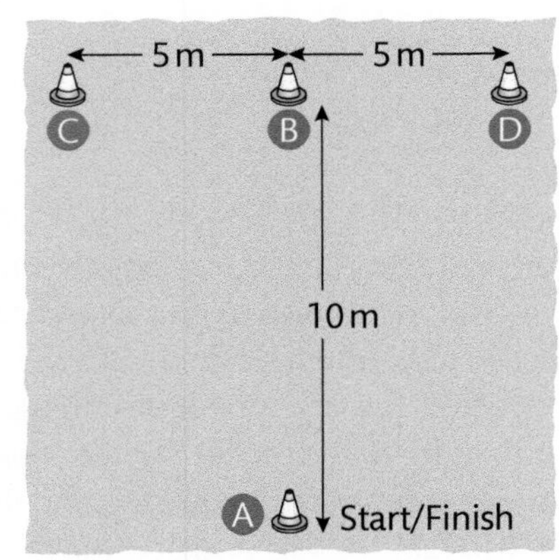

Figure 4.6: Layout of the T-drill test

Table 4.13: Interpretation of T-drill test results for men and women aged 16 to 19

	Male (seconds)	Female (seconds)
Excellent	<9.5	<10.5
Good	9.5–10.5	10.5–11.5
Average	10.5–11.5	11.5–12.5
Poor	>11.5	>12.5

Other test protocols

Some of the other tests and procedures you may encounter have very specific or complex protocols and requirements for the test to be undertaken effectively and ensure its reliability and validity. These are outlined below.

- **Aerobic maximal oxygen uptake methods (VO2)** – a simple VO_2 max test using a flat running area and cone markers. For the bleep test ensure the participant arrives at the end of a shuttle before a bleep. The athlete must wait for the bleep before resuming running. If the participant fails to reach the end of a shuttle before the bleep they are allowed two or three further shuttles to attempt to regain the required pace before being withdrawn from the test.
- **Douglas bag test** – a VO_2 max test using either a cycle ergometer or treadmill. Ensure the participant can breathe through the mouthpiece after the bag has been connected, then vacuum pump the Douglas bag before the start of the test to ensure that it is empty.
- **Blood lactate testing** – all blood testing should use sanitised equipment and the tester should wear protective equipment. It should only take place after a minimum of 3 minutes of exercise.

- **Respiratory and lung function testing** – a static test using a spirometer. For each test, the participant should be provided with a new, clean mouthpiece around which a full seal of the mouth should be checked.
- **Metabolic cost testing and calculation** – measurement of resting metabolic rate (which is similar to basal metabolic rate) is carried out by measuring oxygen input and carbon dioxide output. Hand-held devices are available that perform this function, but they can be costly and not completely accurate.
- **Isokinetic testing** – the participant is seated on a resistance machine from which muscle resistance measurements are taken. This provides an effective, valid and reliable test of specific muscle power, but requires precise positioning and restricted movement of the muscles and joints being worked.

When you are assessing the performance of children, ensure that ethical and legal guidelines/consent are in place to maintain the safety of child participants. It is often better to take measurements such as skinfold when standing at the child participant's side rather than bending down to the child's level as validity and reliability errors are more likely to occur if the tester is crouched. Always have a parent or co-worker present when taking child participant measures.

When carrying out team game assessments while all participants are engaged in game play, it is often better to pull out or concentrate on one participant from each team at the same time to undergo any testing. This ensures validity and reliability and avoids giving either team a competitive advantage.

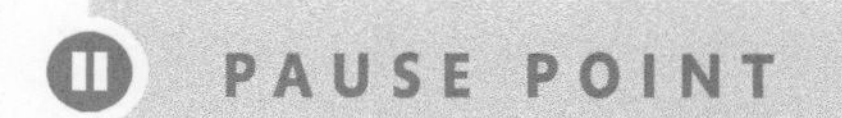

How would you go about selecting a fitness or laboratory test(s) for a specific sport, for example, swimming?

Hint Consider the physiological requirements of the sport and try and match these to a test.

Extend Are there any fitness or laboratory tests that can be used for a variety or range of sports?

Experimental data collection methods

You will need to select the correct method of recording, collecting and handling data depending on the type of test you select. Remember you must follow ethical guidelines for all data, including gaining informed consent, ensuring anonymity and maintaining the secure storage of data. Take steps to ensure the data you collect will be valid and reliable. You must also use correct units of measurement (see Table 4.14).

▶ **Table 4.14:** Correct units of measurement

Measurement	Unit of measurement
Mass and weight	Grams (g) and kilograms (kg)
Length, height, distance and displacement	Millimetres (mm), centimetres (cm), metres (m)
Force	Newton (N)
Work and energy	Joule (J)
Power	Watt (W)
Speed and velocity	Metres per second (m/s)
Angular velocity	Degrees per second (ω)
Torque	Newton metres
Volume	Cubic centimetres
Pressure	Pascal (Pa)
Temperature	Degrees Celsius (°C)

Data recording and collection

There are several different methods you can use to record your data. Some of the most common include:

- video recordings
- commercially available fitness testing and laboratory testing software
- graphical formats.

When you have collected and recorded your data you must ensure it is presented accurately. Your data can be presented differently depending on the type of data or your intended audience. For example, you might use:

- spreadsheets and databases - if you are using ICT, ensure you do so correctly and appropriately
- graphs and/or tables - this could include using bar charts, histograms, cumulative frequency graphs, etc.

Remember that if you carry out any calculations involving your data you should double-check them for accuracy.

You may also need to make variations to any standard testing protocols depending on the type of participants, location and the intention of your test, to avoid experimental errors and to maintain accuracy. Any variations must be maintained in retests or further testing.

Discussion

Select three different fitness tests you could carry out. As a group, discuss what data recording methods you would use to set up these tests and to present your results. What are the reasons for your choice?

Data handling and evaluation of outcomes

Once you have completed your testing you will have collected a range of data as your results. The next stage is to correctly interpret what these results show you. You will need to consider the following points.

- Normative data considerations - each test will usually have a set of data for comparison against, based on the average population norms. You will need to compare your results to these and use them to come to a conclusion about the results of your test and the impact on the athlete(s) you were testing.
- Comparison to sports performers and elite athletes - in some cases the testing data for elite athletes is available and a comparison against these for the sports performers in your test is possible.
- Comparative health ranges - local health authority and NHS guidelines exist for certain health-related tests which can then be used to interpret your test results, for example, by comparing resting heart rates.

Part of the interpretation of your results will require you to use various statistical tools and models. These can help you to formulate scientific conclusions based on your test results. Using these mathematical tools will allow you to draw conclusions from your results.

Link

There are many other statistical tools and methods you need to be aware of to interpret your results. These are covered in detail in *Unit 5: Applied Research Methods in Sport and Exercise Science* and include:

- mean, median, mode and standard deviation (page 171)
- t-tests (pages 176–178)
- critical values (page 175)
- Pearson product-moment correlation coefficient (Pearson's R) (pages 179–180).

When interpreting testing data or statistical evidence, it should be possible to identify trends or relationships that indicate the participant's level of fitness. This can then be compared against norms or averages from either the general population or from elite performers.

Evaluation

Once the data collection is complete an evaluation of the outcomes and test process is required. This will help shape your conclusions and identify any anomalies in your results and potential improvements in your methodology. You will need to ask yourself a series of questions like the ones below.

- Were the results of your test in line with your expectations?
- Do they reflect your original aims and objectives for the test(s)? Have you achieved these aims and objectives?
- Are the findings acceptable or within acceptable ranges? Does this mean your test was a success?
- Are the results valid and reliable?
- Did you encounter any difficulties during the testing or evaluation process?
- Were you able to draw meaningful conclusions?

Discussion

Do you think there is any merit in filming a fitness test? Could this affect the validity and reliability of the test? Could it highlight any issues around the protocols? What negative impacts could it have on the participants?

Significance of findings

Once you have completed your evaluation of your results, you need to understand what your results could mean in terms of their significance to health, sporting performance and potential for improvement. You can then come up with improvement plans that will help you apply your research results in real life.

Your test(s) will have had a series of study aims when you began - these will help guide you to understand the significance and potential limitations of your results when you review future testing and their interpretation and implications.

Your findings may also reveal potential limitations in your original testing investigation, allowing you to suggest possible improvements and changes you could make in the future. It is always sensible to periodically review your testing protocols and data handling to ensure best practice.

PAUSE POINT What possible drawbacks can you think of when comparing a participant's test results against normative data?

Hint Do you know where the normative data comes from or the size of the statistical sample being used?

Extend Research normative data for different countries (e.g. height and weight) and see how they vary from country to country.

D Explore profiling of a sports performer following a practical research design using field- and laboratory-based testing

Scientific application of experimental protocols

The next step in understanding experimental protocols is to apply them to designing and running your own tests. Before you begin you need to prepare a detailed written practical research design. You will return to this document after the tests are complete to help write up your results and conclusions. This document must include:

- the test(s) title and a written introduction, explaining the background and outlining your aims and objectives
- a description of the method and the testing protocols to be used - these must be fit for purpose and observe ethical and health and safety guidelines, and be likely to produce valid and reliable results
- a results table which will be completed after the test with the results and data collected, including evidence of the raw data collection in an appendix or attachment
- an analysis of the data with a brief discussion around the meaning and significance of the results - this should include a discussion of your results' relationship with comparative norms and clear evidence for a methodological approach to a problem analysis
- a conclusion with your interpretation of the results, including a review against original aims and objectives
- a section on research evidence, including a list of all the equipment used and a bibliography containing all relevant sources (such as academic books, articles and websites) that you have consulted.

Research

Create a simple data collection exercise (for example, your classmates' resting heart rate values), analyse the data recorded and present the results in a variety of ways which interpret the results accurately.

Link

More information about interpreting cumulative frequency graphs, including understanding normal distribution and positively and negatively skewed curves, can be found in *Unit 5: Applied Research Methods in Sport and Exercise Science.*

Key terms

Performance profiling – giving objective feedback to performers who are trying to achieve a positive change in performance.

Quantitative – research that collects numerical data and uses statistical analysis to answer questions.

Qualitative – research that collects non-numerical data and is concerned with understanding opinions, beliefs and emotions.

Data collection and presentation

When collecting data you need to use appropriate methods and recording techniques, correctly recording your data in an appropriate format. When analysing data, follow appropriate evaluation and statistical interpretation techniques. Your data can be presented in a variety of ways, including tables and diagrams (e.g. bar charts, histograms, cumulative frequency graphs) depending on what is suitable for your test(s).

Performance profiling through research design

Performance profiling is a method used to identify and organise the training, development and preparation of athletes to help them achieve their goals. The aim of performance profiling is to help:

- focus the participant on improving key aspects of their performance
- focus training on the areas that require adaptation based on an agreed development plan
- structure training programmes to meet these goals and improve fitness levels and testing results.

When preparing your research design, you may need to consider how the protocols and results could be used to build a performance profile for the participant you are working with.

Constructing profiles

The nature of the performance profile you develop will vary greatly depending on the participant you are working with and their aims, goals and sport.

Identifying the key components or physical factors relating to the participant's aims and sport is crucial to profile construction as these will form the basis of the profile. Key physical factors could include heart rate, lung function and body fat percentage. Being able to measure these characteristics will help the coach and athlete develop a training plan to meet the specific requirements of the sport and/or chosen area of fitness. Fitness tests can be conducted to measure each area, and the results analysed to develop a training programme. Focusing on these characteristics and components will produce testing data which can then be interpreted and evaluated to help the participant achieve their long-term aims and goals.

Building a performance profile involves the following considerations.

- To develop a valid performance profile that will help the participant to develop, you need to use normative data from a reliable source as a basis for comparison with the participant's results. These performance characteristics will help identify areas for improvement which can then be built into the profile. Understanding these comparisons is crucial to practical research design.
- **Quantitative** results can be interpreted alongside other normative values to help you identify relative strengths and weaknesses in the participant's performance. From these results you will outline a conclusion containing **qualitative** measures, including your own interpretation of the results and the strengths and weaknesses you identified in the participant's testing data and sporting performance.
- Whatever the results you achieve you will need to establish training priorities based on the results and agree short-, medium- and long-term goals with the participant that will require additional periodical testing.

Case study

Setting up the right tests

A coach is tasked to set up a research design to examine the lung function, resting heart rate and body fat level for three male swimmers at a local swimming club. The aim of the research is to determine whether or not the coaches need to incorporate more longer-distance aerobic swim sessions to improve the three participants' performances.

Check your knowledge

1 What testing protocols might you use - would they be fit for purpose, ethical and follow all health and safety guidelines?
2 How would you present the data recorded?
3 What results format/graphical representation would you use?
4 Is it ethical to make a comparison of the data in a final report without the participants' consent?

PAUSE POINT What circumstances might require you to consider an alteration or amendment to a research design?

Hint A participant may become ill or injured which would have a significant impact on testing results.

Extend How might you compensate for such circumstances in your evaluation and agreed goals?

Assessment practice 4.3

C.P5 D.P6 C.M4 D.M5 C.D3 D.D4

Now that you understand the requirements and protocols of fitness testing, the gym manager is happy for you to carry out a full fitness test on a participant. To achieve this, you will need to:

- create a practical research design
- conduct the fitness tests
- analyse the test data
- use the results to create a performance profile.

For the benefit of this assignment you could carry out the fitness testing on a fellow student, after they have identified their particular sport, fitness or training requirements.

By the end of this assignment you will have produced a suitable research design and report, justifying your test protocols, supported by observation or video evidence, culminating in an evaluation of the effectiveness of your participant's performance profile.

Plan

- Do I understand what the aims and objectives of my testing programme will be? Have I discussed these with the participant?
- Do I know what pre-test preparation I need to undertake to ensure my results will be reliable and valid?

Do

- Am I using the best methods to record my data and to analyse my results?
- Have I considered how the testing protocols can help me to achieve my aims and objectives?

Review

- Have I reviewed my testing protocols and identified areas for improvement to gain the most valid results?
- Does my performance profile reflect the goals and objectives of the performer and can it be used to plan their training needs?

Further reading and resources

Books

Brooks, D. (2004) *The Complete Book of Personal Training*, Champaign, IL: Human Kinetics.

Coulson, M. (2013) *The Complete Guide to Personal Training*, London: Bloomsbury.

Katch, V., McArdle, W. and Katch, F. (2011) *Essentials of Exercise Physiology*, 4th edition, Philadelphia, PA: Lippincott Williams & Wilkins.

Vander, A., Sherman, J. and Luciano, D. (2014) *Human Physiology: The Mechanisms of Body Function*, 7th edition, Boston, MA: McGraw Hill.

Websites

www.uksca.org.uk – UK Strength and Conditioning Association: information and advice about how to become an accredited strength and conditioning coach.

www.bases.org.uk – British Association of Sport and Exercise Sciences: news and other information about sport and exercise sciences.

THINK FUTURE

Cathy Barker Sports scientist

After I completed my BTEC in Sport and Exercise Science course at college, I went to university and studied for a BSc. What I enjoyed most on the BTEC course was fitness testing, particularly using the various equipment to measure fitness levels and identify areas for potential improvement.

While at university I took the fitness instructor award, then the advanced award. This helped me get a job in a local gym where I now have responsibility for carrying out fitness tests. I carry out all the necessary testing protocols and produce a report based on the results with my conclusions and recommendations, which are then passed on to the trainers assigned to the client.

During my final year at university I also wrote a dissertation on the impact of fitness testing in gyms, which was well received and relevant to my career. I'm still working at a gym but I'm hoping to set up as a freelance sports scientist specialising in bespoke fitness testing for elite athletes.

My current role is very rewarding. As well as all the required specialised knowledge, it is vital to have a good rapport with your customers and make them feel calm and relaxed, particularly as you are taking measurements of things they may be self-conscious about, like body fat. It is the day-to-day variety, complexity and the positive impact on performers that makes the role so interesting and worthwhile.

Focusing your skills

Using IT equipment

It is important to know how to set up and use various pieces of fitness testing and IT equipment. If one piece is missing or not working, it may have a knock-on effect for the entire fitness testing process.

- Sports scientists involved in fitness testing should be familiar with the use of various equipment such as blood pressure monitors, spirographs (lung function) or callipers (body fat).
- You should be proficient with spreadsheets and data input software that produces graphs and other graphical interpretations of fitness testing data.
- Ensure all equipment is operational and ready to use, e.g. all batteries are charged and equipment is sterile. The equipment should be clean and safe.

Coaching and fitness knowledge

It is vital for any sports scientist to have a basic underpinning knowledge of fitness. You will require knowledge of how the body moves and functions, especially in sporting scenarios.

- It is often necessary to understand the lifestyle and circumstances of your client. Aid profiling by suggesting goals and motivational techniques that can be built into a training programme.
- Excellent communication skills are needed as it is important to discuss with both your client and their trainer how you have recorded, analysed and presented your findings.

Getting ready for assessment

Ben is working towards completing the second year of his BTEC National in Sport and Exercise Science. He has been given an assignment for Learning aims C and D that asks him to create a presentation which examines the methods for analysing field- and laboratory-based fitness testing. The presentation must:

- describe how to prepare for and carry out different field- and laboratory-based fitness tests
- evaluate the evidence produced by different fitness tests
- profile the performance of the participant and assess their strengths and weaknesses.

How I got started

First I wrote down a list of everything I learned about fitness testing during my lectures at college. I started by dividing my presentation into three key headings:

- Preparation for field and laboratory testing
- Undertaking field and laboratory testing
- Performance profiling of participant using test results.

I decided upon a PowerPoint® presentation so I could include photo images. The first part was quite easy – I looked through my notes and put together a framework of how to prepare for fitness testing. The second heading looked at undertaking tests and the protocols for each. The third heading was more difficult because it required me to think about the design of my report, how to collect and input data and, most importantly, how to analyse that data and provide my own recommendations.

Apart from one practical fitness testing session we'd done at college, I had no other experience. A group of us decided the best way to approach this assignment was to practise using the equipment and designing our own research design. Our tutor agreed to grant us access outside lessons, under supervision. This was invaluable as there is no substitute for hands-on experience when carrying out fitness testing.

How I brought it all together

I'm so glad I took the time to use the equipment in my own time and learn how it all works. This was vital because the more I used the equipment, the more I understood that no two performance profiles are the same. This allowed me to explore the use of field- and laboratory-based protocols, and profile a sport performer after following my practical research design.

What I learned from the experience

I'm glad I gave myself plenty of time to plan my presentation. Had I left everything to the last minute, I wouldn't have had the opportunity to practise using the equipment and gain first-hand experience of how these procedures actually work and how different the results are for each individual.

Studying this unit made me realise how complex fitness testing is – not just extracting the data but analysing it as well. It was encouraging that, during the preparation of my presentation, everything we'd been taught about fitness testing suddenly made sense. I wish I had taken this approach for all my practical-based assignments.

Think about it

- Don't be afraid to look beyond your normal timetable for ideas and inspiration, but always consult your tutor beforehand about what you intend to do.
- For practical-based assignments, make sure you get plenty of practical experience. Once you understand how equipment works, it makes writing an assignment much easier.
- Remember you are a sports student: go to sports events and witness, not only the athletes performing, but also the army of support staff and coaches making it all possible.

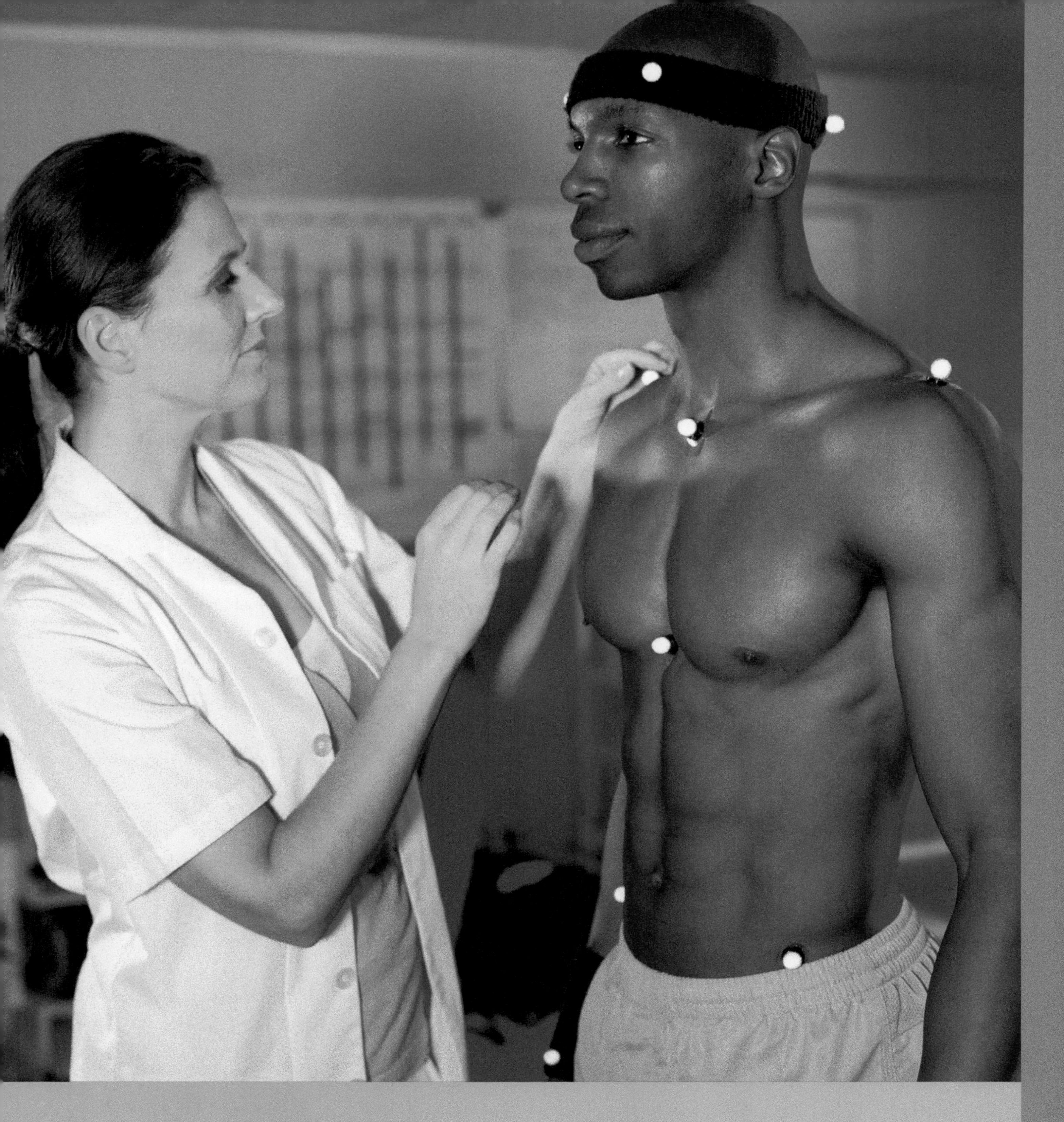

Applied Research Methods in Sport and Exercise Science

5

Getting to know your unit

Assessment
You will be assessed by a series of assignments set by your tutor.

Evidence-based practice has become much more prominent in sport and exercise science in recent years. Having a good skill set and understanding of research methods is central to becoming an effective sport and exercise scientist and, in doing so, being able to offer the highest quality of support to sports performers.

This unit will help you to develop knowledge and skills which you can use to collect and analyse data with a range of sportspeople; in turn this will aid their sport performance, or overall health and well-being. You will learn about what it means to work ethically and why this is central to everything that you do as a sport and exercise scientist. Whether you intend to progress into related work or higher education, studying this unit will set you on a journey to becoming a capable, evidence-based sport and exercise scientist.

How you will be assessed

This unit will be internally assessed by a series of tasks set by your tutor. The assignments set by your tutor may take the form of:

- a written report on the importance of research and factors affecting the quality of research
- a presentation about the different approaches to research and the application of research methods.

The activities within this unit are designed to help you gain knowledge, understanding and skills that will help you complete your assignments. Your understanding of research methods is best gained through using the different concepts and research methods in a practical manner.

The skills that you learn throughout this unit will also be directly beneficial in *Unit 9: Research Project in Sport and Exercise Science* where you will have the opportunity to plan and carry out your own research project.

To pass this unit you must ensure that you have provided sufficient evidence to cover all of the Pass assessment criteria which are listed below.

If you are seeking a Merit or Distinction then you must be able to show both an understanding and application of the concepts and techniques in sport or exercise science-based contexts.

Assessment criteria

This table shows what you must do in order to achieve a **Pass**, **Merit** or **Distinction** grade, and where you can find activities to help you.

Pass	Merit	Distinction
Learning aim A Understand the importance of research in sporting environments		
A.P1 Explain the importance of research in sporting environments. **Assessment practice 5.1**	**A.M1** Analyse the importance of different types of research to inform own work with clients in a sport and exercise science context. **Assessment practice 5.1**	**A.D1** Evaluate the importance of research in sport and exercise science contexts, making justified conclusions. **Assessment practice 5.1**
A.P2 Explain the importance of using research to inform own work with clients in a sport and exercise science context. **Assessment practice 5.1**		
Learning aim B Examine key issues that impact on the effectiveness and quality of research in the sport and exercise sciences		
B.P3 Explain validity, reliability, accuracy and precision and their importance in sport and exercise sciences-based research. **Assessment practice 5.1**	**B.M2** Analyse the relationship between validity, reliability, accuracy, precision, and the ability to conduct ethical research in sport and exercise sciences. **Assessment practice 5.1**	**B.D2** Evaluate the importance of key issues that impact on the effectiveness and quality of research. **Assessment practice 5.1**
B.P4 Explain research ethics and their importance in sport and exercise sciences-based research. **Assessment practice 5.1**		
Learning aim C Examine the three main approaches to research in the sport and exercise sciences		
C.P5 Explain the three main approaches to research in the context of sport and exercise sciences. **Assessment practice 5.2**	**C.M3** Compare quantitative, qualitative and mixed-methods research in the context of the sport and exercise sciences. **Assessment practice 5.2**	**CD.D3** Evaluate the choice of research approach, design and methods for a selected sport and exercise sciences-based research problem, justifying the research skills used. **Assessment practice 5.2**
C.P6 Explain the advantages and disadvantages of the three main approaches to research in the context of sport and exercise science. **Assessment practice 5.2**		
Learning aim D Apply appropriate research methods to a selected sport and exercise sciences-based research problem		
D.P7 Explain the appropriate research methods for a sport and exercise sciences-based research problem. **Assessment practice 5.2**	**D.M4** Analyse the research methods for a sport and exercise sciences-based research problem and the research skills used to address a selected research problem. **Assessment practice 5.2**	
D.P8 Explain the research skills used to address a selected sport and exercise sciences-based research problem. **Assessment practice 5.2**		

Getting started

Many sports teams spend significant amounts of money on developing their athletes. Beyond sport, the government and various government agencies spend large amounts of public funds on health initiatives to try to improve the health of the nation. Produce a mind map of all the ways that research could help to inform how this money is best spent.

A Understand the importance of research in sporting environments

Different types of research

Link

This unit links to *Unit 9: Research Project in Sport and Exercise Science* as it introduces you to the different types of research that could be used in a project.

Research means different things to different people; some believe research is reading around a topic, whereas others believe that research is the collection and analysis of new data. While both of these ideas are correct, it is important that you are familiar with the different types of research that you can use.

There are different definitions of 'research'. However, one definition that encompasses many of the different aspects of research is: a systematic process of discovery and advancement of knowledge, understanding and skills that is guided by seeking answers to specific questions, problems or **hypotheses**.

Key terms

Hypothesis – the predicted, testable relationship between two or more variables (e.g. imagery training will improve basketball free throw performance).

Rationale – the reason for completing a project.

There are two main types of research: primary research and secondary research.

- **Primary research** collects original data specific to a particular project. For example, if you want to investigate the effects of sports massage on hamstring flexibility, you could measure flexibility pre- and post-sports massage and record the results to see if there is any difference.
- **Secondary research** uses previously published data found in books, journals, government publications, websites and other forms of media. Secondary research is used to form **rationales** for your research and to support or counter-argue your research findings.

The importance of research for individuals involved in sport and exercise science

Research is important for those working in sport and exercise science because it helps people to keep up to date with the latest trends and to develop new ideas. In order to carry out effective research, the first stage is to search for sources of information to check that the research you are thinking of doing has not already been done by someone else and, if it has, what their results were.

Literature searching

The first stage of developing a good sport or exercise science-based project is to search for and read appropriate sources of information. At this point you need to look for any differences of opinion or any hot topics within a subject area.

In order to find sources of information, explore basic versus advanced searches in search engines or journal databases, and use key words and filtering using check box options. For example, going to www.google.com/advanced_search will allow you to be more precise about the results you are looking for, by adding details such as an author name or specifying where you want the search engine to look for particular words.

Always judge the literature for validity and reliability, especially if you have found it on the internet. This is explored in more detail later in this unit, from page 160.

Using research to develop knowledge and understanding

There are many examples of research developing knowledge and understanding. The following two studies demonstrate how you can refine and develop subject knowledge through research to benefit the people you are working with.

- Holt and Dunn (2004) produced a theory associated with talent development in elite youth football that made predictions about qualities that would give players the best chance of reaching an elite level. However, as this theory was based mainly on players who had been successful in their youth football career, it was not known if less successful football players did not possess these same qualities.
- As a result, Holt and Mitchell (2006) examined the experiences of less successful and lower level youth players and produced a revised theory. However, both of these studies had the limitation that it was not known if any of the players studied had successfully achieved and maintained a professional career.

Research

Find two articles about the same topic (e.g. PNF stretching or imagery in sport) and produce a short summary - similar to the one above - that shows how these articles build on and develop knowledge and understanding.

The use of research to inform work with clients

When you work within sport and exercise science, you should always use research to plan and review your work. This is called **evidence-based practice (EBP)**. This does not mean you have to read article after article every time you plan a session, but rather that, as a professional, you have a good working knowledge of the research in your area and know how to apply it to the people you are working with.

Key term

Evidence-based practice (EBP) - making sure that evidence uncovered in research is included in your everyday work practices for the benefit of participants.

It also means you should update your knowledge on a regular basis by keeping up to date with the latest research. For example, if you are a strength and conditioning coach or a sports therapist responsible for the post-event recovery of athletes, you should ensure you are familiar with the different recovery strategies available for those athletes, as well as the physiological and psychological benefits of those strategies.

▶ Why would EBP be important for this yoga instructor?

The importance of EBP in sporting environments

As a sport and exercise scientist, the welfare and safety of your participants is always your main concern. In research and practice environments, this means that you should not place any undue physiological or psychological stress on your participants (e.g. conduct any work that might significantly increase the risk of injury). EBP is important in this context, as the available evidence will help you to stay within the normal working limits for participants, or levels of work that will not significantly pose an increased risk to a participant's well-being.

PAUSE POINT What is 'evidence-based practice'?

Hint Close this book and define evidence-based practice.

Extend Discuss why evidence-based practice is important for sport and exercise scientists.

B Examine key issues that impact on the effectiveness and quality of research in the sport and exercise sciences

Link

This content links to *Unit 9: Research Project in Sport and Exercise Science*: whenever you collect data in a project you need to make sure that it is both valid and reliable so that you can reach meaningful conclusions.

Key terms

Validity (in data collection) – whether you are measuring what you intended to measure.

Validity (in data analysis) – the soundness of interpretations of results.

Validity, reliability, accuracy and precision in research

When conducting research, you will need to consider its validity, reliability, accuracy and precision.

Validity

The first important consideration is **validity**. Definitions of validity can vary depending on the context.

- In reference to **collecting** data, 'validity' can be defined as whether you are measuring what you intended to measure.
- In reference to **analysing** data, 'validity' is the soundness of the interpretation of test results.

Validity is also connected to the conclusions drawn through research, i.e. that you correctly draw conclusions from the data that you have collected and analysed.

There are different types of validity but the two key types are 'internal validity' and 'external validity'.

- **Internal validity** relates to whether the results of the study can be attributed to the different treatments in the study. This means that, for your research to claim internal validity, you need to ensure that you have controlled everything that could affect the results of the study.
- **External validity** relates to whether or not the results of the study can be generalised and applied to other people or situations.

Other types of validity include:

- **ecological validity** – relates to the extent to which results of a study can be applied to real-world settings
- **face validity** – relates to whether a measure being used in a study obviously involves the performance variable (e.g. component of fitness) being measured.

Case study

Valid research

As part of a project investigating the effects of sports massage on hamstring flexibility in athletes, a sports massage therapist decides to use the sit and reach test to measure the hamstring flexibility of rugby players. When the massage therapist talks through their idea with their research supervisor, the supervisor points out that sit and reach scores can also be influenced by lower back conditions. The supervisor also asks, if the aim is to measure hamstring flexibility in athletes, why has the sports massage therapist only used rugby players?

Check your knowledge

1. Which types of validity would be affected by the way the sports massage therapist planned the project?
2. How would they have been affected?
3. What advice would you offer to the therapist about potential changes to the project, and why?

Reliability

Reliability refers to the consistency or repeatability of a measure or test or their results. It is important to remember that reliability can be achieved without validity: you could ask the wrong questions and get the same wrong answers consistently. In this case, your work is **reliable** (the answers you received were consistent and repeatable) but not **valid** (you did not find out information about the subject you intended to investigate).

Key term

Reliability – the consistency or repeatability of a measure.

In quantitative research (i.e. research looking at numbers, statistics or other 'countable' data), reliability can be one researcher conducting the same test on the same individual on a number of occasions, and getting the same or similar results. Alternatively, it can be different researchers conducting the same test on the same individual and getting the same or similar results.

In qualitative research (i.e. research looking at non-numerical data such as words, images or behaviours), reliability relates to the same researcher placing results into the same categories on different occasions, or different researchers placing results into the same or similar categories.

Link

You can read more about quantitative and qualitative research in the next learning aim, starting on page 165.

There are certain factors you should take into account that can affect reliability. For example, errors may occur if:

- researchers do not know how to use the equipment correctly
- equipment is poorly maintained
- the wrong type of equipment is chosen.

Types of reliability

There are three types of reliability.

- **Inter-observer or inter-researcher reliability** examines whether different researchers in the same situation would get the same (or similar) results. An example of when inter-observer reliability can be a problem is when measuring body composition. When people are learning to use the skinfold calliper technique of assessing body composition, it is difficult to take accurate measurements from the correct sites, meaning researchers come up with different values. When this happens, you cannot claim to have achieved inter-observer reliability.

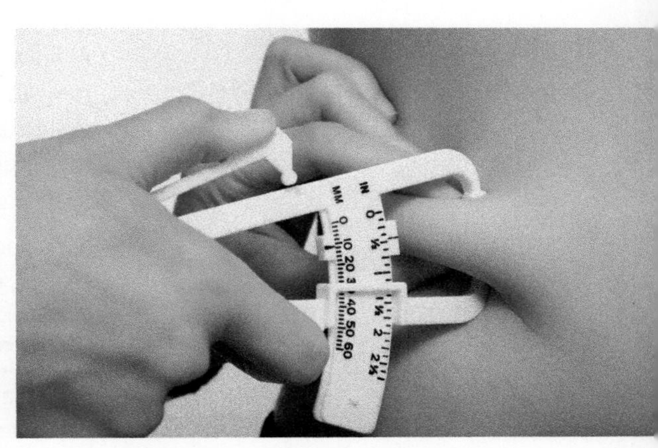

Measuring body composition using skinfold callipers

- **Test-retest reliability** relates to doing the same test on different occasions and getting the same (or similar) results. An example of a test-retest reliability issue is the measurement of heart rate. Heart rate can be affected by different factors such as temperature, time of day, diet, sleep patterns, physical activity levels and alcohol. If you measured the heart rate on the same person at the same time of day but on different days, you could get different measurements.
- **Internal consistency reliability** relates to whether the items in a survey or questionnaire all measure the same thing. For example, if you were measuring sport anxiety and had a seven-item questionnaire, it would have good internal consistency reliability if all of the questions measured sport anxiety appropriately.

Accuracy and precision

Accuracy relates to how close your measurement is to the 'gold standard', or what you are intending to measure. Imagine looking at the weight of a boxer before a fight. If the boxer has an actual weight of 100 kg and your weighing device shows he weighs 100.1 kg, you could say this is accurate. However, if the measuring device shows he weighs 103 kg, you would say this is not accurate as it is not close to his body weight.

Any measurement you take will have some unpredictability. The degree of unpredictability relates to the amount of **precision** the tool selected for measurement has. Precision is related to the refinement of the measuring process. It is concerned with how small a difference the measuring device can detect. Precision is closely related to repeatability/reliability.

Key terms

Accuracy – how close your measurement is to the 'gold standard'.

Precision – how fine or small a difference a measuring device can detect.

An easy way to get to grips with accuracy and precision is to think about target sports such as archery. If you hit the bullseye on the archery board with all of your arrows, you would say that you had been both accurate and precise. However, if you missed the board completely in different directions with your arrows, you would say that you had been neither accurate nor precise. This is shown in Figure 5.1.

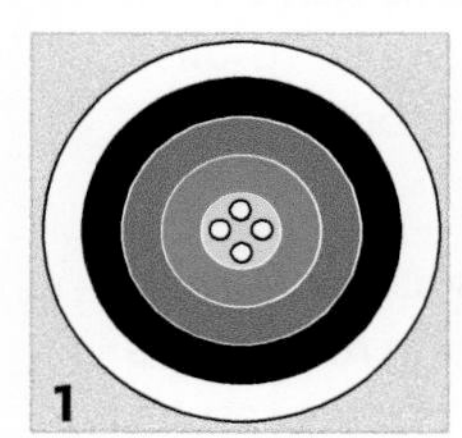

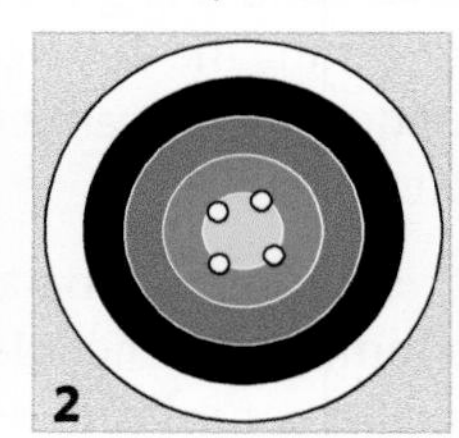

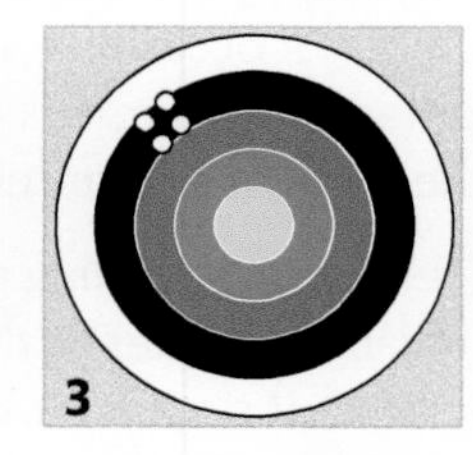

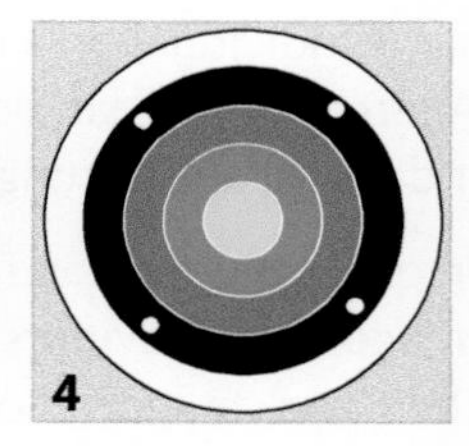

Figure 5.1: Accuracy and precision can affect the validity and reliability of research: 1 – accurate and precise, 2 – accurate but not precise, 3 – not accurate but precise, 4 – inaccurate and imprecise

Impact of accuracy and precision on validity and reliability

Accuracy and precision can affect validity and reliability: if you do not follow the relevant protocol (the way of conducting the data), it is likely the data collected will be less accurate and precise. If this is the case, you are less likely to measure what you intended to measure, reducing the validity of data collection.

Equally, if you are less accurate and precise with your data collection there is likely be a degree of variance in the errors you make. In this instance, you will produce different results, reducing the reliability of your data.

Research

Research measurement of body composition using skinfold callipers. Think about the key errors that could be made when measuring body composition in this way. How would this affect accuracy, precision, validity and reliability?

Ethical issues

There are many different definitions of research ethics. However, a common definition is: standards of conduct that differentiate between acceptable and unacceptable behaviour while conducting research activities. You should always make sure that you adhere to a relevant code of conduct, such as those of the British Association of Sport and Exercise Sciences (BASES) or sports coach UK.

The BASES Code of Conduct

The ethical issues relevant to you are outlined in the BASES Code of Conduct. This governs how you work as a practitioner and as a researcher, and outlines ethical standards essential for safe research within sport and exercise science.

Ethical clearance

When conducting research, to ensure that you are working ethically and legally, you need to gain ethical clearance from an appropriate body before you start. If you conduct any research as part of your course, ethical clearance will come from your tutor, college or school **ethics committee**.

Informed consent

Once you have gained ethical approval for your research project, it is an ethical and legal requirement for you to gain informed consent from your participants. This can be given verbally but it is safer for both you and your participants if you obtain it in writing. An informed consent form consists of:

- a description of the investigation
- details of the procedure to be followed
- details of any risks to the participant
- details of the potential benefits of taking part in the research
- a section that offers to answer any questions and confirms these have been answered fully
- an indication that the participant can withdraw at any time without being penalised
- a section which explains that any information collected about the participant will remain confidential
- a section for you, the participant and any other relevant individual (such as a parent or carer) to sign and date.

Confidentiality, data protection and responsibility

Any data you collect is protected under the terms of the Data Protection Act (1998). You may only disclose information important to the study you are conducting, and no data that makes the participants personally identifiable should be included in your research project. Data collected should be stored in a locked filing cabinet or on a password-protected computer, accessible only by you and your research supervisor.

Competence

Competence refers to you only working within your specific skill sets. If you are not suitably qualified, experienced or skilled in a certain technique, you should not perform it during research without adequate supervision. You should also not interpret results from areas where you have insufficient subject knowledge, as this may mislead participants and bias the results of your study. It could also affect participants' safety and well-being if they change their lifestyle based on your interpretations.

Key terms

Ethics committee – a panel that looks at your research proposal and says whether it is safe and ethical. It will confirm whether you can start work on your project.

Competence – having knowledge, skills and experience within a given area and recognising your limitations associated with this.

Key term

Referral – when you recognise that you are not competent to work with a particular person or conduct research in a particular area based on your skill set, contacting another professional who is competent so that they can conduct that work.

If you are ever asked to work in an area in which you are not competent, you should **refer** this to another appropriate professional (e.g. someone in a different discipline of sport and exercise science, a sports therapist or a sports medicine professional).

Personal and professional conduct

Working in a professional manner is the cornerstone of being an effective sport and exercise scientist. In addition to the factors discussed above, some of the key considerations within this context are outlined below.

- **Safety of the participants** – when conducting research, this is the key concern. The researcher must maintain the highest professional standards so as not to endanger participants or themselves. This is especially important if the research involves participants exerting themselves towards their maximum effort. The researcher should treat all participants equally and only work within their own area of competence.
- **Acting with due regard for equality and impartiality** – to preserve the reputation of sport and exercise science, you must remain totally unbiased in your actions and practices. This means you cannot let factors such as race, age or gender affect your work with participants or your interpretation of results. You must not exploit personal relationships for personal gain. Any decisions must be completely objective (based on facts rather than on opinions).
- **Responding to member or client queries** – there may be a time when a senior member of BASES or your client asks why you have worked in a particular way. As a sport and exercise scientist, you have the professional responsibility to answer these queries in an honest and timely manner.

Research

Research the Society of Sports Therapists' standards of conduct, performance and ethics. What are the similarities and differences between these standards and the BASES Code of Conduct?

Impact of ethical issues in research settings

The primary role of research ethics is to ensure the safety and well-being of the research participants and the researcher. Without consideration of ethical issues, it is not possible to offer these safeguards.

Centring more on the research process, ethical issues also play a role in helping to ensure a high quality of data collection and analysis, allowing you to investigate research aims in an optimal manner, resulting in research of the most use for the widest audience. Working in this manner is also likely to reduce the potential for bias in the research, enhancing the credibility of sport and exercise science as a professional discipline.

PAUSE POINT What are the key ethical considerations when conducting research?

Hint Think about a specific topic you would like to research. What are the key ethical considerations relating to this project?

Extend Why are these ethical considerations in place and what might be the consequences of breaching these ethical considerations?

Assessment practice 5.1

A.P1 A.P2 A.M1 A.D1 B.P3 B.P4 B.M2 B.D2

You are applying for an internship at a local football club. The head of sport science is very keen on evidence-based practice, so part of the application process requires you to write a report that examines the importance of research when working with participants within a football setting and the factors that can influence the effectiveness of research.

Within your report, consider how you can use football-specific examples to enlighten the work (e.g. why is evidence-based practice used in football; football-specific examples of validity and reliability). You may also find it helpful to use the work completed for the pause points and research activities in this section.

Plan

- What am I being asked to show about research and the factors affecting the quality of research, and why is this important?
- Are there any areas that I think I might struggle with?

Do

- Have I spent some time planning out my approach to the task?
- Have I recorded any problems I am experiencing and looked for ways/solutions to clarify queries?

Review

- Can I explain how I approached the task and how I could approach it differently next time?
- Did I meet the task's criteria?

Examine the three main approaches to research in sport and exercise sciences

There are three main approaches to research: quantitative, qualitative and mixed-methods. Remember that there is no 'best' approach to research, only research approaches that are more suited to certain types of research questions. During your career you are likely to find a preference for a certain research approach, but it is important that you appreciate each approach to research on its own merits.

Quantitative research

Quantitative research is a formal, objective and systematic process in which numerical data is used to obtain information. It involves testing a hypothesis or trying to discover relationships. It is generally deductive: a scientist will start with a hypothesis and then begin observations to prove the hypothesis. It is designed to establish differences, relationships or causality (does one thing cause another?).

Because quantitative research relies on measurement and statistical analysis, its success often depends on the accuracy and precision in data collection.

As an example of quantitative research, Soligard *et al* (2008) investigated the effectiveness of a warm-up programme to prevent injuries in female youth football players. Their investigation used 1892 female football players and had treatment and control groups. They found that the treatment group had fewer injuries than the control group, and this comprehensive warm-up programme is now widely used in female football.

Advantages

Quantitative research is useful for researching large groups. This is beneficial as some researchers think it is important to be able to **generalise** results.

One of the key advantages of quantitative research is that, if the investigation is designed correctly, it allows the researcher to assess cause and effect. This allows researchers to investigate the effectiveness of different treatments or supplements.

Key term

Generalise – the extent to which research results are applicable to other settings.

Quantitative research allows the testing of **(null) hypotheses** and theories, allowing researchers to assess the accuracy of any theoretical predictions. Using this information, researchers can be more confident in their advice to clients having tested a theory and knowing it is correct, or they can develop a theory further if they find any inaccuracies after testing it.

Quantitative research also provides objective, numerical data which some people see as more credible because the data is seen to be free from **bias**.

Disadvantages

As you will sometimes conduct quantitative research with large sample sizes from many different backgrounds, the findings may be too general: you may get a less specific level of knowledge from a broad cross-section of the population than if you were to examine a specific single sporting population.

Case study

Quantitative research and well-being

In their work examining psychological well-being and ill-being in sports coaches, Stebbings *et al* (2011) used anonymous data collection with correct statistical analysis to show that coaches who had a better work-life balance saw more opportunities for development, and perceived greater job security, demonstrating higher levels of psychological well-being. People were then able to use these findings to structure a working environment to benefit the psychological well-being of coaches.

Check your knowledge

1 What do you think are the key strengths of this study and why?

Key terms

Null hypotheses – a prediction that there will be no relationship/no significant difference between two or more variables or groups.

Bias – misrepresenting facts about a study, e.g. selectively reporting results or structuring the design in such a way that it will always support your hypothesis.

Subjective – based on or influenced by personal feelings, beliefs or opinions.

Qualitative research

Qualitative research is generally **subjective** and involves collecting non-numerical data, such as words or images. It looks at feelings, opinions and emotions and aims to explain **why** rather than **what** or **how many**. It tends to be inductive, which means you collect data and then analyse it to create explanations, models or theories. It tries to explain differences, relationships or causality. Qualitative data can produce quantitative data, for example, you may record how many people said that they like playing sport because they can spend time with their friends; you might explore why this is the case.

Advantages

Qualitative research can provide a richer understanding than quantitative research because you can explore a topic in greater depth and detail, often immersing yourself in the environment.

It also tends to be more flexible and dynamic in design, meaning a researcher can respond to the needs or directions of participants to explore a topic in a slightly different manner. Equally, if results of interest arise during qualitative research, the flexible nature of the design can allow you to adapt the research to explore these results further.

Finally, qualitative research may help to understand how or why a particular event or experience occurred, from the perspective of the participants. This may lead to changes to improve the participant's sporting experience.

Case study

Qualitative research

Gledhill and Harwood (2015) investigated the developmental experiences of four elite female youth football players using interviews over a 20-month period. They gained an in-depth understanding of a very specific population and used this to make suggestions about how these players had been successful in their career. This helped them to provide explanations that parents, coaches and sport scientists could use to help develop talented female football players.

Check your knowledge

1 What do you think are the key strengths and limitations of this study and why?

Disadvantages

Because of the nature of its data collection and analysis, qualitative research can be much more time consuming than quantitative research. Whereas conducting statistical analysis can take a matter of minutes, conducting qualitative data analysis involves, for example, repeatedly listening to and reading interviews, which is far more time consuming but is necessary for good data analysis.

In addition, as qualitative research tends to use smaller sample sizes, the results are often said to be more difficult to generalise. However, while some researchers view this as a disadvantage of qualitative research, others see it as a strength as it suggests a more specific level of knowledge about a focused topic.

Reflect

Who you are and how you think about things may affect your preference for an approach to research. Do you think you have a natural tendency towards quantitative or qualitative research? Why?

Mixed-methods research

Mixed-methods research combines qualitative and quantitative principles and methods in the same study.

Advantages

Mixed-methods research has the combined benefits of quantitative and qualitative research and can add a level of insight that may not be gained from one approach alone. It typically uses the strengths of one approach to overcome the limitations of the other (e.g. getting follow-up in-depth opinions using qualitative work after gaining a superficial level of understanding from a quantitative measure). In doing so, this type of research may lead to a stronger conclusion.

Case study

Mixed-methods research

Giacobbi *et al* (2008) used a mixed-methods approach to investigate the links between physical activity and quality of life. By using a quantitative measure to assess physical activity levels and qualitative techniques to investigate physical activity experiences, they were able to find out that physical activity had a number of physical, psychological and social benefits that improved overall quality of life. Without the use of both quantitative and qualitative measures, the researchers would not have gained this depth of information.

Check your knowledge

1 Why do you think that it is important for sport and exercise scientists to understand a topic from multiple perspectives (e.g. physical, psychological, and social)?

2 Using this example as a guide, can you think of another type of study that would benefit from mixed-methods research?

Disadvantages

While mixed-methods research has many advantages, it can be more time consuming than qualitative research due to the volume of data collection and analysis that needs to take place.

There can also be problems because one researcher may not have the skill set to conduct both the qualitative and quantitative aspects of the research, meaning a research team has to be assembled. Although this is regularly seen as good practice, it may increase the research costs.

Similarly, mixed-methods research tends to require more equipment or research tools than using one approach alone, which can also increase costs.

PAUSE POINT What are the advantages and disadvantages of the different approaches to research?

Hint Close this book and create a mind map of all the advantages and disadvantages.

Extend Provide specific examples of why you think these are advantages and disadvantages.

D Apply appropriate research methods to a selected sport or exercise sciences-based research problem

Quantitative research designs

A research design is the overall structure of your research. The main quantitative designs are experimental, cross-sectional or survey-based, and longitudinal.

Experimental research design

The aim of experimental research is to explore the effects that something has on something else that depends on it. To use this research design effectively, you need to understand the terms 'independent variable' and 'dependent variable'. The independent variable affects the dependent variable. For example, an athletics coach might want to find out whether lower back flexibility training is benefiting an athlete's high jump performance. As the coach wants to find out if flexibility affects performance, in this example:

- the independent variable is flexibility
- the dependent variable is high-jump performance – it depends on the flexibility.

In this type of design, having **treatment** and **control groups** is important so that you can isolate any treatment effects – you need to know for sure that it is the independent variable affecting any changes, not something else. Other variables that might 'skew' the results need to be controlled and reduced as much as possible.

Key terms

Treatment group – a group of participants who undergo the treatment condition in an investigation.

Control group – a group of participants who undergo the control condition (e.g. receiving no treatment or 'sham treatment', where they think they are being treated but they are not).

Cross-sectional or survey-based design

Cross-sectional research involves using a range of participants with different backgrounds, ages and gender from the overall population. For example, if you want to look at preferences for team sports or individual sports in people in the UK, cross-sectional research would be useful. This would allow you to obtain opinions from a range of people from different backgrounds.

Cross-sectional research is often questionnaire- or survey-based. You would send your participants a survey-type questionnaire that allowed them to say which type of sport they prefer. Then you could produce some descriptive statistics for the results of the study (for example, 73 per cent of men prefer team sports, 20 per cent of men prefer individual sports and 7 per cent of men have no preference).

This type of research can identify trends or relationships within or between different groups of people.

Longitudinal design

Longitudinal research involves measuring the same variables over a long period of time. It requires greater resources than other research types, so be careful when approaching it. Measurements are taken at multiple time points over a period of weeks, months or even years, and you then see how and when these change.

Longitudinal research is useful if you want to examine developmental characteristics of a group. For example, it would be a good option if you were investigating factors associated with talent development in a particular sport, allowing you to focus on developmental issues over an extended period of time.

Longitudinal designs can be used in either quantitative or qualitative research, but the application is slightly different.

Theory into practice

In small groups, discuss how you think the application of longitudinal research designs would differ between qualitative and quantitative research?

Quantitative data collection methods

Laboratory-based data collection

Laboratory-based data collection involves collecting data in an environment where all the conditions and potential **extraneous variables** are controlled, so that you are only measuring the variables that are the focus of your research.

One advantage of laboratory-based data collection is that it has high levels of internal validity: you are controlling all your variables so you know that you are only measuring the aspect you mean to measure, making it more possible to isolate treatment effects.

One disadvantage of laboratory-based data collection is that it has low levels of 'ecological validity' because the data is not collected in an environment that reflects the situation in which the activity is performed. Another disadvantage is that it normally requires the use of expensive or technical equipment to collect data, making it difficult to use if you have few resources.

Key term

Extraneous variable – a variable outside the scope of the study that could adversely affect the results, reducing the validity and reliability of findings.

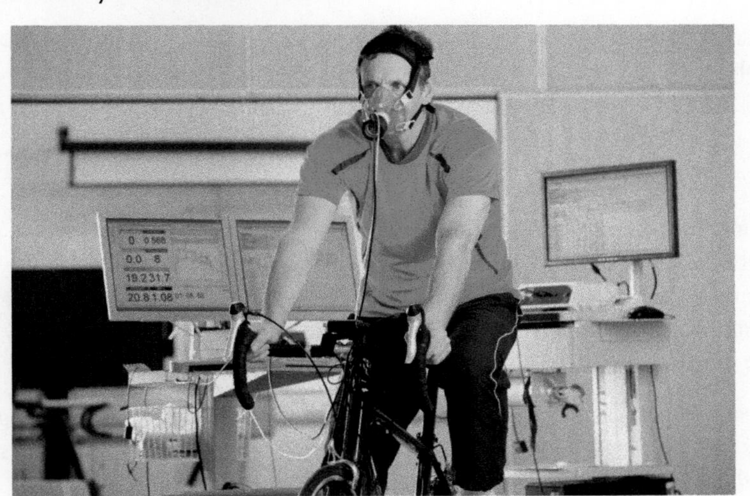

▶ VO_2 max tests are a form of laboratory-based data collection

Field-based data collection

Field-based data is collected in an environment that simulates the one in which the sport is played. One of the key strengths of field-based data collection is that it mimics the performance environment so you can claim ecological validity when you are collecting data in this setting.

Field-based data collection can be cheaper than laboratory-based collection, making it more accessible to people with fewer resources. However, one limitation is that you do not control all of the extraneous variables in this setting, so it can be difficult to claim internal validity.

Survey-based data collection

Surveys are used when you are trying to collect a large amount of data from large groups and when the data you want to collect is not in-depth. As such, surveys predominantly use **closed questions**. If you need to obtain more in-depth information, surveys would not be suitable alone. However, they could be effective if used alongside other qualitative methods of data collection (such as interviews). As with other data collection methods, surveys have advantages and disadvantages, shown in Table 5.1.

Key term

Closed questions – questions that are worded to provoke a single-word response, such as 'yes' or 'no'.

Table 5.1: Advantages and disadvantages of surveys

Advantages	Disadvantages
They are people-friendly if the form is designed correctly.	Questions can be too complex if the form is designed incorrectly.
They can reduce participant bias.	There is a potential for a low response rate.
The participant can be anonymous.	There is no opportunity for probing questions.
The data is structured so you can analyse the results more easily.	There are control issues (e.g. potential issues with controlling the return rate; clarity and understanding of questions).
They are usually accessible to most people.	

When designing your survey, you need to consider a number of factors including:

- what you want to find out
- your sample (this will affect how you write your survey)
- the length and appearance of your survey (when you design it, do not make it too long or difficult to answer)
- how and when you are going to distribute your survey. If by hand, wait for it to be completed rather than going away and returning later. Another way is by post or email, but this reduces the chances of it being returned. Include a return address and a covering letter to explain why your questionnaire is being sent out
- how you will analyse the results.

If your survey looks poorly organised and unprofessional, it may be thrown away, particularly if you post your surveys to people or conduct the survey online. If it looks well-organised and purposeful, you have a better chance of it being completed. Ensure your design is geared towards your audience, for example by making it easy and simple to use for young children if that is who you are investigating.

When designing your survey, remember that if it is more than one page long it is much less likely to be filled in, so keep it as short as possible while still containing sufficient information to answer your research question.

Always consider why you are asking a question – this will stop you including unnecessary ones. The quality of your survey will increase as its validity increases. Decide which format would be most appropriate for the question you want to ask, i.e. a closed question that invites a one-word answer or an open question (who? what? where? when? why? how?) that invites a longer response.

PAUSE POINT You want to find out about the physical activity habits of the students at your school or college. Which quantitative data collection method would you use?

Hint List the different quantitative data collection methods. What would you use each method for and which method would be most suitable in this case?

Extend Justify your choice of collection method, explaining how it would allow you to answer the question.

Quantitative data analysis methods

Quantitative data analysis involves using different statistical methods to answer your research questions. The first group of statistics to consider are descriptive statistics.

Descriptive statistics

Common descriptive statistics are the mean, median, mode and standard deviation.

- **Mean** – the average or 'measure of central tendency', calculated by adding up all the values and dividing the answer by the number of values. For example, if eight values add up to 125, the mean is 15.625.
- **Median** – the middle value in a series of numbers. For example, in the series 4, 6, 7, 10 and 11, the median is 7 because it is the middle number in the series.
- **Mode** – the value that occurs most frequently. For example, if the values are 3, 4, 6, 6, 7 and 8, the mode is 6 because it occurs twice.
- **Standard deviation** is a number that indicates how much each of the values in the distribution deviates from the mean (or centre) of the distribution. If the data points are all close to the mean, then the standard deviation is close to zero. If many data points are far from the mean, then the standard deviation is far from zero. If all the data values are equal, then the standard deviation is zero. The formula for calculating standard deviation (*sd*) is as follows:

$$sd = \sqrt{\frac{\Sigma(X - M)^2}{n - 1}}$$

Where:

- Σ = sum of
- X = individual score
- M = mean
- n = number of participants

Here is how to calculate standard deviation.

1. Calculate the mean.
2. Subtract the mean from each subject's score $(X - M)$.
3. Square the answer $(X - M)^2$.
4. Sum the squared scores $\Sigma (X - M)^2$.
5. Divide by the number of participants minus 1 $(n - 1)$.
6. Take the square root of the answer.

Organising data

There are different methods for organising your data during quantitative data analysis, each of which provides a good starting point to the appropriate research project. The methods include range, rank order distribution, simple frequency distribution and grouped frequency distribution.

- **Range** is the distance in numerical value from the highest to the lowest value collected. You calculate the range by subtracting the lowest value from the highest value. For example, if the highest value was 15 and the lowest value was 7, the range would be 8.
- **Rank order distribution** means placing your data into an ordered list from the lowest to the highest in a single column, ensuring you include all the scores. Rank order distribution is used when the number of participants is less than or equal to 20 ($n \leq 20$).
- **Simple frequency distribution** is used when the number of participants is greater than 20 ($n > 20$) and when the range is less than or equal to 20 ($r \leq 20$). You use simple frequency distribution with a table that has two columns, one for raw data scores (X) and one for frequency scores (f). The frequency column is the number of times that particular score was achieved.

Table 5.2: Simple frequency distribution example

Number of missed shots (*X*)	Frequency (*f*)
7	3
6	5
5	14
3	2
1	1
	$n = 25$

Worked example

A basketball coach is looking at the number of free throws missed in each game over a season. He has 25 games to assess ($n > 20$) and the number of missed shots per game ranges from 1 to 7 ($r \leq 20$), so simple frequency distribution is suitable. The data is set out as shown in Table 5.2.

Grouped frequency distribution

In quantitative research, you often work with ranges greater than 21 ($r > 21$) and with more than 20 participants ($n > 20$). This is when to use grouped frequency distribution. As with simple frequency distribution, the table has two columns (*X* and *f*) except this time the *X* column is for groups of scores and the *f* column is for frequency.

To keep your data on a single sheet of paper, you normally have between 10 and 20 groups of scores; the ideal number is 15. You need to decide on the **interval size** for each group, which is calculated using the formula i = range ÷ 15.

Key term

Interval size – the range of values that each group will cover.

Worked example

An athletics coach is looking at the times recorded (in seconds) of athletes who want to represent the college at 5000 metres. She has 30 times to look at ranging from 900 seconds to 1094 seconds. Grouped frequency distribution is a suitable method because both $r > 21$ and $n > 20$. The interval size for each group is 13 seconds (r = 194 seconds; 194 ÷ 15 = 12.93 seconds, which is rounded up to 13). The data is shown in Table 5.3.

Table 5.3: Example of grouped frequency distribution

Time (*X*)	Frequency (*f*)
1082–1094	1
1068–1081	1
1054–1067	1
1040–1053	1
1026–1039	5
1012–1025	8
998–1011	3
984–997	2
970–983	2
956–969	1
942–955	1
928–941	1
914–927	1
900–913	2
	$n = 30$

Although using grouped frequency distribution is a useful way of organising large amounts of data, some information is lost through this process. Once scores have been placed into groups, it is impossible to know the individual values. For example, if you look at the 1012–1025 seconds row in Table 5.3, you only know that eight athletes fell within that range; you will not know what the individual times were.

Distribution curves

Distribution curves show the relationship of your data to the mean value.

Normal distribution curves

A normal distribution of data means that most of the examples in a set of data are close to the 'average', while a few examples are at one extreme or the other. In a normal distribution graph (see Figure 5.2):

- the curve is bell-shaped, with a single peak
- the mean (average) lies at the centre of the distribution and the distribution is symmetrical around the mean
- the two 'tails' of the distribution extend indefinitely and never touch the *x* axis
- the shape of the distribution is determined by the mean and standard deviation.

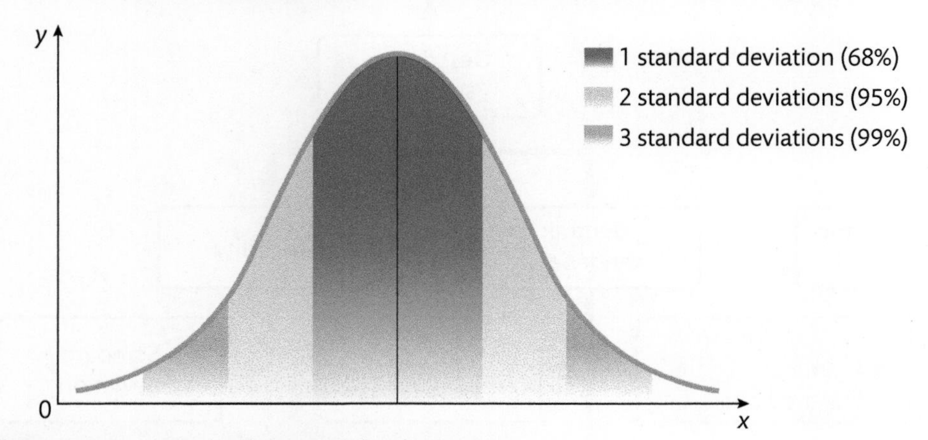

Figure 5.2: An example of a normal distribution curve

Not all sets of data have graphs as neat as the one in Figure 5.2. Some have relatively flat curves, others will be steeper. Sometimes the mean will lean to one side or the other. However, all normally distributed data will have something similar to this bell-shaped curve. Generally, if you go right or left one standard deviation from the mean (the red area on the graph) you will include about 68 per cent of the scores in the distribution. Two standard deviations away from the mean (the red and yellow areas) account for about 95 per cent of scores, whereas three standard deviations (red, yellow and green areas) account for about 99 per cent of scores.

Standard deviation tells you how tightly all the various examples are clustered around the mean in a set of data. When the examples are tightly bunched together and the bell-shaped curve is steep, the standard deviation is small. When the examples are spread apart and the bell curve is flat, this tells you that you have a relatively large standard deviation.

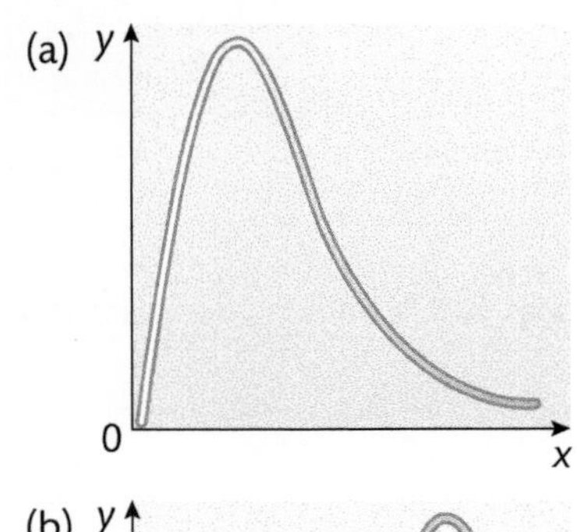

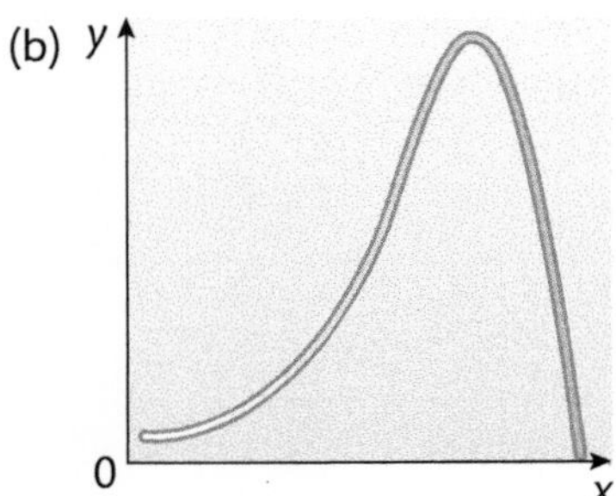

Figure 5.3: Examples of (a) positively and (b) negatively skewed curves

Positively skewed curves and negatively skewed curves

If the shape of the curve is asymmetrical, your data is not distributed normally and is said to be positively or negatively skewed.

- Positively skewed means the longer tail of the curve points to the positive (higher) end of the scale and the scores are bunched to the left of the centre.
- Negatively skewed means the longer tail of the curve points to the negative (lower) end of the scale and the scores are bunched to the right of the centre.

Figure 5.3(a) shows an example of a positively skewed curve and Figure 5.3(b) demonstrates a negatively skewed curve.

Inferential statistics

Inferential statistics assess relationships or differences between data sets. For example, if you wanted to find out whether PNF stretching increases hamstring flexibility, you could use an appropriate inferential test to get your answer. They are further subdivided into two groups: **parametric tests** and **non-parametric tests** (see Figure 5.4). The over-arching purpose of inferential statistics is to test your null hypothesis so that you are able to either accept or reject it.

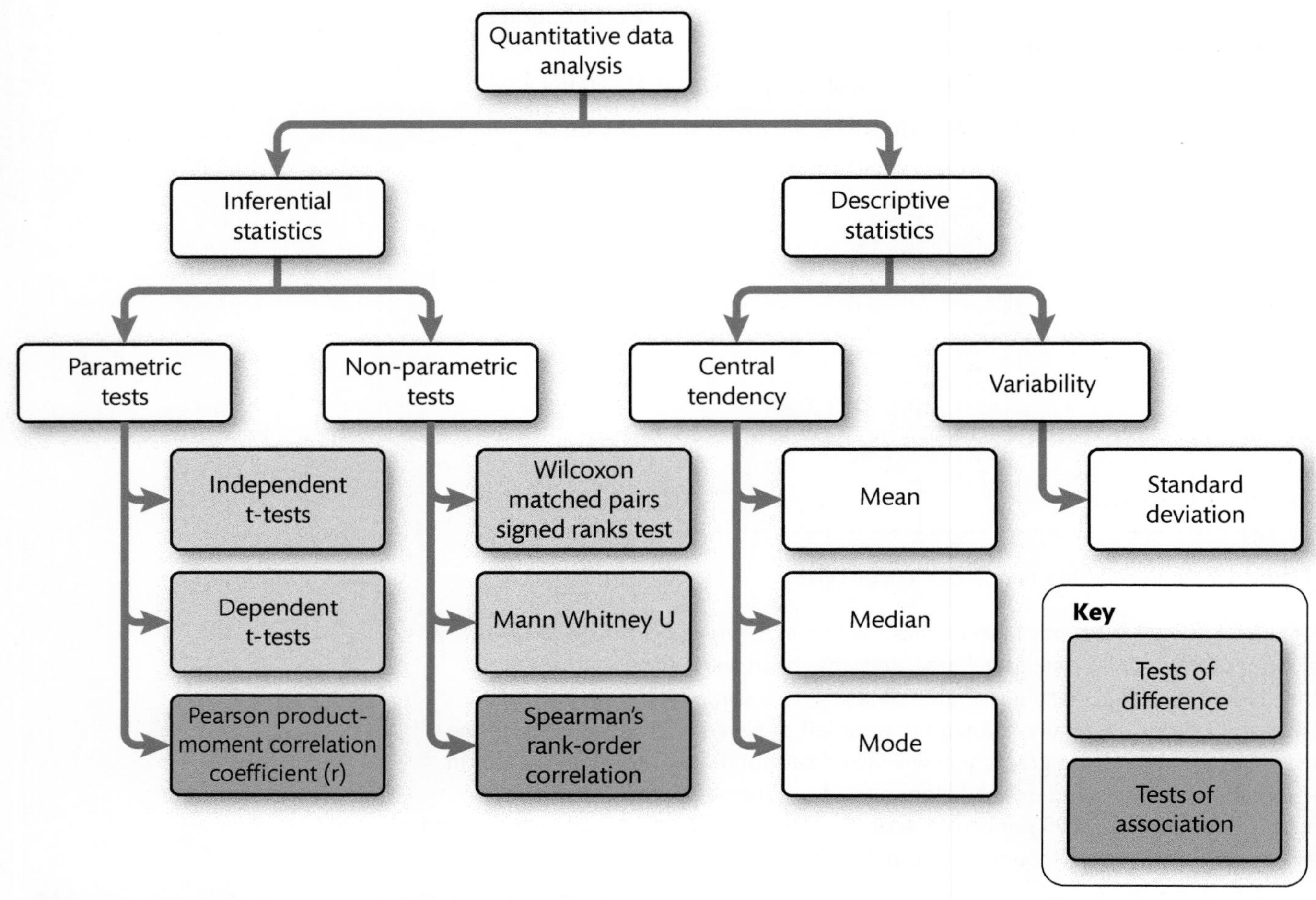

Figure 5.4: Inferential and descriptive statistics used in sport and exercise science

Selecting appropriate inferential tests

A good way to select your test is to use a decision tree like the one in Figure 5.5. If you follow the decision tree using the information available, you will find the test that you need to use. The process of using the decision tree is similar to planning a bus or a train journey – follow the line and find your stops to get to the destination!

To be able to use this decision tree and appropriately select parametric or non-parametric tests, you need to understand the types of data: nominal, ordinal, interval and ratio data.

- **Parametric tests** use **interval or ratio data** and assume that the data is drawn from a normal distribution and has the same variance.
- **Non-parametric tests** use **ordinal or nominal data**.

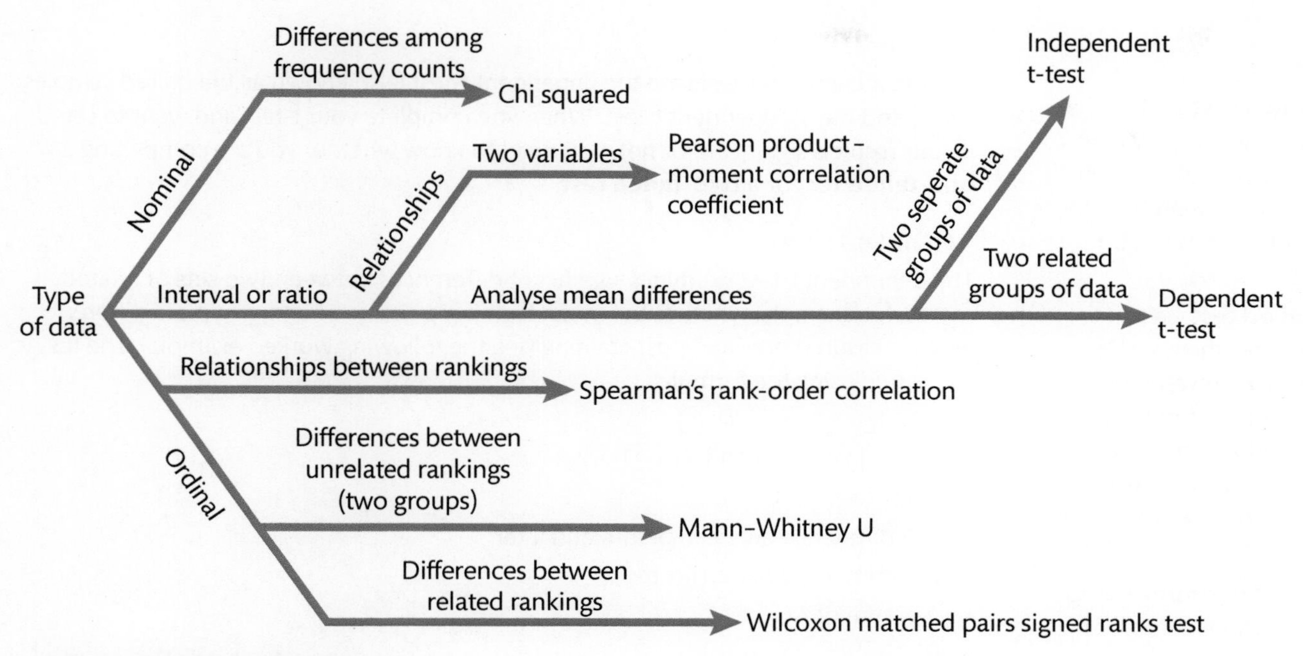

Figure 5.5: Statistics decision tree

Nominal data

A nominal scale is where participants are put into categories and counted, for example, grouping basketball players under the team they play for. You would group the players in this way to count them, not necessarily to say that one group is better than another.

Ordinal data

Ordinal data is ranked data that gives no indication of the difference between levels. It allows you to say who is best and second best, but does not tell you the difference between the two.

This type of data provides the researcher with a rank order, but does not give an exact value. For example, on a badminton ladder, the person at the top is assigned a rank of 1, the person second down is awarded a rank of 2, the third person is awarded a rank of 3, and so on. There is nothing to say, however, that the person at the top of the ladder is three times as good as the person in third place on the ladder.

Interval

Interval data is based on a scale that has equal intervals of measurement with equal intervals between each score. For example, in a figure skating scoring scale there is the same difference between scoring 5 and 5.5 as there is between scoring 5.5 and 6.

Ratio

Ratio data has proportional equal units of measurement. Ratio scales range from zero upwards and cannot have negative scores. For example, if a rugby team scores 40 points, it is worth twice as much as their opponents who have scored 20 points.

How to conduct appropriate inferential statistical tests

This section contains step-by-step instructions, formulae and **tables of critical values** for each of the statistical tests listed in your unit specification. While these will help you learn how to conduct the tests by hand, they will not show you how to complete the tests using different ICT packages (such as Microsoft Excel or IBM SPSS statistics). For these programmes, you should refer to the appropriate user manual.

Key term

Table of critical values – a table of values to which you compare your results of statistical testing to find out if they are significant at a given level.

Key terms

One-tailed test – a test that assumes one group will be better than the other, or at least no worse than the other. For example, girls will be better than boys.

Two-tailed test – a test that assumes there will be a difference between both groups, but does not say which will be better. For example, there will be a difference between girls and boys.

Degree of freedom – used as a correction factor for bias and to limit the effects of outliers, based on the number of participants you have.

Parametric tests

The most common t-tests are the dependent t-test (also known as the paired samples t-test) and the independent t-test. When you complete your t-test and want to see if your result is significant or not, you need to know whether you are completing a **one-tailed test** or a **two-tailed test**.

Dependent t-test

The dependent t-test examines significant differences between two sets of related scores, for example, whether the mean high jump scores of one group are different when measured pre- and post-training (see the following worked example). The test is calculated using the formula:

$$t = \frac{\Sigma D}{\sqrt{[n\Sigma D^2 - (\Sigma D)^2] \div (n - 1)}}$$

Where:

- D = difference between before and after
- n = number of paired scores
- Σ = sum of

Follow the steps below to carry out the dependent t-test.

1. Calculate your t value using the formula above.
2. Calculate your **degree of freedom** (df) using the formula $df = n - 1$.
3. Compare your t value to the critical values shown in Table 5.5. Find your df value (in this case 9), then go across and see if your result is greater than or equal to the number in the column below the 0.05 level. If the value achieved for your t-test is equal to or greater than the number shown, your results are significant to that level. Note that if $df > 120$, use the infinity row at the end of Table 5.5 (∞).

Worked example

Dependent t-test

An investigation explored the effects of a 12-week plyometric training programme on high jump performance using a dependent t-test. The investigation generated the data shown in Table 5.4.

$$t = \frac{43}{\sqrt{[2490 - 1849] \div 9}}$$

$$t = \frac{43}{\sqrt{641 \div 9}}$$

$$t = \frac{43}{\sqrt{71.22}}$$

$$t = \frac{43}{8.44}$$

$$t = 5.09$$

The t value calculated (5.09) is greater than the critical value of t (2.262) so the result is significant to the 0.05 level. We can say that there is a significant difference between high jump scores pre- and post-training.

Table 5.4: Effects of a 12-week plyometric training programme on high jump performance

Subject	Pre-training height (cm)	Post-training height (cm)	D (post-training minus pre-training)	D^2
1	176	179	3	9
2	169	172	3	9
3	171	175	4	16
4	173	177	4	16
5	164	166	2	4
6	170	171	1	1
7	161	168	7	49
8	159	169	10	100
9	163	166	3	9
10	170	176	6	36
n = 10			D = 43	D^2 = 249

▶ **Table 5.5:** Critical values of t

	Level of significance for one-tailed test					
	.10	**.05**	**.025**	**.01**	**.005**	**.0005**
	Level of significance for two-tailed test					
df	**.20**	**.10**	**.05**	**.02**	**.01**	**.001**
1	3.078	6.314	12.706	31.821	63.657	636.619
2	1.886	2.920	4.303	6.965	9.925	31.598
3	1.638	2.353	3.182	4.541	5.841	12.941
4	1.533	2.132	2.776	3.747	4.604	8.610
5	1.476	2.015	2.571	3.365	4.032	6.589
6	1.440	1.943	2.447	3.143	3.707	5.959
7	1.415	1.895	2.365	2.998	3.499	5.405
8	1.397	1.860	2.306	2.896	3.355	5.041
9	1.383	1.833	2.262	2.821	3.250	4.781
10	1.372	1.812	2.228	2.764	3.169	4.587
11	1.363	1.796	2.201	2.718	3.106	4.437
12	1.356	1.782	2.179	2.681	3.055	4.318
13	1.350	1.771	2.160	2.650	3.012	4.221
14	1.345	1.761	2.145	2.624	2.977	4.140
15	1.341	1.753	2.131	2.602	2.947	4.073
16	1.337	1.746	2.120	2.583	2.921	4.015
17	1.333	1.740	2.110	2.567	2.898	3.965
18	1.330	1.734	2.101	2.552	2.878	3.922
19	1.328	1.729	2.093	2.539	2.861	3.883
20	1.325	1.725	2.086	2.528	2.845	3.850
21	1.323	1.721	2.080	2.518	2.831	3.819
22	1.321	1.717	2.074	2.508	2.819	3.792
23	1.319	1.714	2.069	2.500	2.807	3.767
24	1.318	1.711	2.064	2.492	2.797	3.745
25	1.316	1.708	2.060	2.485	2.787	3.725
26	1.315	1.706	2.056	2.479	2.779	3.707
27	1.314	1.703	2.052	2.473	2.771	3.690
28	1.313	1.701	2.048	2.467	2.763	3.674
29	1.311	1.699	2.045	2.462	2.756	3.659
30	1.310	1.697	2.042	2.457	2.750	3.646
40	1.303	1.684	2.021	2.423	2.704	3.551
60	1.296	1.671	2.000	2.390	2.660	3.460
120	1.289	1.658	1.980	2.358	2.617	3.373
∞	1.282	1.645	1.960	2.326	2.576	3.291

Independent t-test

The independent t-test is used when you have two groups and are trying to discover if the mean scores of the two groups can be considered to be significantly different.

This test is suitable when the data you have collected is interval or ratio data, when your groups are randomly assigned, and when the variance (or spread) in the two groups is equal. It is calculated using the formula:

$$t = \frac{M_1 - M_2}{\sqrt{s_1^2/n_1 + s_2^2/n_2}}$$

Where:

- M_1 = mean value of group 1
- M_2 = mean value of group 2
- s_1 = standard deviation of group 1
- s_2 = standard deviation of group 2
- n_1 = number of participants in group 1
- n_2 = number of participants in group 2

Worked example

Independent t-test

A research team produced Cooper 12-minute run data (see Table 5.6) and then used the independent t-test formula to see if there was a significant difference between the two groups.

Calculate the degrees of freedom (*df*) using the formula: $df = n_1 + n_2 - 2$ and then compare the *t* value calculated to critical values in Table 5.5.

Where:

$s_1 = 238.3$ $M_1 = 3183.3$ $s_1^2 = 56786.89$ $n_1 = 10$

$s_2 = 94.6$ $M_2 = 2468.7$ $s_2^2 = 8949.16$ $n_2 = 10$

$$t = \frac{3183.3 - 2468.7}{\sqrt{(238.3)^2 \div 10 + (94.6)^2 \div 10}}$$

$$t = \frac{714.6}{\sqrt{(56\,786.89) \div 10 + (8949.16) \div 10}}$$

$$t = \frac{714.6}{\sqrt{5678.69 + 894.92}}$$

$$t = \frac{714.6}{\sqrt{6573.61}}$$

$$t = \frac{714.6}{\sqrt{81.07}}$$

$$t = 8.81$$

As you can see, the *t* value calculated (8.81) is greater than the critical value of *t* (1.734) meaning the result is significant to the 0.05 level. This means we can say that there is a significant difference between Cooper run data in the two groups.

Table 5.6: Cooper 12-minute run data

Subject	Group 1 (run after 70% VO_2 max training)	Group 2 (run after 40% VO_2 max training)
1	3200 m	2513 m
2	3600 m	2601 m
3	2894 m	2444 m
4	3001 m	2361 m
5	3187 m	2541 m
6	3651 m	2486 m
7	3109 m	2611 m
8	2997 m	2419 m
9	3056 m	2400 m
10	3138 m	2311 m
Mean	3183.3 m	2468.7 m
Standard deviation	238.3	94.6

Pearson product-moment correlation coefficient (r)

A correlation is the value of the relationship between two or more variables, which can be positive or negative. Whether it is positive or negative depends on the direction of the line when the results are plotted on a graph. The graphs in Figure 5.6 show examples of perfect positive and perfect negative correlations, but it is rare to record such correlations during data analysis.

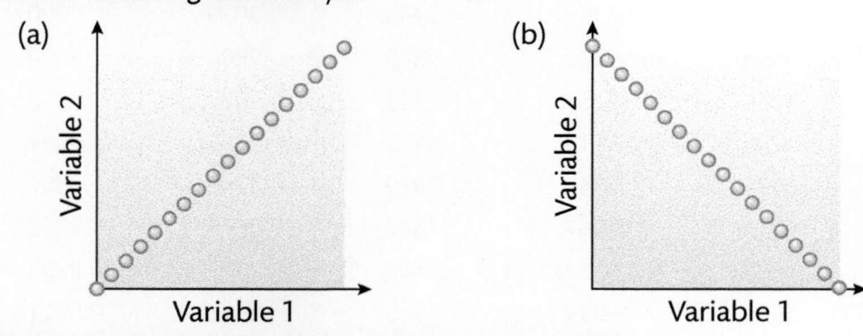

Figure 5.6: Examples of perfect positive and negative correlations

The Pearson product-moment correlation coefficient is a parametric test that is suitable when you have interval or ratio data and you are trying to identify a relationship between two variables. It is a test of association, which means it looks at whether two or more variables are related.

The test can be used in two ways:

- either you can try to find out a relationship between two variables
- or you can try to predict one score from another.

In a simple correlation that is trying to find out a relationship between two variables, it does not matter which variable is assigned *X* and which *Y*. However, if you are trying to predict one score from another, then *X* is the independent variable and *Y* is the dependent variable.

There are three stages to using the Pearson product-moment correlation:

1 summing each set of scores
2 squaring and summing each set of scores
3 multiplying each pair of scores and obtaining the cumulative sum of these products.

The formula for this is:

$$r = \frac{n\Sigma XY - (\Sigma X)(\Sigma Y)}{[\sqrt{n\Sigma X^2 - (\Sigma X)^2}][\sqrt{n\Sigma Y^2 - (\Sigma Y)^2}]}$$

Where:

- n = number of paired scores
- Σ = sum of
- X = scores for one variable
- Y = scores for the other variable
- ΣX^2 = sum of raw scores for X, squared
- ΣY^2 = sum of raw scores for Y, squared
- $(\Sigma X)^2$ = sum of all of the X^2 scores
- $(\Sigma Y)^2$ = sum of all of the Y^2 scores

To interpret the significance of your *r* value, select your level of significance (remember that in sport and exercise science this is normally 0.05) and find your degree of freedom (*df*) for your test. For this test, use the formula $df = n - 2$ and compare your *r* value to Table 5.7 to find whether your results are significant. If your result is equal to or greater than the critical value in the table, your result is significant.

Table 5.7: Critical values of Pearson product-moment correlation coefficient

	Level of significance for one-tailed test				
	.05	.025	.01	.005	.001
	Level of significance for two-tailed test				
df	**.10**	**.05**	**.02**	**.01**	**.001**
1	.9877	.9969	.9995	.9999	1.000
2	.9000	.9500	.9800	.9900	.9990
3	.8054	.8783	.9343	.9587	.9912
4	.7293	.8114	.8822	.9172	.9741
5	.6694	.7545	.8329	.8745	.9507
6	.6215	.7067	.7887	.8343	.9249
7	.5822	.6664	.7498	.7977	.8982
8	.5494	.6319	.7155	.7646	.8721
9	.5214	.6021	.6851	.7348	.8471
10	.4973	.5760	.6581	.7079	.8233
11	.4762	.5529	.6339	.6835	.8010
12	.4575	.5324	.6120	.6614	.7800
13	.4409	.5139	.5923	.6411	.7603
14	.4259	.4973	.5742	.6226	.7420
15	.4124	.4821	.5577	.6055	.7246
16	.4000	.4683	.5425	.5897	.7084
17	.3887	.4555	.5285	.5751	.6932
18	.3783	.4438	.5155	.5614	.6787
19	.3687	.4329	.5034	.5487	.6652
20	.3598	.4227	.4921	.5368	.6524
25	.3233	.3809	.4451	.4869	.5974
30	.2960	.3494	.4093	.4487	.5541
35	.2746	.3246	.3810	.4182	.5189
40	.2573	.3044	.3578	.3932	.4896
45	.2428	.2875	.3384	.3721	.4648
50	.2306	.2732	.3218	.3541	.4433
60	.2108	.2500	.2948	.3248	.4078
70	.1954	.2319	.2737	.3017	.3799
80	.1829	.2172	.2565	.2830	.3568
90	.1726	.2050	.2422	.2673	.3375
100	.1638	.1946	.2301	.2540	.3211

Non-parametric tests

If the data is non-parametric, t-tests cannot be used. In this case, the Wilcoxon matched pairs signed ranks test is used in place of the dependent t-test, and the Mann-Whitney U test is used in place of the independent t-test. Spearman's rank-order correlation test is similar to the Pearson product-moment correlation coefficient in its purpose.

Wilcoxon matched pairs signed rank test

The Wilcoxon matched pairs signed rank test is used when you are trying to find out if there is a significant difference between two scores (or 'conditions') that are taken from the same participant (or from matched participants). It is used when the data is ordinal (ranked). To do the test, work through the following steps.

1 Disregard any results for participants who scored the same in both conditions, then count up the number of paired scores left. This is your *n* score.
2 Calculate the difference between the two scores of each participant, assigning plus or minus signs (*d*).
3 Rank the differences, giving the smallest a rank of 1 (ignoring plus or minus signs, i.e. +2 is of the same value as –2). When two scores are tied, each is given the mean of the two ranks and the next rank is missed out (for example, if two participants are in level sixth place, they are both given the rank of 6.5 and the next place is given a rank of 8).
4 Add up the ranks of all the minus scores.
5 Add up the ranks of all the plus scores.
6 Take the smaller of the two figures calculated in points 4 and 5 to gain your *w* value.
7 Look up your value for *w* in a significance table (you will be able to find one online). If it is equal to or less than the figure in the 0.05 column, the result is significant at that level.

Table 5.8: Using the Wilcoxon matched pairs signed rank test to assess effect of imagery training

Subject pair	Condition A (run times pre-imagery training)	Condition B (run times post-imagery training)	*d* (A minus B)	Rank of *d*	Rank of plus differences	Rank of minus differences
1	11.09	11.00				
2	11.23	11.25				
3	11.55	11.32				
4	11.46	11.36				
5	11.22	11.73				
6	11.13	11.43				
7	11.01	10.86				
8	10.93	10.55				
9	10.99	10.90				
10	11.39	11.10				
					Total	Total
						w =

Mann-Whitney U test

The Mann-Whitney U test is the non-parametric equivalent of the independent t-test. You will use this if you have ranked data, or data that is not normally distributed. You use the 'U' value to find out if one group ranks significantly higher than the other, when measured against the same variable (e.g. the number of 180s scored by darts players in the British Darts Organisation against the Professional Darts Corporation).

Research

Some data analysis is completed using data analysis packages, such as Statistical Package for the Social Sciences (SPSS). Using the website www.statisticssolutions.com answer the following questions.

1 What is SPSS?
2 Why are electronic data analysis packages useful in sport and exercise science?
3 How do you complete a Mann-Whitney U test?

Spearman's rank order correlation test

Spearman's rank order correlation test has a similar purpose to the Pearson product-moment correlation coefficient. However, it is a non-parametric equivalent and should be used when you want to find a relationship between two sets of ordinal (ranked) data (for example, goals scored and final league position in football, or serving accuracy and final ladder position in badminton, or golf driving distance and final leader board position).

The first step is to rank your data (goals scored/serving accuracy/golf driving distance) from highest to lowest, with 1 being the highest. After this, determine the difference between your data and the place in the tournament. This must be squared and then summed. The formula used for the test is:

$$r_S = \frac{6(\Sigma D^2)}{n(n^2 - 1)}$$

Where:

- n = number of ranked pairs
- D = difference between each pair
- ΣD^2 = the sum of the squared differences between rank

To interpret the significance of your r_s value, select the level of significance (0.05) and calculate the degree of freedom (*df*) for your test using the formula $df = n - 2$. Compare your value to the degree of significance in Table 5.9.

Table 5.9: Table of critical values for Spearman's rank order correlation

df	.10	.05	.01
5	0.90		
6	0.83	0.89	
7	0.71	0.79	0.93
8	0.64	0.74	0.88
9	0.60	0.68	0.83
10	0.56	0.656	0.79
11	0.52	0.61	0.77
12	0.50	0.59	0.75
13	0.47	0.56	0.71
14	0.46	0.54	0.69
15	0.44	0.52	0.66
16	0.42	0.51	0.64
17	0.41	0.49	0.62
18	0.40	0.48	0.61
19	0.39	0.46	0.60
20	0.38	0.45	0.58
21	0.37	0.44	0.56
22	0.36	0.43	0.55
23	0.35	0.42	0.54
24	0.34	0.41	0.53
25	0.34	0.40	0.52
26	0.33	0.39	0.51
27	0.32	0.38	0.50
28	0.32	0.38	0.49
29	0.31	0.37	0.48
∞	0.31	0.36	0.47

Practical meaningfulness statistics

Inferential statistics are used in quantitative research to accept or reject your null hypothesis, and therefore your hypothesis. However, inferential statistics do not give you information about the practical significance of your results, such as how effective a treatment has been. To do this, you need to use practical meaningfulness-based statistics. Two of the most common involve looking at percentage change or effect size.

Discussion

If you were a sport and exercise scientist working with sportspeople on a daily basis, why would you find practical meaningfulness statistics useful?

Percentage change

Calculating percentage change is a simple statistic that gives you basic information about the effectiveness of a treatment or an intervention (such as how beneficial a particular training method has been) in a way that most people can understand quite easily. The greater the percentage change, the more effective the treatment has been. The formula for calculating percentage change is:

$$\text{percentage change} = ((X_2 - X_1) \div X_1) \times 100$$

Where:

- X_1 = pre-test mean values
- X_2 = post-test mean values

Effect size

As its name suggests, you use the effect size calculation to determine how effective a particular treatment has been, with the test providing a result that equates to a small, moderate or large effect size. A value of 0.2 to <0.5 equates to a small effect size, a value of 0.5 to <0.8 equates to a moderate effect size, while a value >0.8 equates to a large effect size. The larger the effect size, the more effective a treatment has been. The formula for effect size is:

$$\text{effect size} = \frac{(X_1 - X_2)}{SD_{control}}$$

Where:

- X_1 = treatment group
- X_2 = control group
- $SD_{control}$ = standard deviation of the control group

Qualitative research designs

There are four main types of qualitative research design: case studies, historical/retrospective design, grounded theories and ethnographic design.

Case study

Case study research is where you investigate a particular phenomenon (e.g. an individual or team) over a long period of time. It takes into account the development of the area of investigation over time and the environment in which the research resides. Multiple case studies can also be used, where two or more cases are examined at the same time.

For example, to investigate the psychological effects of injury at different stages of injury and recovery, a case study design would be suitable. It allows you to investigate one person over a period of time and at different times throughout the stages of injury. This means you can draw conclusions relating to that individual and suggest these conclusions as directions for future research on a larger scale.

Historical/retrospective design

A historical or retrospective research design aims to collect and analyse data relating to past events to try to explain how or why those events happened. For example, you could speak to retired athletes to investigate the role of injury in their decision to retire.

Grounded theory

You would use a grounded theory design when you aim to produce a theory from the data that you collect and analyse. You will usually show the theory you have produced as a diagram. For example, you could interview former professional players in a particular sport, and the people involved in their development, and use the information you gathered to develop a theory about the factors that contribute to a successful career in that sport.

Ethnographic design

Ethnographic design aims to study a group or culture by becoming immersed within that group to carry out observations. For example, Atkinson (2007) used an ethnographic design to study how gym-goers linked supplement use to their desire for enhanced masculinity.

Reflect

Think about your favourite topic within sport and exercise science. Can you think of a way that the different qualitative designs could be used to investigate the topic?

Qualitative data collection techniques

Interviews

Interviews can be separated into individual and group-based interviews. There are three main types of individual interview.

- **Structured interviews** – a set interview plan that you follow without change, regardless of participant responses.
- **Unstructured interviews** – this type of interview has a start question and then the conversation goes from there. You must be skilled at focusing your conversation to get a lot out of this type of interview.
- **Semi-structured interview** – an interview that follows the original plan but allows scope for follow-up **probe questions** if a topic of interest is brought up. This is a good technique as it allows you to get deeper information from your participant through additional questioning, as well as giving the participant the opportunity to discuss things further.

Key term

Probe questions – questions used to further explore a topic when it appears as part of an interview. Examples of probe questions include elaboration, clarification and continuation probes.

Focus groups

Focus groups are similar to individual interviews but involve more than one participant. There are usually between six and 12 participants and the researcher acts as a discussion facilitator rather than an interviewer. In this context, your role as the researcher is to ensure that the focus group stays on topic and does not wander.

Focus groups are more effective if everyone joins the discussion. They can provide a better quality of data because the discussion gets deeper as the ideas develop. They are useful for finding out opinions and ideas.

Advantages and disadvantages of interviews

No one type of interview is perfect - it should be matched to the situation or participant. Interviews are used in qualitative research because they are a useful way for researchers to understand the beliefs, opinions and emotions of participants: the researcher gets a view of what the participant thinks in the participant's own words. This gives the researcher a greater understanding of the meanings that the participant attaches to their experiences.

▸ **Table 5.10:** Advantages and disadvantages of interviews

Advantages	Disadvantages
Participants can express their views in their own words.	They require more resources and are more time consuming than using questionnaires.
Participants can provide information from their own perspective.	They tend to use small sample sizes because interviews are time consuming.
Unexpected data may come out in the interview.	The participant(s) can take the interview off in a number of directions.
Body language, tone and pitch of voice, and speed of speech can be assessed.	Data analysis is more difficult and takes longer than using questionnaires.
The researcher can establish a rapport with the participant(s) and investigate target groups.	The quality of the data is dependent on the quality of the questioning and quality of responses.

Conducting effective interviews

Interviews are used in qualitative research as they help you get lots of information about a topic quickly, but this only works if you have developed your interview skills. In interviews, you will only get answers to the questions you ask. If you ask the wrong questions you will never find out what you want.

To get the most out of an interview, establish a rapport by setting the tone of the interview; have a friendly chat before starting or break the ice with more general questions at the start that do not need much thought to answer. You can then progress to more specific questions likely to lead to more detailed responses. Guide the conversation around your research problem. Question the participant further to provide you with examples of things they have experienced, rather than hypothetical examples.

When interviewing in research, a three-stage technique is often used.

1. The researcher asks the main question (for example 'What motivates you to...?'). This gets the ball rolling.
2. This is followed by probe questions (for example 'Can you give me a specific example of...?'). This clarifies or deepens understanding or knowledge.
3. The final aspect is a follow-up question (for example 'So, am I correct in saying that...?'). This gives the researcher the opportunity to check they have understood what the participant has said and that it is taken in the correct context.

Remember that the listening part of an interview is as important as the speaking part. A good interviewer knows when to keep quiet and listen, and when to speak. Do not interrupt the participant when they are speaking as this can prevent them from wanting to answer further questions.

Observations

Observations are qualitative data collection methods that take place in a natural setting. They allow you to observe behaviours a participant may not know they display, or would not like to disclose during an interview. As such, observations can add a different dimension to your research.

Data is often recorded in field notes, which can be handwritten or typed/recorded on a smartphone. Field notes should describe the activity or setting you are observing (e.g. behaviours you have seen and when) and be as detailed as possible without spending more time writing than observing. You should reflect on your thoughts and feelings as the researcher during your observations.

Table 5.11 shows some of the advantages and disadvantages of using observational data collection methods.

Table 5.11: Advantages and disadvantages of observations

Advantages	Disadvantages
They can be 'here and now' rather than being dependent on memory.	There is potential for the researcher to misunderstand what they are seeing.
They can take place in natural settings rather than research settings.	It can be difficult to identify and record the correct type of data.
They allow for the identification of behaviours that may not be apparent to the person and may not have been discovered through interviews.	The Hawthorne effect: if the person knows they are the subject of research, they may act differently and could invalidate the whole project – the researcher must be very careful exactly how they approach the people in observational research.
They allow for the identification of behaviours that the person may not wish to disclose.	

Participant observation

Participant observation involves active participation in the topic you are researching. For example, if you were studying team cohesion in rugby, you could join a rugby team to observe 'from the inside' and gain your own experiences of cohesion as a player. Data would then be recorded in the form of field notes with you recording your own thoughts, feelings, opinions, emotions and experiences. This method is useful when trying to discover the more delicate aspects of group behaviour that are not easy to see from the outside.

Non-participant observation

Non-participant observation involves observing 'from the outside'. There is no interaction with the individuals or activity being observed. For example, if you wanted to look at injuries during a basketball match, you could watch how many injuries happened, what types of injuries they were and record the numbers on a data recording sheet.

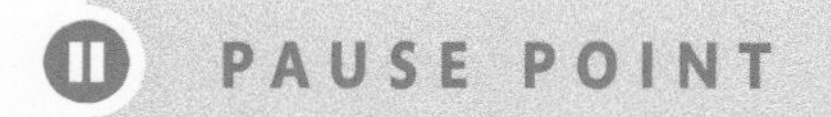

You want to investigate team cohesion in netball using observations. What type of observation would you use?

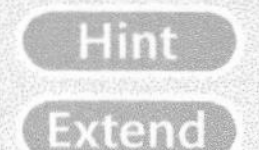

Hint: Produce a table that contrasts the two types of observation.

Extend: Discuss the advantages and disadvantages of each type of observation, then conclude by stating which method you have selected.

Qualitative data analysis methods

Selecting an appropriate method of analysis for your qualitative data is an important aspect of the research process. Three common qualitative data analysis methods are content analysis, coding and thematic analysis.

Content analysis

Qualitative content analysis is an umbrella term used to describe methods of analysing qualitative communications – such as interviews or focus groups – with a specific focus on the context in which the communication took place as well as the content of the communication. It involves you looking at the content of the interview and grouping data together under themes, which are then refined and developed until you have your final data analysis.

The key differences between this and other methods (such as coding and thematic analysis) is that content analysis does not aim to develop a specific theory in the same way as coding does within grounded theory, and it is more flexible in its use than thematic analysis.

Research

Research the analysis method of hierarchical content analysis. What are the stages involved and why do you think this version of content analysis is popular with qualitative researchers?

Coding

Coding involves organising raw data (sentences, phrases or words from your questionnaires or interviews) into categories. Each category must have a valid heading and a **rule for inclusion**, which helps to guide which category each piece of data is placed in.

Key term

Rule for inclusion – a statement used to define which data is included in a category.

For example, if you were researching 'factors affecting talent development in football', you could have a category called 'importance of tangible parental support'. A rule for inclusion could be 'statement made refers to concrete support given to player from parent (for example, the purchase of playing kit or transport to matches), being either a positive or negative influence on the player's development'.

Before starting your coding, you should read and re-read your transcribed data. This is so you gain an in-depth understanding of the data. The process of coding starts with open coding, progresses to axial coding and ends with selective coding.

- **Open coding** – data is broken down and examined. Your aim is to identify all the key statements in the interviews relating to the aims of your research and your research problem. After identifying the key statements, you can start to put the key points into categories, but each category must be given a suitable heading. When you start to organise your data into categories, you have started the coding process.
- **Axial coding** – the next stage is to put the data back together. Part of this process means re-reading the data you have collected so that you can give precise explanations about your area of interest. To do this, you need to refine the categories that you started to create during open coding. During this stage you may develop new categories. To allow you to refine your codes at this stage ask more questions about the categories (and the codes) you have created. Some questions you may consider are:
  - Can I relate certain codes together under a more general code?
  - Can I place codes into a particular order?
  - Can I identify any relationships between different codes?
- **Selective coding** is the final stage. It involves finalising your categories (and codes) so that you can group them together. When you group them together, you will produce different diagrams to show how your categories link together. The key part of this is to select a main category that will form the focal point of your diagram. You also need to look for data that contradicts previous research, rather than data that supports it. This helps you to make better arguments and draw more conclusions based on your data.

Thematic analysis

Thematic analysis is a common qualitative data analysis technique originally put forward by Braun and Clarke (2006). It is different to other methods of qualitative data analysis as it has six stages that you progress through in order to reach your final analysis. This process is useful for some novice qualitative researchers as it provides a framework for analysis that you can follow while still offering you the flexibility of qualitative analysis.

Step by step: Thematic analysis

6 Steps

1 **Immersion** – become familiar with your data by, for example, reading interview transcripts repeatedly so that you gain a deep understanding.

2 **Generate initial codes** – create codes across the full data set and produce a list of all of the initial codes. You can then ensure that you have included all of the relevant data under each code.

3 **Search for and identify themes** – think more broadly beyond codes and progress to themes that are more general. Collate into themes all codes that are relevant to each other, then give the theme a working title. At this stage it is common that you will produce a thematic map – a form of mind map – that shows how the different codes link to form a particular theme.

4 **Refine themes** – think critically about the themes that you produced in stage 3, looking at, for example, any potential overlap or repetition so that you can produce themes that more succinctly represent the data. Within this, you should consider any data that did not fall into any of the codes at stage 1 and see if they can feed into your themes.

5 **Define and name themes** – write a short definition (two or three sentences maximum) about the content of the theme and give the theme a name that accurately represents the content. This is another opportunity to ensure that your themes are not too broad as, by writing your description of the theme, you will be further reflecting on the content of each theme.

6 **Write the report** – write your report of the thematic analysis. You should use rich quotes or extracts from data that clearly demonstrate the themes in your study. Even at this stage, you should reflect on your analysis so far, to ensure that it fairly represents the data you collected.

Discussion

What do you think are the advantages and disadvantages of using thematic analysis in qualitative research?

Stages of qualitative data analysis

Qualitative research will generally go through three stages, originally put forward by Miles and Huberman (1994). These stages are data reduction, displaying data, and drawing conclusions and verifying data.

Data reduction

Data reduction involves taking all of your data (e.g. field notes from observations, interview transcripts, etc.) and organising it into more manageable chunks. This can involve any of the methods of qualitative data analysis explored in the previous section (i.e. content analysis, coding, thematic analysis).

When going through this stage, you might be tempted to permanently discard some of your data. However, you should avoid doing this until your project is finished and you are certain that you no longer need it.

Displaying data

There are different ways to display your data. The way that you display it will affect the argument or point you are trying to make. Diagramming is a technique that can be used throughout your data analysis to help you to understand relationships between different aspects of your data, as well as being used at the end of your data analysis to represent these relationships.

Network diagrams show hierarchical relationships between different ideas. Figure 5.7 shows that there are a number of benefits to the use of imagery (the top of the hierarchy or the most important part of information to take away) and that these benefits include increased self-efficacy, skill acquisition and injury rehabilitation.

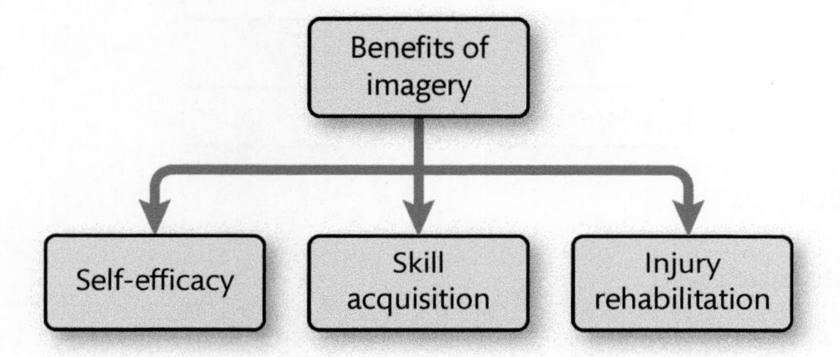

Figure 5.7: A network diagram

Venn diagrams consist of two or more overlapping circles. They show how different topics relate to each other. In the example in Figure 5.8, you can see how the different disciplines within sport and exercise science (SES) interact to make up the overall discipline.

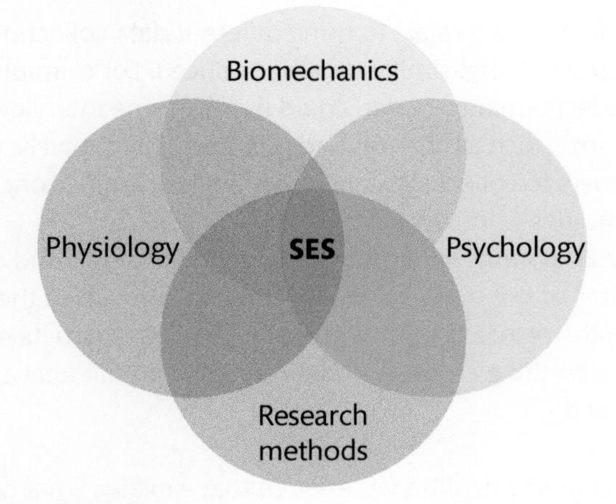

Figure 5.8: A Venn diagram

A **radial diagram** (also known as a **spider diagram**) illustrates a relationship where each item is linked to a central item. This diagram can be thought of as a simple organisation chart that starts from the centre rather than the top (see Figure 5.9).

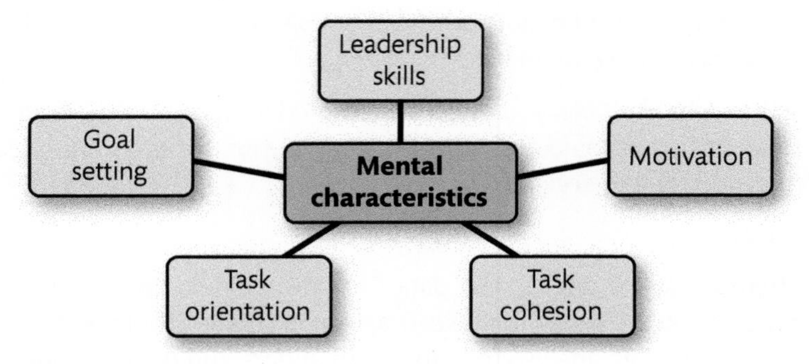

Figure 5.9: A radial diagram

A **cycle diagram** shows the stages in a process as a continuous cycle. The process is shown as a circle, with a break at each stage, and an arrowhead to show the direction of the process. In the example in Figure 5.10, the diagram shows that team cohesion affects team performance, which in turn affects team cohesion further, and so on.

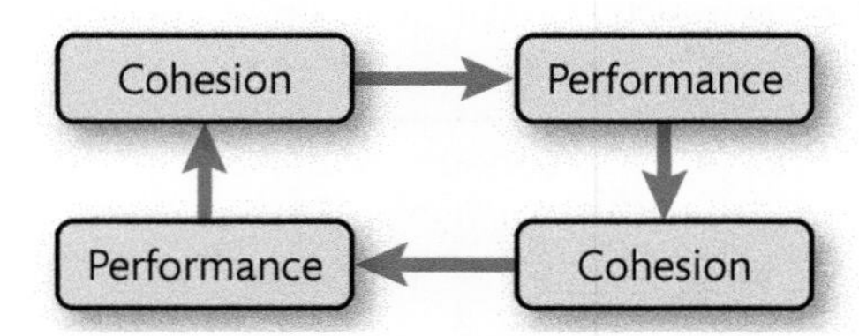

Figure 5.10: A cycle diagram

Theory into practice

Write down when you would use each of the diagrams that are covered in this section and why.

Drawing conclusions and verifying data

Your data analysis should allow you to draw meaningful conclusions about your data and then verify these conclusions. Doing this can help you to ensure the validity and reliability of your research. Two common techniques used to do this are triangulation and member checking.

- **Triangulation** in one sense refers to using different data collection methods in the same study to check that similar data is produced. For example, you could use interviews and questionnaires or you could use the same interviews with different types of participants (such as athletes and coaches). Alternatively, you could ask different researchers to collect data and independently draw conclusions before checking their findings with each other.
- During **member checking**, you complete your data analysis and draw conclusions relating to the aims of the study. You then show the analysis to the participants who took part in the research so that they can check that you have understood and communicated everything correctly. If they agree with your analysis, you can say that the data is valid.

PAUSE POINT Produce a 'novice guide' to qualitative research that explains what happens at the different stages.

Hint What are the different stages of qualitative data analysis?

Extend Think of an example research project and explain how you would apply the different stages of qualitative data analysis to this project.

Mixed-research designs

Mixed-research has gained more prominence in recent years as researchers have sought multiple layers of understanding about topics.

Discussion

What do you think are the advantages and disadvantages of each type of mixed-research design?

Mixed-research designs fall under two common headings, relating to the interaction of the quantitative and qualitative methods within the overall design on the study.

- **Sequential research design** involves you using one set of research methods followed by another (i.e. qualitative followed by quantitative, or vice versa).
- **Parallel research design** involves you using qualitative and quantitative research methods alongside each other, at the same time.

Mixed-research data collection

Data collection in mixed-research involves using appropriate qualitative and quantitative methods. When deciding which to use, you should consider their advantages and disadvantages, and use them in either a sequential or parallel manner, as appropriate for your study. For example, you might conduct a quantitative survey to measure adolescent athletes' attitudes toward concussion in sport and then conduct follow-up interviews with a sample of the participants to gain a deeper understanding of their attitudes.

Mixed-research data analysis

As with data collection, data analysis in mixed-research involves the appropriate use of qualitative and quantitative data analysis methods, in either a parallel or sequential manner.

Using the concussion example again, you could use descriptive statistics such as mean and standard deviation to gain an overall understanding of attitudes, then use an appropriate inferential statistic (such as an independent t-test or Mann-Whitney U test) to assess any differences in opinion between males and females. You might then conduct a content analysis of the follow-up interviews to identify the key common opinions.

PAUSE POINT You want to investigate physical and psychological benefits of sports massage. Which type of mixed-research would you use and why?

Hint Explain what mixed-research data analysis involves and how it would work in this situation.

Extend Why might mixed-research be more beneficial for this project than either qualitative or quantitative research alone?

Assessment practice 5.2

C.P5 C.P6 C.M3 CD.D3 D.P7 D.P8 D.M4

Great news! Following on from Assessment activity 5.1, your application report has got you an interview for the internship. As part of the selection process, in the interview you are required to deliver a presentation that:

- first introduces the three main approaches to research in sport and exercise science so that the football club can see how well you will be able to apply these if you conduct any research with the players
- presents the methods and results from a mini-investigation that you have conducted, so that the club can see your ability to correctly select a method for a topic and your ability to appropriately present results about a topic.

Plan

- What are the key parts to the presentation that form the whole task?
- Do I need clarification on anything, such as interpreting the results of my statistical test?

Do

- Can I make connections between what I am reading/researching and the task, and identify the important information?
- Can I set milestones and evaluate my progress and success at these intervals?

Review

- Can I explain how I would use this type of activity in working life or in another unit on my course?
- Do I know which research methods I am confident with, which I am not, and how I can improve this in the future?

Further reading and resources

Books

Gratton, C. and Jones, I. (2010) *Research Methods for Sports Studies*, 2nd edition, Oxford: Routledge.

Smith, M.F. (2010) *Research Methods in Sport*, Exeter: Learning Matters.

Sparkes, A.C. and Smith, B. (2014) *Qualitative Research Methods in Sport, Exercise and Health: From Process to Product*, Oxford: Routledge.

Thomas, J.R., Nelson, J.K., and Silverman, S.J. (2011) *Research Methods in Physical Activity*, 6th edition, Champaign, IL: Human Kinetics.

Journals

Gledhill, A. and Harwood, C. (2015) A holistic perspective on career development in UK female soccer players: A negative case analysis, *Psychology of Sport and Exercise*, 21: 65–77.

THINK ▶▶FUTURE

Nicola Johnson
Sport Scientist

I've been working as a sport scientist in professional rugby for three years. During this time I have encountered so many different athletes that sport science has been beneficial for, across physiology, biomechanics and psychology. When I completed my BTEC Level 3 Sport and Exercise Science, I went to university and completed a BASES-endorsed course in Sport and Exercise Science as I wanted to be confident that the programme had been scrutinised by my professional body. This complemented my existing rugby coaching qualifications so I'm happy that I have the subject-specific knowledge as well as an understanding of the sport. I think this blend means that I can relate to both players and coaches, as well as understanding their needs.

Having an understanding of the sport you work in is essential for effective work as a sport scientist. So is the ability to develop and maintain effective working relationships with different individuals. In doing so, you are more likely to be able to get to know your players which is really useful when it comes to trying to get them to 'buy-in' to things like new training methods. This is important as the safety and well-being of your players is always your main concern when you are working in sport, even before their levels of performance, so having them train and perform in the way they should be is more likely to mean they will stay safe and well.

Focusing on your skills

Conducting research with athletes

Research is important for the continued development of sports teams and athletes as it helps to develop knowledge, understanding and skills. You should think about the following points.

- Before completing any research with a participant, make sure that you have their consent.
- Make sure that you provide them with a clear information sheet so that they know exactly what will be required of them.
- Make sure that you have a good depth of knowledge, understanding and skills across each of the main approaches to research.
- Remember, there is no 'best' approach to research, only approaches that are best suited to answering research questions.

Getting ready for assessment

Jess is working towards a BTEC National in Sport and Exercise Science. She was given an assignment with the following title 'The role of research in sport: Why is it important and what factors can affect it?' to cover Learning aims A and B. The report had to:

- discuss the importance of research in sporting environments
- examine the key issues that impact on the effectiveness and quality of research in sport and exercise science.

How I got started

First, I decided which sport I wanted to base my report on. I chose a sport that I am interested in because I knew this would make me more motivated and committed to doing a good job on the work.

I collated all of my notes for these learning aims and separated them out into different sections: the importance of research and the different factors that can impact on the quality and effectiveness of research.

Finally, I wrote a plan for my assignment that included key headings that I was going to include and a mind map for each section that showed what I wanted to include. The mind map started with each of the topic areas and developed out into what I needed to say about each of them.

How I brought it all together

To start, I wrote a short introduction that outlined the purpose of the work that I was doing. After this, I separated out my assignment into six different sub-sections:

- a definition of research, that I referenced from an appropriate source
- a discussion of the different types of research
- a discussion of the importance of research for those working in sport and exercise and for informing your work with clients. Within this, I talked about things like the importance of evidence-based practice
- the roles of validity, reliability, accuracy and precision in research
- ethical issues associated with sport and exercise science research
- a conclusion.

What I learned from the experience

There are lots of different things to think about when you are looking at how research applies in sport and exercise settings. It is important to know how they apply in these settings, not just what they are. This application made the assignment a little bit difficult at times, but using examples in my assignment made it easier to get to grips with it, as I was talking about it in a context that I understood.

I think I spent a bit too much time focusing on defining key words like validity and reliability, rather than looking in depth at the different types. I would look at understanding the different types in more depth as they each have different roles to play and just looking at validity and reliability in general is a little too basic.

Think about it

- Have you planned out your assignment so that you know you will be able to complete it by the submission deadline?
- Do you have the recommended resources as well as your class notes to help you to provide evidence and references to support and develop the arguments that you plan to make?
- Is your assignment written in your own words?

Coaching for Performance and Fitness 6

Getting to know your unit

Assessment

You will be assessed by a series of assignments set by your tutor.

There is more to being a good coach than producing good athletes or excellent teams. The best coaches are those who give athletes a positive experience and motivate them to continue. The role of a sports coach can go beyond that of a skilled and knowledgeable coach who is dedicated to developing athletes. A coach might be called on to act as a fitness trainer, social worker, motivator, disciplinarian, friend, mentor, manager or secretary, as well as many other roles.

With sport participation increasing throughout the UK, there is a strong demand for coaches who can develop athletes' performance and fitness. In this unit you will investigate the work of successful coaches and examine the skills and techniques required to develop sports performance and fitness. You will plan and deliver a coaching session; after its completion, you will reflect on your performance and how the session could be improved in future.

How you will be assessed

Coaching is fundamentally a practical skill and as such there will be a strong emphasis in this unit on practical learning. Throughout this unit you will find a range of assessment activities designed to consolidate your learning, give you valuable experience and assess your learning. Completion of these activities will give you the opportunity to demonstrate your knowledge but will not guarantee you any particular grade.

It is important that you follow a structured approach to these activities to ensure that you cover all the learning aims. This will be good practice for when you tackle your actual assignments, helping you provide the required evidence to achieve a pass grade.

For a Merit or Distinction grade additional information will be required and presented in the appropriate format. For example, for a Merit grade, you may be asked to compare or analyse whereas for a Distinction you may be asked to evaluate.

Your tutor will design tasks that will challenge you and provide opportunities to evidence your understanding at all levels. This may take the form of:

- providing a written document to explain and analyse the skills and knowledge required to be a strong coach
- developing a plan for an individual session and showing how it links to an extended series plan
- delivering the individual practical performance session and afterwards reflecting on how it could be improved.

Assessment criteria

This table shows what you must do in order to achieve a **Pass**, **Merit** or **Distinction** grade, and where you can find activities to help you.

Pass	Merit	Distinction
Learning aim A Investigate coaching for performance and fitness		
A.P1 Describe coaching for performance and fitness and the methods used to support athlete development. **Assessment practice 6.1**	**A.M1** Explain coaching for performance and fitness, the methods used to support athletes and the role technology may play in athlete development. **Assessment practice 6.1**	**A.D1** Analyse coaching for performance and fitness, and the use of technology and supporting professionals to support athlete development. **Assessment practice 6.1**
A.P2 Describe the role technology and professionals may have to support athlete development when coaching for performance and fitness. **Assessment practice 6.1**		
Learning aim B Explore practices, adaptations and measures used to develop performance and fitness		
B.P3 Explain practices and adaptations used to develop athletes when coaching for performance and fitness. **Assessment practice 6.2**	**B.M2** Analyse practices and adaptations used to develop athletes when coaching for performance and fitness. **Assessment practice 6.2**	**B.D2** Evaluate the practicality, suitability and effectiveness of practices and measures used to develop athletes when coaching for performance and fitness. **Assessment practice 6.2**
B.P4 Explain measures used to develop athletes when coaching for performance and fitness. **Assessment practice 6.2**	**B.M3** Analyse measures used to develop athletes when coaching for performance and fitness. **Assessment practice 6.2**	
Learning aim C Demonstrate effective planning of coaching to develop performance and fitness		
C.P5 Produce a detailed plan for an individual performance and fitness coaching session that reflects planning considerations and measures, and fits within an overall series plan. **Assessment practice 6.3**	**C.M4** Discuss the interrelationship between own individual plan, planning considerations, measures and the overall series plan. **Assessment practice 6.3**	**CD.D3** Evaluate the impact of the planning and delivery of the performance and fitness session, justifying adaptations to future sessions and personal coaching developments. **Assessment practice 6.4**
Learning aim D Explore the impact of coaching for performance and fitness		
D.P6 Deliver the individual performance and fitness session, showing consideration of health and safety factors. **Assessment practice 6.4**	**D.M5** Analyse the impact of the planning and delivery of the performance and fitness coaching session, suggesting adaptations to future sessions and personal coaching developments. **Assessment practice 6.4**	
D.P7 Review the delivered performance and fitness session, reflecting on own planning and coaching performance. **Assessment practice 6.4**		

Getting started

Positive coaching takes practice and skill. You will probably have worked with a coach in real life and should be able to assess how they performed. Consider a coach you have observed. What strengths did they exhibit? What do you feel they could have done better? What skills and qualities do you think you possess that would help you as a coach?

A Investigate coaching for performance and fitness

Link

This unit has strong links with *Unit 8: Specialised Fitness Training.*

Skills and knowledge for coaching

Organisation of session

Planning training programmes and sessions requires high levels of organisation to motivate athletes and maintain interest. To be fully prepared and organised for a session a coach should ensure that:

- they know how many participants are taking part and the activities are appropriate for all the participants
- they have decided what equipment they will need prior to the event and checked that it is available and ready for use on the day of the session
- the facility is booked well in advance and that they are aware of its safety procedures
- at the end of the session the facility and equipment are left as they were at the start
- they have clear methods of stopping and starting the session, for example, when the coach blows the whistle, all participants must stop.

Reflect

Consider the sport you feel most confident in and imagine you have been tasked with providing a coaching session for a group of Year 9 students. How many students would you coach at any one time? What would you cover in your coaching session? What resources and facilities would you need for successful delivery?

Rapport building

A coach should have an excellent relationship with, and trust of, their performer(s). This helps the coach get the best out of their performers in training and competition. To develop a good rapport a coach needs to find common ground between themselves and the athletes.

Communication

Communication is possibly the most important skill required to coach effectively. Remember also that listening skills are vital for coaches - communication is not just about speaking.

- In **verbal communication** it is important to keep language simple. A coach should ensure what they are saying is correct and appropriate, and that they have the attention of the people they are speaking to. Check for understanding by questioning the audience or observing the performance of the athlete.
- **Non-verbal communication** can take many forms, for example, body language. Most body language is unconscious (done without thinking). An athlete will be able to read positive and negative body language and this information will indicate the coach's mood. Hand signals can direct athletes or provide instructions during training and competitions. Demonstrations are used to show correct techniques and to outline each component of a skill, technique or tactic.

Reflect

Consider your classmates. Decide who you think is the best communicator in the class, noting down your justifications. What is it about them that makes them strong at communication?

Diplomacy

It is important that a sports coach can communicate to sports performer(s) and/or teams using **diplomacy**. This is particularly important when performers are struggling with form or injury. Coaches have to use diplomacy to communicate key messages without upsetting athletes.

Key term

Diplomacy – the art of dealing with people in a sensitive and tactful way.

Case study

Dave Brailsford, former performance director of British cycling

Sir Dave Brailsford is widely credited with turning British cycling around over the last decade. Brailsford is famous for his 'marginal gains' philosophy that if you break a sport down into its component parts and improve your performance in each of those parts by just 1 per cent the total gains will be significant. He is also known for his 'no compromise' attitude in which he sees only the best as close to good enough.

Brailsford's hunger for success is apparent: he leads by example, never asks anyone to do something he is not prepared to do himself and places himself firmly in the driving seat of the team. But without the 'buy in' from his team and athletes, it is of little value.

Check your knowledge

1 Considering Dave Brailsford's approach to coaching, what skills do you think he needs to ensure that his team follows him and accepts his vision?
2 Can you name any other famous coaches with a no nonsense approach who inspire their team and are fundamental to the success of their athletes?

Motivator

Success and enjoyment are critical when trying to motivate sports performers of all ages and abilities. A sports coach needs to adequately plan for progressive and challenging practices to ensure they maintain their participants' **motivation** and drive to take part and persist during a competitive situation. There are two different types of motivation which a sports coach could use to motivate the sports performers: **intrinsic** and **extrinsic**.

Link

More information about intrinsic and extrinsic motivation can be found in *Unit 3: Applied Sport and Exercise Psychology*, page 82.

Knowledge of a range of sports' characteristics and demands

A coach must have an understanding of the three different components used by sports performers during competitive performance.

- **Technical** – a technique is the way an athlete performs a skill. In some sports, players use different techniques to produce the same outcome. A coach should have a clear understanding of the technical requirements of the sport which they are coaching and the ability to analyse the technical ability of a sports performer, spotting areas which require development.
- **Tactical** – tactics are the skills and strategies a player uses in sport to be able to win. A coach needs to be able to develop sports performers' understanding of applying tactics in a competitive performance.

- **Fitness** – fitness is the ability to meet the demands of the sport. A sports coach must know and understand the components of fitness required for the sport and be able to develop this.

Knowledge of correct technical performance models

When learning skills and techniques, sports performers require progressive challenges. The challenges presented to a sports performer should focus on a complete or whole experience of the skill or technique, or can be broken down into smaller parts. Teaching using a combination of the two methods is often effective.

A sports coach would generally introduce a skill to a sports performer by a demonstration and/or an explanation of the skill and then let the sports performer have a go. After observation the sports coach should then consider the most appropriate method to coach the correct technical application of the skill. Possible methods are outlined below.

- **Whole and part learning** – for struggling performers a coach may break the skill down into its component parts and practise each part separately. When it has been broken into parts it can be put back together again easily by linking the movements until the performer can undertake the whole movement.

Research

Rowing is a popular water sport that requires great skills and coordination. The paddle stroke can be broken down into distinct phases and this is how performance is coached. Can you list the various phases of a paddle stroke in rowing?

- **Chaining** – this links the skill together in the same way that a chain links together. Again this method is suitable for complex skills with parts which can be broken down easily into different sub-parts. In this method the coach demonstrates the whole skill, then just the first part. The performer then practises just this first part. The coach then demonstrates the first and second part (the first two links). The performer then practises these two parts. This continues until the performer has mastered all the parts of the 'chain'.
- **Shaping** – breaking things into parts does not work as well when the parts of the skill need to be carried out simultaneously and/or quickly, such as a somersault or a backflip in gymnastics. The time between each part of the skill is so quick it is very difficult for the coach to break down each part of the skill. Instead the coach can simplify the action, adding more in as the performer masters the other parts.

Knowledge of correct tactical performance models

Before coaching tactical knowledge, a coach needs to analyse the existing performance of the sports performer(s) they are coaching and the performances of opponents. The coach will then need to develop strategies (or tactics) that their performer(s) can use to overcome the strengths or capitalise on weaknesses of the opponent, or which allow the athlete to focus on their strengths and avoid exposing their weaknesses.

Once a sports coach has devised and considered these strategies they need to go through how the sports performer(s) will implement these strategies in a competitive situation. For most sports coaches this will be done in either **conditioned practices** or **competitive situations** during training – you can read more about these later in this unit (starting on page 209).

Knowledge of components of fitness for different sports

Different sports require different fitness components. A sports coach can develop a further understanding of a sports performer's training needs around the components of fitness which are relevant and important within a particular sport. There are two different types of fitness: physical and skill-related fitness.

Link

More information about how to train the components of fitness can be found in *Unit 8: Specialised Fitness Training*.

- The six components of **physical fitness** are aerobic endurance, muscular endurance, flexibility, speed, muscular strength and body composition.
- The five components of **skill-related fitness** are agility, balance, coordination, power and reaction time.

Knowledge of sports activities to challenge and develop performers

It is important a sports coach has a bank of activities they can use when coaching. Using a range of activities is important to maintain interest and motivation. This also enables a coach to develop a programme to ensure sports performers develop as required and remain appropriately challenged as they progress.

Discussion

When working with sports that use frequent and accurate passing of a ball, coaches spend a lot of time looking at moving the ball between players quickly and accurately. Consider a ball sport. As a group, discuss some ways in which you might adapt the usual rules of play to encourage passing during a training session.

It is important when planning sessions that the coach considers what challenges each performer needs and how the session is going to challenge each performer to progress. To do this the coach must have a good knowledge of the performers and the ability to analyse their performance effectively. A coach may adapt a competitive situation to enable performers to develop a greater understanding of the skills and tactics which should be applied in particular situations.

Sport adaptations to challenge and develop performers

It is important that a sports coach has the ability to adapt their sessions as appropriate to ensure that the sports performers are challenged and entertained for the duration of the session. The adaptations that a coach can make can relate to:

- the **space** that the session takes place in – the coach could expand or reduce the amount of space available to challenge participants in different ways
- the **time** available – time restrictions can further challenge the participants and make good planning and organisation crucial
- the **equipment** used – different pieces of equipment can be introduced to further challenge participants or shift the focus onto specific areas that need addressing
- the **pace** – the speed with which a drill is performed can also be adapted to present new challenges
- the **people** involved – for instance, in a team sport the coach might set up a 'defence v attack' drill in which one side has a numerical advantage. Coaches may also need to take into account factors such as age, ability level and any physical disabilities
- the **intensity** and **duration** of the session – the amount of work the performer does during the session and the length of time spent on it.

You can read more about these adaptations later in this unit (see page 210).

Planning for changing conditions

A good coach should be prepared for every eventuality; this is known as contingency planning. When undertaking a contingency plan it is important to:

- consider everything that could possibly go wrong or not quite work as originally planned – for instance, with the athletes, the equipment or other resources, the weather, the location or the facilities
- do everything you can to ensure that none of these things does happen – so check all equipment, the availability of the facility, the number of participants and the specific needs of the participants at least the night before the event
- have an alternative plan and be prepared in case something does go wrong.

Coaches have to be able to adapt sessions to changing weather conditions

Maintaining safety in changing conditions

As conditions change, a sports coach must make sure the health and safety of participants is maintained. An environment that was safe at the start of a session might not be safe by the end of it. A coach should be prepared to end a session early if safety becomes affected. Alternatively, they may be able to adapt the session as the conditions change, for instance, by moving from an outside environment to indoors.

Planning for progression

When planning for progression it is important to set appropriate goals. Progression may be mapped out over a longer period of time and a coach may plan a series of sessions rather than hoping to achieve progression of all performers in a single session. This is known as 'programme planning'. You can read more about planning for progression later in this unit (starting on page 215).

Reflect

Have you ever been involved in training where progression was mapped over an extended period? What goals were you set during this journey?

PAUSE POINT What skills and knowledge do you need to be an effective coach?

Hint Close the book and list as many examples as you can in 2 minutes.

Extend Of all these examples, which do you think are most important? Justify your thoughts.

Qualities for coaching

There are several desirable qualities for coaches (see Table 6.1). A coach displaying these qualities is more likely to earn the respect of participants, colleagues and others, and is therefore more likely to achieve success. Coaches should have a high level of experience and this can only be developed by practising. Try and observe other coaches in practice or attend workshops to add to your skill set. Remember that coaches also need to have a clear understanding of their performers' ability level, experience and fitness in order to develop appropriate coaching plans.

▶ **Table 6.1:** Qualities for coaching for performance and fitness

Quality	Description
Professionalism	Always behave appropriately. The coach's conduct and behaviour will determine the experience and future behaviour of the athletes. A good coach will: • dress appropriately for the coaching session (personal appearance can have a major impact on the perception of you as a coach) • be personally prepared for the session, with everything planned and the correct equipment available • speak clearly, using appropriate language at all times • respect all athletes of all abilities and treat them all equally • respect and support all officials and their decisions • promote fair play and honesty, and reward effort • follow any National Governing Body (NGB) codes of conduct.
Time keeping and organisation	Always arrive with enough time to set up and prepare the session. Make sure that the session ends on time. Make sure that: • all the athletes attending the session are aware of its location and start time • the facility is booked • the equipment required is prepared and ready for use • the session is planned and all appropriate arrangements are made.
Positive attitude	An enthusiastic, positive coach will encourage sports performers to succeed. Treat performers with the same level of respect and fairness you would expect to receive yourself. Ensure the needs of the performers are placed first and any feedback is positive and constructive. Being positive does not mean you cannot highlight areas of development for a performer, but relates to the method and communication style you use to do this.
Positive role model	Set a good example to the participants, demonstrating appropriate behaviour and using appropriate language.
Knowledgeable	You should have a wealth of knowledge about the sports you are coaching, specifically around the technical and tactical demands, the fitness requirements and the rules and regulations of each sport.
Adaptable and a proactive problem solver	Find solutions to problems quickly; the quicker a coach can resolve an issue and provide an alternative solution the more efficient they will become. When possible always look for a solution to a problem, even in the most adverse situations, using experience and quick thinking to adapt.

▶ **Table 6.1:** Qualities for coaching for performance and fitness – *continued*

Quality	Description
Empathy	Show empathy for the circumstances, ability and pressures of performers. Do everything you can to support performers to enable them to develop. You may need to be patient due to factors beyond their control, such as a family bereavement.
Approachable	Performers should be able to approach their coach to discuss anything – they should feel able to ask questions and seek advice and guidance when appropriate. Demonstrate approachability by maintaining a friendly demeanour. However, be careful not to become too friendly and get too close to the performers, but maintain a professional relationship.
Enthusiastic and positive	Combine knowledge of the sport with a love for it, demonstrating a high level of enthusiasm and passion. Innovative ways of delivering sports sessions will help performers to build their enthusiasm. Appearing positive at all times, and a positive mindset will 'rub off' on performers.
Appropriate levels of confidence	You should have the confidence to stand in front of a group of performers and direct them towards achieving an agreed objective. You will need confidence in your own ability to identify areas for development of performers, and apply tactics using your own judgement in specific situations. At times coaches may also have to deliver messages to the performers which are not going to be well received. When delivering such messages, the coach must demonstrate faith in their own opinions and deliver this to the sports performer(s) in a way which inspires confidence.
Reflective	A coach has to learn from their experiences if they are to develop. Evaluate each and every session you deliver, considering its strengths and weaknesses. Then consider what you would do in the future should a similar circumstance arise to ensure the session is a complete success.
Analytical and observant	Demonstrate the ability to observe sports performance and analyse each component to identify areas for development. Objective judgements will need to be made about the performer's ability and fitness levels. You should have a clear expectation of their stage of development. This skill takes time to develop, and many athletes change coaches regularly for a 'fresh pair of eyes'. You should also analyse the personality and motivation of the athletes. Much of this will be done during competitive situations.
Responsive and reactive	Coaches must make the right decisions at the right time. Events in sessions may require a fast response and quick adaptation. The more experience you have, the easier it will become to make the right decisions quickly.

Key term

Empathy – understanding another person's condition from their perspective.

Case study

Argentina in the 2015 Rugby World Cup

Few people expected Argentina to do as well as they did in the 2015 Rugby World Cup. Compared to countries like England and France, Argentina has far fewer grass roots players and a smaller pool of talent to pick from.

In the years leading up to 2015, Argentina's rugby performance came a long way. They also benefited from being refused permission to join the Northern Hemisphere Six Nations Championship, instead joining the Southern Hemisphere Tri Nations Series: Southern Hemisphere rugby is currently dominant as a world force and Argentina's performance has been strengthened by consistent competition against the world's best teams.

However, their coaches have had much to do with Argentina's fantastic performance.

Check your knowledge

1 Carry out research to identify the type of atmosphere that Argentina's coaches try to promote in their team, starting with preparing in the changing rooms to getting on the field.
2 What would you say is the main difference between Southern and Northern Hemisphere rugby and what is the difference in the focus of coaching?
3 Do you believe that Argentina can continue to improve or has their coaching peaked?

 PAUSE POINT

Which qualities do you consider most valuable for a coach?

Hint: Are there any qualities that you might have already which will help you as a coach?

Extend: Are there any qualities that you may need to develop? How might you go about developing these qualities?

Best practice for a coach for performance and fitness

Away from the training pitch or practice court, there are other requirements to being a successful sports coach. A sports coach can fail if they do not follow certain practices, no matter how good their grasp of the principles of delivering a session.

Safeguarding and DBS checks

All coaches who work with children have a responsibility for safeguarding them while they are under their care and supervision. The definition of safeguarding is to protect children and young people from harm or damage with an appropriate measure. Safeguarding relates to following a process to protect children from abuse and neglect, but also to prevent the impairment of a child's development.

▶ Coaches need to be aware of safeguarding issues

Any professional working with children has a duty to place the child's welfare as their paramount concern at all times. All organisations must have clear safeguarding policies and procedures in place that should be followed. It is common for NGBs to have standardised procedures that should be followed for specific activities.

You should also be aware that coaches have caused harm to children through over-training, bullying and other forms of mistreatment, and that it is vital that a coach always treats children fairly and with respect.

Before working with children in any capacity a coach must be the subject of a Disclosure and Barring Service (DBS) check to check if they have a criminal record. Any previous convictions will be listed and a decision will be made by the organisation after they have viewed the DBS's feedback.

Equal opportunities

A sports coach will need to deliver their coaching sessions to a range of sports performers with a variety of abilities and from a range of ethnic and social backgrounds. It is important that the coach gives everyone the same opportunities to develop and improve their performance – this is what equal opportunities is about. A sports coach should ensure that they demonstrate **equality** at all times. Sports coaches should coach sports sessions without any **inequality** or **prejudice** and must ensure that all participants are treated equally and included in all of their sessions.

Key terms

Equality – treating everyone equally.

Inequality – social disparity, e.g. inequality between the pay of men and women in sport.

Prejudice – intolerance or a dislike for people based on race, religion, sexual orientation, gender, age or disability.

Duty of care – a legal obligation imposed on an individual, requiring that they adhere to a standard of reasonable care while performing any acts that could possibly harm others.

Risk assessment of environment and activity

Sports coaches have a **duty of care** at all times to provide a safe environment for the athletes who participate in their sessions. Risk assessments reduce or remove the risk of harm or injury to players, spectators and coaches. Risk assessment requires the coach to examine all equipment and the facility/playing surface where the activity is taking place. Once a hazard has been identified, the coach must eliminate the hazard and/or reduce the risk. If the hazard can be eliminated then the session can proceed; if not, the coach must classify the degree of risk before continuing with the session and decide if the session can go ahead.

Discussion

As a group, plan a circuit session for a group of 17-year-olds and think about the risks associated with it. Then carry out the session. Individually, as the session takes place, look for any other health and safety considerations which you have missed and add these to your risk assessment. Discuss your findings with the rest of the group.

A coach also needs to be aware of all the **emergency procedures** for the facility and ensure they follow them. These will include fire drills and evacuation procedures, first aid procedures, location of telephones and the risk assessment procedures. Before a coaching session, the coach should carry out last minute health and safety checks to ensure the facility is prepared and safe for physical activity to commence.

Qualifications and CPD

Coaches must also look to continue their professional development (CPD). CPD can be set by the coach themselves, but a coach can also be directed towards CPD through a supervisor or mentor. CPD is mostly done through the attainment of recognised qualifications. NGBs have developed coaching and leadership awards to support a developing coach. Some academic qualifications also enhance coaching ability, such as relevant degrees or other BTEC courses.

Administration for coaching

Administration refers to the paperwork that becomes part of the role of coaching sports performers. Coaches now have a number of administrative tasks to carry out before, during and after delivering a session. All sessions should be planned in advance and a clear record kept of attendance through a register. Attendance records and any other records - such as payment - should be kept safe and secure and updated regularly.

Record keeping is also important to record consent from the performers to take part in the session. To gain informed consent you need to explain the purpose and nature of the session - and any risks - in advance. For minors, a parent or guardian must give consent.

You must have insurance cover to participate in and lead physical activities. If an athlete is injured during a session, the coach is liable (legally responsible) and could be considered negligent (at fault). Insurance companies may wish to see session plans and risk assessments - another reason for record keeping.

Pre-activity readiness questionnaires (PARQ) ask specific questions relating to past or current illnesses and identify any conditions that could worsen due to participation. The coach uses the questionnaire to judge whether the performer is at an appropriate level of health and fitness for the session(s).

Supporting the development of performers

To develop performance, sports performers need relevant, informative and positive feedback. This can come not only from the coach but also from other performers, spectators, officials and the performer themselves.

When providing feedback a coach should always make sure that it promotes learning and builds self-confidence and motivation. Too often feedback is negative, which has been proven to have a negative impact on development.

- **Hot and cold feedback** - when providing feedback, the coach needs to consider appropriate timing. Coaches may decide to deliver feedback to the sports performer during performance, straight after the performance or after the performer has reflected on their performance.

Key terms

Hot feedback - feedback provided to sports performers by coaches, as soon as the coaching session has finished or during the session when a skill, technique or tactic has been applied.

Cold feedback - feedback provided after the sports coaching session. This allows the coach to reflect on the performance of the performers in more detail, and then provide detailed feedback.

- **Feedback to groups** - a coach may choose to provide feedback to a group of performers at one time. This can promote team development. The focus should remain positive. The feedback should be clear and concise, with any information kept simple and specific to make sure all performers can follow it. The focus should be on areas for development and strengths as a team, and should be planned in advance.
- **Feedback to individuals** - coaches often speak to performers to provide them with feedback. During one-to-one feedback sessions the coach can highlight individual areas for development and consider how to develop the performer over the next few sessions. When giving feedback to individual performers, coaches should plan what they are going to say in advance.

- **Feedback based on performance** – feedback should be linked to specific sporting areas, such as technical and tactical performance, fitness, effort and intensity, including highlighting areas for development. Coaches should ensure that solutions are provided to the performers, rather than just outlining areas where performance is not meeting its full potential.

Goal setting

Having goals is a key part of the planning process – when coaches do not set goals or set imprecise goals, their coaching plans can lack focus and performers can fail to develop. Goals should provide clear direction for the coach and performer, and motivate both to achieve. Goals should be SMART (specific, measureable, achievable, realistic and time-related). As a coach you will need several types of goals such as those outlined below.

- **Primary and secondary goals** – primary goals are the end goals that are the ultimate focus for the performer. Secondary goals occur as the performer works towards the primary goal.
- **Outcome/competition goals** – a coach may set performer goals that focus on the end of a competitive situation, for example, 'we will win this football match by two goals'.
- **During the session/training** – a coach may set performers goals to achieve during a coaching session. Goals like this can be used to further motivate the performer or team.
- **Process goals** – the coach may challenge a performer to master a specific technique or skill by a certain date or event.
- **Short-term goals** – set to be achieved between a day and a month, these goals could be a target that a sports coach wishes to be achieved after the next training session or in the next competitive situation.
- **Long-term/seasonal goals** – set to help performers and teams determine where they want to go, what they want to achieve and the best way of getting there, these goals should shape coaching schedules. In sports that have seasons, coaches may set long-term goals for the season.
- **Future development goals** – a coach may consider developing a performer's technique or tactical application to make an overall improvement to their performance. For example, a 400-metre runner may set the goal to improve their first 100-metre split by 0.5 of a second.

Technology and sports professionals

Over the last decade a range of technologies have been introduced to support coaching and the analysis of sports performers. Similarly, there are now several different professionals in the sporting industry that can support the coach to develop specific areas of an athlete's performance. See Tables 6.2 and 6.3 for more information.

For all of these technologies and professionals, coaches need to consider whether the support supplied for the desired goal justifies any cost involved. Coaches should also consider the practicality of accessing any additional support and how relevant it might be to helping the athlete develop.

▶ **Table 6.2:** Supporting technologies

Technology type	Description
Video analysis software	Used to observe performers' movements, correct bad technique and further develop performance. Elite coaches use gait analysis to analyse how athletes can run more efficiently. Other programmes include Coach's Eye, Dartfish and Kandle. Video analysis is expensive and requires a lot of training to be used effectively. Usability is limited to those who can afford the software and are trained to use it. However, non-professional video analysis can be done using video-recording facilities on smartphones.
Electronic training logs	Software used to support the planning of sessions and monitor progress towards achieving set goals. It allows coaches and performers to log their coaching sessions to see if goals have been met. Smartphones can monitor speed and distance through the use of an app. GPS devices can also be used. Examples of training logs include TrainingPeaks, Strava and RunKeeper. Often free with paid-for upgrades also available, sometimes they may only be used with specific devices. The more advanced the technology, the more expensive the equipment required. A wide range of sports performers use electronic training logs, and the software is often user-friendly and practical.
Heart rate (HR) monitors	Measures the HR of the performer in real time. Often used to measure the intensity a performer is working at. Used by a range of performers and available at a reasonable cost. To record HR and use the data, you must have access to appropriate software to store data.
GPS tracking units	Can be worn as a watch, as part of a GPS vest, or on the handlebars of bicycles. They track the precise location of the performer and monitor their movement, speed and distance covered. They are used to measure the intensity that a performer is working at. They are more expensive than HR monitors and you must have the correct software to record and use the data.
Power meters	Used on a bicycle to measure the rider's power output. Most use strain gauges to measure force applied to the pedals and, when combined with GPS tracking information, calculate the power applied by the cyclist. Coaches need training to interpret the data they produce. They are expensive and need specific software to measure and store data.
Laboratory testing	Performed in sports and exercise laboratories, it uses specialist equipment with complex **protocols**. A scientist measures elements of the athlete's body, such as blood lactate levels. Measurements are highly accurate and often require funding as equipment is complex and expensive. Staff must be highly trained to administer the test and record results. Very few performers have access to these facilities due to the cost.
Online resources	The internet contains a huge number of resources to support performers. Specialist websites provide support and guidance. Other resources include forums, video sharing sites and social media. These are very accessible and cheap to use. Coaches can share their own good practice and pick up tips and hints from others. The sites and the guidance they contain should always be assessed for reliability.

Key term

Protocol – a step-by-step process for conducting a specific test that can be followed every time it is carried out to ensure accurate and consistent results.

Link

For more about laboratory testing, see *Unit 4: Field- and Laboratory-based Fitness Testing*.

▶ **Table 6.3:** Supporting professionals

Professionals	Description
Sports nutritionist	Provides nutritional education and guidance to sports performers, helping performers improve their eating habits
Sports masseur	Uses massage to rub and manipulate muscles and soft tissues of the body to help relieve stress, tension and pain. Often used to help people with sports injuries
Physiotherapist	Helps performers affected by injury by giving them exercises, physical therapy, education and guidance, rehabilitating them back to achieve and maintain full health
Chiropractor	Focuses on identifying and treating neuromuscular disorders, with a focus on treatment through physical adjustment and/or manipulation of the spine
Osteopath	Detects and provides treatment for injuries, and helps prevent additional injuries, through movement, stretching and massaging of a performer's muscles and joints
Sports psychologist	Assesses the psychological factors affecting performance and considers how participation in sport and exercise affects psychological and physical factors
Strength and conditioning coach	Uses exercise specifically to improve performance. Works on strength and conditioning to help athletes avoid injury by ensuring performers are in the best physical condition to withstand the demands of their sport

PAUSE POINT

There is a huge range of resources available for a coach to help an athlete to set and achieve goals. What options are available to you as a coach to help support performers?

Hint Why is goal setting important? Why should you make sure goals are realistic and achievable?

Extend What extra steps could you take to stretch a performer to achieve or exceed short-term or long-term goals?

Assessment practice 6.1

A.P1 A.P2 A.M1 A.D1

Imagine that you are the head coach for a sports team. You have six junior coaches working under you who are all new to their roles and lacking experience.

Create a presentation for your junior coaches that carefully explains the skills, qualities and best practices associated with being a strong performance coach, analysing why you feel they are relevant. You should also explain and analyse how technology and other professionals can help coaches to support athlete development.

Plan

- What resources do I need to do to complete this task?
- Have I enough experience as a coach to complete this task or do I need to gain some practice?

Do

- Do I clearly understand what makes a good coach?
- Do I have a clear structure that I can use to communicate this through a presentation?

Review

- Am I able to justify why I tackled this task as I did?
- Can I suggest improvements I would make if I had to re-do this task?

B Explore practices, adaptations and measures used to develop performance and fitness

It is important to understand that coaches use different practices in different sports to develop the specific skills, techniques and tactics for that sport, with a focus on developing them in competitive situations. A coach must have a thorough understanding of these skills, techniques and tactics for their sport.

▶ Isolated practices can be used to develop specific skills or techniques

Practices to develop skills, techniques and tactics

Isolated practices

Isolated practices are used by coaches during a coaching session to develop skills and techniques. An isolated practice is often a drill or exercise that breaks the skills or techniques being coached into parts; such practices are usually used to introduce skills and techniques the performer has not fully mastered, or has never used before. They are used mainly for beginners and intermediates but, as performers develop their ability, isolated practices are also used to rehearse and refine the skill or technique.

Isolated practices can be adapted to help a performer struggling to master a technique or skill. They can also be adapted to increase in difficulty when performers have mastered a skill and require further challenges.

Isolated practices can also develop a performer's ability to apply tactics. In team sports, like rugby union, a coach will replicate a particular component of the game, like a line-out, then continually work with the players to ensure they understand the tactics the coach would like them to use in that situation.

Conditioned practices

Conditioned practices are used to recreate elements of specific competitive situations during coaching sessions. The focus is for the performer to master the correct application of skills, techniques and tactics in these situations; after rehearsing them, the performer can apply them in specific competitive situations. During conditioned practices, a coach will often stop the practice to coach performers, providing specific guidance, feedback and reinforcement to shape their behaviour.

An example of this is practising a line-out in rugby and the subsequent moving of the ball back into attacking play. The coach might split the team into attack and defence and play the game on for just one minute after each line-out, each time practising a different scenario.

A coach would normally only use conditioned practices for performers who already have a very good understanding of a sport and who have mastered all, or the majority of, that sport's skills and techniques.

Discussion

There are many sports which involve individuals performing on their own, one-by-one, for example, tennis. Although there might not initially appear to be many tactics in these sports, in reality there are. In a small group, list a few examples of such sports and discuss ways athletes might use tactics to gain an advantage over competitors.

Case study

Usain Bolt

It has been remarked that you cannot make a world class athlete: the athlete must already be there. The coach's job is to facilitate the use of the athlete's assets to enable success.

When coaching an activity such as the 100-metre sprint you might think that the options for coaching are limited due to the brief nature of actual competition. However, this is not so. When working with world class athletes where success is dictated by tiny margins, small adjustments to technique can lead to big results.

A great deal of science is utilised in Usain's training, as with many top level performers. It took two years of focused training before the 2008 Olympic Games, a milestone in Usain's career, to redevelop his technique to bring his performance to the next level.

Allowing small errors in technique can result in an athlete wasting time when developing their performance later in their career. Coaches must make a judgement about when to enforce changes to technique and when to allow them to be overlooked, focusing on improvements that might result in larger short-term rewards.

Check your knowledge

1. In what scenario is it advisable to ignore small mistakes in technique and focus on fast-paced development?
2. What other sports could be compared to the 100-metre sprint in that coaching very small adjustments to technique can give big rewards?
3. To be able to work with a world class athlete such as Usain, what additional skills and knowledge might a coach need to develop?

Competitive situations

Competitive situations are created by coaches in coaching sessions to rehearse the tactics taught throughout the coaching sessions. They mimic a real-life competitive event, following the usual rules/laws and regulations of the sport. They provide performers with the opportunity to apply skills and techniques they have developed and previously mastered, in a competitive situation. They are often used to improve particular components of performance and observe **offensive** (attacking) and **defensive** ability.

Theory into practice

Think about a sport you have played where points are awarded through scoring goals. Draft three brief plans for practice sessions which focus upon shooting accuracy, one each for isolated, conditioned and competitive practice. Which session do you feel might be most effective?

Adaptation of practices to promote development

A coach can consider a variety of ways of adapting practices to further challenge performers and develop performance. Performers learn at different speeds, and ability levels within groups will differ. At times this may mean practices are changed for some performers but not all.

- With younger performers the **size of the group** may be large to ensure the coach can include lots of competitive games to develop skills and techniques through competition. As performers become more advanced, the size of the group may generally reduce. For older performers, a coach may reduce numbers to make the practice easier or increase the number to make it harder.

Research

Can you find any examples of sports which involve competitors competing individually, but in which it is common practice to develop skills or techniques in large groups?

- A coach may give different performers **different roles** within a session. More advanced performers may support other members of the group or have roles which require more advanced application of skills and techniques. Less advanced performers may be given roles involving them in the session while allowing those with a higher skill level the opportunity to also develop and be challenged. However, coaches must be careful to avoid this being seen as favouritism or isolating performers from the session.
- A coach may adapt a practice to increase its difficulty to challenge more advanced performers. For example, in football a coach may allow some performers to play with their favoured kicking foot while the rest of the performers have to play with their weaker foot - this is known as a **technique restriction**. When coaching beginners, coaches may adapt to enable weaker players to work on particular components. For example, in football when delivering a dribbling drill a coach may ask the group to only dribble with certain parts of their feet, and then **progress** the activity to work with other parts when the coach is satisfied that all performers have mastered that component.
- The **environment** can be altered to enhance training sessions and focus upon specific skills, for example, using a five-a-side pitch to help footballers develop and improve touch and control. Space can also be adapted to increase or decrease the difficulty level.
- In some sports when working with beginners, using the least **equipment** possible will help performers settle. However, as players progress the amount of equipment a coach uses to develop skills will increase. In other sports, because of the amount of safety implications involved, more equipment is needed from the start. For example, when a gymnastic coach coaches a somersault on a trampoline, a sports performer will initially perform the activity with a number of coaches supporting a safety harness. As the performer develops their confidence and skill level, the amount of equipment supporting the performer will be reduced until eventually no coach or equipment is supporting them.
- A coach needs to consider the **intensity** the performers display during each session. Technology (see page 207) can be used to measure intensity. Alternatively, a performer can be asked what level of intensity they are working towards using a scale of perceived physical exertion (with 1 the lowest and 10 the highest). A coach can also adapt physical demands by altering the **duration** or **distance** of the session: often the longer a session is, the more aerobically demanding it will be.
- Sessions can also reproduce some of the **psychological demands** a performer may face by creating realistic competitive situations. A coach can also measure the performance of the athlete to create pressure for them to demonstrate high-level performances. For example, a netball coach may give a goal shooter 60 seconds to score as many goals as they can, with the outcome measured and used as a benchmark. Alternatively, a coach could apply disadvantages to the performer. For example, a road cyclist could be placed three minutes behind a pacer and told to catch them within 20 km.

Research

Can you find any examples where a coach might work with an athlete by fine-tuning their equipment to try and find a mechanical advantage over competitors?

In 1 minute, create a spider diagram showing examples of ways a coach might adapt a session.

Hint Which of these adaptations are you most likely to use? Justify your thoughts.

Extend Are there any adaptations that might prove challenging for a coach? How might they adapt a session in these scenarios?

Measures of performance and fitness

It is important to measure the ability of sports performers against the correct **benchmark**, which may depend on their age, level of ability or experience.

In some sports, such as athletics, benchmarks can be measured using time or distance. For example, you could judge a 21-year-old sprinter's performance against the world record 100-metres time for 21 year olds. But in team sports a coach needs to use **objective** or **subjective analysis** to measure performance against other teams with similar aspirations, for example, in objective analysis, comparing the number of goals scored from corners in football.

When working with a new group, a coach may start by measuring fitness and performance against the rest of the group in order to establish weaker and stronger performers. They may also measure the performers again during and after a period of training in order to measure how much the performers have improved during the training plan.

Field tests

A coach can use **field tests** to assess specific skills, techniques and levels of fitness. For example, when assessing agility, a football coach may ask a footballer to dribble in and out of cones, timing their effort and noting how many cones were knocked over.

Conditioned practices can be used to assess a performer's ability to perform skills and techniques which can be used during competitive games. Success can be measured in terms of accuracy of application of the skill, time taken to apply the skill, or distance covered while the skill is applied.

Coaches can also set up sessions assessing the application of tactics, using **notational analysis**. A coach may set up a practice and inform the sports performers what he or she would like them to do, then assess their effectiveness at applying the tactic.

Key terms

Benchmark – a reference mark against which you can assess the performers' current performance and fitness.

Objective analysis – based on measured, statistical performance data.

Subjective analysis - based on observational judgements, personal interpretations and opinions.

Field test – a physical test carried out in similar conditions to those in a competitive situation.

Notational analysis – a coach keeps a record of the number of successes or failures in a particular situation.

Coach-devised field tests

A coach may develop their own system of assessing technical, tactical or physical attributes. For example, a basketball coach may assess the effectiveness of a player's shooting by keeping a **tally** of the number of successful and unsuccessful shots during training or competition. The coach would then compare these against previous results from the same or other players. A coach may use **observational analysis** to subjectively assess the abilities of a performer; the accuracy of this often depends on the experience and opinion of the coach.

Standard tests

Standard tests can assess the attributes of sports performers. Standard tests have comparable data (benchmarks or normative data) which can be used to assess results. Fitness tests provide sports performers with an evaluation of their current level of fitness and have a specific protocol, or way of administering the test, that must be followed to gain accurate results. Examples of standard tests include the Cooper 12-minute run test and the Illinois agility run test.

Link

More information about fitness testing can be found in *Unit 4: Field- and Laboratory-based Fitness Testing.*

Evaluation of practices, adaptations and measures

It is important that a coach evaluates every practice they use and considers whether they should be used again to support the development of sports performers (see Table 6.4). They should do this both for the original session as they planned it and for any adaptations they introduced. The coach also needs to evaluate any measures they took to assess performance and fitness against the same criteria.

▶ **Table 6.4:** Evaluating practices and adaptations

Aspect	What coach should consider
Practicality	• The time it took to set up the activity • The amount of and use of equipment during the activity • The outcome of the activity
Suitability	• Whether the activity adequately challenged the performers within the session • Whether or not the activity supported the coach to achieve their own outcomes (aims and objectives) for the session
Effectiveness	• Which practices were effective in developing performers and which practices were not as effective • How easy it would be to adapt practices to ensure they are more effective in the future
Relevance	• Whether the activities were appropriate to meet the session's aims and objectives

Assessment practice 6.2

B.P3 B.P4 B.M2 B.M3 B.D2

Think back to Assessment practice 6.1. For the next stage in the development of your junior coaches, you must produce a written guide that explains a variety of practices to develop skills, techniques and tactics for sports performance. Evaluate these practices within this guide, discussing their practicality, suitability and effectiveness within your sports club. Suggest ways that you might adapt these practices for your chosen sport.

Plan

- Do I understand how to plan a document so that it is clear and easy to read as a guide?
- Have I done appropriate research into a variety of practices?

Do

- Am I able to motivate myself to generate a document that is thorough?
- Do I have the IT skills to ensure that it is presented in a professional manner?

Review

- Am I able to identify ways in which I could improve this document in the future?
- Do I have access to classmates and tutors who can give me feedback on my work?

Demonstrate effective planning of coaching to develop performance and fitness

Planning considerations

Several areas must be considered before planning a coaching session. Coaches need to gather as much information about the performers as possible to develop a greater understanding of the athletes participating. The activities must be suitable for the performers. The performers' needs determine the types of activities and the method of delivery and instruction for a particular session that the coach chooses. The information the coach gathers should include:

- the group's size and gender mix
- the age and ability or fitness level of the sports performers
- any individual needs of participants.

When a coach has this information, they can start to plan the session. The coach should initially consider the overall aim for the group and any specific targets for individuals within the session – the targets set for a performer may be very different than the session's aim. The plan should document these individual targets.

Environment and equipment

Session planning should understand the environment of the session and the equipment available. Coaching sessions can take place in a number of different spaces, as shown in Figure 6.1.

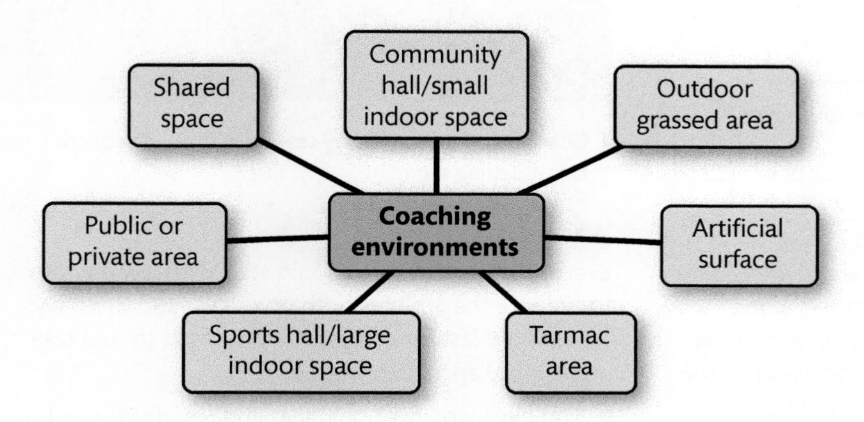

▶ **Figure 6.1:** Coaching environments

A coach should ensure they know the equipment requirements for each part of the session and what is available on the site. A rationale should be provided on the session plan that details the purpose of the equipment for each activity, such as using equipment for different purposes to challenge performance. This rationale should also include diagrams to show how to set up each activity. Sometimes there will be little or no equipment available and the coach will have to plan around this.

Planning activities

- **Selection of skills and techniques** – the coach must choose which skills and techniques are used to ensure the session aims are met and that performers are challenged and developed appropriately. The coach should ensure they have appropriate knowledge of the correct technical model to coach the sports performers correctly, and identify the correct coaching practice for each skill, technique or tactic to be coached during the session.
- **Set clear learning aims and outcomes** – each aim should be an expected outcome that will be achieved by all or some of the performers within that session, for example: 'By the end of the session everyone will be able to correctly complete a long lofted pass, and some performers will be able to correctly complete a long swerve pass.' To achieve the aim, a sports coach will need to set out some **objectives**. These should also be written clearly on the session plan and express how the coach will meet each of the aims.
- **Selecting activities/adaptations to develop skills and techniques** – a variety of activities should be used within every session, each included to support the coach to achieve the aims they have set for each performer, challenging them and supporting the development of every performer. Within a session plan a coach should include appropriate detail about how they will deliver and set up each activity.

Discussion

Imagine that you have been given a 20-metre piece of rope. In a small group choose a sport and think of three ways in which you might use the piece of rope to enhance a training session.

Research

Are there any examples where coaches might use a completely different sport or activity to coach skills fundamental to their actual discipline? Why might this be an effective coaching tool?

Link

You can read about suitable intensities and durations of practices later in this unit (page 215). Benchmarks and field testing were covered earlier in the unit on page 211.

Key term

Objective – how a sports coach is going to meet their aim.

- **Differentiation through adaptation of activity** – there will be parts of some sessions in which performers of all abilities participate. During these activities, a good coach should look to challenge performers of different abilities by adapting activities. Each adaptation should be clearly stated in the session plan.
- **Contingency plans** – within each session plan, consider plans for every eventuality, indicating a number of alternative options if something goes wrong or even if the session has to be stopped.

Reflect

Have you any specific examples in which you have seen a coach adopt a contingency plan?

Health and safety considerations

The key priority should be to manage the health and safety of the participants before, during and after the session. Assess all the potential risks which could occur during the session. This involves considering risks posed to and by the athletes, the environment and the equipment. Refer back to the section earlier in this unit on risk assessment of the environment and the activity (starting on page 204).

Planning for an individual session

Individual session plans normally cover all of the elements outlined below. Remember sessions may need to be adapted to meet the requirements of different athletes to resolve any problems. Time should also be allowed for feedback to both the whole group and individual athletes (see pages 205–206). Doing this at the end of the session is known as a 'plenary' and should include reflection on future progression.

Benchmarks and field testing (see page 211) will also be important for session planning for athletes.

Discussion

Why might it be important that a coach focuses on strengths as well as areas for improvement during all plenary sessions?

Introduction and target setting

At the start of every session the coach should outline the aims of the session and, if required, set individual targets for sports performers. The session should start with all the performers together, where the coach clearly communicates the aims and objectives of the session. Individual targets should not be shared in front of the group (to prevent possible embarrassment) but on a one-by-one basis.

▸ Coaches should start every session with an introduction and target-setting segment

Warm-up

Every coaching session should start with a warm-up to prepare the athletes both physically and mentally. This should last for at least 10 minutes. It should take a methodical approach which:

- initially increases body heat and respiratory and metabolic rates
- stretches the muscles and mobilises the joints that will be used in the session
- includes rehearsal and practice of some of the skills/techniques from the main body of the session.

Theory into practice

Imagine that you are preparing a warm-up for a group of young gymnasts. Consider the three elements listed above which should be seen in every warm-up. Write a brief plan, keeping in mind the age of your learners and how you might engage them at the start of a session as well as fulfil your other objectives.

Technique/tactic introduction

It is important that a coach appropriately introduces the performers to each activity within a session. This is particularly important when introducing a technique or tactic: the content the performers are required to take on board is key. This is why both communication and the method used are carefully considered. Verbal and non-verbal communication (see page 198) should be used correctly.

When instructing athletes, it is important to explain the significance and relevance of the instruction in relation to their overall development. When providing technical instructions, a coach should:

- plan what they are going to say and how they are going to deliver the information
- gain the attention of all the athletes before they speak
- keep the instructions simple but ensure the information is accurate
- when possible, use demonstrations/visual examples to reinforce the instructions
- check at the end of the instructions that all members of the group have understood.

As with any learning process, an athlete's ability to take in information will depend on what stage of learning they are at. The fresher the participants are to the sport or element being coached, the simpler the activities, instructions and feedback should be. As the participants gain competence, the activities, instructions and feedback should also develop to keep the participants challenged.

Technique/tactic development and advancement

Once the technique or tactic has been introduced, it can be developed. When a performer has mastered the application of a technique or tactic, it is important the coach develops the practice to increase the difficulty level and to apply increased pressure. For example, if a sports performer has developed a technique by taking part in an isolated practice, the sports coach may make it more complex by adding conditions which require the sports performer to apply the technique in a more competitive, game-like environment.

The timing of any progression is crucial. If a performer is left on the same practice for too long they will quickly become bored and lose interest. Similarly, advancing a struggling performer too quickly will negatively affect motivation. Remember, learning more complex skills will require performers to have mastered more advanced skills, so the timing of their introduction should be carefully considered.

Coaches also need to know which skills and techniques should be combined and then applied in competitive situations. The coach should be able to provide opportunities in coaching sessions for sports performers to practise combining skills. It is important that conditioned and competitive situations are used by coaches to develop sessions and ensure performers enjoy taking part (see page 209).

Cool-down

At the end of the session a coach should ensure all participants spend an appropriate amount of time cooling down. This brings the body back to the pre-exercise condition gradually. It should prevent muscle stiffness, injury and improve flexibility, provided stretches are performed correctly and controlled effectively by the coach.

Intensity and duration of practice

When planning a session, a coach needs to consider the level of intensity which a performer should be working at. For example, warm-up intensity starts at a low level and gradually increases to prepare the performer. A coach must consider intensity in relation to each part of the session, and the intensity level of each session when planning a series of sessions. Intensity will also affect the duration of the practice. Duration will also be affected by the need to achieve the overall aims and objectives of the session.

Link

Intensity will also be affected by the element of fitness that you are targeting - see *Unit 8: Specialised Fitness Training*, for more information.

Planning for a series of sessions

When planning a programme for a group of performers, a coach should consider how many sessions it will take to fulfil the aim and target. A series normally lasts a minimum of four sessions and may cover the build-up to a major competition or a whole season. The coach has to consider how they are going to link the sessions in order to progress and develop the performers to meet the aim in full by the end of the series. The sports coach may build a series of sessions to develop:

- **different skills and techniques combined** – a coach would work on different skills and techniques through specific practices, linking them together to create the desired outcome
- **a selected technique** – a coach would need to ensure each session progresses the development of the performers and appropriately challenges them. The final outcome is measured through the ability of the performers to undertake the selected technique
- **a tactical application** – it may take a series of sessions to coach performers in the skills and correct timing when applying a tactic. The outcome is easily managed by observing the performers' ability to demonstrate the tactic successfully, both during training and in a competitive situation
- **relevant fitness components** – a coach may use a series of sessions to develop a particular fitness component.

The end product of a series of sessions

A series of coached sessions will always work towards a particular end product. The end product will either be a competitive aim or target, or a non-competitive element.

- A **competitive element** can be demonstrated through a performer(s) completing a series of sessions prior to a particular race or tournament. This can include an element of 'tapering' where the physical demands of training are eased off in order to leave the participant fresh for the competitive event.
- A **non-competitive aim** or target could be the performer acquiring additional skills or competency in a particular component of a sport by a certain date.

A coach may also repeat field tests at the end of a series, comparing them with field tests conducted at the start of the series to measure progress. They also need to plan when they will conduct field tests during the series in order to gauge progress and, if necessary, adapt the series.

Assessment practice 6.3

C.P5 C.M4

Choose the sport you are most confident in delivering. Choose an individual or group you feel you can work with to practise your coaching skills. Generate a session plan that meets a pre-defined purpose for the session, ensuring that it links into an overall series plan. Write a document that discusses the relationship between your individual plan, planning considerations, measures and the overall series plan.

Plan

- Have I chosen a sport that I am confident in delivering?
- Do I understand what the objectives of the session and the series are?

Do

- Is my plan detailed and clear?
- Have I considered my objectives and do I believe my plan is both realistic and practical?

Review

- Am I able to highlight strengths within the plan and areas where it might need improvements?
- Am I able to implement my suggestions for improvement thus enhancing my own performance?

Explore the impact of coaching for performance and fitness

Performance analysis

A coach should be able to effectively analyse performers within each session. This analysis can then be used to develop future coaching plans.

The most effective way to do this is through observation analysis. Coaches need to be effective observers so they can identify strengths and weaknesses during performance. Observation analysis should be used to identify an athlete's needs, with the coach analysing their whole performance and developing a training programme around it, aiming to improve significant weaknesses. There are two basic ways of formulating judgements:

1. **subjective analysis** – which is based on observational judgements, personal interpretations and opinions
2. **objective analysis** – which involves measuring and comparing performance data.

For example, the ability to perform a basketball free throw could be assessed objectively by counting how many free throws a player scores out of ten. The same assessment could be carried out subjectively if a coach compares the player's technique and skill against a mental image of an ideal technique.

When carrying out observation analysis, a coach must be careful not to be biased. They will have built up a relationship with the athlete they work with but must view their performance in as unbiased a light as possible.

Reflection on session and planned series

Self-assessment and self-reflection are something we all undertake. For example, the last time you played sport at a competitive level you probably considered how well you played, and the last time you delivered a presentation in class you will have reflected on your presentation skills. When you reflect on yourself in this way you also consider what you would do differently if you were put in that situation again. Reflection enables you to learn from your experiences and consider what to do if the same situation arises again.

A good coach should ensure they reflect after each session they deliver. Coaches work on the principle that performers learn as much from their mistakes as their successes. The same applies to coaches. When reflecting on each session, a sports coach should consider each of the areas shown in Figure 6.2.

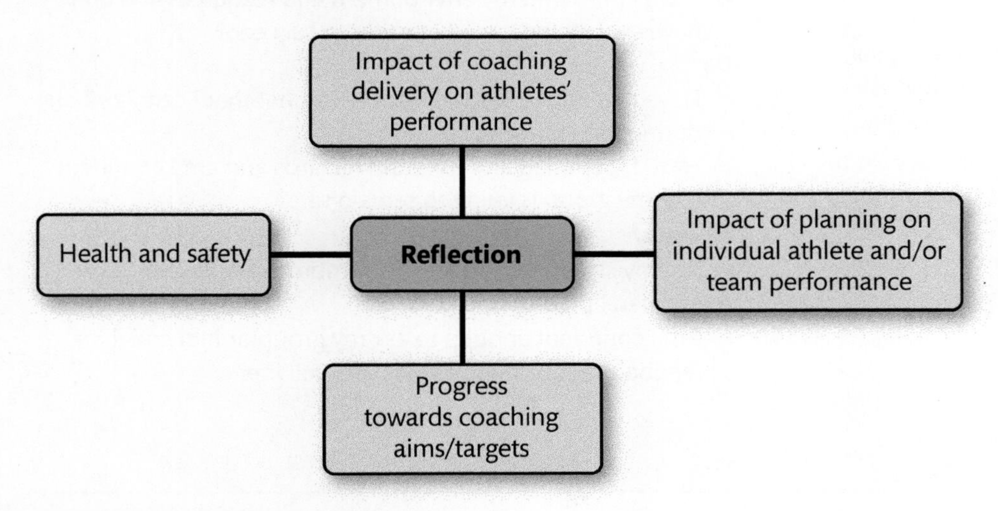

Figure 6.2: Carrying out post-session reflection

The reflection stage of the coaching process is when the coach should reflect on the effectiveness of each session. It should influence the planning of future sessions. The cycle should continue, each time benefiting from the experience of the previous stage. The questions below should help in assessing a session.

1. Did the session meet the aims and targets set at the start?
2. Did the session improve the performance of the participants?
3. What went well in the session and why?
4. What did not go well in the session and why?
5. Did the session progress the overall plan for the participants?
6. Were the participants and spectators safe at all times?
7. What could be done to improve the session if it was delivered again?

Theory into practice

Observe an experienced coach's session. Use the seven questions to give structure to your observation. Make sure that you have some notes for every question. If they are comfortable with it, discuss your thoughts with the coach.

Coaching development based on reflection

Personal development recommendations

After reflection, coaches should consider how to address the feedback and opinions they have developed. The coach should consider what personal development they need to undergo in order to improve their qualities, skills and knowledge in order to deliver better coaching sessions. Conclusions should form the basis of a development plan with targets for improvement set by the coach.

As with the athletes they coach, who should have a perfect and ideal model in mind that they are trying to replicate, a coach should use role models and consider how they deliver sessions. They can then aim to mirror the behaviours and practices of their role models, helping them move towards best practice. In their development plan, the coach should identify specific goals, for example, completing specific coaching qualifications, working with specific sports coaches and/or observing sports coaches working with specific groups.

Session development recommendations

A coach should also use their reflection to consider the practices and measures they used during each session, judging their effectiveness, how appropriate they were and how manageable they were in reality. Most importantly, they should consider how they might adapt the sessions and the series next time they deliver it.

Assessment practice 6.4

D.P6 D.P7 D.M5 CD.D3

Look back to Assessment practice 6.3. Deliver your pre-prepared plan to your group or individual. Ensure that during the delivery you use appropriate skills and techniques and demonstrate the qualities of a strong coach. Consider health and safety factors during your session and keep your group or individual safe.

Afterwards, analyse your performance and the impact of both your planning and delivery on the individual or group. Evaluate your performance, suggesting and justifying adaptations to future sessions and their impact on your own personal coaching development.

Plan

- Am I confident in my plan and do I believe it will engage and benefit my group or individual?
- Have I prepared my environment and resources and do I have everything I need in order to succeed?

Do

- Have I identified areas for improvement that I can work on during delivery of my session?
- Have I identified any risks and hazards and am I confident that my group is going to remain safe?

Review

- Are my strengths and areas for improvement clear to me and can I practise further?
- Am I confident enough to ask my group or individual for feedback and act upon what they tell me?

Further reading and resources

Books

Cassidy, P. (2005) *Effective Coaching: Teaching Young People Sports and Sportsmanship*, Yardley, PA: Westholme Publishing.

Cassidy, T., Jones, R. and Potrac, P. (2009) *Understanding Sports Coaching: The Social, Cultural and Pedagogical Foundations of Coaching Practice*, Abindgon: Taylor and Francis Ltd.

Earle, C., Craine, N. and Andrews, W. (2004) *How to Coach Children in Sport – Coaching Essentials No. 6*, Leeds: Coachwise Ltd.

Websites

www.topendsports.com – Topend Sports: a range of fitness tests and normative data.

www.1st4sport.com – 1st4sport: an online shop for a range of resources to help you work as a sports coach.

www.coachwise.ltd.uk – Coachwise UK: advice and support for people involved in sports coaching and increasing participation in sport.

www.sportsleaders.org – Sports Leaders UK: information and advice about awards and qualifications for sports leaders.

www.sportscoachuk.org – sports coach UK: information, advice and learning resources for anyone interested in sports coaching.

THINK FUTURE

Natalie Ward

Sports coach

Sports coaching is a great job. I get to work with lots of really keen young people, which is fun. Helping them to develop is really fulfilling. It isn't all easy though and there are some difficult parts. One of the biggest problems that I face is when I am working with different age groups. I currently coach girls' hockey teams at the following ages: under-10s, under-12s and under-14s, so there are lots of different things that I need to take into account when I am planning and running sessions.

At times it can get a little confusing, especially when I'm working with some of the 'older' 12-year-olds who are more mature or more advanced than some of the 'younger' 14-year-olds! I often think that working with people based on their age group is not the best way to work, especially between the ages of 10 and 14. This is where there are some of the biggest differences in growth and maturity and I'm always trying to find better ways of working with my players to meet their individual needs rather than the needs of their age group.

Focusing your skills

Managing people

Coaching is not just about teaching people how to play a sport. You need to be a leader and manager as well as an expert in your sport.

- Developing your team working and leadership skills is important. Try and identify any opportunities to do this. For example, if you take part in a group discussion in class, volunteer to lead the discussion.
- Coaching is a professional environment. Make sure you are familiar with the attitudes and responsibilities you will need to follow in a professional environment.
- Part of leading sessions is understanding that everyone is different - both in personality and how people are best motivated. Talk to friends and family: how do they motivate themselves? What do they look for in a leader? The different answers you receive will show you the range of options for leadership styles that coaches have.

Organising your time

One of the major things Natalie needs to deal with professionally is organising other people's time as well as her own. Understanding how to plan and organise your time is a crucial skill. The more organised you are, the more authoritative and professional you will become - and the more respected you will be as a coach.

- Try to plan your time - get used to organising yourself and work out the best ways you can structure your time. It may help to organise your tasks into achievable chunks.
- When working in a group in class, review and organise the tasks you have been given. Work out a plan that will allow you to achieve everything you need to do within the time you have been given.

Getting ready for assessment

Mark is working towards his BTEC National in Sport and Exercise Science. He particularly enjoys the practical units and hopes to find a job in coaching or sports leadership. He has gained plenty of experience by volunteering as an assistant coach at his local swimming pool. It has helped him to practise his own skills and allowed him to learn from more experienced coaches.

His tutor has encouraged each learner to organise their own coaching assessment for learning aim D. This way, she explains, they will be able to perform in an environment that they feel comfortable in and will enable them to do their best. Mark discusses his experiences below.

How I got started

I have managed to gain quite a lot of experience by volunteering as an assistant coach. However, having my tutor attend a session and observe me was quite nerve-racking. To ensure I could deliver my session confidently, I planned thoroughly and made sure I understood the needs of my group and the desired outcome.

The session was 45 minutes long and in my plan I broke it down into bite-sized chunks, each with a clear objective. I arrived early so I had time to prepare my resources and go over my plan one last time. I also brought a stopwatch to make sure I kept to my plan!

How I brought it all together

I already knew the group I was working with as I had helped coach them before. I ensured that when I welcomed them my instructions were very clear so everyone knew what we were going to do, what was expected of them and what the objective was. I knew that my group had a slight mixture of abilities so I tried to differentiate between individuals using floats to help develop their strokes.

It soon became clear that individuals develop at different speeds. I had to adapt my plan slightly, splitting the group in two and giving the more able group a slightly more challenging task to ensure that they were pushed.

What I learned from the experience

It was clear that my practice helped me with my session. My planning and preparation gave me a good basis to work from. However, I soon discovered that it isn't always possible to keep to a plan and that you might need to adapt a session so everyone gains as much as they can from it.

I tried to gather plenty of feedback after the session from my group to help with my evaluation. Although I felt uncomfortable initiating this exercise, there were plenty of positive comments as well as areas for improvement. One of my group reminded me that I was still inexperienced and so there were obviously going to be areas for improvement – the only way I was going to get better was by taking advice and practising.

I used the feedback and my own reflection to update my session plan, and the comment about practising helped me think about my own future personal development.

Think about it

- Are you confident in your plan and is your preparation sufficient?
- Are you able to communicate this plan effectively and make adaptations if needed?
- Do you have the tools to collect feedback and are you confident that you can make improvements to your own personal performance as a coach?

Biomechanics in Sport and Exercise Science 7

Getting to know your unit

Assessment

You will be assessed by a series of assignments set by your tutor.

Sports biomechanics examines human movement, the movement of sporting objects and the forces that act on and are produced by the human body in a sports environment. It involves giving objective feedback to athletes or coaches based upon the investigation of linear and angular motion, and the forces acting on performers and equipment, to help athletes improve or enhance performance.

In this unit, you will gain an understanding of the types of motion the human body undertakes in sport and the forces that impact on the human body, such as reaction forces, friction and buoyancy. You will examine concepts that explain what happens when the body or sporting objects move through the air. The application of this knowledge is particularly important as it will enable you to become a more effective coach or sports scientist.

How you will be assessed

This unit will be assessed by a series of internally assessed tasks set by your tutor. There will also be a strong emphasis upon your practical analysis skills, which may be observed.

The assignments set by your tutor may take the following forms.

- Creating a portfolio that details an investigation into linear motion in sport and exercise science.
- Producing a report that examines the forces acting on sports performers and their equipment.
- Creating a presentation that details an investigation into angular motion in sport and exercise science activities.

The exercises within this unit are designed to help you practise and gain the skills that will help you complete your assignments. The theories you will learn will give you the background information to enable you to complete the unit but not necessarily guarantee you a particular grade.

Assessment criteria

This table shows what you must do in order to achieve a Pass, Merit or Distinction grade, and where you can find activities to help you.

Pass	Merit	Distinction
Learning aim A Investigate linear motion in sport and exercise activities		
A.P1 Describe speed, velocity, acceleration, deceleration and momentum in sport and exercise contexts. **Assessment practice 7.1**	**A.M1** Explain speed, velocity, acceleration, deceleration and momentum in sport and exercise contexts. **Assessment practice 7.1**	**A.D1** Analyse speed, velocity, acceleration, deceleration and momentum using relevant calculations from sport and fitness contexts. **Assessment practice 7.1**
Learning aim B Examine forces acting on sports performers and their equipment		
B.P2 Describe how forces impact on sport and exercise performance referencing Newton's three laws of motion. **Assessment practice 7.2**	**B.M2** Explain how forces impact on sport and exercise performance referencing Newton's three laws of motion. **Assessment practice 7.2**	**B.D2** Analyse, using examples, how forces impact on sport and exercise performance. **Assessment practice 7.2**
Learning aim C Investigate angular motion in sport and exercise activities		
C.P3 Describe how different types of levers and axes of rotation are used in sport and exercise activities. **Assessment practice 7.3**	**C.M3** Explain how different types of levers and axes of rotation are used to complete different movements. **Assessment practice 7.3**	**C.D3** Analyse how different types of levers and changes in the centre of mass combine to affect performance in sport and exercise activities. **Assessment practice 7.3**
CP.4 Describe how changes in the centre of mass affect performance in sport and exercise activities. **Assessment practice 7.3**	**C.M4** Explain how changes in the centre of mass affect performance in sport and exercise activities. **Assessment practice 7.3**	

Getting started

Biomechanics examines the causes and consequences of human movement and the interaction of the body with equipment through the application of mechanical principles in sporting settings. You will start by looking at linear motion, how forces influence the outcomes of performance and why angular motion can play an important role in the difference between success and failure. How can knowledge of this help you analyse sports performance and improve the athletes of tomorrow?

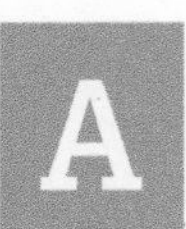

A Investigate linear motion in sport and exercise activities

Linear motion is important in sports. Linear means in a straight line and linear motion is movement in which parts of a system move in the same direction at the same speed or acceleration – for example, a cyclist freewheeling downhill, maintaining a static posture on a bicycle moving in a straight line.

However, pure linear motion – in which a body moves as a unit with its different parts (limbs) not moving – is uncommon in sport. For example, even when a cyclist is travelling in a straight line, their limbs are moving in various different directions to produce the movement (e.g. when pedalling).

Linear motion can occur in a straight line (**rectilinear motion**) or in a curved line (**curvilinear motion**). Some sports, such as the 200 metres in athletics, are part rectilinear and part curvilinear as the athlete starts from the blocks on the curve of the track, then finishes in a straight line.

When looking at linear motion, you need to look at factors such as distance, displacement, speed, velocity and acceleration – all covered in this learning aim.

Key terms

Rectilinear motion – motion along a straight line or path.

Curvilinear motion – motion that occurs along a curved line or path.

Vector quantity – a physical quantity that has both size and direction.

Magnitude – a term used in science to describe the size of something.

Scalar quantity – a physical quantity that has only size.

Vector and scalar quantities

There are two categories of quantity used in sport and exercise science. **Vector quantities** have both **magnitude** (size) and direction (movement), while **scalar quantities** only have magnitude. The different vector and scalar quantities are explored in more detail in the following text but also summarised in Table 7.1.

Table 7.1: Vector and scalar quantities used in sport and exercise

Category	Quantity	Description
Vector quantities	Displacement	The straight line distance an object or athlete has travelled in a given direction between start and finish points. Not to be confused with distance
	Velocity	How quickly an object or athlete has moved in a given direction and measured in ms^{-1}
	Acceleration	The rate of change of velocity, measured in metres per second per second (ms^{-2})
	Deceleration	A reduction in acceleration, measured in negative metres per second per second (ms^{-2})
	Weight	A force exerted on an object or person by the gravitational pull (g) of the Earth
	Momentum	Quantity of motion of a moving body measured as a product of its mass and velocity
Scalar quantities	Distance	The sum of all movement, regardless of direction. Not to be confused with displacement
	Speed	How quickly a body moves, measured in metres per second (ms^{-1})
	Mass	Measure of how much matter is in an object
	Inertia	Resistance of an object to a change in its state of motion

Vector quantities

When analysing the biomechanics of sports performance, the common vector quantities used are displacement, velocity and acceleration/deceleration.

- **Displacement** – refers to the distance an object or athlete has travelled in a given direction. It is measured as the length of a straight line between start and finish points (see Figure 7.1). For example, if you look at a 200-metre sprint race on a running track, the sprinter will travel a distance of 200 metres from start to finish, but using basic trigonometric calculations, you can determine that the athlete will have displaced 123.8 metres at an angle of 36°.

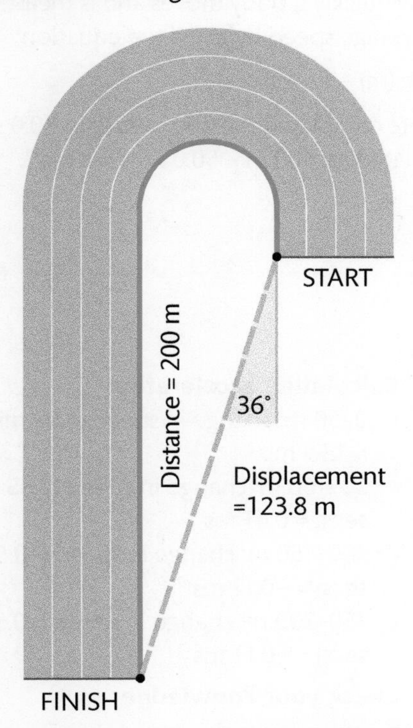

Figure 7.1: Displacement versus distance (not to scale). Note that the angle will vary depending on the configuration of the track

- **Velocity** – refers to how quickly an object or athlete moves in a given direction and is measured in ms^{-1}. You can calculate velocity using the equation:

  velocity (ms^{-1}) = displacement (m) ÷ time (secs)

  For example, the sprinter completed the 200 metres in 24.10 secs. Therefore, the average velocity is calculated as: 123.8 m ÷ 24.10 secs = 5.14 ms^{-1} (to 2 decimal places).

- **Acceleration** – refers to the rate of change of velocity over a set period of time and is measured in metres per second per second (ms^{-2}). You can calculate acceleration using the equation:

  change in velocity (ms^{-1}) ÷ time (secs) *or*

  (final velocity in ms^{-1} – initial velocity in ms^{-1}) ÷ time (secs)

  For example, the sprinter completed the 200 metres crossing the line with a final velocity of 10 ms^{-1}. Therefore, the average acceleration is calculated as: (10.0 ms^{-1} – 0 ms^{-1}) ÷ 24.10 secs = 0.41 ms^{-2} (2dp). Note the sprinter's initial velocity is given as 0 ms^{-1} because, at the start, the sprinter was still (i.e. in the blocks and not moving).

- **Deceleration** – a vector quantity that refers to a reduction in acceleration and is measured in negative metres per second per second (ms^{-2}). Deceleration can be calculated using the acceleration formulae, only producing a negative outcome.

Scalar quantities

Scalar quantities are described in terms of size. When analysing the biomechanics of sports performance, the following scalar quantities are used.

- **Distance** – describes the sum of all movements regardless of direction (whereas displacement is the straight line distance between start and finish points). For example, in a race around one complete lap of a running track, an athlete's distance travelled will be 400 metres whereas the displacement will be 0 m – because the athlete has finished where he started.
- **Speed** – describes how quickly a body moves and is measured in metres per second (ms^{-1}). You calculate average speed by using the equation:

  speed (ms^{-1}) = distance (m) ÷ time (secs)

  For example, the athlete completed the 400 metres in 50.0 secs. Therefore, the average speed is calculated as: 400 m ÷ 50.0 secs = 8 ms^{-1}.

Discussion

When a sprinter runs the 100 metres, what distance do they actually run? Is it 100 metres, is it slightly more or slightly less? Discuss this with the rest of the group and explain your answers.

Case study

Usain Bolt and the 200-metre world record

At the IAAF World Championships in Berlin in 2009, Jamaican sprinter Usain Bolt broke the 200-metre world record by running a time of 19.19 seconds. Using this information, you can calculate the average speed.

Average speed: distance (200 m) ÷ time (19.19 seconds) = 10.42 ms^{-1}

It is often important for coaches to know split times or the velocity or speed at different points during the race to further analyse the performance. Each of Bolt's split times (below) is for a 50-metre interval:

Calculating average speed at each interval

- 0–50 m = 5.60 secs = 8.93 ms^{-1}
- 50–100 m = 4.32 secs = 11.57 ms^{-1}
- 100–150 m = 4.52 secs = 11.06 ms^{-1}
- 150–200 m = 4.75 secs = 10.53 ms^{-1}

Now you know the average speed for each stage of the race, you can calculate the average acceleration through each stage. Remember that at the start of the race, the starting or initial velocity is 0 ms^{-1}.

Calculating acceleration

- 0–50 m: change in speed (8.92 ms^{-1}) ÷ time (5.60 secs) = 1.59 ms^{-2}
- 50–100 m: change in speed (2.65 ms^{-1}) ÷ time (4.32 secs) = 0.61 ms^{-2}
- 100–150 m: change in speed (–0.51 ms^{-1}) ÷ time (4.52 secs) = –0.12 ms^{-2}
- 150–200 m: change in speed (–0.54 ms^{-1}) ÷ time (4.75 secs) = –0.11 ms^{-2}

Check your knowledge

1. During which split was the greatest rate of acceleration and why?
2. Explain why you think Bolt's time for 100–200 metres is faster than his time for 0–100 metres.
3. How do the accelerations for 0–100 metres and 100–200 metres differ?

Mass and weight

Two other important related vector and scalar quantities are mass and weight.

- **Mass** is the quantity of matter that makes up an object or person. Mass depends on the density and volume of an object and is measured in kilograms (kg). Mass is a scalar quantity.
- **Weight** is a force exerted on an object or person by the gravitational pull (g) of the Earth. Weight is a vector quantity as its direction of force is always towards the centre of the Earth. The acceleration of the Earth's gravitation pull (g) is a constant 9.81 ms^{-2}

Weight is often discussed in terms of kilograms, for example, 'My weight is 75 kilograms'. However, this is not scientifically correct as weight is a force and should be measured in Newtons (N). You can calculate weight using the equation: weight (N) = mass (kg) × acceleration of gravity (g). For example, an athlete with a mass of 75 kg will weigh: 75 kg × 9.81 ms^{-2} = 735.75 N.

Inertia and momentum

It is also important to understand the concepts of inertia and momentum.

- **Inertia** is the tendency of a body to maintain its state of rest or motion in a straight line. Inertia has no units of measure, though the more massive an object is, the more it resists any change of state in its motion. Inertia is a scalar quantity.
- **Momentum** is the amount of motion possessed by a moving object or body. Linear momentum is calculated using the equation:

  momentum (M) = the object's mass (m) × the object's velocity (v)

  Therefore, an object or body's momentum can be altered by changing its velocity. For example, for a 100-metre sprinter with a mass of 80 kg and sprinting at a velocity of 10 ms^{-1}:

  momentum (M) = 80 kg × 10 ms^{-1} = 800 kg ms^{-1}

  Momentum is a vector quantity.

PAUSE POINT What sports can you name in which inertia plays an important role?

Hint Think about sports in which an athlete (or their equipment) can glide in a relatively straight line as part of their performance.

Extend What might prevent inertia playing too much of a role in these sports and, ultimately, the athlete's performance?

Assessment practice 7.1

A.P1 A.M1 A.D1

You have secured a position on the coaching staff at a local university's cricket club. The club has decided to use biomechanical analysis of all its players to improve their coaching and performance. The club coach has asked you to prepare a short presentation for the players that outlines linear motion and how it affects sports performance.

You have a 30-minute slot at the pre-season meeting: 20 minutes for the presentation and 10 minutes for questions and answers. Your presentation must include:

- a brief introduction to biomechanics
- an explanation of the terms speed, velocity, acceleration, deceleration and momentum
- an analysis of how these measures are used, with calculations.

Plan

- What is my presentation being asked to address?
- How confident do I feel in my ability to complete this task? Are there any areas I may struggle with?

Do

- Do I know how to examine methods for analysing sports performance?
- Have I thought about the questions people might ask and how to answer them?

Review

- Can I explain how I approached the task?
- What would I do differently if I had to complete a similar task in the future?

B Examine forces acting on sports performers and their equipment

Newton's three laws of motion

Sir Isaac Newton was a scientist who discovered gravity. He produced three laws, outlined in Table 7.2, that are essential if you are going to understand linear motion.

▶ **Table 7.2:** Newton's three laws of motion

Law of motion	Meaning of the law	Application to sport and exercise
First Law: law of inertia	A body will remain at rest or at a constant velocity unless compelled to change by an external force acting on it.	Applicable when an athlete is stationary or moving with a constant speed or velocity in a fixed direction. For example, for a cyclist to maintain a constant speed or velocity in a straight line, all other forces acting upon the cyclist must cancel each other out.
Second Law: law of acceleration	The acceleration of a body is proportional to the force causing the acceleration, and the acceleration takes place in the direction that the force acts.	Applicable when an athlete undergoes a net force which changes their velocity and acceleration (and possibly direction). For example, a footballer dribbling may suddenly change direction to go round an opponent. The friction force (see page 229) to the ground on the footballer's feet causes a change of direction but no change of speed. Because there has been a change of direction, there must also have been a change in acceleration in the direction of the force (opposite to the direction of travel).
Third Law: law of action/reaction	For every action, there is an equal and opposite reaction – when any object exerts a force on another, then it experiences an equal force exerted by the other but in the opposite direction.	Applicable when an athlete pushes hard on the ground resulting in an upward acceleration, or when, for example, a golfer strikes a ball from a tee, a force hits through the ball, but an equal and opposite force also travels back through the club head in the opposite direction.

Theory into practice

Which of Newton's Laws of motion are involved in the following sporting scenarios?

- A gymnast vaulting off a horse
- A rugby player running at and tackling another player with the ball

Reaction forces

Reaction forces are produced as a result of Newton's Third Law of Motion. Force is the push or pull effect that will cause a body to change its state of motion. It is measured in Newtons (N).

Ground reaction forces are caused as the athlete pushes downwards on the ground. The size of the ground reaction force depends on the mass of the body and the gravity acting on this mass, and is equivalent to the force that is being exerted downwards by the body.

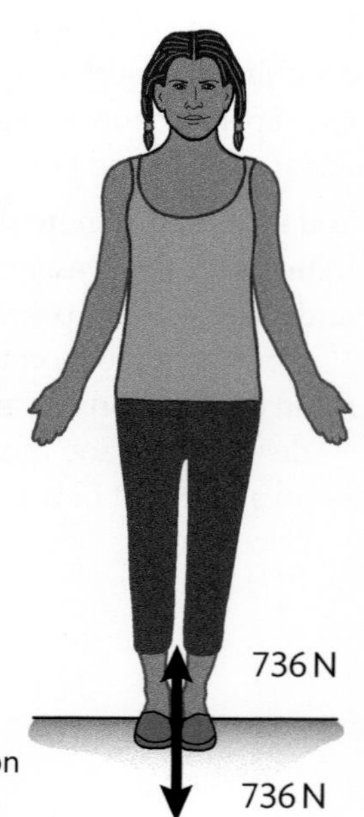

▶ **Figure 7.2:** Reaction forces of an athlete

Worked example

At rest an athlete whose mass is 75 kg is standing upright without moving (see Figure 7.2). The athlete's weight is calculated as:

$9.81\ ms^{-2}$ (g) × 75 kg (m) = 736 N (1dp)

The athlete's weight is pushing downwards onto the ground with a force of 736 N.

Newton's Third Law states that, at the same time, a force of 736 N is being pushed in the opposite direction - from the ground up through the athlete.

In a sports context, it is these forces that allow the ground to 'push back' in the opposite direction to the direction in which the athlete is moving, resulting in an upward acceleration of the athlete. Without ground reaction forces the athlete would just sink into the ground.

The ability of a runner to drive a large force into the ground by pumping the arms and pushing the legs onto the ground surface allows the rapid acceleration associated with a 100-metre sprinter.

Friction

Friction is a force that resists the motion between two surfaces that are in contact with each other. Friction acts at the area of contact between two surfaces in the direction opposite to that in which an object or body is moving.

The **coefficient of friction** is a number that is used to represent the relative ease of sliding between two surfaces that are in contact. Surfaces with a coefficient of zero are perfectly smooth and frictionless. Factors affecting the coefficient of friction are the roughness or hardness of the surfaces and whether or not the two surfaces in contact are moving or static.

Types of friction

There are four types of friction that can affect sports performance.

- **Static friction** - occurs when a body or object is forced to move on a surface but movement does not happen. This is because the magnitude of the static friction is equal to the applied external force while the direction is always opposite the direction of motion. The magnitude of the static friction depends on the coefficient of friction. An example of static friction in sport is the moment you strike a tennis ball with the strings of a racket: the static friction causes a 'grip' on the ball and initiates the ball's change in direction.
- **Kinetic friction** - occurs when a body or object begins moving along a surface. When an external force is enough to move a body or object along a surface, the force that opposes this motion is called kinetic friction. An example of kinetic friction can be seen in skiing, where skiers require the lowest possible amount of kinetic friction to glide along the surface of the snow.
- **Rolling friction** - a force that slows down the motion of a rolling object or body.
- **Fluid friction** - resistance to motion of an object or body in a fluid due to friction exerted between the body or object and the fluid. An example of fluid friction occurs when water passes around the body of a swimmer which will, without additional muscular force, slow the swimmer down.

Kinetic friction and fluid friction are both types of **sliding friction**.

Implications of friction on sports performance

Friction plays an important role in sports performance. For example, skis are made from special materials that are regularly cleaned and waxed to minimise the amount of friction from the snow, allowing a skier to achieve greater speeds. Track sprinters wear spiked running shoes to create a greater amount of friction with the running surface, allowing them to generate more force through their legs to increase their speed during a race.

The design of equipment to control friction is increasingly advanced. Swimming costumes are made from materials that minimise fluid resistance, allowing performers to swim faster. And football boots are continually evolving as manufacturers change the stud type and configuration in attempts to allow for greater friction between boot and pitch – this enables players to change direction quicker or achieve greater acceleration or deceleration during a game.

Case study

An unfair advantage?

In 2010 the world swimming governing body, FINA, announced that certain types of hi-tech swimming suits made from polyurethane were banned from competition. FINA was aware that swimmers wearing these suits were breaking numerous long- and short-course world records.

Check your knowledge

1. Which frictional force acts on swimmers in a swimming pool?
2. Explain how the use of polyurethane suits may have contributed to the setting of so many world records.
3. Do you consider the use of such suits any different to waxing the bottom of skis to reduce kinetic friction during a downhill race?

The friction between the tyres on a Formula 1 car and the track surface is arguably the most important factor in the car's performance. The tyres are manufactured to allow for maximum grip and allow the car to achieve optimal accelerations and velocities throughout a race. This has to be achieved while other forces such as inertia and momentum are constantly working against the car's performance.

Air resistance

Air is often thought of as 'nothing' or as an empty space. In fact, air is made up of a complex structure of molecules containing oxygen, nitrogen, carbon dioxide and water vapour. These molecules give air a composition which we encounter as air resistance every time we move.

Air resistance (also known as 'drag') is a frictional force between the surface of an object or person and the air moving in the opposite direction of travel. It plays a major role in all sports, especially those involving balls or throwing.

When thrown, objects or balls become 'projectiles' and the main frictional forces acting on them are the molecules that make up the surrounding air, or air resistance, and the weight of the projectile. Projectiles follow a flight path and there are two major types, outlined below.

- **Parabolic flight path** – in the absence of any air resistance, the dominant force acting upon the flight path of any projectile (e.g. a long jumper) is weight. Therefore, the athlete would follow a parabolic flight path (shown in Figure 7.3).

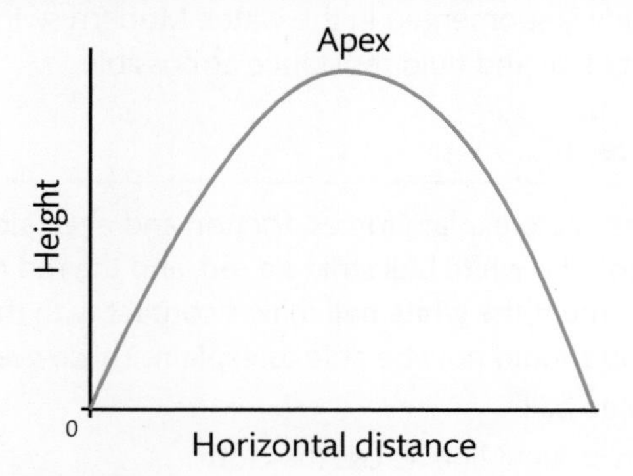

Figure 7.3: Parabolic flight path

- **Nearly parabolic or asymmetric flight path** – occurs when the air resistance of a projectile becomes dominant compared to its weight (e.g. a shuttlecock). The shuttlecock would follow an asymmetric flight path (see Figure 7.4).

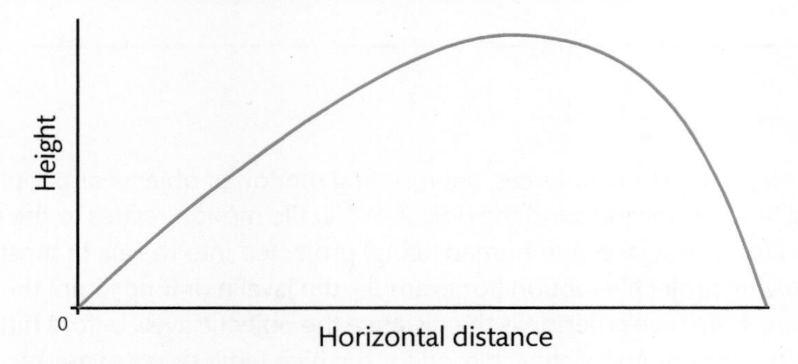

Figure 7.4: Nearly parabolic flight path

The distance travelled (or height achieved) by a projectile depends on three major performance criteria:

- angle of release (also known as projection angle)
- velocity of release/velocity of take-off
- height of release/height of take-off.

The **angle of release** is the angle between the projectile's velocity and the horizontal at the instant of release or take-off. Different sports require different angles of release. If the height of release and velocity of release are the same, an angle of release of 45° is the angle that provides optimal performance. However, in sports that require maximum horizontal distance, such as the long jump, smaller angles are required. In comparison, in sports like the high jump where height is key, the optimal angle is larger.

The **velocity of release** is recorded at the instant of release (for example, when the long jumper leaves the take-off board).

The **height of release** is the distance from the ground (in metres) at which the object leaves the thrower. If the angle and velocity of release are the same for two shot putters, the athlete who has a greater height of release will have a longer flight time and, therefore, record a greater range.

Air resistance increases with speed: a football with an average velocity of 35 ms^{-1} will encounter greater air resistance than one with an average velocity of 30 ms^{-1}.

Certain types of clothing, such as skin-moulded Lycra, are designed to minimise the amount of air resistance by streamlining and are popular in cycling and running. In swimming, the initial dive into the water will result in the swimmer encountering air resistance until the body is submerged in the water. Modern swimsuits are designed to offer the least amount of air and fluid resistance as possible.

Theory into practice

Snooker is an ideal sport to explain forces, friction and even air resistance. In the example of a long pot, the white ball strikes a red, and the red runs into a corner pocket. From the moment the white ball makes contact with the cue, a series of events occur that you should now be able to explain. These events are:

1. cue tip impacts cue ball
2. cue ball travels in straight line across the cloth
3. cue ball impacts red ball
4. red ball travels in different straight line towards a pocket
5. red ball drops into the pocket and white stops moving.

Think about these five stages and try to explain the forces and types of friction that occur.

Aerodynamics

Aerodynamics is the study of forces, the resulting motion of objects or people through the air, and how air flows around the object. Projectile motion relates to the motion of an object (such as a javelin or human being) projected into the air. In most athletic events involving projectile motion (for example, the javelin or long jump) the most important performance criterion is the distance the object travels before hitting the ground (or the maximum height achieved for the high jump or pole vault).

The aerodynamic properties of an object depend on its size and shape. The cross-sectional shape of an object will determine the drag created by the pressure variation around the object, while the smoother the surface of the object, the less turbulent flow it is likely to create (see the next section). Consider the shape of a javelin: it has a small cross-section and a smooth surface which results in a low level of drag, making it very aerodynamic. Contrast this with a football which has a much larger cross-section and a patterned surface resulting in a high level of drag making it less aerodynamic.

Now consider the flight paths of both objects: the javelin will travel a large distance in a near-parabolic curve due to its aerodynamic properties, whereas the football will take a very different path or curve due to its greater air resistance that can influence the ball to swerve or to remain airborne for longer.

Types of flow

There are two types of air flow around an object:

- **laminar flow** – the smooth flow of fluid or air around an object or person. During laminar flow all fluid or air particles move in distinct and separate layers around an object or person which lessens the amount of air or fluid resistance
- **turbulent flow** – also known as 'turbulence', this is the flow of air in which the motion of fluid or air particles varies and, instead of the particles moving in distinct and separate layers (as with laminar flow), the layers mix in a chaotic manner resulting in a turbulent wake, which increases the amount of air resistance.

Laminar and turbulent flows can have a significant impact on sports performance. In time trial cycling, competitors wear specially designed suits and helmets which, when cycling at speed, are designed to reduce the turbulent flow of air and increase the laminar flow of air. This results in a more aerodynamic design and reduced turbulent wake which allows the cyclist to achieve higher speeds using less force and energy.

The dimples on a golf ball work by creating a thin turbulent boundary layer of air at the ball's surface (see Figure 7.5). This layer allows the laminar flow around the back of the golf ball, decreasing the turbulent wake. This decrease allows the ball to travel further.

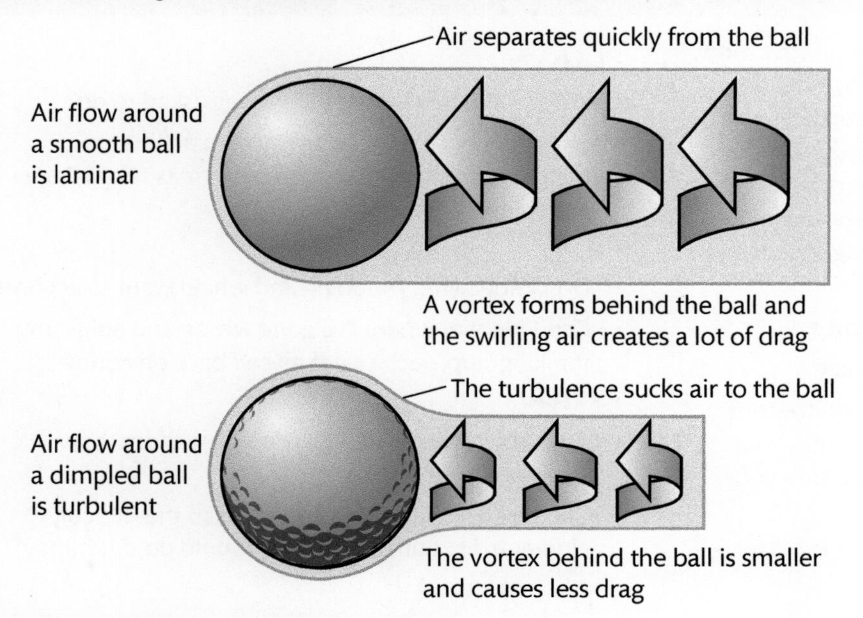

Figure 7.5: Benefits of laminar flow for a golf ball

Theory into practice

What biomechanical explanations can you put forward for the sudden increase in performance witnessed during events such as the javelin, long jump and discus at the Mexico City Olympic Games in 1968?

Lift and Bernoulli's principle

Lift is the force which directly opposes the weight of an object or body and holds it in the air. It is also referred to as the **Bernoulli principle**. This describes the upward force caused by air flowing at different speeds above and below an object or person. The amount of lift is affected by:

- the size and shape of an object
- the angle at which the object meets the moving air
- the speed at which the object moves through the air.

The **Magnus effect** is the variation in the trajectory of a rotating (spinning) projectile caused by the 'Magnus force'. Spin creates an area of low velocity and high pressure on one side of the projectile, and an area of high velocity and low pressure on the other side. This pressure differential creates the Magnus force, a lift directed from high pressure to low pressure, and allows objects that have spin applied to them to move laterally through the air. This principle can be seen when footballers put spin on a ball to curl a free-kick over the wall, when a swing bowler gets the cricket ball to move in the air, and when applying backspin or topspin to a tennis shot.

Research

Find out how Bernoulli's principle can affect sports performance. Consider:

- the flight of projectiles such as the discus or shot
- the optimum angle of take-off for ski jumpers and long jumpers
- the design of aerofoils in Formula 1 racing.

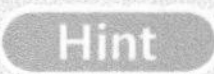

PAUSE POINT How can the shape of projectiles affect their projectile motion?

Hint Think about the difference between a cricket ball and a shuttlecock, then consider their relative flight paths.

Extend Of all the athletic throwing events, why do you think the javelin travels the furthest?

Assessment practice 7.2

B.P2 B.M2 B.D2

Your presentation on linear motion was a success. Now, the cricket club president would like you to prepare a report on how forces affect sports performance, with particular emphasis on cricket (although you can also refer to other sports for additional reference). This report will be studied by the club's coaches and will play an integral role in the season's training schedule. Your report should analyse:

- how forces impact on sports performance
- how these forces are applicable to cricket.

You will need to carry out some research on these points and show that you understand how they may apply to cricketers and their training. Make sure your report is relevant and informative.

Plan

- What is the task? What am I being asked to do?
- How confident do I feel in my own abilities to complete this task? Are there any areas I think I may struggle with?

Do

- Do I know what I'm doing and what I want to achieve?
- Can I identify where I've gone wrong and adjust my thinking/approach to get myself back on course?

Review

- Am I able to explain what the task was and how I approached it?
- Can I explain how I would approach the difficult elements next time (i.e. what I would do differently)?

C Investigate angular motion in sport and exercise activities

Centre of mass

The centre of mass, also referred to as the centre of gravity, is an imaginary point at which the weight of an object (for example, the athlete) can be considered to act and be equal on both sides. The position of the centre of mass varies according to the size and shape of the object or body. Objects with a low centre of mass have better balance and are more difficult to tip over.

In objects with a regular shape (e.g. a football) the centre of mass equates to its geometric centre. In objects with an irregular shape (e.g. the human body) the centre of mass is less easily defined and changes according to the position of the body. If you stand in the anatomical position, your centre of mass is around your belly button. But if you raise an arm above your head, your centre of mass will move upwards. Sometimes, the centre of mass can actually be outside the body, such as in the 'Fosbury Flop' technique in high jump (see Figure 7.6).

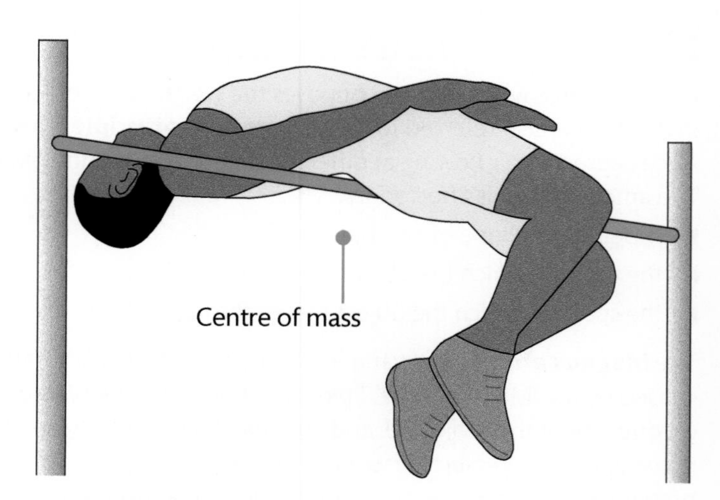

Figure 7.6: How does the centre of mass move outside a body and how can it benefit performance?

Impact of position of centre of mass on sports performance

Using the example of an athlete jumping over a hurdle, a combination of reaction force (1070 N), friction (105 N), air resistance (50 N) and weight (520 N) produces a net force on the hurdler, as shown in Figure 7.7.

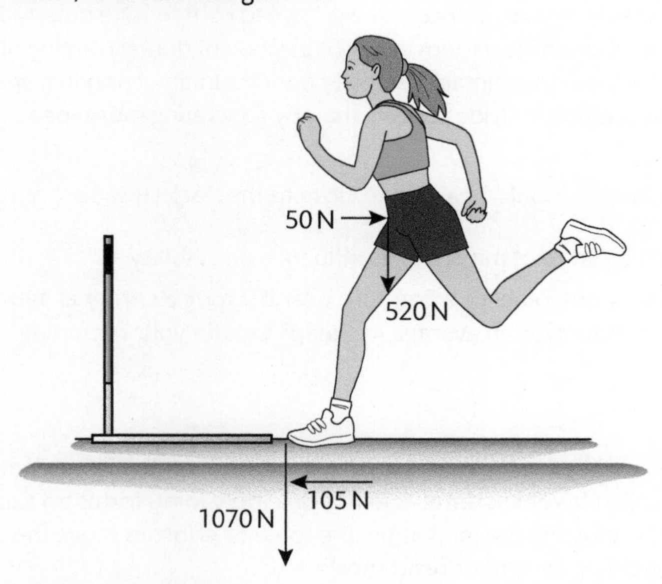

Figure 7.7: The impact of centre of mass on a hurdler

Net upward force produces an upward acceleration of the body. At the instant of take-off, the foot leaves the ground and the net upward force gives the body a velocity of, for example, 5 ms^{-1}. Therefore, the centre of mass of the athlete will have a velocity of 5 ms^{-1} resulting in the centre of mass moving up the body.

As the athlete jumps the hurdle, the body becomes a projectile and is subject to two forces: weight and air resistance. As air resistance is small, the resultant force is almost entirely downwards so the athlete's centre of mass will accelerate vertically downwards and produce a parabolic curve (see page 231).

As the body travels through the air, it changes its shape during flight due to its flexibility and working muscles. However, the path of the centre of mass remains parabolic, resulting in the athlete landing the other side of the hurdle.

Centre of mass and stability

'Stability' is the tendency of an object or body to maintain its resting position or constant velocity. The factors affecting stability include the mass and height of the object or body, plus the position, size and shape of its supporting base. In humans, it can also be affected by the position of limbs in relation to the body and the posture or stance adopted.

The stability of an object or body is related to the height of its centre of mass above its supporting base. An object or body tends to be more stable if the line of mass falls closer to the centre of its base of support. The further a part of the object or body moves from the vertical line through the centre of mass, the more stability will decrease unless compensatory movements are undertaken.

Athletes are required to perform movements of balance, which is achieved by ensuring that their centre of mass lies above their base of support. If the centre of mass lies above a point outside the base of support, an athlete is unstable and is likely to lose their balance or topple over.

To increase stability boxers or martial artists often bend both their legs. This lowers the centre of mass and increases the amount of external force needed to unbalance the athlete. A gymnast on a balance beam requires careful control of their centre of mass: if the centre of mass shifts outside the line of gravity which goes through the beam, the gymnast is likely to lose balance and will have to compensate quickly. Runners are conscious about their stride pattern and foot placement during running or sprinting. This placement helps them to maintain a stability during running/sprinting, enabling them to execute the most efficient stride pattern, thereby generating more speed.

PAUSE POINT Why do you think Formula 1 cars sit so close to the track surface?

Hint Think about the centre of mass and its influence on stability.

Extend What is the likely outcome for a Formula 1 car if it took a corner at 140 mph if it was as high off the ground as an average 4×4 jeep? Explain your reasoning.

Link

This section links with *Unit 2: Functional Anatomy*.

Levers

Muscle, bones and ligaments work together to create human movement using mechanisms called **lever systems**. A joint (e.g. elbow joint) forms an axis or fulcrum, and the muscles crossing the joint apply the force or effort to move the arm and anything it is holding (weight or resistance).

There are three classes of lever system, and all three classes are found in the human body, though the majority are third class lever systems. They depend on the relationship between fulcrum, effort and load. The functions of levers help sports performers increase the resistance that any given effort can move, increase the speed at which a body can move or increase the mechanical advantage of a specific movement.

First class lever system

A first class lever system is one which has its fulcrum between the resistance and the point of effort. An example of a first class lever system in the human body is when the head is raised off the chest (see Figure 7.8).

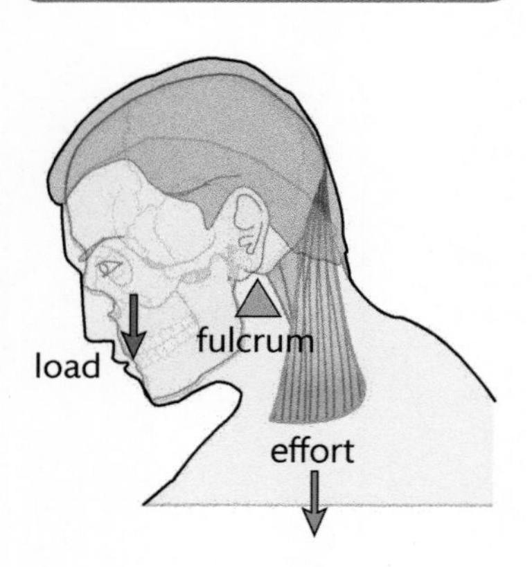

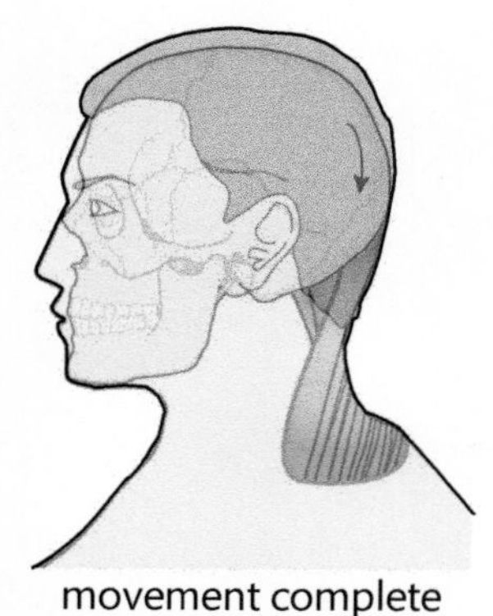

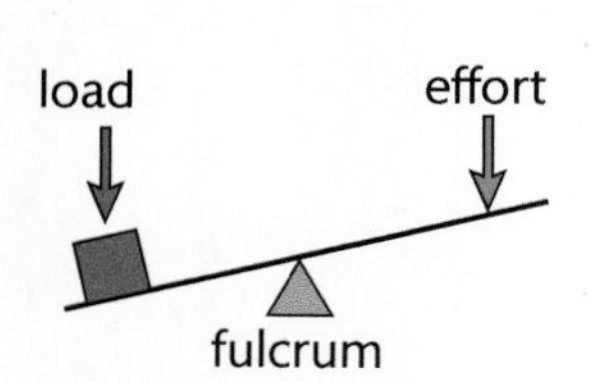

Figure 7.8: Lifting the head away from the chest involves a first class lever system

Second class lever system

A second class lever system is one in which the resistance (load) is between its fulcrum and the point of effort. An example of a second class lever system in the human body is when a person stands on tiptoe (see Figure 7.9).

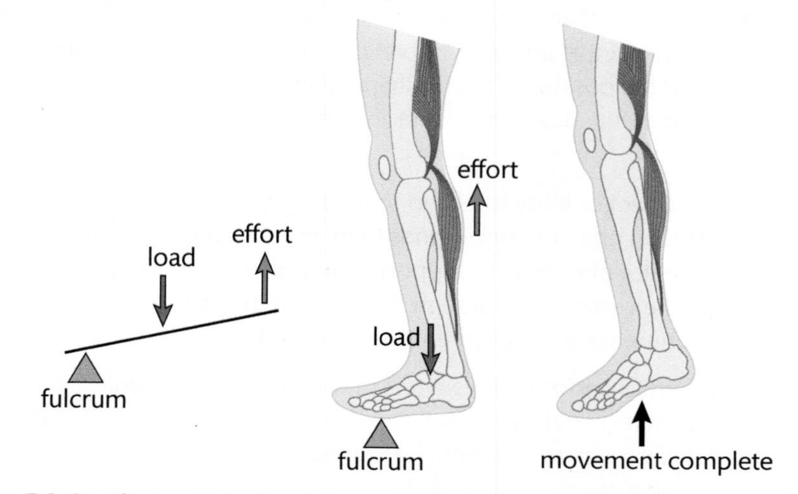

Figure 7.9: Standing on tiptoe involves a second class lever system

Third class lever system

A third class lever system is one in which the effort is between the fulcrum and the resistance. An example of a third class lever system in the human body is a bicep curl (see Figure 7.10).

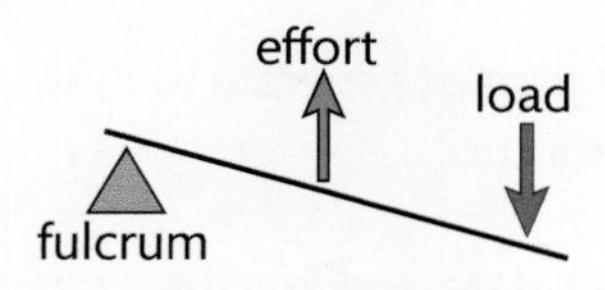

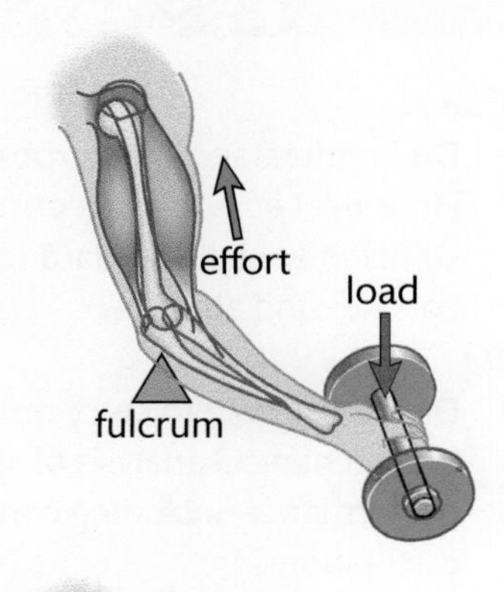

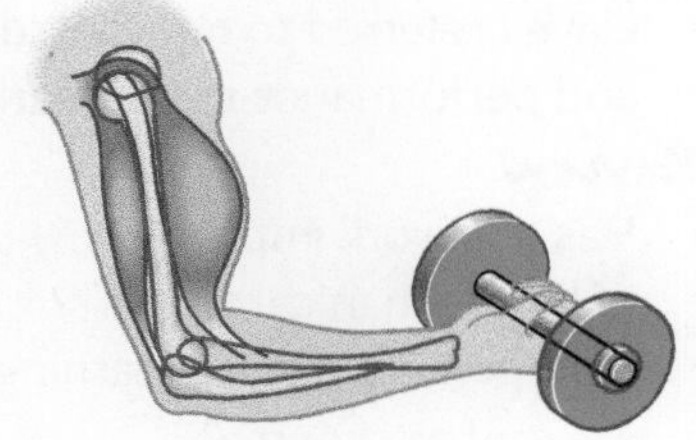

▶ **Figure 7.10:** The bicep curl involves a third class lever system

Research

How many different lever systems can you see operating at the moment a footballer strikes the ball at a free kick? Draw a sketch of the body at this moment and indicate where the systems are in operation from head to foot, and classify each system class 1, 2 or 3.

Turning effects

Torque is a force that produces a twisting or rotational movement. In the human body, torque occurs when the lever systems are called into play, as bones move around a joint in response to a force applied by a muscle or muscles.

Torque is a measure of the turning effect on a lever, so that torque = magnitude of force × lever arm distance from fulcrum (moment arm). It is measured in Newton-metres (Nm).

Axes of rotation

An axis of rotation is an imaginary straight line around which you rotate when you move. There are three axes of rotation (shown in Figure 7.11).

- **Vertical axis** (also known as **longitudinal axis**) – an imaginary line drawn from your head to your toe. A sports example of this axis in use would be an ice skater rotating their body while their foot/boot remains spinning at the same spot.
- **Sagittal axis** (also known as **frontal axis**) – an imaginary line drawn from your back to your front. A sports example of this axis in use would be a gymnast performing a cartwheel where the axis of rotation would go through the stomach and out the back.
- **Transverse axis** – an imaginary line drawn from your left to right. A sports example of this axis in use would be a high diver performing a tuck front somersault as part of a dive where the axis of rotation would go through the hips.

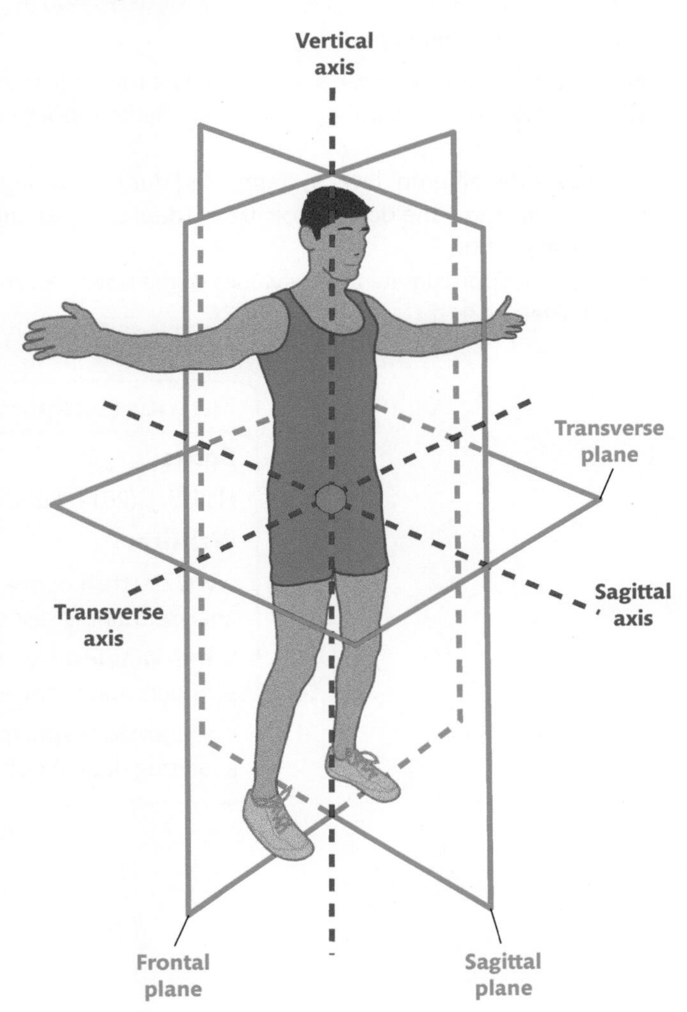

▶ **Figure 7.11:** The three axes of rotation

PAUSE POINT Can the use of lever systems help coaches plan their training programmes for specific movements or exercises?

Hint: Lever systems can help identify the location of an axis or fulcrum (joint), the muscles crossing the joint and the location/direction of the force or effort to move the limb or anything it is holding.

Extend: Can you calculate the amount of force a muscle must generate to move a dumbbell using your knowledge of turning effects and torque?

Assessment practice 7.3

C.P3 C.P4 C.M3 C.M4 C.D3

The cricket club president is delighted with your efforts so far in explaining linear motion and forces. The first match of the season is in a month's time, so he would like the biomechanical analysis of the players' techniques to begin soon.

The club's coaches would like to see if your proposals work in practice before the cricketers start training. They agree that the bowlers should undergo a full biomechanical analysis in a gym environment, using video equipment and motion analysis software to see first-hand how you carry out an analysis, review the data and present your findings.

First, though, you have been asked to write a report that explains what will be assessed during your analysis. In the report, you should:

- analyse the different lever systems used during bowling action
- determine how the bowler's centre of mass changes during the bowling action
- calculate approximate torque values of the bowler's arm during a delivery.

Plan

- Do I understand the purpose of the report?
- How will I ensure my report is of a sufficiently high standard to be shared with coaches and athletes?

Do

- Do I know how to carry out a biomechanical analysis of sports performance, including correct calculations?
- Have I referred to relevant ideal models and performance benchmarks?

Review

- Has this work improved my understanding of biomechanical analysis?
- How can I apply this learning to other areas of my course?

Further reading and resources

Books

Hall, S. J. (2014) *Basic Biomechanics*, 7th edition, Boston, MA: McGraw-Hill.

Websites

www.dartfish.com – Dartfish: video software that can be used to record and analyse training sessions.

http://kandlesoftware.co.uk/index.html – Kandle Software: video analysis products and services.

www.prozonesports.stats.com – Prozone: a range of tools for collecting and analysing data about sports performance.

THINK FUTURE

Ravindra Pandya
Sports Science student

Since completing my BTEC National Sport and Exercise Science course, I've been at university studying the same subject. The BTEC course got me interested in biomechanics and I knew that I wanted to take my interests to degree level once I finished.

While at college, I filmed my classmates during an athletics training session, particularly javelin throwing and the long jump. I analysed the footage using motion analysis software and used the results as my course project. I really enjoyed it - measuring the angles of take-off or release, calculating the velocities using displacements and accurate timings, then showing the results to my classmates and looking for ways to improve their techniques.

As part of my application to university, I was interviewed by the course leader and asked to give a short presentation on an aspect of biomechanics. I talked about the biomechanical analysis I did with my fellow students and demonstrated my work using the software and subsequent calculations.

In addition to all the required specialist knowledge, it is important to have a good rapport with those you are filming and analysing. I don't mind which sport I end up working in – it is the positive impact on performers that makes the role so interesting.

Focusing your skills

Using IT equipment

- Sports scientists involved in biomechanical analysis need to know how to use cameras and camcorders, how to track a moving athlete, and how to download data to a laptop or hard drive.
- You will need good knowledge of motion capture software and must be able to carry out screen annotations for performance profiling.
- You should be proficient in mathematics and the use of formulae, spreadsheets and graphical interpretations of raw numerical data.

Biomechanical and fitness knowledge

The majority of your role will be gathering data for performance profiling, but you will need a basic knowledge of fitness and coaching to interpret this data.

- A sports scientist needs to know how the body moves and functions, and understand the techniques and skills involved in the sport they are analysing (e.g. cricket or athletics).
- You will need excellent communication skills to discuss with the coach and athlete how you will record, analyse and present your findings.

Getting ready for assessment

Josh is working towards completing the second year of his BTEC National in Sport and Exercise Science. He has been given an assignment that asks him to create a presentation examining the methods for biomechanical analysis of sports performance. The presentation can be in a format of Josh's choice but must address forces acting on sports performers and their equipment.

Josh shares his experience below.

How I got started

I decided on a PowerPoint® presentation so I could include photos. The first part was quite easy: I looked through my notes, wrote a list of everything I had learned during the course, and created a list of all the different forces I wanted to talk about. Then, I found plenty of diagrams to illustrate how these forces influence athletes' motion. Finally, I used annotated motion analysis screenshots of my friends performing in athletic events to reinforce my findings.

How I brought it all together

Although my college course taught me a lot about biomechanics, I'm glad I enjoyed maths when I was at school. An understanding of basic geometry, trigonometry and algebra is important if you want to succeed in biomechanics. It is also important to be comfortable using IT software and recording equipment. This allowed me to investigate the biomechanics of different sporting techniques, including the influence of forces along with other components such as linear and angular motion, and highlight areas for potential improvement.

What I learned from the experience

I'm glad I gave myself plenty of time to plan my presentation. Had I left everything to the last minute, I wouldn't have had the opportunity to film real athletic performances and gain first-hand experience of the various biomechanical components that contribute to sports performance. Studying this unit made me realise a camera can be useful – not just for analysis but for recording events that you can use in your assignments.

My friends at college were keen to find out the results of my investigations. My analysis of their performance was well-received and many asked to study the footage and results with a view to improving their own performance.

Think about it

- Make sure you feel confident in your own abilities to complete your assignment.
- Don't be afraid to record your own observations and thoughts, especially when giving feedback to others.
- Biomechanics is a specialised sports science topic that requires an understanding of mathematics. Make sure you have a calculator handy and ask your tutor for help if you want clarification of your calculations.

8 Specialised Fitness Training

Getting to know your unit

Assessment

You will be assessed by a series of assignments set by your tutor.

Effective fitness training is needed alongside tactical and technical training in order to develop the performance of athletes. The type of fitness training used with an athlete will depend on the sport/event. It is important to first understand the demands of the sport in order to select the most effective training methods. Yearly periodised training plans are often developed to maximise the training benefits and reduce the risk of injury. Therefore, understanding how to develop these plans is a requirement of a developing Sport and Exercise Scientist.

How you will be assessed

This unit will be assessed by a series of internally assessed tasks set by your tutor. Throughout this unit you will find assessment practice activities that will help you work towards your assessment. Completing these activities will not mean that you have achieved a particular grade, but you will have carried out useful research or preparation that will be relevant when it comes to your final assignment.

In order for you to sucessfully complete the tasks in your assignment, it is important to check that you have met all of the Pass grading criteria. You can do this as you work your way through the assignment.

If you are hoping to gain a Merit or Distinction, you should also make sure that you present the information in your assignment in the style that is required by the relevant assessment criterion. For example, Merit criteria require you to analyse whereas the Distinction criteria require you to evaluate.

The assignment set by your tutor will consist of a number of tasks designed to meet the criteria in the table. This is likely to consist of a mixture of written and practical assignments and include activities such as:

- researching to produce a report about the different fitness demands of a series of sports
- engaging in different training methods to help you evaluate their effectiveness
- designing training plans and programmes for a range of different athlete case studies.

Assessment criteria

This table shows what you must do in order to achieve a **Pass**, **Merit** or **Distinction** grade, and where you can find activities to help you.

Pass	Merit	Distinction
Learning aim A Examine the fitness requirements, physical characteristics and demands of sport that contribute to effective training and performance		
A.P1 Explain how the fitness demands, characteristics and movement patterns of the sport influence the planning of an athlete's training. **Assessment practice 8.1**	**A.M1** Analyse how the fitness demands, characteristics and movement patterns of the sport influence the planning of an athlete's training. **Assessment practice 8.1**	**A.D1** Evaluate how the fitness demands, characteristics and movement patterns of the sport influence the planning of an athlete's training. **Assessment practice 8.1**
Learning aim B Investigate methods of training for physical and skill-related fitness		
B.P2 Explain methods of training and their effectiveness in improving physical fitness for a chosen sport. **Assessment practice 8.2**	**B.M2** Analyse methods of training and their effectiveness in improving physical fitness for a chosen sport. **Assessment practice 8.2**	**B.D2** Evaluate the effectiveness of methods of training used to improve physical and skill-related fitness, justifying how they contribute to enhance performance in a chosen sport. **Assessment practice 8.2**
B.P3 Explain methods of training and their effectiveness in improving skill-related fitness for a chosen sport. **Assessment practice 8.2**	**B.M3** Analyse methods of training and their effectiveness in improving skill-related fitness for a chosen sport. **Assessment practice 8.2**	
Learning aim  Explore the planning of fitness programming		
C.P4 Explain the principles of training to be considered when planning for periodised training and fitness programming. **Assessment practice 8.3**	**C.M4** Analyse the design of the training session plan as part of the periodised training programme. **Assessment practice 8.3**	**C.D3** Evaluate the effectiveness of the training programme towards enhancing sports performance, making justified suggestions for adaptations or alternative methods of training. **Assessment practice 8.3**
C.P5 Produce a detailed periodised training programme to improve performance for a chosen sport. **Assessment practice 8.3**		
C.P6 Produce a detailed training session plan for a selected aspect of the periodised training programme. **Assessment practice 8.3**		

Getting started

The fitness training industry needs high quality specialised fitness coaches and trainers. Fitness trainers are required to understand the demands of a range of sports in order to prescribe the most effective training methods. Observe or watch a video of a sport being played and create a list of the fitness-related demands you think are being placed on the performer(s) during the event.

A Examine the fitness requirements, physical characteristics and demands of sport that contribute to effective training and performance

The fitness demands and physical characteristics required to be successful vary depending on the sport being performed. Fitness trainers need to assess the characteristics of the sport.

- How long is the event? Is it short, long or sustained? Does it last seconds, minutes, hours or even days?
- What level of physical contact is there? Contact sports where additional loads may be applied to the body (e.g. rugby or boxing) need additional considerations.
- What are the recovery periods during or between performances? Some events, such as the 100 metres, allow 12–24 hours between races, and weeks between competitions. Other sports feature two or three matches per week.

Types of activity and performance cycles

A sport is made up of several different types of activity which directly influence the training methods used.

- **Multi-sprint activities** – most team sports, like football, rugby, netball and hockey, require performers to repeatedly carry out sprint activities.
- **Skill-based activities** – agility, speed, power, reaction time, balance and **proprioception** are required.
- **Fitness-based activities** – sports requiring different components of fitness such as endurance, strength or power, e.g. marathons and open water swimming require cardiovascular endurance.
- **Multi-discipline** – where the sport consists of several events, such as triathlon and decathlon.

Key term

Proprioception – the ability to sense where the body is in space.

Case study

Balanced weekly training

Jasper has been training in a range of athletic events over the last two years. He is performing well in several events such as the 100m hurdles, long jump and shot put. His coach has suggested that he competes in the heptathlon next season.

Check your knowledge

What type of activity is the heptathlon categorised as? How would the inclusion of additional events influence Jasper's training?

The different performance cycles of sports must also be taken into consideration when planning training as it will affect when peak fitness needs to be achieved.

- The **type of competition** (i.e. whether a tournament, one-off performance or in a league) will affect the fitness training undertaken. For example, a boxer may only have two or three fights per year while football players play 60 games each season. Sprint athletes are building towards high profile competitions such as the Olympics, so athletes aim to be at peak fitness at these events.
- The **repetition and frequency of performance** also has to be considered. For example, the football World Cup takes place at the end of a domestic season, when players tend to already be in a heightened state of fatigue, so high-intensity training sessions between matches in the World Cup is unrealistic.

PAUSE POINT For a sport you are unfamiliar with, identify the characteristics of performance, the type of activities and competition involved, and the repetition and frequency of performance.

Hint The National Governing Body (NGB) website for the sport will be a good source of information.

Extend If the sport takes place in your local area, go and watch it being played or speak to a coach/fitness trainer to find out more.

Fitness demands of sports

Understanding the specific fitness demands of a sport, as shown in Table 8.1, will help you structure and plan appropriate training.

▶ **Table 8.1:** Different fitness demands of sports

Component of fitness	Definition
Strength	The ability of a single/group of muscles to exert a maximal force or overcome a maximal resistance in a single contraction. Strength generated is in direct proportion to the size of muscle or group. Some sports require specific muscle training to improve muscle size and strength. • **Isometric strength** – ability to contact and hold a movement – the muscles contract but no movement occurs (for example, in a rugby scrum). • **Isotonic strength** – can be concentric (muscles contract and shorten in length) or eccentric (muscles contract and lengthen under tension). In the upwards phase of a bicep curl, biceps contract concentrically; in the downwards phase they contract eccentrically to lower the weight.
Cardiovascular endurance	The ability of the heart, lungs, blood vessels (arteries and veins) and skeletal muscle to take in, transport and use oxygen efficiently over a prolonged period.
Localised muscular endurance	The ability of a muscle – or group of close-together muscles – to make repeated contractions against light-to-moderate resistance over a prolonged period of time.
Explosive power	Actions where the movement requires a rapid rate of force development. This means recruiting a high number of motor units (motor neurons and muscle fibres) to generate a rapid force of contraction in the shortest time possible, for example, a high jump take-off.
Speed	Requires movement over a certain distance in the shortest time possible, for example, a 100-metre sprint.
Agility	The ability to coordinate the body to change direction quickly while maintaining control, for example, a netball player being able to change direction quickly on the court to receive a ball.
Balance and proprioception	Balance and proprioception work together. Balance is the ability of the body to retain the centre of mass over the base of support. Proprioception is the awareness of body position in space. A rhythmic gymnast will need to possess excellent balance and proprioception.
Sustained anaerobic exercise	Anaerobic exercises are of high intensity, producing lactic acid. Sustained anaerobic exercise can be separated into **anaerobic power** and **speed endurance**. Anaerobic power exercises are greater in length than explosive power exercises, e.g. a sprint finish in the Tour de France. Speed endurance is the ability to work anaerobically over a longer period of time, e.g. a 200-metre freestyle swimmer.
Flexibility	The ability to move a joint through a complete – and natural – range of motion without discomfort or pain. A javelin thrower requires good shoulder flexibility.
Reaction time	The time taken to respond to a stimulus, for example, to respond to a serve in table tennis.

Movement patterns

Human movement involves the coordination of several joints all at the same time. Exercises should be chosen to mirror the movement patterns of the sport. Sporting movement patterns include:

- changes of direction
- sustained repeated movements (anything where the same movement pattern is repeated over and over, for example, running, cycling and swimming)

- pre-programmed movements (patterns of movements the body has learned, allowing movements to be produced with relative ease)
- reactive movements (movements that change frequently in response to external stimuli such as a ball, opponent, the court position of an opponent or an object on a course).

Theory into practice

Select a sport of your choice and work out what type of movement patterns are required during the event (a combination may be required). Research a range of different exercises/activities that you could include in a training plan to mirror the movement patterns of the sport.

Interaction of body parts

Movement patterns are coordinated in **kinetic chains**, the ordered, sequential movement of a series of body segments. These ensure the **distal segments** (the body segments that are further away from the body, like the hands and feet) are placed in the correct position for the sporting movement.

The **core** of the body is the centre of most movement patterns in sport and is the base of successful coordination of movements in the distal segments. For example, in a tennis serve the transverse abdominals are activated before the upper body limbs start to move – the core generates power which then translates into the shoulder, elbow, wrist and then the ball. During sporting movements, the core is usually dynamic, ensuring movements are carried out efficiently without compromising their **base of support**. It also helps maintain balance and maintain good posture.

Several sports require the reach distance of the upper or lower limbs to be high, for example, the upper body in tennis reaching for a return ball and the lower body when trying to intercept a pass in football. Successful reach requires the coordination of the upper and lower limbs in combination with reaction time.

Reach is different in tennis (upper body) and football (lower body)

Poor movement patterns can increase landing forces and the stress placed on muscles and joints, potentially increasing the risk of injury. Exercises should encourage the athlete to work through the range of motion they need during their sport. The correct technique must be mastered before an athlete adds any additional weight or progresses to an unstable surface.

Figure 8.1 shows range of movement at the shoulder. Figure 8.1(a) shows good shoulder mobility. Figure 8.1(b) shows a limited range of motion but the spine has extended to allow the shoulders to appear to have good mobility. Figure 8.1(c) shows poor shoulder mobility with a neutral spine. An athlete with poor shoulder mobility is likely to have an incorrect technique for overhead squats – developing mobility would avoid additional stress on the spine.

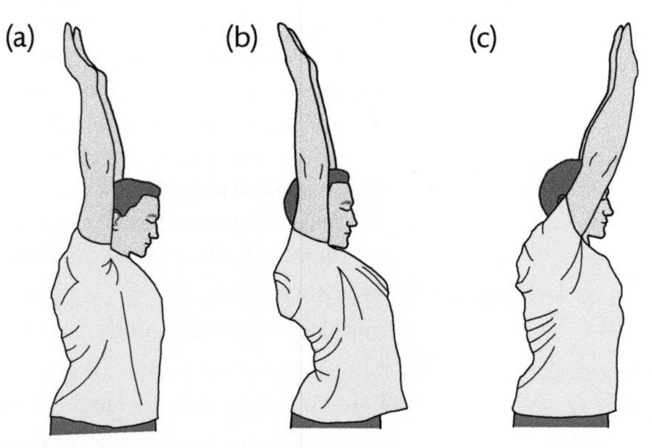

Figure 8.1: Shoulder mobility: (a) good mobility, (b) poor mobility with extended spine, (c) poor mobility with neutral spine

Sporting actions consist of **unilateral** and **bilateral** movement patterns. For example, during the approach and take-off in high jump movement patterns are unilateral while a jump shot in basketball is bilateral.

Key terms

Core – the muscles of the trunk and pelvis that stabilise the spine and pelvis.

Base of support – the area of surface below an object or person (e.g. base of support is increased when the feet are hip width apart in comparison to touching at the ankles).

Unilateral – movement on one side of the body or when each limb is working independently.

Bilateral – movement that occurs on both sides of the body in unison.

In fitness training, unilateral exercises can be particularly useful for identifying imbalances between the dominant and non-dominant sides of the body. Training using unilateral movements can improve these imbalances which can, in turn, improve overall movement quality and sport performance. Bilateral exercises use a greater number of skeletal muscles and can result in greater training gains (e.g. strength gains) that last for a longer period of time. A combination of unilateral and bilateral exercises should be used, with a specific focus on the demands of the event (e.g. whether it needs greater contribution from unilateral or bilateral movements).

Discussion

How can understanding unilateral and bilateral movement patterns help with injury prevention and performance enhancement?

PAUSE POINT Select two contrasting sports and consider how the movement patterns in the sports differ. Why is the core important in the movements? What does it allow the athlete to be good at? Are the movements unilateral or bilateral?

Hint Watch examples of the sport. Are there any times when the movement pattern does not occur successfully?

Extend Why will understanding the movement patterns in the sport help you draw up training exercises?

Energy systems and expenditure

Different sports require the use of different energy systems. Understanding how the body produces energy in order for an activity to be carried out helps a fitness instructor prescribe exercises. If energy needs to be produced either rapidly or over a long period of time, then training will focus on developing this. But sports often demand energy production from both the aerobic and anaerobic energy systems; for example, a basketball player uses anaerobic energy to jump and uses the aerobic system to work at a high intensity through the quarters.

Link

For more information on energy systems and energy production, see *Unit 1: Sport and Exercise Physiology*.

For more information on planning training sessions so that they are not too intense, see *Unit 6: Coaching for Performance and Fitness*.

Factors affecting training programme design

You must also be aware of other factors that affect the design of training programmes.

- **Time** – this will vary for every person you work with, with other commitments like work, education and family life often balanced alongside training and competing. Training needs to maximise the time available.
- **Injury prevention** – if you overload a participant without rest and recovery time, the injury risk increases. For athletes returning from injury, training that does not stress the injury but helps maintain fitness should be used.
- **Performance outcomes** – what a participant needs or expects from their performance will affect the training programme. For example, a 400-metre sprint athlete aiming for the Olympics will need training to support this goal, usually across a four-year period.
- **Pre-season/post-season** – the pre-season period helps participants return to their competitive levels, progressively adapting towards competition without fatigue. Post-season consists of restorative practices and low-intensity training.
- **Manager requirements** – a manager may want a player to fulfil a specific role within a team, for example, jumping higher for an attacking header in football to increase scoring chances. In this example you would be expected to develop the player's lower body power.
- **Personal, team and position goals** – a participant's specific personal goals need to be appreciated. Athletes may also need to work towards team goals (such as improving cardiovascular endurance) and/or positional goals relating to where they play in the team (such as improving strength for a rugby scrum).

Assessment practice 8.1

A.P1 A.M1 A.D1

The chair of a local volleyball league has asked you to produce a presentation for local coaches on the importance of identifying a sport's requirements and the influence these have on planning training.

The presentation should look at the requirements of the sport focusing on its:

- fitness demands
- characteristics
- movement patterns.

Explain why each requirement is important and analyse how each requirement influences the planning of training. Your analysis needs to consider interrelationships between the requirements, for instance, how do the characteristics of the sport link with the fitness demands and how does this influence training?

Then help the coaches to evaluate which requirements may have the most significance in planning training. To do this, draw conclusions about the influence that each aspect has on planning, including a range of specific examples to support your conclusions.

Plan

- Why is it important that I know about the requirements of the sport and their influence on training?
- Are there any areas where I might struggle? What could I do to avoid this?

Do

- Have I researched the requirements of the sport?
- Have I watched the sport being played live and talked to some of the players?

Review

- Did my approach help me achieve the task?
- How could I apply what I have learned to other areas of my work?

B Investigate methods of training for physical and skill-related fitness

Physical fitness training: flexibility

Flexibility training aims to allow everyday movements to be completed with ease. A hurdler may focus more on range of movement at the hip joints compared to a sprint athlete, as a wide range of movement is required to clear the hurdles. Flexibility can also improve posture and the power and strength of a joint. It can also help prevent injury.

Methods of flexibility training

Static flexibility stretching

Static stretches are usually slow and controlled. There are two types: passive and active.

- **Passive (assisted) stretching** – requires the help of another person or an object such as a wall. This applies an external force (push or pull) to increase the range of movement at the joint.
- **Active stretching** – can be achieved by an individual alone and involves voluntary contraction of specific muscles.

For both active and passive stretching the range of movement at a joint should be increased until the individual can feel the stretch developing (but not to the point of high pain) and hold this position for 15–30 seconds. This can be repeated across each muscle group, with a rest between each muscle group stretched. This is best done at the end of a training session or in a specific session targeted at improving flexibility.

Ballistic stretching

This requires an individual to make fast, jerky movements – usually bouncing and bobbing – through the full range of motion. It should be specific to a movement pattern in the relevant sporting activity. It can lead to soreness and may cause injury such as strains so must be undertaken carefully and with the correct technique.

Proprioceptive neuromuscular facilitation (PNF)

This is an advanced form of passive stretching and one of the most effective forms of increasing flexibility. There are three types of PNF stretching techniques.

- The **hold-relax technique** requires a trainer to stretch the target muscle group to the upper limit of its range of movement. The participant isometrically contracts the muscle(s) against the trainer for 6–10 seconds. The trainer should ensure they have a strong base of support as no movement should occur during the contraction phase. Once the isometric phase is complete the participant relaxes and the trainer stretches the muscle(s) to the new upper limit. This can be repeated up to three times.
- The **hold-relax-contract technique** is nearly identical to hold-relax but the contraction is isotonic, meaning the participant contracts against the trainer to move through the range of movement.
- The **hold-relax-swing technique** involves the trainer moving the participant through a passive stretch after the isometric contraction phase, with the athlete moving straight into a dynamic or ballistic stretch.

Communication with the participant is key during this type of stretching. If the participant is experiencing too much pain this may suggest the stretch has been taken too far.

Research

Research the different types of PNF stretches that can be conducted and practise them with a peer (under supervision).

Effectiveness of training methods

These methods are designed to increase flexibility by stretching the muscle spindle, a sensory receptor found in the belly of a muscle between muscle fibres that detect changes in length of the muscle. When a muscle spindle is stretched, a series of signals are sent to the spinal cord via sensory neurons. Rapid signals via motor neurons are then sent back to the muscle fibres to create muscle action (to prevent the muscle fibres from being overstretched). This is known as the **stretch reflex**.

Overuse of muscle spindles reduces the effectiveness of the stretch – static stretching in particular is slow and controlled so that the stretch reflex is not activated. Static stretching can effectively increase range of motion and is less likely to cause injury than ballistic stretching.

PNF stretching can be superior to other methods as it facilitates muscular inhibition. This is experienced when a muscle actively undergoes contraction before a passive stretch of the same muscle. The active tension during contraction causes receptors located near the join between a tendon and muscle to be activated, causing a reflexive relaxation of the muscle during the following stretch.

Physical fitness training: strength

A number of resistance training methods can be employed to improve maximal strength, **core stability** and muscular endurance. Strength training has four main functions.

- Poor posture can be a result of muscle imbalances – effective strength training will train the weakened muscles and improve posture.
- Stability provided by muscles of the trunk supports whole-body function – core stability can help this.
- Joint integrity refers to the expected movement pattern at a joint. When the joint becomes unstable, normal function is altered. Joint strength and stability can be improved by training the muscles supporting them.
- Force production is the ability of a muscle(s) to recruit the appropriate **motor units** to overcome resistance. The ability to generate force is improved through strength training. Different training will lead to different gains in force production. For example, a weightlifter will have a greater absolute strength than a high jump athlete, therefore they can exert a greater force.

Discussion

Discuss which sports require a specific type of strength and which require a combination of strength types.

Key terms

Core stability – the ability of the muscles deep within the abdomen which connect to the spine, pelvis and shoulders to maintain good posture – the foundation for all movements.

Motor unit – a motor neuron and all associated fibres it affects. Motor units work together to coordinate contractions of a single skeletal muscle.

Methods of strength training

▶ Weights are a common method for strength training

> **Key terms**
>
> **Maximal strength** – the maximum force that a muscle or group of muscles can exert in a single contraction (e.g. the maximum weight that you can lift once).
>
> **Muscular endurance** (also known as strength endurance) – the ability to exert a sub-maximal force for a number of repetitions or over a sustained period of time.

- **Traditional strength training** – consists of repeated bouts of repetitions against resistance on stable surfaces. The type of strength being developed determines the load, repetition target and rest periods.
    - **Maximal strength** training typically requires loads greater than 85 per cent of a person's repetition maximum (1RM), with a repetition goal of less than six. Rest periods for maximum strength training (1–6 reps) will require a rest of 2–5 minutes between sets. The higher the RM target, the longer the rest needed between sets (e.g. if a 2RM has just been performed a rest period of 4–5 minutes is likely to be needed).
    - To improve **muscular endurance** a load less than 65 per cent of a person's 1RM and a repetition target of more than 12 is required. The rest can be much shorter than maximal strength training due to the lower load lifted – a rest of less than 30 seconds between sets should be sufficient.
- **Core stability** – consists of repeated bouts of repetitions on unstable surfaces. The principles are similar to traditional strength training but the surface is unstable. This can be achieved by using BOSU balls, core stability balls, wobble boards and suspension bands.
- **Circuit training** – can be designed to target specific types of strength training. It works particularly well for developing muscular endurance and core stability but can also develop strength. It is particularly beneficial for participants with limited time. The circuit design can be used to maximise work while not compromising effectiveness, as muscle groups can be alternated so rest times can be reduced. Muscular endurance-based circuits usually take place in a facility with a large floor space. Strength circuits are likely to be in a gym, to access the heavier loads, and the floor usually needs to be reinforced.
- **Complex training** – combines traditional strength training and plyometrics (see page 256). The underlying principle is that heavy loading prior to explosive activity (such as a plyometric exercise) creates a heightened central nervous system stimulation resulting in a greater motor unit recruitment in the later activities. A five-repetition maximum followed by a 4-minute rest and then a plyometric exercise is widely accepted. It is suitable for trained participants but evidence is inconclusive about its effects.

PAUSE POINT If a participant can lift 30 kg in a 1RM frontal raise, what weight would they need to lift if they wanted to work at 60% of their 1RM for 12 reps?

Hint To work out the percentage repetition maximum use the following: (12 × 60) ÷ 100

Extend Now calculate 70% and 80% of 30 kg.

Types of strength training exercise

- **Compound exercises** involve using more than one main muscle group at a time. Usually one larger group is predominately activated, with other smaller groups recruited to support movement. Examples include squats, lunges, deadlifts, bench press and pull-ups. Rest and recovery needs to be carefully planned. For example, if you trained your chest one day (where triceps are likely to be supporting movement) and triceps the next day, you will not have provided enough rest for the triceps.
- **Isolated exercises** are any exercise in which only one major muscle group is trained. The exercise is done in a way so that other muscle groups are not used, leaving the one group to be isolated to complete the work. Example exercises include bicep curls, triceps extension, leg curl/extension and calf raises.

Research

There is a large amount of strength and conditioning equipment on the market, including free weights, weight-resistance and gravity-based machines, elastic resistance and calisthenics/body weight exercises. Carry out some research into these and the training methods and exercises they best support.

Effectiveness of training methods to improve strength

All training methods can be adapted to further challenge an individual's strength. A common debate within resistance training is whether to use free weights or resistance machines. Table 8.2 shows when free weights or resistance machines may be more effective.

Table 8.2: Differences between free weights and resistance machines

Free weights	Resistance machines
Wider range of exercises available for training a particular muscle/ muscle group.	Limited number of resistance machines to develop strength of a particular muscle/muscle group.
Enhance postural developments and engage stabilising muscles as well as fixator muscles (the muscles assisting the main muscles creating the action and the ones that prevent any unwanted movements).	Isolate a single muscle or group of muscles without requiring the assistance of synergist and fixator muscles.
Risk of injury is high with the use of free weights, particularly in strength training.	Reduced injury risk due to set range of movement.
More suitable for intermediate and advanced resistance-trained athletes.	Useful for beginners and for athletes returning from injury.

Theory into practice

When working with experienced strength-training athletes, you may want to use advanced weight training techniques to increase training effectiveness. Research the following: supersets, dropsets, partials and forced reps.

Physical fitness training: cardiovascular endurance

Link

Cardiovascular endurance training improves the endurance of the aerobic and anaerobic energy systems. Refer back to *Unit 1: Sport and Exercise Physiology* to remind yourself about these.

The main function of cardiovascular endurance training is to:

- improve stamina (working at a higher intensity for a longer period of time)
- sustain performance (maintaining performance levels throughout the duration of an event)
- improve recovery between bouts of exercise to improve the quality of performance
- increase the ability to train at a higher intensity to improve performance during events.

Methods of cardiovascular endurance training

Continuous training

Also known as steady-state or long, slow distance training, continuous training involves training at a steady pace over a long distance and time. Continuous training should be moderate intensity (≤70% VO2 max). This method of training is suited to long-distance runners or swimmers. Due to the lower intensity, an athlete can train for longer.

It can be useful for beginners, athletes recovering from injury, and children and the elderly.

Disadvantages of this type of training are that:

- there is a higher risk of injury when running long distances on harder surfaces
- some people find it boring
- it offers few sport-specific benefits.

Fartlek training

Fartlek training is designed to improve aerobic endurance. It is based on running outdoors and varies the intensity of work according to the athlete's requirements. Intensity is changed by varying terrain, such as sand, hills or woodland.

Research

Some common examples of fartlek sessions include Astrand, Gerschler, Saltin and Watson methods. As a group, research each of these methods and prepare a short written report or presentation about their benefits.

Benefits include improving aerobic endurance, muscular endurance, and balance and proprioception in the ankle, knee and hip, improving performance and aiding injury rehabilitation. Fartlek training can also be more individual and sport-specific and uses both aerobic and anaerobic energy systems to improve aerobic endurance. It also involves changes in direction, so it is useful for team sports as it can mimic game conditions. There is no rest period but the athlete has more control and is able to decrease intensity at any time to rest.

Interval training

Interval training improves anaerobic endurance components and aerobic endurance by varying the intensity and length of the work periods. In interval training, athletes perform a work period followed by a rest or recovery period, before completing another work period. When designing an interval training programme, you should consider:

- the number of intervals (rest and work periods)
- the intensity and duration of the work interval
- the intensity and duration of the rest interval.

An example of an interval training session for aerobic endurance is 1 set of 3 repetitions of 5-minute runs interspersed with 2 minutes and 30 seconds of rest. This would be written in a training diary as 1 × 3 × 5:00 Work:Rest 2:30.

Interval training allows clear progression and overload to be built into the programme by increasing the intensity of work periods, increasing the number of intervals, decreasing the duration of the rest period or increasing the intensity of the rest period (for example, by using a slow jog rather than a walk).

Skill-related fitness training: agility

Agility is the ability to coordinate the body to change direction quickly while maintaining control. Agility helps athletes at speed to do the following.

- **Change direction** – many sports require the ability to change direction. For example, a football player rarely runs in a straight line and many changes of direction are required.
- **Lose an opponent** – an athlete who can change direction faster than an opponent, is likely to be more successful.
- **Create space** – an athlete can create space through changing direction at speed, giving them more time to complete a subsequent movement, for example, in netball if a wing attack can change direction quickly without the opposition's wing defence following her, she will be able to create space to receive a pass.

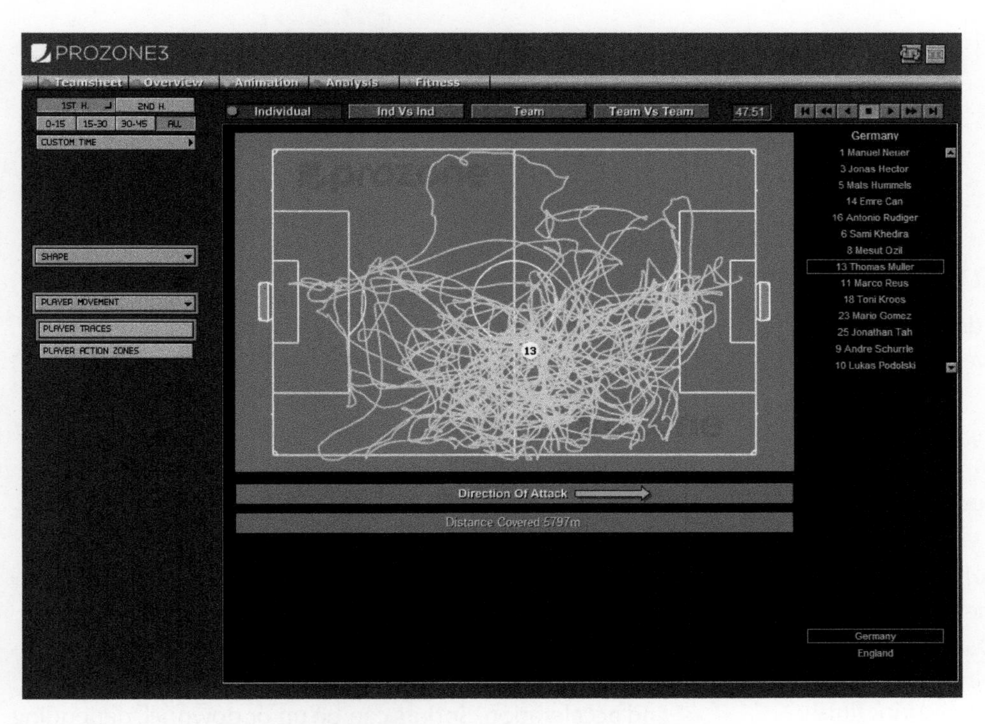

▶ Football players often change direction and rarely run in a straight line

Methods of agility training

Three methods of agility training exercise are shown in Table 8.3.

▶ **Table 8.3:** Agility training exercises

Methods of agility training	Training details
Speed, Agility and Quickness (SAQ®)	This often involves the use of cones, mini hurdles, poles and agility ladders to create a course that the athlete needs to manoeuvre through. (Due to its speed requirements, agility training often follows the principles of speed training.)
Agility ladders	An agility ladder is a piece of equipment in the shape of a ladder laid down on the ground. The athlete then moves through the gaps in the rungs of the ladder quickly. Ladders can be joined together to form a pattern, or different movement patterns can be used to travel between the rungs.
Shuttle runs (multi-direction)	Shuttle runs are simple courses of a short number of marked points or lines that the athlete sprints between or around. Figure 8.2 shows examples of how shuttle runs can be set out for agility. The shuttle should be designed to match the movement patterns that are required for the sport. For example, the baseline inside M could be used with a badminton player and an inside X could be used with a football player.

(a)

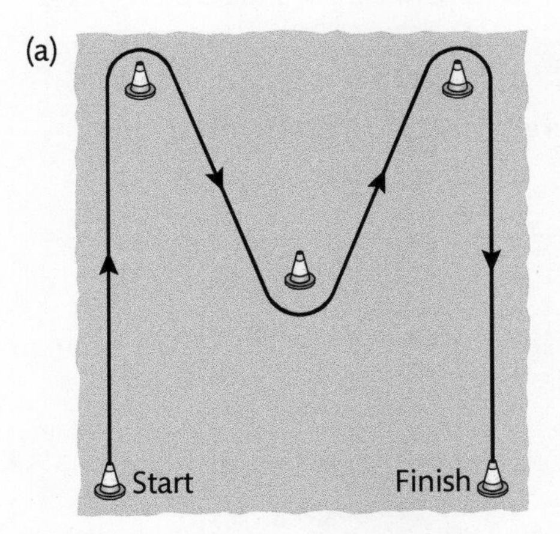

(b)

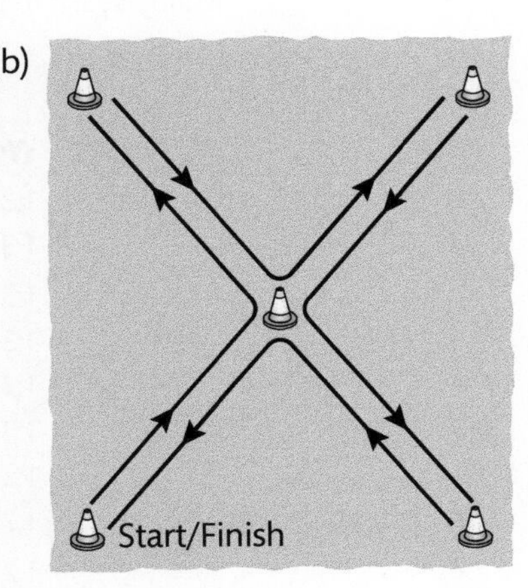

▶ **Figure 8.2:** Shuttle run layouts: (a) baseline inside M and (b) inside X

PAUSE POINT Watch two contrasting sports that require agility. Design two different shuttle runs to help develop agility in that sport.

Hint You could adapt shuttle run layouts you have used in your training.

Extend Could you adapt the shuttle run to include SAQ® equipment?

Skill-related fitness training: speed

Speed training has several functions depending on the type of speed required. It can improve acceleration, improve pace or improve cadence.

- **Acceleration** – the ability to change your speed is a key requirement of many sports. An athlete who can change speed faster than their opponent will have a competitive advantage.
- **Change of pace** – this is particularly useful in team sports, for example, in netball if the goalkeeper wins the ball, the wing defence will need to change their pace quickly to create space to receive a pass. In cycling, a change of pace may be required for a sprint finish.
- **Cadence** – this refers to stride rate, so in terms of speed the ability to move the legs quickly. Speed is stride length × stride rate. The person with the longest stride and quickest stride rate or cadence is likely to be the fastest. Usain Bolt took 41 steps to win the 2012 Olympic 100-metre final, whereas his rival Yohan Blake took 46 steps.

Methods of speed training

Acceleration sprints

- **Resisted sprints** use a weighted vest or sledge to increase resistance during the acceleration phase, placing additional stress on joint range of movement and activation of the muscular system. A resisted weight of 10–15 per cent of body weight should be used over short distances such as 20–50 metres. Parachutes and resistance sprint bands can also be used.
- **Short acceleration sprints** cover 5 metres, 10 metres, 15 metres and 20 metres with 10 repetitions of 5 sets. The starting position can also be manipulated if this is required for the sport, For example, a sprint athlete could use a sprint start or a 3-point start, whereas a team sport athlete may use a rolling start (where a jog precedes the acceleration phase). A work-to-rest period of 1:3 is often used in speed-related training. Each sprint should be performed at the same speed as previous ones to stress the correct energy system. If the sprint times become slower over the set, increase the rest time.

Hill sprints

Athletes use hill sprints to increase speed, coordination and acceleration. Sprints can be up or downhill, depending on the content and aims of the session. Hill sprints involve a shorter stride length and longer contact time with the ground than flat sprints. The knee, hip and ankle joints are more flexed during hill sprints and there is greater muscle activity in the gastrocnemius, quadriceps muscle group and gluteus maximus muscle. These all play a key role in sporting activities involving sprinting and jumping. The incline used should only be around 5 degrees to create the increase in contact time.

Overspeed training

This should only be used with experienced speed-trained athletes. Overspeed training requires the athlete to work at speeds higher than willingly possible. It is designed to override the current speed to create improvements that will mean a faster unassisted speed. Overspeed training can be done using a decline sprint, wind assistance or an elastic pulley system. The decline sprint grade should be very slight

▶ **Table 8.4:** Speed training guide

Energy system targeted	Time (min:sec)	Sets	Reps per set	Work:relief ratio	Relief interval type
Phosphocreatine Acceleration	0:10 0:20	5 4	10 10	1:3 1:3	Walking
Phosphocreatine – Lactic acid Acceleration – maximum speed	0:30 0:40 0:50 1:00 1:10 1:20	5 4 4 3 3 2	5 5 5 5 5 5	1:3 1:3 1:3 1:3 1:3 1:2	Jogging
Lactic acid – Aerobic Speed endurance	1:30–2:00 2:00–3:00	2 1	4 6	1:2 1:1	Jogging

and not go beyond a couple of degrees; it is designed to help the athlete go faster but not so fast that it cannot be maintained. Table 8.4 can be used to prescribe speed training.

Skill-related fitness training: balance and proprioception

Balance depends on the area of the base of support, the position of the centre of gravity and the mass of the performer. A wide positioning of the feet (such as for a wicket keeper in cricket) will enhance static balance but many sports require dynamic balance, as athletes react to changes. Improving proprioception can also increase an athlete's ability to change direction and coordinate movements to perform activities consistently, as well as reducing the risk of injury by helping the body react to sudden changes.

Balance and proprioception can also maintain and improve **aesthetics**. Gymnasts and dancers are particularly concerned with this. Mechanoreceptors (sensory areas that detect changes in pressure) found in the joints, muscles, tendons and skin help improve the neural control of a movement. The more controlled a movement is the more aesthetically pleasing it will be.

Balance training and proprioceptive training should be incorporated into everyday sessions where possible – 20 minutes per day should improve both (see Table 8.5). Training should progress to ensure balance is continually being stressed.

Key term

Aesthetics – the way a person moves and how the movement looks.

A gymnast needs extremely good balance

Table 8.5: Methods of training balance and proprioception

Training method	Details
Wobble balance board	Provide an unstable surface on which to conduct movements and challenge static balance. Exercises can include press-ups, lunges, side plank and single leg standing. It is important to develop static balance before using wobble balance boards; the Bongo board is particularly challenging so should be used only with athletes with high levels of balance.
Gait exercises	The following gait exercises can be completed once to twice daily: • One-leg balance – one leg should be bent at the knee and held at 90 degrees for as long as possible. • Heel-to-toe walking – place heel of one foot at the front of the toes on the other foot and repeat for 10–20 metres without looking at the feet. • Hip stabilising – sit on the edge of a chair, lean back slightly and raise one leg straight out in front, so the hip, knee and ankle are all in line. Hold for 30 seconds and repeat on each leg.
Weighted ball exercises (e.g. medicine ball)	Can be used to develop static balance. In contact with the floor, throwing a medicine ball backwards and forwards between athletes, developing one-foot contact. The challenge can be increased by using a weighted ball while standing on a wobble balance board, either moving the ball to a different position, e.g. holding above the head and passing from side to side, or while completing a torso twist.

Skill-related fitness training: power and reaction time

Power is required by actions that need a rapid rate of force development. Reaction time refers to the time it takes to respond to a stimulus. The functions of power and reaction time include:

- **responding to a stimulus** in the shortest time, providing athletes with a competitive advantage
- **changing direction at speed** using a combination of agility and power, again to provide a competitive advantage
- **increasing vertical and horizontal jump height**, recruiting a high number of motor units and developing force rapidly.

Methods of training power and reaction time

These include any exercise that engages two or more different joints to fully stimulate entire muscle groups and, indeed, multiple muscles.

Power

Power needs to be developed from a foundation of strength, so strength needs to be trained in order to generate maximum power. Compound training (exercises that engage two or more different joints to stimulate entire muscle groups) should be used to establish base strength, with exercises such as lunges, squats and calf raises. Plyometric training is one of the most common methods to develop power. Plyometric exercises are designed to engage the stretch-shortening cycle. The stretch shortening cycle involves three phases, shown in Table 8.6.

▶ **Table 8.6:** Stretch-shortening cycle phases

Stretch-shortening cycle phases	Process
Eccentric phase	Stretch the agonist muscle to build up elastic energy.
Amortisation phase	The paused stage where the sensory signal is processed by the spinal cord and then a rapid motor response is sent to the agonist muscle. This phase must happen quickly otherwise the stored energy from the eccentric phase is lost.
Concentric phase	Once the motor signal is received the agonist muscle fibre shortens.

Plyometric exercises can vary in intensity and careful consideration must be given to ensure the correct exercises are selected for the participant's experience level. Plyometric training volume is determined by the number of repetitions or 'contacts' performed during a session. Appropriate contacts are suggested in Table 8.7.

▶ **Table 8.7:** Contacts in a session based on experience of plyometric training

Plyometric experience	Contacts
Beginner with no experience	80–100
Intermediate with some experience	100–120
Advanced with considerable experience	120–140

Plyometric exercises can also be categorised by intensity, with exercise selection based on the athlete's experience of plyometric training.

- **Low-intensity** – two-foot ankle hops, squat jump, jump and reach, skipping, two-hands side to side throw, two-hand overhead throw.
- **Medium-intensity** – single arm alternate leg bounding, front barrier hop, double leg hop, single arm throws.
- **High-intensity** – single leg hop, double leg zig zag hop, depth jumps, power drop.

Research

Research the different types of plyometric exercises suitable for a beginner in comparison to an advanced athlete with significant experience.

Reaction time

Reaction speed drills are designed to improve the reaction time of the athlete. Depending on the sport the reaction time drill will vary. Some events require the reaction to occur after a command, such as a starting pistol in sprinting or a beep in swimming. Other sports may require the athlete to respond to an object such as ball.

Reaction drills to improve reaction time after commands include changing the starting position, such as lying, sitting or facing a different way. Sprint athletes often react to the starting pistol in between 0.12 and 0.18 seconds, but it can be difficult to develop reaction time for these sports.

A four-cone reaction drill is a good method to improve reaction time. The trainer points and calls which cone they want the athlete to run to and the athlete responds. This type of drill is used with team sports. In racquet sports a serving machine can be used to develop faster reactions.

Effectiveness and suitability of training methods

Each type of training method covered in the previous pages can improve performance of the related component of fitness. However, the most effective and suitable method will vary depending on the athlete's goals. Consider:

- their ability in the sport (beginner, development, performance or elite)
- their experience of the training method (beginner, intermediate or advanced)
- their age (young athlete, adolescent, adult or mature adult)
- the facilities and equipment availability
- their motivation levels
- how the method can support recovery
- how the method can aid the required progression
- the training improvement required to counteract the opposition's tactics.

Research

Research further the different methods of training, building on the information provided in this book to help you determine the most suitable methods of training for the following participants:

- an adult beginner cyclist
- an experienced strength trained athlete
- an intermediate, adolescent high jump athlete who wants to improve their jump height.

Assessment practice 8.2

B.P2 B.P3 B.M2 B.M3 B.D2

A local sprint athlete asks you to help improve the fitness training at the athletics club. Before you go to the club you need to research more on physical fitness and the skill-related demands of sprinting in order to select the most effective training methods. Then you can explain the methods of training that can be used to develop the physical fitness and skill-related fitness demands.

Consider the effectiveness of each method of training in contributing to enhanced performance.

1 What are the advantages, disadvantages and relevance of each method of training to help you make judgements regarding the effectiveness of the training methods?

2 Would the training methods need adapting in any way to maximise their effectiveness with the sprint athletes?

Plan

- Where can I find more information about training methods?

Do

- Have I researched training methods that would help a sprinter to develop in different areas?
- Have I considered the demands of sprinting and ensured my training methods are relevant?

Review

- Have I reviewed the advantages and disadvantages of different training methods?
- Have I analysed the training methods and evaluated their effectiveness in terms of the task criteria?

C Explore the planning of fitness programming

One of the biggest problems for anybody trying to improve their fitness is that they often do the wrong type of training or their training programme is not structured properly. This leads to a lack of motivation for the individual as well as few training gains, which will make the training programme useless.

Collecting personal information

You will produce a more effective programme if you start by collecting appropriate information about your client. You should focus on collecting information about the individual's:

- **short-, medium- and long-term goals** – these will help you to know what to direct the training towards. Short-term goals are usually between one day and one month
- **aims and objectives** – the aim is what the programme ultimately wants to achieve (e.g. improve cardiovascular endurance to complete a half marathon in 12 months); the objectives show how the aim will be met (e.g. train five times a week, with an increasing continuous training run each week)

- **lifestyle, medical and physical activity history** – the programme should reflect the participant's history (for example, if they have been involved in a structured programme before) as well as any medical conditions and lifestyle factors (such as time availability, occupation, etc.). Questionnaires are often used to gather this information
- **attitudes towards training and their personal motivation** – it is a trainer's responsibility to help improve the participant's attitude and motivate them. Motivation can decrease for many reasons, including lack of improvement, boredom, poor sporting performance and external pressures such as work
- **baseline ability level** – before any training takes place, a trainer will need to complete baseline fitness tests. The result of these tests can be compared to benchmarks and normative data to identify the participant's baseline ability level. Targets for training can then be set based on these initial results.

Case study

Setting goals

Anouska would like to improve her sprinting ability. She is 14 years old and is running the 200 metres in 26 seconds. In the next summer season, she would like to improve her personal best by 1 second. At present she trains once per week with her club and once at school lunch-time.

Check your knowledge

Write short-, medium- and long-term goals for Anouska. You might need to research further about the season duration in athletics to help.

Principles of training and their application

Any fitness programme is based on the principles of training. Following these principles results in the greatest training gains.

- **Specificity** – plan a training programme around the needs of the sport (specific muscle groups, components of fitness and sporting actions) and the individual (specific targets). For example, a pole vaulter will focus their training on speed and power alongside a considerable amount of technical training.
- **Progressive overload** – training needs to be demanding enough to cause the body to adapt. Without correct levels of overload, training gains will level off (plateau). Poor performances may result from too little progression or too much. Excessive overloading may also lead to injury and should be avoided at certain points of the season, such as off-season or close to a major competition.
- **FITT principle** – proper overload can be achieved by gradually adjusting the FITT principle.
  - **Frequency:** the number of sessions a week, for example, increasing from two to four.
  - **Intensity:** how difficult a training session is, for example, increasing percentage maximum heart rate or rate of perceived exertion, reducing recovery time between intervals, increasing or decreasing repetitions/sets in resistance training, etc.
  - **Time:** the total time an exercise session or activity takes, for example, increasing a 20-minute session to 30 minutes.
  - **Type:** there are several types of training methods for the different components of fitness. Manipulating the type of training can help prevent boredom, e.g. fartlek training instead of continuous training. Changing the mode of training, such as swapping running for cycling, can also help.
- **Reversibility** – if training stops, is not frequent enough or is done with insufficient intensity, training gains will reverse. Reversibility is expected during the off-season but needs to be avoided during the competitive season. Finding the right balance between overload and reversibility is challenging. Too much overload can lead to stress/injury but too little overload can lead to reversibility.
- **Variation** – varying the type of training used can improve motivation and exercise adherence, so you are less likely to become disengaged with training.
- **Individual differences** – all individuals are different and a training programme should be tailor-made for each individual. For example, someone who has never trained before may improve their 1 repetition max by 60 kg after a long period of resistance training. An Olympic weightlifter might increase their personal best by only 1 kg during the same time frame, but this could mean breaking the world record. Both achievements need to be judged separately.
- **Rest and recovery** – recovery time is essential within any training programme to allow for repair and renewal of the body's tissues. Without this time to recover, you will reduce the progression rate.

- **Adaptation** – training must help an athlete adapt to improve performance. Monitoring performance and testing fitness can help identify how well an athlete has adapted to the training demands. Training can then be modified to ensure the adaptations required are going to be met.

Designing periodised training programmes

Most training programmes are based on a structured cycle. This is known as **periodisation**. Periodisation ensures continued physiological and psychological changes, prevents over-training injuries and boredom, and helps to achieve peak performance for key events. Training programmes must be specific to the athlete's personal information and fitness testing data. Fitness testing data can help set SMART targets, identify priorities and improve the design of the programme.

Performance cycle

A traditional periodised model splits a programme into specific time periods. The largest time period is called a **macrocycle**. This is typically a year but could reflect a period of months or many years (for example, an Olympic athlete will have a four-year periodised programme to fit with the Olympic Games). Within a macrocycle are two or more **mesocycles** lasting several weeks to months. The number depends on the sporting event, the athlete goals and the number of competitions. Each mesocycle is then broken down into a **microcycle** which lasts usually one week but may be longer if the macrocycle is long in length. Table 8.8 gives an overview of the cycles in a periodised programme.

Table 8.8: Overview of periodisation cycles

Macrocycle											
Mesocycle 1				Mesocycle 2				Mesocycle 3			
Microcycle 1	Microcycle 2	Microcycle 3	Microcycle 4	Microcycle 1	Microcycle 2	Microcycle 3	Microcycle 4	Microcycle 1	Microcycle 2	Microcycle 3	Microcycle 4
work	work	work	rest	work	work	work	rest	work	work	work	rest

Calendar-based phases can be applied to the periodisation cycles to help design and monitor training.

- **Preparation phase** – usually the longest and the period that includes no competition. The main focus is establishing base levels of conditioning to increase the athlete's tolerance to training. Conditioning activities start at a low intensity and high volume, e.g. low-intensity plyometrics but a high number of contacts. As time progresses the intensity increases and the volume decreases.
- **Pre-competition phase** – consists of sport-specific training. Training intensity is close to competitive pace, drills replicate performance, plyometric exercises that are similar to performance demands are completed, and resistance training is focused on high intensity, low volume with exercises that follow movement patterns similar to the event.
- **Competition phase** – here the performance peaks. Training intensity will rise again but volume will decrease. The main focus is practising skills and event strategies with decreases in physical conditioning. Many sports have long competitive seasons so physical condition needs to be maintained; moderate intensity training with a moderate volume is used to help preserve condition. Tapering will be planned, where reductions in physical training intensity and volume occur to aid recovery and reduce injury risk.

- **Recovery (transition) phase** – the final phase, between the end of the competition phase and the start of the next macrocycle. Commonly includes active rest and can last between one and four weeks depending on the sport. Athletes often want to remain active during these phases but the intensity and volume should be low, encouraging recreational activities such as playing another sport.

Research

The type of periodisation model described is known as a linear model because there is a gradual progression in intensity over time. Research the other types of periodisation models – **undulating** and **non-linear**.

The performance cycle and the way the periodised programme is designed depends on:

- **event identification** – the number of necessary competitions. Many sport competition phases last no more than 20 weeks (e.g. athletics) but others, such as a golf season, last much longer. In these sports the focus in the competitive phase is maintaining condition
- **event prioritisation** – certain events that will be a priority for peak performance, e.g. major tournaments
- **season goals** – such as ranking one position higher or increasing a personal best performance
- **SMART targets** – these will be set for different components of fitness and skills and monitored across the programme to ensure training is developing the athlete to meet the targets.

Case study

Principles of training

A friend has referred an individual to you who has just signed up to complete her first half marathon. She has not run a half marathon before but does run for 30–45 minutes, three to five times per week. The event is in six months.

Check your knowledge

Consider the principles of training. How are you going to ensure they are met over the six months of training?

Scheduling fitness testing to monitor progress

Fitness testing needs to be planned and built into the macrocycle to monitor progress. Too frequent fitness testing is unlikely to show significant adaptation. The amount of fitness testing planned depends on the length of the macrocycle.

Continuous collation of fitness test results across a macrocycle will also allow for comparison across seasons/training cycles. This is useful for coaches because they can check a player's condition in comparison to previous seasons. Training can if necessary be altered after comparing these results to ensure training is allowing an athlete to at least match the fitness results of previous years.

Testing should always take place at the start of the preparation cycle to set baseline results, which results at later stages can be compared against – this will demonstrate improvement and help motivation. Testing at the end of the preparation phase will also check if the training planned in the pre-competition phase is suitable. Testing might also be required part way through this cycle to ensure it is on track for the competition phase.

Before the competition phase, either testing can be carried out or initial competition results could be used instead of fitness testing. It is unlikely fitness testing will take place during the competitive phase unless the athlete is returning from injury.

Link

You can read more about fitness testing in *Unit 6: Coaching for Performance and Fitness* (starting on page 211) and especially in *Unit 4: Field- and Laboratory-based Fitness Testing.*

Planning training sessions

Planning a training session is covered in *Unit 6: Coaching for Performance and Fitness* (from page 214). However, remember that certain components of fitness require the selection of a combination of exercises for individual sessions. Remember to ensure that recovery time is included too.

- **Cardiovascular training** tends to focus on one mode for an entire session, e.g. running/cycling/swimming. However, within a weekly plan and full periodised programme, the mode of training will vary.
- The focus of **flexibility training** determines the combination of exercises included. A session focused on whole-body flexibility may include one or two different types of stretches per area of the body. A specific flexibility session focusing on the lower body will include a range of stretches for the focused area.

- **Muscular endurance training**, due to its high volume and low intensity, tends to allow for a greater range of exercises in a training session. Several areas of the body can be trained but a session can also focus specifically on a few areas. Avoid two exercises in a row that train the same area of the body.
- **Strength training** focuses on certain areas of the body with only a few exercises per session due to the high intensity and longer rest periods required. Only one or two areas of the body are trained in one session.

PAUSE POINT Suggest a series of appropriate exercises for a sport of your choice.

Hint: Watch the movement patterns of the sport closely. What do participants need to do?

Extend: Revisit movement patterns and re-familiarise yourself with the importance of selecting exercises to suit these.

Theory into practice

Select two sports and suggest two types of exercises the athletes could complete for the following methods of training:

- speed, agility and quickness (to train agility)
- wobble and balance board exercises (to train balance and proprioception)
- plyometrics (to train power).

Training intensity to suit method

A participant's training goals will determine the training intensity of the selected method.

- Cardiovascular training can be planned using heart rate zones (see Table 8.9).

Table 8.9: Heart rate training zones

Heart rate zone	% of maximum heart rate
Warm-up or cool-down	Around 50% and mainly for sedentary or unfit person starting training
Active recovery	Approximately 60%. Useful for aiding recovery, removing waste products and good next step for those new to cardiovascular training
Aerobic fitness	70–80%. Develops aerobic endurance, suitable for more active or trained individuals
'Target heart rate'	Approximately 60–75% (but sometimes as high as 85%). Has the greatest benefits for cardiovascular health and improving the body's ability to use fat as energy source
Peak performance	80–90%, the highest zone of cardiovascular training. Geared towards competitive sport. Will alter anaerobic threshold. Uses up-tempo training methods (fartlek and interval training) when training through the aerobic fitness and peak performance zones

- Strength training intensity can be determined by the percentage of repetition maximum (see Figure 8.3).

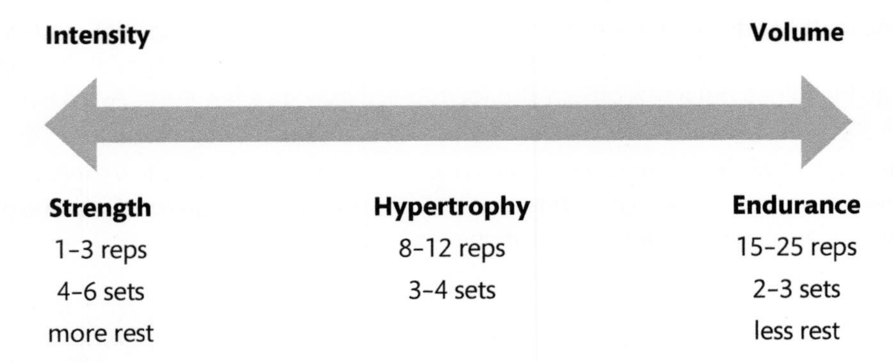

Figure 8.3: Strength training intensity

- The intensity of plyometrics is determined by the number of contacts and the intensity of the exercise.
- Agility and speed training is often conducted at high intensity (95-100 per cent maximum speed) for the given distance or time. For speed training, rest periods need planning so subsequent intensity can be high.
- Balance and proprioception training stresses the neuromuscular system so the exercise selected will determine the stress placed on the system.

Monitoring intensity

You must monitor the session's intensity to ensure it is as effective as possible and your client is not at any risk. Common methods of monitoring intensity include the following.

- **Observation** - a subjective way of monitoring progress, but can be very useful. Look for changes in exercise technique, skin colour or breathing patterns, and excessive sweat levels.
- **Talk test** - if you are able to hold a conversation at the same time as breathing rhythmically while exercising, you are probably working at an acceptable level for cardiovascular training.
- **Rating of perceived exertion (RPE)** - a scale used by athletes to quantify how hard they feel they are working during exercise. This is based on physical sensations such as heart rate, breathing rate, sweating and muscle fatigue. Perceived exertion relates to how the athlete feels, so this is a subjective measure of exercise intensity. It is best to use this system with other methods of assessment until you get used to it.

Research

The original rating of perceived exertion scale was devised by Dr Gunnar Borg. Use the internet to find two different versions of Borg's scale and explain the differences between them.

- **Heart rate monitoaring** - effective particularly in cardiovascular endurance training. Training zones can be calculated from percentages of maximum heart rate. Maximum heart rate is calculated using the following formula: 220 - age. The target heart rate zones can then be calculated.

Training duration to suit methods

Training duration depends on the participant's time availability, and should be planned to maximise benefits if time is limited. Time can be reduced between exercises by alternating working body areas and ordering exercises to minimise rest without compromising recovery. Higher intensity sessions can be shorter. In order to see training results, the durations outlined in Table 8.10 should be followed approximately.

Table 8.10: Ideal duration for different methods of training

Type of training	Ideal duration	Description
Cardiovascular	30 mins	Continuous training tends to be longer in length and a low intensity. Interval training could be shorter in length but higher in intensity.
Strength	30–60 mins	High-intensity sessions have fewer exercises but longer rest periods. Low-intensity sessions have more exercises and less rest so session time tends to be similar.
Flexibility	20–30 mins	Can be a specialist session or typically at the end of another type of session.
Speed/power	30–60 mins	High-intensity with a long rest period. Overspeed training and plyometrics may only contribute a small part of a session (e.g. 10–15 minutes) due to high intensity.
Balance and proprioception	30 mins	If exercises are low in intensity, length may be longer. Particularly challenging sessions are likely to be shorter or have longer rest periods.

Evaluating the effectiveness of training plan design

Training programmes should be reviewed regularly to evaluate their effectiveness and whether personal goals and objectives have been met. As well as the considerations outlined in *Unit 6: Coaching for Performance and Fitness* (Table 6.4 on page 212), the coach/fitness instructor and the athlete should consider:

- **the intensity and duration of the training** – will the planned intensity and duration of the sessions allow the individual to progress, allow for adaptation and prevent excessive overload?
- **the scheduling of the session and how it fits the periodised programme** – does the session meet the needs of that part of the periodised programme?

Being critical of a planned programme will help ensure the most appropriate training methods, intensities, duration and exercises have been selected. The more critical and questioning you are of the methods selected and what you are doing, the more the quality of the planned programme and training plan will improve.

Assessment practice 8.3

C.P4 C.P5 C.P6 C.M4 C.D3

Imagine you have been approached by an athlete competing in a sport of your choice. You can also decide their individual needs (e.g. if they are a track athlete you can decide whether they compete in a sprint or an endurance event).

The athlete wants to be involved in developing their training programme so first you need to explain to them the principles of training to be considered when planning a periodised programme. Following this, produce an initial programme, identifying their key events, goals, and the start and end of cycle phases. Once the programme is complete, pick one phase and produce a detailed session plan to support it.

Evaluate the appropriateness of the programme design. Does it support the principles of training and meet the performance requirements of the sport? Produce a brief report considering the plan, how relevant it is in relation to the performance cycle, and why the activities, durations and intensities selected are appropriate and relevant for the performance cycle.

Make recommendations for adaptation and alternatives for the training programme and plan. Use examples throughout as to why these have been suggested.

Plan

- Do I know what I need to do to produce an effective periodised programme and plan?
- Have I selected a cycle to produce a session plan for? Can I justify my choice?

Do

- Have I talked to a relevant athlete to identify key cycles and events?
- Do the exercises, durations and intensities I have chosen match the overall aim of the selected performance cycle?

Review

- Have I reviewed my work?
- Could I apply my learning from this task to another, similar, assessment task?

Further reading and resources

Books

Bompa, T. and Buzzichelli, C. (2015) *Periodization Training for Sports*, Champaign, IL: Human Kinetics.

Dick, F. (2014) *Sports Training Principles: An Introduction to Sports Science*, London: Bloomsbury Publishing.

Haff, G. and Triplett, T. (2015) *Essentials of Strength Training and Conditioning*, Champaign, IL: Human Kinetics.

Shephard, J. (2013) *The Complete Guide to Sports Training*, London: Bloomsbury Publishing.

Websites

www.sport-fitness-advisor.com – Sports Fitness Advisor: a range of training methods and links to training plans.

www.strengthandconditioningresearch.com – Strength and Conditioning Research: sport-specific training guidance and research.

THINK FUTURE

Amy Hind

Strength and conditioning coach

I've been working as a strength and conditioning coach in athletics, specialising in jumps. During this time I have trained many athletes competing in high jump, long jump, triple jump and pole vault.

After I completed my BTEC Level 3 in Sport and Exercise Sciences I went to university and completed a BSc in Strength and Conditioning. While I was at university I completed my UKSCA Strength and Conditioning Accreditation - this was important as it provided me with professional body recognition.

A strong foundation of knowledge about the demands of a sport is required in order to write effective training programmes, but it is also important to understand and work closely with the athlete. All athletes are different and even if they compete in the same event, it does not mean their training will be the same.

Identifying key competition phases and event priorities helps me start to plan training. Frequent fitness testing also helps to check that the training is creating the adaptations required.

Focusing your skills

Writing effective training sessions

- Safety must be your upmost concern - always ensure appropriate risk assessments have been completed for the planned activities and that the individual participants are screened before taking part in any training.
- Plan appropriate warm-up and cool-down activities that help support the demands of the session.
- Select a combination of exercises that are appropriate for the time duration.
- Monitor the intensity of your training, e.g. using heart rate training zones or rate of perceived exertion.
- Select an appropriate duration for training - effectively managing work-to-rest ratios will help you manage the duration of a session.

Calculating training zone intensities

- Start by calculating maximum heart rate (beats per minute, bpm). The basic way of doing this is to calculate 220 - age, e.g. 220 - 30 years = 190 bpm
- Now calculate the percentage heart rates to match the different training zones, e.g. 70 per cent of maximum heart rate for the aerobic training zone: 70 × 190 bpm = 13,300. Then divide this by 100 = 133 bpm
- For the athlete to work in the low end of the aerobic training zone they need to reach a target heart rate of 133 bpm.

Getting ready for assessment

Lily is working towards a BTEC National in Sport and Exercise Sciences. She was given an assignment with the following title: 'Effective Training' for learning aim B. She had to take part in and research the different methods of training in order to produce a report that evaluated the effectiveness of the methods. The report had to:

- analyse the different methods of training and their effectiveness for improving skill- and physical-related fitness in a selected sport
- evaluate the effectiveness of the methods, including which methods would provide additional benefits over other methods.

How I got started

First, I wrote a list of all the physical- and skill-related components of fitness required to be successful in my selected sport (I selected hockey). I then wrote a list of training methods that could be employed to improve each component. Following this I researched the different training methods and when they would be used. I used the following questions to help guide my research.

- What are the requirements of the training method?
- How does the training method attempt to improve the component of fitness (what is the theory behind the training methods)?
- Are there any advantages or disadvantages of the training method?

I then carried out the different methods of training to experience how the method is employed. This helped me to further understand the training methods and the reasons why the method would be used.

I also visited the local hockey club to speak to the coaches about the training methods they employed and why they thought these were the most effective.

How I brought it all together

To start, I wrote a short introduction that outlined the purpose of the work that I was doing. After this, I briefly discussed hockey and the specific components of fitness that are required to be successful in the sport. Following this I analysed the different training methods that can be used to develop each component of fitness.

To evaluate the effectiveness of the methods I considered the advantages and disadvantages of the training methods in developing the specific component of fitness.

What I learned from the experience

I had detailed information on the different training methods and their effectiveness but needed to focus more on the advantages and disadvantages of the training methods. Carrying out further reading and sourcing specific journal articles on training methods would have helped. Also, when discussing the training methods used at the hockey club, it would have been useful if I had asked the coach what they thought were the advantages and disadvantages of the training methods.

Think about it

- Have you planned your assignment so you know you will be able to complete it by the submission deadline?
- Do you have the recommended resources as well as your class notes to help you provide evidence and references to support and develop the arguments that you plan to make?
- Is your assignment written in your own words? Have you got a reference list that includes all the resources used to help produce the assignment?

Physical Activity for Individual and Group-based Exercise

10

Getting to know your unit

Assessment
This unit is internally assessed using a series of assignments set by your tutor.

Since the growth of private sector health clubs in the last 20 years, the range and number of exercise sessions available for groups and individuals has grown within the sector. The growth of gym membership has led to a demand for instructors to deliver these sessions to a wide-ranging participant group.

In this unit you will discover the methods used by exercise instructors to screen their participants before participating in exercise sessions and a range of different exercises suitable for different groups and individuals. Finally, you will be given the opportunity to plan and deliver an exercise session to a particular group or individual.

How you will be assessed

Instructing physical exercise is fundamentally a practical skill and as such there will be a strong emphasis in this unit on practical learning. In this unit you will find two assessment practice activities designed to consolidate your learning, give you valuable experience and assess your learning. Completion of these activities will give you an opportunity to demonstrate your knowledge but will not guarantee you any particular grade.

It is important that you follow a structured approach to these activities to ensure that you cover all the learning aims. This will be good practice for when you tackle your actual assignments, helping you provide the required evidence to achieve a Pass grade.

For a Merit or Distinction grade additional information will be required and will need to be presented in the appropriate format. For example, for a Merit grade, you may be asked to compare or analyse, whereas for a Distinction you may be asked to evaluate.

The assignments set by your tutor will consist of a number of tasks designed to meet the criteria in the table opposite. This is likely to consist of a written assignment but may also include activities such as:

- preparing contrasting participants for a safe gym-based exercise session
- examining different types of exercise for individual and group-based exercise sessions
- undertaking the planning and instructing of safe individual and group-based exercise sessions
- evaluating and reviewing your own performance when supervising an individual or group-based session.

Assessment criteria

This table shows what you must do in order to achieve a Pass, Merit or Distinction grade, and where you can find activities to help you.

Pass	Merit	Distinction
Learning aim A Explore the processes of health screening prior to physical activity participation		
A.P1 Perform participant screening and interpret the results for one individual. **Assessment practice 10.1**	**A.M1** Perform effective screening using methods that are appropriate to the needs of one individual. **Assessment practice 10.1**	**A.D1** Evaluate the screening from one individual, justifying suggestions for progression to safe exercise participation. **Assessment practice 10.1**
A.P2 Explain factors that can affect safe exercise participation for three individuals in different specific groups. **Assessment practice 10.1**	**A.M2** Assess the factors affecting the safe exercise participation of three specific individuals, making recommendations for their safe exercise participation. **Assessment practice 10.1**	
Learning aim B Examine different types of exercise for individual and group-based exercise sessions		
B.P3 Explain different methods of cardiovascular endurance training and resistance training for an individual exercise session. **Assessment practice 10.2**	**B.M3** Compare different methods of cardiovascular and resistance training for individual and group exercise sessions, justifying the uses of each for participants with different needs. **Assessment practice 10.2**	**BC.D2** Evaluate own performance in the planning and delivery of an individual or group-based exercise session to specific participants, justifying choices of adapted and alternative exercises, session strengths and recommendations for self-improvement. **Assessment practice 10.2**
B.P4 Explain different methods of cardiovascular endurance training and resistance training for a group exercise session. **Assessment practice 10.2**		
Learning aim C Undertake planning and instructing of individual and group-based exercise sessions		
C.P5 Plan and deliver a safe and effective individual or group-based exercise session that includes the performance of safe and effective cardiovascular and resistance-based exercises. **Assessment practice 10.2**	**C.M4** Plan and deliver a comprehensive individual or group-based exercise session using effective communication and offering adapted and alternative exercises for different specific participants. **Assessment practice 10.2**	**C.D3** Evaluate the impacts of participant assessment and choice of exercise on the planning and instruction of safe and effective exercise sessions. **Assessment practice 10.2**
C.P6 Review own performance in the delivery of an individual or group-based exercise session, identifying strengths and areas for improvement. **Assessment practice 10.2**	**C.M5** Review own performance in the delivery of an exercise session, explaining strengths and providing recommendations for self-improvement. **Assessment practice 10.2**	

Getting started

To lead successful individual or group-exercise sessions takes practice and skill. You will probably have observed or participated in sessions led by instructors in real life and should be able to judge how they performed. Consider a fitness and exercise instructor that you have observed. What strengths did they exhibit? What do you feel they could have done better? What skills and qualities do you think you possess that would help you as an instructor?

A Explore the processes of health screening prior to physical activity participation

Link

You can read more about the questionnaires that can be used to gather participant information in *Unit 8: Specialised Fitness Training*

Before a participant can undertake any exercise, and as part of designing a training programme, you must gain a full picture of their exercise history, including any health-related issues or recent illnesses. The participant's health and safety before, during and after a training session is of the utmost importance. This full health screening process will give you a clear picture of the exercises that are safe for the participant to undertake.

Participant screening

Before they participate in any exercise session it is essential that you assess the participants' current level of activity as well as their health and any medical conditions or injuries. Each participant should complete a screening session. These were covered in more depth in Unit 4, but can include:

- short, informal interviews
- pre-exercise questionnaires such as a PAR-Q and a lifestyle questionnaire
- observation
- health monitoring tests, e.g. blood pressure, resting heart rate, body mass index (BMI), waist to hip ratio and lung function.

If you are uncertain about any response given as part of a pre-exercise questionnaire or interview then you should not allow the participant to complete an exercise session. Remember, the health and safety of your participant is your primary concern.

You must also obtain the participant's informed consent before the exercise session starts – this was covered in Unit 4.

Reasons for deferring start of exercise programme

You must be aware of a participant's **contraindications** before they start any exercise programme. This can be covered in your interview or questionnaires and will ensure you are aware of any conditions that are likely to affect a person's ability to train safely. Common examples of contraindications include asthma, pregnancy, heart disease, diabetes, and recent operations or injuries.

If you have any concerns regarding the participant's health or any contraindications are indicated, then you should refer the participant to a professional medical expert such as their GP.

Key term

Contraindication – a physical or mental condition or factor that increases the risk involved when someone is engaged in an activity.

Maintaining participant confidentiality

You must ensure that any personal information you gather about a participant during the initial screening process is kept confidential and not revealed to anybody else without the participant's consent. This means keeping the information secure by using a locked filing cabinet (if stored on paper) or a password-protected file (if stored on computer).

PAUSE POINT Why is health screening so important?

Hint What methods can be used to screen a participant prior to exercise? What are the benefits of each method?

Extend How can these health screening processes affect the shaping of your session plans?

Factors affecting safe exercise participation

All individuals have different needs, abilities, goals, skills, physical attributes, lifestyles, medical history and exercise preferences. Therefore a training programme should be tailor-made for each individual. Your expectations should be specific to the different individuals.

The pre-exercise questionnaire and interview will allow you to determine the participant's current level of activity. This will help you to design a programme that is safe for the participant while also pushing them to progress.

Discussion

In a group or pairs, think of the things which need to be considered to ensure that exercise sessions are delivered to individuals or groups in a safe manner. What factors can you control to ensure that the performers are safe at all times? Which factors are out of your control?

Exercise intensity

Exercise intensity is the level of effort required to perform an exercise session – in other words, how hard the exercises are. It can be measured in a number of ways for a variety of exercises. Intensity is sometimes referred to as **overload**. This means that for any improvements to be made, you must work the body beyond what it is normally used to. If overload is not achieved, the best a person can expect is to maintain his or her current level of fitness.

Key term

Overload – stretching the body systems beyond their normal functional level – essential for gaining training benefits.

Intensity can be adjusted by adapting exercises/movements to increase or decrease the demand put on specific participants. In group-exercise situations, you may have to demonstrate a range of options of different intensities that can be chosen by participants based on their own particular health-related needs.

Percentage of heart rate maximum

Exercise intensity is often measured as a percentage of your maximum heart rate (MHR), using equipment such as a heart rate monitor. Commonly, exercises aim for low, medium or high intensity.

- **Low intensity** – training at up to 70 per cent of MHR – used to improve general fitness.
- **Medium intensity** – training at up to 80 per cent of MHR – used to improve aerobic threshold or endurance.
- **High intensity** – training at up to 90 per cent of MHR, used to improve strength or anaerobic threshold.

Link

The aerobic and anaerobic energy systems are covered in *Unit 1: Sport and Exercise Physiology.*

Training zones for cardiovascular health and fitness

Training zones can determine the level of intensity you are working at. This is particularly important for cardiovascular training or exercise. Heart rate training zones are calculated by taking into consideration your maximum heart rate (MHR) and your resting heart rate (RHR). A simple way to work out your MHR is by subtracting your age in years from 220:

MHR = 220 – age

Your RHR can be measured by taking your pulse at rest, preferably before any form of movement or exercise. Because it is difficult to exercise and measure your heart rate manually, it is useful to use a heart rate monitor.

Another method of determining heart rate training zones is the Karvonen formula. The Karvonen formula allows you to determine how fast your heart should be beating when you are in one of the heart rate training zones (shown in Table 10.1):

desired heart rate (HR) = RHR + [(MHR – RHR) × % intensity]

Table 10.1: The four main training zones

Zone	Percentage of MHR	Training
Fitness	60–70	Develops basic endurance and aerobic capacity – all easy recovery running should be completed at a maximum of 70% MHR.
Aerobic	70–80	Develops your cardiovascular system – the body's ability to transport oxygen to, and carbon dioxide away from, the working muscles is developed and improved; as fitness improves it will be possible to run at up to 75% MHR and get the benefits of fat-burning and improved aerobic capacity.
Anaerobic	80–90	High intensity – your body cannot use oxygen quickly enough to produce energy so relies on energy that can be used without oxygen, namely glycogen stored in the muscles. This can be used for only a short period – a build-up of lactic acid will rapidly cause fatigue.
Red line	90–100	Maximum level of exercise – training possible only for short periods, effectively trains fast-twitch muscle fibres and helps develop speed. This zone is reserved for interval running – only for the very fit.

Case study

Calculating target heart rate

Otis is an 18-year-old male athlete with a resting heart rate of 70 beats per minute (bpm) and a maximum heart rate of 202 bpm. So, using the Karvonen formula:

- for 65% intensity: 70 + [(202 – 70) × 0.65] = 156 bpm
- for 75% intensity: 70 + [(202 – 70) × 0.75] = 169 bpm
- for 85% intensity: 70 + [(202 – 70) × 0.85] = 182 bpm

Check your knowledge

1. How could Otis ensure that he is training at the selected intensity?
2. At what intensity should Otis train to improve his aerobic fitness?
3. Work out your own target heart rate for 65%, 75% and 85% intensities.

Rating of perceived exertion (RPE)

Rating of perceived exertion (RPE) is a method by which athletes assess how hard they are working during exercise, based on how they are feeling. The rating depends on physical sensations such as heart rate, breathing rate, sweating and muscle fatigue. There is more information about RPE in Unit 8, on page 262.

Safe participation for specific groups

When planning an exercise programme you must consider the specific needs of different types of participants. Participants can be divided into different categories depending on age, condition and physical ability. Some of the common groups are described in Table 10.2.

Table 10.2: Considerations for specific groups of participant

Age group	Specific issues
Children	Caution needed for certain types of training. For example, a 14–16 year old's bones are still growing so lifting heavy weights should be avoided as the risk of injury is high. However, moderate strength training is beneficial and would be considered low risk. Children should take part in short periods of exercise with clear rest periods for recovery.
Antenatal women	Covers pregnant women from conception to birth. Exercise can help circulatory problems, fatigue and varicose veins. Good circulation supplies the baby with more oxygen and nutrients. Exercise can also reduce haemorrhoids, cramps and constipation. Care should be taken during exercise and certain types of exercise should be avoided including: • high-impact and high-intensity exercises • exercises involving the abdominal area • after 16 weeks of pregnancy exercises involving participants lying on their front (prone) as this may put too much pressure on the abdominal area • overhead resistance exercises as this can increase curvature of the lower spine and cause hyper-**lordosis**.
Post-natal women	Post-natal women are the group that have just given birth. Post-natal exercises help the body regain shape but ligaments and joints will still be soft for at least three months following birth, so vigorous stretching and high-impact activities should be avoided. During pregnancy the weight of the baby alters the mother's centre of gravity. This, combined with the softening effects of the hormone relaxin on ligaments, may lead to bad posture. Exercise can strengthen abdominal and back muscles improving posture.
Older people (+50)	This group can have a wide variety of exercise needs with a range of possible medical conditions, ability levels and participant interests. Consider the following approaches. • Use a longer, more gradual, warm-up period – older people take longer to warm up as their circulatory system is not as efficient. A cool-down should also be longer and gradually tapered as part of the recovery period. • Avoid high-impact exercises – such as running and jumping, especially where **osteoporosis** has been previously diagnosed. Older people have less dense bones so are more susceptible to impact fractures. Exercise involving balance also carries risk of fractures, such as in the hip and waist, if the participant loses their balance. Support should be on hand to prevent falls. • Exercises should incorporate general everyday movements to aid mobility such as toe, heel and leg rises (to improve ankle strength), balancing exercises, side stepping (to increase leg and hip strength and balance), etc.

Clients over the age of 50 are one group who might need their exercises to be adapted

Key terms

Antenatal – during pregnancy from conception to birth.

Lordosis – an inwards curve of the spine associated with cervical and lumbar regions.

Post-natal – the period after the baby has been born.

Osteoporosis – a medical condition that weakens bones due to a loss of stored calcium. This makes bones fragile, brittle and more likely to break.

PAUSE POINT

Why is exercise important and beneficial to pregnant women?

Hint

List the benefits of exercise during pregnancy and explain the main considerations when providing exercise advice.

Extend

Now explain why some exercises should be avoided during pregnancy. You should consider the different trimesters.

Assessment practice 10.1

A.P1 A.P2 A.M1 A.M2 A.D1

While gaining work experience as a gym assistant at a private health club, you have been asked to help one of the class instructors. The instructor is delivering a series of circuit sessions to a group of new participants. She asks you to help with the screening of three of the new participants:

- **participant A** – Shazia, a 30-year-old woman who runs twice a week and cycles to work every day
- **participant B** – Bruce, a 60-year-old man who recently took early retirement from his desk job and is now hoping to take up exercise for the first time since he played football in his mid 30s. He is currently overweight
- **participant C** – Mel, a 25-year-old woman who gave birth to twins two months ago.

Before the instructor does the screening, produce a brief report that explains and assesses the factors that could affect the safe exercise participation of each individual. Make recommendations for their safe exercise participation, evaluating why your recommendations are best for each individual.

Plan

- Do I know the screening procedures to be followed before delivering a physical activity session?
- Do I know the likely screening results for each of the three participants?

Do

- Have I considered all relevant factors to ensure all participants are safe during physical activity sessions?
- Is my report well laid out and are my recommendations clear?

Review

- Am I confident that my recommendations are appropriate for each individual?
- How can I use my learning from this task in the future?

B Examine different types of exercise for individual and group-based exercise sessions

Performing exercises safely

There are several key stages and processes you need to follow in order to set up and run exercise sessions safely. Remember to consider intensity of exercise (see page 271) when setting up a session. Risk assessments must also be performed before a session begins and all equipment and the environment reviewed and checked. More information on checking equipment and facilities can be found on page 276.

Warm-up

A warm-up is performed before participation in exercise. It generally consists of a gradual increase in intensity of physical activity. Any warm-up should be specific to the activity that will follow, so preparing the muscles to be used and activating any energy systems required.

- A **pulse raiser** is a simple cardiovascular exercise that raises the heart rate ready for further exercise. It should gradually increase in intensity and normally lasts 5–10 minutes leaving the heart rate near to the level expected during the main activity. Common pulse raisers include jogging, static cycling or using a rowing machine.

- **Stretches** are used to improve joint mobility by encouraging the body to produce more fluid in synovial joints in readiness for exercise. The joints become warmer and allow a full range of motion to be achieved. Stretching should start with small movements and then progress to larger, full ranges of motion. The main joints that should be mobilised by stretches are the shoulders, elbows, spine, hips, knees and ankles.
  - **Static stretches** are used while the body is at rest and use techniques that gradually lengthen a muscle to a point of mild discomfort, at which point the position is held for a period (10–30 seconds).
  - **Dynamic stretching** involves moving muscles through their full range of motion in a controlled manner, using momentum.

Cool-down

A cool-down returns the body to its pre-exercise state. It keeps the metabolic rate high and capillaries dilated to enable oxygen to flush through the muscle tissue, helping remove lactic acid waste created by exercise. This should stop the blood from staying in the veins, which can cause dizziness if exercise is stopped too quickly.

- **Pulse lowerers**, such as walking, or using a cross-trainer or rowing machine, can be used to slowly reduce the intensity of exercise and allow the body to lower its pulse and to readjust to a resting state.
- **Maintenance stretches** aim to return the muscles to their normal length. They should be held for 10–15 seconds and aim to maintain the body's flexibility, reducing the risk of injury and muscle tension, and improve muscle coordination.
- **Developmental stretches** involve stretching and holding the working muscle for about 10 seconds until it relaxes. Following this, the muscle should be stretched again but at an increased level, and again held for 10 seconds. This process should be repeated three times. Using stretching as part of a cool-down will improve flexibility as at this time the muscles will be warm and more pliable. This means that they will be able to extend beyond their normal length and increase the range of motion at the joint.

PAUSE POINT Why are warm-ups and cool-downs such an important part of an exercise programme?

Hint Describe the purpose of a warm-up in relation to physiological changes to the body.

Extend What different exercises can be used as part of a warm-up and why? How could these be adapted for different participants?

Safe alignment of exercise position

The development of 'core stability' is a fairly new phenomenon in the fitness world. It basically seeks to develop an equilibrium or balance throughout the skeletal and muscular systems. Body alignment targets areas of posture and balance as fundamental factors to ensure the body remains functional and efficient. Core stability achieves this by highlighting the core (abdominal and lower back regions) as the framework to generate a solid platform to work from. You should be aware of the benefits of developing this platform, not only in the core region, but also throughout the body.

Body alignment also deals with creating a balance between muscle groupings. For example, the quadriceps are capable of producing substantial power output but should not be too powerful for the opposite muscles – the hamstrings – to deal with, otherwise one of the hamstrings is likely to be damaged.

Developing participant coordination

Some participants will have little experience of exercise or being in a gym environment. As such you must consider the techniques used to perform an exercise. Any recommended exercises you use should be demonstrated clearly and you should allow the participant to gradually develop their movement and exercise techniques so they develop both their coordination and confidence.

Impact

Broadly, exercises can be categorised into two types: high-impact and low-impact.

- **High-impact exercises** put force on the body, especially on bones and joints, for example, running. Studies suggest the correct amount of high-impact exercise can increase bone density but too much can place excessive strain on the body and cause injury to bones and joints. High-impact exercises should be avoided if participants have suffered from previous joint issues, have osteoporosis or are in the later stages of pregnancy.
- **Low-impact exercises** such as walking or using a rowing machine or cross trainer put far less force on the body and are suitable for participants who should avoid high-impact exercises.

Wall presses are sometimes a useful adaptation for older participants

Alternative exercises for specific participants

Many exercises can be adapted so that they support the needs of specific participants. For example, a wall press-up will be more suitable for an older adult, especially if they have low levels of fitness. For antenatal participants, low-impact exercise such as walking should be included in a training programme.

Some exercises could also be harmful for certain participants, depending on their level of fitness. You will need to identify any issues and ensure that all the exercises you are asking participants to perform are safe and carry no risk.

Health and environmental factors

Risk assessments must be performed before a session begins, with all equipment and the environment reviewed and checked. Factors to consider include:

- **equipment** – this must be fit for purpose and includes the clothing that is to be worn. Equipment should be checked for quality and condition and whether it has been maintained correctly
- **facility** – this includes the space available, whether it was designed for the selected activity, accessibility of emergency exits, noise/acoustics (for example, if there is a lot of echo, making it difficult to hear instructions) and accessibility and suitability for people with particular needs such as wheelchair users
- **suitability of participants** – if you have planned well, you will have planned your session around the needs of the people who you are working with. When planning your sessions, consider participants' age and experience, the number of participants, how well they know you and any specific individual needs.

Types of cardiovascular exercises

There are a number of cardiovascular exercises that can be used to help strengthen the body and stimulate the heart and breathing rate to increase. This is very useful for building up a participant's strength and exercise potential. Good cardiovascular exercises to use with participants include jogging, skipping, jumping jacks, step-ups and shuttle runs.

- **Cardiovascular machines** are sometimes referred to as cardio machines and are used for improving and maintaining the cardiovascular system. The machines are designed to replicate common exercises to increase heart and respiration rates. They can also be used as part of a warm-up or cool-down.
- **Treadmills** have many adjustable features to alter the exercise intensity, for example, adjusting the speed or degree of incline. They are suitable for participants who are used to, or who enjoy, running. They can be used as part of aerobic and anaerobic training.
- **Static cycles** have adjustable features affecting exercise intensity, such as changes in resistance making it easier or harder to turn the pedals. Cycling is a low-impact exercise so it is a good choice for participants suffering from joint or bone conditions, or who may be returning from a skeletal injury. Upright cycles can be used as part of aerobic training and to improve muscular endurance and power. A recumbent cycle allows the user to cycle in a reclined position, which is particularly good if they suffer from lower back pain.
- **Indoor rowing machines** are used to simulate the action of rowing a boat and use the same muscles. It is a low-impact exercise piece of equipment that can help build and tone muscles, strengthen cardiovascular function and increase stamina. Rowing machines are particularly effective for older participants because they place no strain on the back and joints. They can be used to train anaerobically by increasing the speed of the rowing action and the resistance on the pulley chain.

Treadmills are a cardiovascular machine common in gyms

Types of resistance-based exercises

Weight training exercises

Weight training can be done using either free weights or resistance machines.

Free weights

The most common free weights are barbells and dumbbells. The reason they are called free weights is that there are no pins, cables or pulleys and they rely purely on muscular contractions to move.

- **Barbells** are usually 1.2 to 2 metres long and have removable weights at each end. The weights attached to the ends of the bar provide resistance while both arms are used to lift the bar. These weights are normally removable so different amounts can be added to the bar, and are fixed in place with a collar.

- A **dumbbell** is a short barbell which can be held in one hand. They usually have fixed weights at each end and a range of different weighted dumbbells will be used depending on the goals and needs of the participant. Dumbbells enable you to strengthen both sides of your body equally as well as allow you to do some exercises (like front raises) that cannot be done with a barbell.

Resistance machines

Resistance machines combine weights with pulleys and cables, offering a wide range of exercises for many different muscle groups. Because resistance machines use cables and pulleys they do not require another person to support or 'spot' a participant during an exercise and allow you to do some exercises you cannot do with barbells, such as leg curls, lat pull-downs and leg extensions.

Fixed resistance machines allow individuals to change the load based on their training programme. The variable resistance ranges from 0–100 kg on most machines, allowing the programme to include overload and progression. They have an increased safety element compared to free weights and an individual can change the range of movement at a specific joint by adjusting the machine's settings.

PAUSE POINT State the different uses of cardiovascular equipment, free weights and resistance machines.

Hint Describe the equipment used to train aerobic endurance, muscular strength and muscular endurance.

Extend Explain the advantages and disadvantages of using free weights rather than resistance machines.

There are a number of different exercises that can be performed using weight training to develop muscle strength, as shown in Table 10.3.

Table 10.3: Weight training exercises

Type of exercise	Main muscles used	Technique
Front raise	Deltoids	• Position yourself with a wide stance and knees slightly bent. • Hold a dumbbell in each hand with arms straight by your sides and palms facing behind you. • Lift your arms out in front, until the hands are at shoulder level. • Return the arms back to the starting position, maintaining control throughout. • Ensure you do not arch your back in an attempt to lift the weight.
Bent arm pull-over	Pectorals Latissimus dorsi	• Lay on your back on a bench with your feet on the floor. • Hold a dumbbell in both hands, with the palms facing each other and arms straight above your chest. • Lower the dumbbell over and behind your head, with a slight bend in the elbow. • Keep your abdominals braced throughout to avoid arching your back. • Lower to as far as you are comfortable and then reverse the movement.
Shoulder press	Deltoids Triceps	• Position a bench with the back support up and sit on the seat pad, leaning your back against the support. • Hold a dumbbell in each hand at shoulder height. • Push directly upwards until the elbows are almost completely straight. • Slowly return back to the starting position.

▸ **Table 10.3:** Weight training exercises – *continued*

Type of exercise	Main muscles used	Technique
Lateral raise	Deltoids Trapezius	• Position yourself with a wide stance and knees slightly bent. • Hold a dumbbell in each hand with the arms straight by your sides and palms facing inwards. • Lift your arms out to the sides, maintaining a small bend in the elbow until the hands reach shoulder level. • Return the arms back to the starting position, maintaining control throughout.
Dumbell flye	Pectorals Deltoids	• Lie on your back on a bench with your feet planted on the floor. • Hold a dumbbell in each hand, with the palms facing together, above your chest. • Maintain a small bend in the elbows throughout the exercise. • Take your arms apart, leading with the elbows, until they are just below the level of your shoulders. Maintain control throughout the lowering phase especially. • Return to the starting position.
Bicep curl	Biceps brachii	• Stand with the feet shoulder width apart, knees slightly bent and back straight. • Hold a dumbbell in each hand with the palms facing forwards and elbows straight. • Bend the elbows to lift the dumbbells from by your thighs, up towards your shoulders. • Avoid swinging the weights or arching the back to help lift the weight. • Slowly return the weights back to the starting position.
Lunge	Quadriceps	• Stand with feet shoulder width apart. • Hold a dumbbell in each hand. Step forwards with one foot in a long stride. • Make sure your feet are in line and pointing straight forwards. • Keep your back upright as you slowly bend and lower the back knee towards the floor, raising the heel off the floor. • At the same time bend the front knee, making sure it does not go past your toes. • Do not let the back knee touch the floor before returning to the starting position.
Squat	Quadriceps/hamstrings	• Place feet shoulder width apart. Weight comes down through the heels. • Hip drive backwards during first part of movement. • Do not let your knees come any further forward than your toes. • Face looking forwards and slightly upwards. • Aim for knees at 90 degrees with top of quads parallel to floor.

Body weight resistance exercises

Body weight exercises only use the body's mass and gravity to provide resistance – they do not use any additional weights to provide resistance. Popular body weight resistance exercises are shown in Table 10.4.

▸ **Table 10.4:** Body weight resistance exercises

Type of exercise	Main muscles used	Technique
Press-up	Pectorals Triceps brachii Deltoids	• Kneel on all fours with the hands a little wider than shoulder width. • Straighten your legs out behind you so that your weight is distributed between your hands and toes. • Bend the elbows outwards to lower the chest towards the floor. • Push back up to the starting position.
Triceps dips	Pectorals Triceps brachii Deltoids	• Sit on a bench. • Position your hands on the bench beside your hips. • Push down with your hands to raise your body off the bench. • Slowly bend your elbows to lower your body towards the floor, keeping your elbows at a 90 degree angle and back close to the bench.

▶ **Table 10.4:** Body weight resistance exercises – *continued*

Type of exercise	Main muscles used	Technique
Plank	Rectus abdominis Erector spinae	• Lie on your front and place your forearms and palms flat on the floor. • Lift your chest, stomach and legs off the floor and maintain your balance between your forearms and toes. • Keep a straight line from your shoulders, across your back to your feet. • Hold for up to 60 seconds.
Sit-ups	Rectus abdominis Tensor fasciae latae	• Lie on your back with knees bent and feet flat on the floor and your fingertips behind your ears. • Raise your body up towards your knees, shoulders lifted off the floor and head straight. • Return to starting position and repeat.
Lunge	Quadriceps Hamstrings Gluteus maximus Gastrocnemius Soleus	• Step forwards with one foot in a long stride. Make sure your feet are in line and pointing straight forwards. • Keep your back upright as you slowly bend and lower the back knee towards the floor, raising the heel off the floor. • At the same time bend the front knee, making sure it does not go past your toes. • Do not let the back knee touch the floor before returning to the starting position.
Squat	Quadriceps Hamstrings Gluteus maximus Gastrocnemius Soleus	• Stand with your feet shoulder width apart and toes pointing straight forwards. • Keep the back straight as you initiate movement at your hips. • Push your buttocks out behind you and bend your knees. • Do not let your knees move in front of your toes. • Do not squat deeper than a 90 degree (right angle) at the knee. • Start with shallow squats and increase gradually.
Prone back raise	Erector spinae	• Lie on your front with your arms bent and fingers on your temples. • Slowly lift your chest and stomach off the floor, keeping the hips and legs still. • Hold for 2–3 seconds before slowly lowering the upper body back to the floor. • Movement should only be coming from your lower back.

Research

Another way of introducing resistance into an exercise is to use resistance bands – strips of rubber that can be held in the hands or placed under a foot, providing resistance to the participant's movements. Using the internet, identify some popular resistance band exercises. Do you think there are some participant groups that might find resistance bands more useful than others?

Activities for group-based and individual sessions

The content of **individual sessions** will vary depending on the goals of your participant. However, for a gym-based session they are likely to focus on the cardiovascular and resistance-based exercises that were introduced in the previous section of this unit.

For a **group-based session**, many instructors use circuit sessions. Circuits usually consist of a series of stations and at each station there will be a different type of exercise. The exercises included in the circuit will depend on the objectives of the session and the participants' needs. Table 10.5 shows a variety of exercises that can be used within a circuit session to improve different components of fitness.

Table 10.5: Exercises to train different components of fitness

Stations to improve aerobic endurance	Stations to improve muscular strength and endurance
• Shuttle runs • Jogging on the spot • Jumping jacks • Spotty dogs • Squat thrusts • Knee lifts • Step-ups • Skipping	• Shoulder press • Dumbbell flyes • Upright row • Lateral raise • Bicep curl • Triceps extension • Dumbbell lunge • Barbell squat • Calf raise • Triceps dips • Press-ups • Lunges • Squats • Side-bends

Circuit cards

Circuit cards are used to help the participants identify the requirements of the exercise station. They should include the following details:

- name of the exercise
- diagram
- teaching points
- adaptations, including progressions and alternatives.

See Figure 10.1 for an example layout.

Research

Table 10.5 shows a variety of different exercises that can be used to target different components of fitness. See if you can create your own list of exercises that could be used to improve the different components of fitness.

Press-up (with wobble board)

Muscles involved:
- pectoralis
- deltoid
- abdominal muscles
- triceps brachii
- serratus anterior
- coracobrachialis

Level 1 | Level 2 | Level 3

Figure 10.1: An example layout for a circuit card

Circuit training layouts

A range of different circuit training layouts can be used depending on the session aim and the variety you wish to bring to the session. See Table 10.6 for a range of popular layouts.

▶ **Table 10.6:** Popular circuit training layouts

Layout name	Overview	Comments
Square	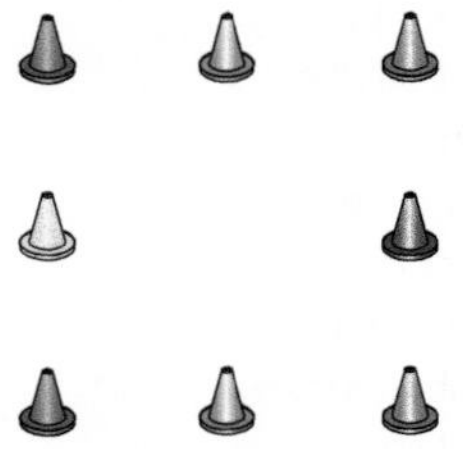	Exercises can be placed in a square shape. Usually all stations are facing towards the middle.
Lined circuit	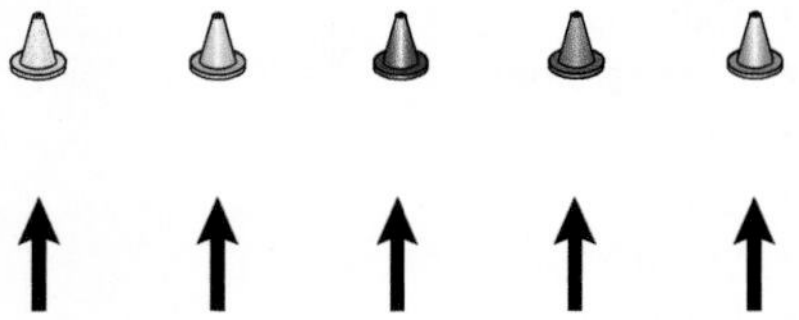	Cards are usually placed on the wall at the front with participants lined up behind each other, as shown by the arrows. Participants complete the exercise in their line for the set duration then all move up a station.
Bow tie	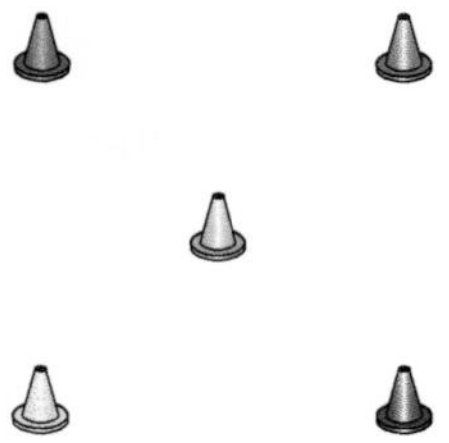	Stations are placed in each corner with another station in the middle of the room.
Circular	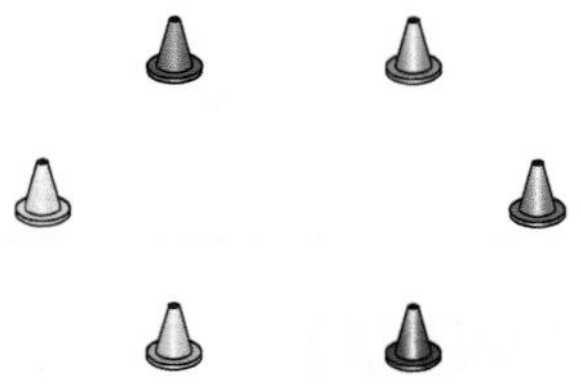	As many stations as you wish can be placed in a circular layout. The outside of the circle is also useful as a shuttle run station.
Corners		A corner circuit is where each corner has a target muscle group and three exercises which work that targeted muscle group. It is designed to overload one target area and then move on to another.

Other considerations

The practicalities of the session will depend on the number of participants and the space available.

- If there are few participants, you may have one person working at each station at a time.
- If there are more participants but plenty of space at each station, you may have several people at each station at a time. (If the exercises require specific equipment, you will need to make sure there are sufficient facilities for everyone.)
- If there are a lot of participants but limited space at each station, you may have half the group working at stations at any given time, with the rest of the group performing shuttle runs or running laps around the outside of the room.

The time spent at each station can be determined in two main ways:

1 Each participant completes a specific number of reps of the given exercise (e.g. 20 press-ups) before moving on.
2 Each participant repeats the exercise as many times as they can within a set time (usually between 30 seconds and 3 minutes, depending on the intensity of the exercise) before moving on.

PAUSE POINT What type of circuit training layout would you use with a group of 30 experienced participants?

Hint Thirty participants is a large number so this should be factored in when selecting the layout.

Extend How would you ensure you made the most effective use of the space available?

Case study

Planning and delivering a safe physical activity

Daisy is a fitness instructor at a local leisure centre. She has planned a circuit session for a group of 16-year-old girls. The focus of the session is to increase the all-round physical fitness of the participants. Daisy would like to develop further understanding of this participant group and has approached you for some information.

Check your knowledge

1 Summarise the types of activity Daisy could use in her session.
2 Create a proposed plan for one of the sessions with this participant group.
3 Outline the types of issue that Daisy may need to look for when conducting her risk assessment of the session you have planned, to ensure that all of her participants are safe at all times.

Undertake planning and instructing of individual and group-based exercise sessions

Aims and objectives of the exercise session

One of the biggest problems for anybody trying to improve their fitness is that they often do the wrong type of training. This leads to a lack of motivation for the individual as well as few training gains. Collecting appropriate information about your participants - such as their goals, lifestyle information, medical history and physical activity history - means you will be able to produce more effective sessions for them by keeping in mind their aims and objectives.

Each individual has different ambitions and aspirations, and your sessions should reflect these. The athlete's goals should be broken up into short-term (up to one month), medium-term (one to three months) and long-term goals (three months to one year). Your session's aims and objectives should feed into these goals, and to help you do this the goals should be based on SMART targets (specific, measureable, achievable, realistic, time-bound).

Leading group-based exercise sessions can present more of a challenge as you need to incorporate a variety of different participants' aims and objectives within one session. You can do this by providing different intensities to the exercises and adaptations that allow your participants to find a challenge that is suited to their own goals.

Research

Find out more information regarding the importance of health and safety in a gym environment by visiting the Register of Exercise Professionals website (www.exerciseregister.org).

Individual exercise session planning

Identify appropriate exercises and equipment

Any fitness session is based on the principles of training; if you follow them, the greatest gains through training can be achieved. You should plan your training programme around the needs of the sport or activity (such as specific muscle groups, components of fitness or sporting actions) and any individual needs (such as targets specific to the participant rather than general targets). For example if your participant is trying to improve cardiovascular fitness, a training programme involving heavy weights would not be relevant. Ensure you have the correct equipment for any exercises planned and that you are familiar with how it operates.

Appropriate sequences of exercises

Structure is very important if the participant is to enjoy the exercise and avoid injury. In general terms, a session will follow this order: warm-up, main activity, cool-down (or 'warm-down').

When using resistance training, it is important that corresponding muscles are trained equally. Muscles help stabilise a joint, so if one is stronger than another this may cause joint instability and injury. It can also cause long-term problems with posture and may affect sporting performance.

A simple exercise will involve only one joint (e.g. bicep curl), while a more difficult exercise will involve two or more joints (e.g. chest press). The more difficult exercises will need more focus, so they should be done early on before the onset of fatigue. Likewise you should train the large muscles first. The main reason for exercising these muscles first is that they will require the most effort, so they should be exercised before they start to fatigue. The smaller muscles help the larger muscles work, so they should remain relatively fresh when exercising.

Finally, exercise the abdominal muscles last. The abdominal and muscles of the lower back provide support to the main core of the body. These should remain free from fatigue so injury to the back can be avoided and correct posture be maintained.

Appropriate timings of each exercise to ensure progression

For a training programme to be effective the principles of overload and progression should be followed. Progression and overload is where the body adapts to training, allowing training to become progressively harder (increasing the levels of overload). Without correct levels of overload and progression, training gains start to level off (plateau).

Be careful when planning progression because poor performances may result from too little progression or a training programme that overloads the system. Excessive overloading may also lead to injury or illness through over-training.

When training consider adapting the duration of each exercise as well as the total length of the session. Increasing time will increase overload and progression, but it is important to consider recovery between exercises and sessions. Always allow adequate recovery time between sets to allow for repair and renewal of body tissues and to avoid fatigue which can lead to reduced performance and injury.

Group exercise session planning

A training programme session will start with a warm-up before the main component of the session and end with a cool-down (refer back to earlier in this unit on page 275).

Depending on the fitness level of your participants you may have to change the time given for each component of the programme. For example, a participant with a low level of fitness may need more time for a low-intensity warm-up. But the time allowed for elements within the main component of the session should also be reviewed periodically as participants progress - you should review the amount of time allocated to each component to ensure that overload is maintained and that progress is made.

Main component

The main component of a session can focus on a range of different areas.

- **Cardiovascular endurance** - the ability of the cardiovascular and respiratory systems to supply muscles with oxygen to maintain exercise. Aerobic endurance forms the basis of fitness for most sports and a reduced aerobic endurance leads to a decrease in other fitness components.
- **Muscular strength** - the ability of a specific muscle or muscle group to exert a force in a single maximal contraction. Strength training is typically low repetition with very high loads.
- **Muscular endurance** - needed where a specific muscle or muscle group makes repeated contractions over a significant period of time (possibly over a number of minutes), for example, a boxer making a repeated jab, continuous press-ups or sit-ups or 400-metre sprint in athletics. A number of training methods used for muscular strength can also be adjusted to improve muscular endurance, such as by altering the weight, number of repetitions and/or number of sets.

PAUSE POINT How would you plan for a group activity session for 15 older people (aged between 60 and 65 years old)?

Hint What planning would you need to undertake before, during and after the session for this participant group?

Extend What activities would need to be undertaken for each component of the exercise session for this participant group?

Pre-exercise session preparation

Before you start any exercise programme, it is essential that health and safety have been fully considered. Before the session starts, check the equipment that is to be used and the facility.

- Equipment must be checked for damage before and after a session, with any damaged equipment either repaired or replaced before the next session. All equipment should be stored correctly, and in a way that helps to set up the next session quickly and safely.
- Inspect the area you intend to use to make sure it is suitable and safe, including checking for hazards such as slip hazards. If working with a group of people, ensure the area is large enough for the group so people have enough space and can exercise freely.
- Ensure that the environment is a suitable temperature to prevent overheating of the participants and possible dehydration. Good ventilation will provide 'fresh' air to aid training and prevent overheating.

Preparing participants for an exercise session

Before a participant can start a gym-based exercise programme you must prepare them so that they are ready to undertake any prescribed exercise.

- **Checking ability and medical conditions** – collecting appropriate information (see page 283) about your participants, means you will produce a more effective programme. Establishing the participants' specific goals will help with motivation as well as ensuring your programme presents no danger to their health.
- **Confirm or revise plans with the participants** – the participants' individual goals will allow you to direct your training. The sessions must be flexible and capable of meeting these goals. Goals should be short-term (up to one month), medium-term (one to three months) and long-term (three months to one year). Confirm these goals with participants and use regular reviews to help them remain motivated and on target.
- **Advise participants of any emergency procedures** – you must be familiar with the facility's emergency procedure and communicate this to the participants. Emergencies could include fire evacuation, bomb alerts and injury or first-aid situations. It is good practice to make everybody aware of the procedures to be followed.
- **Inform the participants of the demands, purpose and value of the exercises** – consider each planned exercise and explain the physical and technical demands of it to the participants. They should be aware of what is expected of them and how the exercises should be completed, as well as any variations for individuals.
- **Demonstrate any specific movements** – each exercise must be demonstrated and explained clearly and the participants given an opportunity to practise, using any equipment, while you supervise.

Case study

Post-injury exercise

Georgina is a 21-year-old female who has been unable to participate in exercise for almost a year due to a complex fracture of her tibia. Before her injury, she was very active, playing netball for a local team and visiting the gym at least three times per week. After a year of rehabilitation and several operations, Georgina has been given the all-clear to exercise again. She is looking for a programme to support both her physical fitness and her rehabilitation.

Check your knowledge

1. What health screening procedures should you undertake with Georgina?
2. What considerations should you take into account when planning a session for Georgina?
3. Suggest a range of activities you would include in the first sessions with Georgina. Justify your choices.

Instructing an individual or group-based exercise session

Once you have designed your session, with an effective warm-up, main components and a cool-down, there are a number of best practice techniques you can follow to provide the best service possible for your participants.

Explain and demonstrate each exercise

To demonstrate a session effectively, the abbreviation IDEA presents a natural progression suitable for group-exercise classes and one-to-one personal training. IDEA stands for:

- **Introduction** - of the exercise, its purpose, its benefits and basic technique
- **Demonstration** - this allows participants to observe the movements
- **Explanation** - of the basics of the exercise - mention perhaps two or three technique-related points but avoid information overload
- **Application** - give participants an opportunity to practise the movements and gauge whether there are any potential problems or areas for improvement. It is essential to ensure correct technique.

Remember each exercise you provide for your participants may need to be adapted, both to allow them to progress but also to support a participant if they are having trouble completing the exercise (regression).

Appropriate communication

Communication is an essential tool for developing relationships and interacting. The key to good communication is to provide the amount of information the receiver can use effectively. Your message should be transmitted in a clear voice and be free from jargon. The use of jargon and slang terms is commonplace, but they can often cause 'grey areas' and be the cause of real confusion.

Ensure the information you provide allows enough guidance for individuals to take part safely and to establish good technique performance. Further information can be delivered over time when the basic principles have been mastered.

Your communication should also be appropriate for the environment. It might be pointless trying to communicate vocally if the exercise session is accompanied by loud music, unless you have a microphone headset and speakers. Similarly, during the cool-down when you might be trying to create a more relaxed environment you should also change your communication to match, e.g. by speaking softly.

Change position to observe participants

When leading an exercise session, you will be able to gauge levels of experience and potential by simply watching. During the session make sure you are not static and that you move around the participant or participants so you can observe their technique from different angles.

Monitor the safety and intensity of each exercise

When working with a participant, you must monitor the intensity of the session to ensure that it is as effective as possible and so that your participant is not at any risk. Common methods of monitoring intensity include:

- **observation** - this is a subjective method but it can give good early warning signs. When observing people, look for changes in exercise technique, skin colour and breathing patterns, and excessive sweat levels
- **talk test** - generally speaking, if you can hold a conversation while breathing rhythmically during exercise, you are probably working at an acceptable level for cardiovascular training. This test can quickly establish whether participants are working at a safe intensity for cardiovascular training.

Observation can be used to help monitor the safety and intensity of exercise

Progression and regression

A fitness programme should be reviewed regularly to ensure that progression is being made according to the client's goals and needs. You should support your client to evaluate their progress to make sure any prescribed exercises are not too easy or too difficult. Simple questioning after a session will help you and your client review their progress.

You may need to adapt exercises during their delivery, either to help progression if a participant is coping easily with the exercise or to add regression and simplify it if the participant is struggling.

Clear instructions and feedback

To ensure your participants are training correctly and to ensure their safety you must provide clear instructions. Any instructions need to be timed correctly so that a participant can act on them, correcting their technique to avoid injury or wasted effort. You should also provide clear feedback as this will not only ensure that they are training correctly but it will also provide motivation through your encouragement.

End-of-session feedback

At the end of the session you should also allow sufficient time for your participants to recover and reflect on the session. This time should also be spent giving the participants feedback. Explain how you thought they did and areas you think that may need improving. Remember any feedback should be clear, free from jargon or technical language and always check the participant's understanding.

You also have the opportunity to ask participants how they feel it went. This should include how they felt during each exercise, how they felt with the whole session and whether there are any additional goals they wish to work towards. You should also allow time for your participants to ask you any questions about their programme, goals or progress. This will allow you to refine their training programme.

This time is important as it gives you valuable feedback as part of your own personal evaluation, helping you to amend the client's programme and improve your delivery.

Theory into practice

To help with feedback it is useful to practise with a friend. Adopt the role of a fitness instructor and prepare an individual exercise session. You should conduct a pre-exercise questionnaire and instruct your friend on the exercises you have recommended. During the session you should encourage and motivate your friend.

1. Following the session you should reflect on your own performance. What were your strengths and what would you change next time?
2. Now discuss with your friend the areas of your performance that they thought were good and the areas they suggest you could improve on. Consider how you will improve on these areas.

Leaving the area after a session

Once your training session has been completed you must ensure that the area you have used is ready for the next person or session. Store any equipment correctly, checking that it is free from damage, clean and assessed for wear and tear, and always report any equipment that is broken.

Communication is an important skill that will underpin your work with participants. Describe the different types of communication.

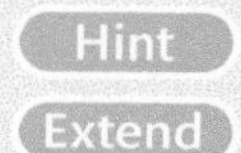

Hint: Explain what is meant by 'verbal' and 'non-verbal' communication.

Extend: Now consider how these different types of communication can be used effectively to motivate your participants.

Reviewing your own performance

To keep developing, it is important that you review your own performance. Being open and honest with yourself and considering your strengths and areas for improvement will help you to become better at instructing. You should spend time considering aspects of your personal performance that you think you could improve.

Evaluate how exercises met participants' needs

By reviewing your performance, you can identify whether your selected activities are fit for their purpose. This means making sure the exercises are addressing the short- and long-term goals of the participants.

- **Track progression** - have clear targets that are measurable, so that any improvements can be tracked. If a specific aspect of the programme is not effective, then changes can be made and the session adapted.
- **Session adaptation** - perform regular session reviews. If the participant's goals are not being met, it is important the session is amended, taking into account their needs, and address whether a participant has become demotivated. Adaptations will also allow variety, which can further enhance enjoyment.
- **Modify activities** - activities may be modified to take into account factors such as injury, illness, unexpected changes to the length of sessions, and participant demotivation. Modifications should be discussed fully with participants so that they are aware of what to expect in the future.

Relationship with the participants

A common reason why people leave exercise and training programmes is a drop in motivation. This may be caused by previous poor experience, lack of enjoyment, or failure to achieve aims and objectives. Therefore, you must motivate your participants, especially when the going gets tough.

You must be positive at all times to make sure you are pushing the participants into working as hard as is reasonable to achieve their goals safely. Likewise, build a rapport with your participants - match your instructing style to their needs, and be friendly and open with them. Being honest and respectful will also keep up the participants' motivation. Participants should feel that they are able to discuss their sessions with you, and feel comfortable in trying to achieve their targets.

Ways to improve personal practice

Once you have completed your reflection on your personal practice, consider steps you can take to improve your performance. Are there training courses you can take to help address any areas of weakness? Do you need to complete some additional study? Should you complete other methods of continued professional development, such as work shadowing?

Relevant professional bodies may offer training courses, or you might be able to plan to progress to further education. It might even be possible to take courses that aim to improve your communication skills and self-confidence. The value of reflective practice is that it can help you identify these weaknesses and get you thinking about ways to address them.

PAUSE POINT

When considering what went well when delivering a session, it is important to consider the methods used to assess your performance. Explain the feedback methods that can be used to review the performance of an exercise instructor.

Hint: Think back to initial participant screening before the exercise session – many of the methods used then can be adapted to help review your performance.

Extend: Consider the most effective methods of feedback when delivering a group or individual exercise session.

Assessment practice 10.2

B.P3 B.P4 B.M3 BC.D2 C.P5 C.P6 C.M4 C.M5 C.D3

During your work placement at a private health club, you have been asked to plan and deliver a safe and effective group-based exercise session that includes safe and effective delivery of cardiovascular endurance training and resistance training exercises. You need to:

- plan your session carefully, including adapted and alternative exercises for a range of individuals and justifying your choice of activities
- produce a written report that evaluates the information from participants' initial assessments and explains your choice of exercises
- show that you have considered the health and safety of the participants
- review and assess your own performance, explaining any strengths and areas for improvement
- create a personal development plan, explaining what you could do next to develop as an instructor.

Plan

- Do I know the different methods of cardiovascular endurance and resistance training?
- Do I know what activities to undertake before delivering an exercise session safely?
- Do I know how to collect feedback from participants and observers of the session?

Do

- Does my written report contain all the necessary information?
- Am I using the most appropriate exercises for the participants in my session?

Review

- Was the session a success? If so, why? If not, why not?
- How can I use my experience from this task to improve my planning in the future?

Further reading and resources

Books

Coulson, M. (2013) *The Fitness Instructor's Handbook: A Complete Guide to Health and Fitness*, London: Bloomsbury.

Crossley, J. (2012) *Personal Training: Theory and Practice*, London: Routledge.

Delavier, F. (2010) *Strength Training Anatomy (Sports Anatomy)*, Champaign, IL: Human Kinetics.

Websites

www.brianmac.co.uk – Brian Mac Sports Coach: a wide range of information related to fitness and training.

www.pponline.co.uk – Peak Performance Lite: free advisory newsletter that discusses strength and fitness.

www.teachpe.com – Teach PE: a variety of resources to support learners with all aspects of physical education including health and fitness.

THINK FUTURE

Paul Damas
Fitness instructor

Being a fitness instructor is a great job, albeit demanding. I get to work with a variety of people and helping people to improve their fitness, mobility or even social well-being is really fulfilling.

One of the perks of my role is that everyone who comes into my classes wants to be there. I work hard to make sure my sessions are varied and interesting, and that the intensity is right for each group. One of the biggest challenges I had to overcome was nervousness. It's very daunting standing up in front of a group of people and telling them what to do and how to do it – and correcting them if they do something wrong. You have to be very confident in what you're delivering and able to adapt what you're doing if something isn't working: improvisation is key if you want to make sure all your clients get the most out of the session.

It is important that your clients trust you as an instructor. In order to gain this trust, you have to prove that you know what you're doing and that you're good at what you do.

Focusing your skills

Planning

Being a fitness instructor is not just about developing people's fitness. You need to be a leader and organiser as well as knowing a wide range of cardiovascular and resistance-based exercises.

- Before any session, you must understand the personal needs of each of your clients. You can gather this information through client screening; make sure you are familiar with screening processes.
- Plan each session, using the information from client screening to decide which activities you will use and how you will structure the session. Make sure you have a good understanding of the different types of exercise you can use when delivering individual or group-based sessions.
- Consider planning a series of sessions, so you are clear about how you would like your clients to progress and you can share this information with the participants.

Leadership

- When delivering sessions, it is important to understand that everyone is different – both in personality and in how they are motivated. Your clients will have different fitness needs and objectives, and your role is to support each client individually to achieve their aims.
- Fitness instruction requires high levels of professionalism. Make sure you are familiar with the attitudes and responsibilities you will need to follow in a professional environment.
- Try to identify any opportunities to develop your team working and leadership skills. For example, if there is a group discussion in class, you could volunteer to lead the discussion.

Getting ready for assessment

Bridie is working towards her BTEC National in Sport and Exercise Science. She particularly enjoys the practical units and hopes to pursue a career in sports conditioning. For learning aim C, Bridie had to organise, deliver and evaluate a group exercise session. She needed to:

- plan the session, choosing exercises to suit her clients and adapting the exercises to make them more or less challenging if necessary
- evaluate her planning and delivery of the session, identifying strengths and areas for improvement.

Bridie discusses her experiences below.

How I got started

I've gained a lot of experience by volunteering as a gym floor assistant at a local health club. Although I can't deliver any sessions or work directly with clients, the opportunity to observe fitness instructors and personal trainers has been invaluable. I was also able to deliver my exercise session at the club, which was really useful as I had knowledge and experience of using the equipment.

I had to plan a 30-minute exercise session for ten of my classmates. Before the session, I gathered all the appropriate screening information and used this information to design a session that would suit the group. It helped that I knew the group, although I was still very nervous. On the day of the session, I arrived early so I had plenty of time to prepare the equipment and check that it was safe to use, and to go over my plan one last time.

How I brought it all together

When I welcomed the group, I made sure I was very clear about what we were going to be doing in the session. I was aware that there was a mix of abilities in the group, so I tried to use different activities for different people, and to vary the intensity of certain activities when necessary, by asking some people to work at a higher intensity and others to work at a lower intensity.

During the session, I realised that the weights I'd chosen were too heavy, so I had to adapt my plan slightly and change the exercise from bicep curls to press-ups.

What I learned from the experience

Observing fitness instructors and personal trainers definitely helped me with the planning and delivery of my session, as I'd improved my knowledge of the different types of exercises and how to administer them during a session. This helped me feel far more confident during the session.

I spent a long time planning and preparing, which gave me a good basis to work from. However, I soon discovered that it isn't always possible to keep to a plan and that you might need to adapt a session so everyone gains as much as possible from it.

I tried to gather plenty of feedback after the session to help with my evaluation. Although I found this a little uncomfortable, there were plenty of positive comments as well as some areas for improvement. One of my classmates reminded me that, 'You're still inexperienced, so there are obviously going to be areas for improvement. The only way to get better is by taking advice and practising.'

Think about it

- Have you developed an appropriate process to screen all your clients before planning your session?
- Are you familiar with a variety of exercises you can use for each part of your plan?
- How are you going to obtain feedback from your group after you have delivered the session?

11 Sports Massage

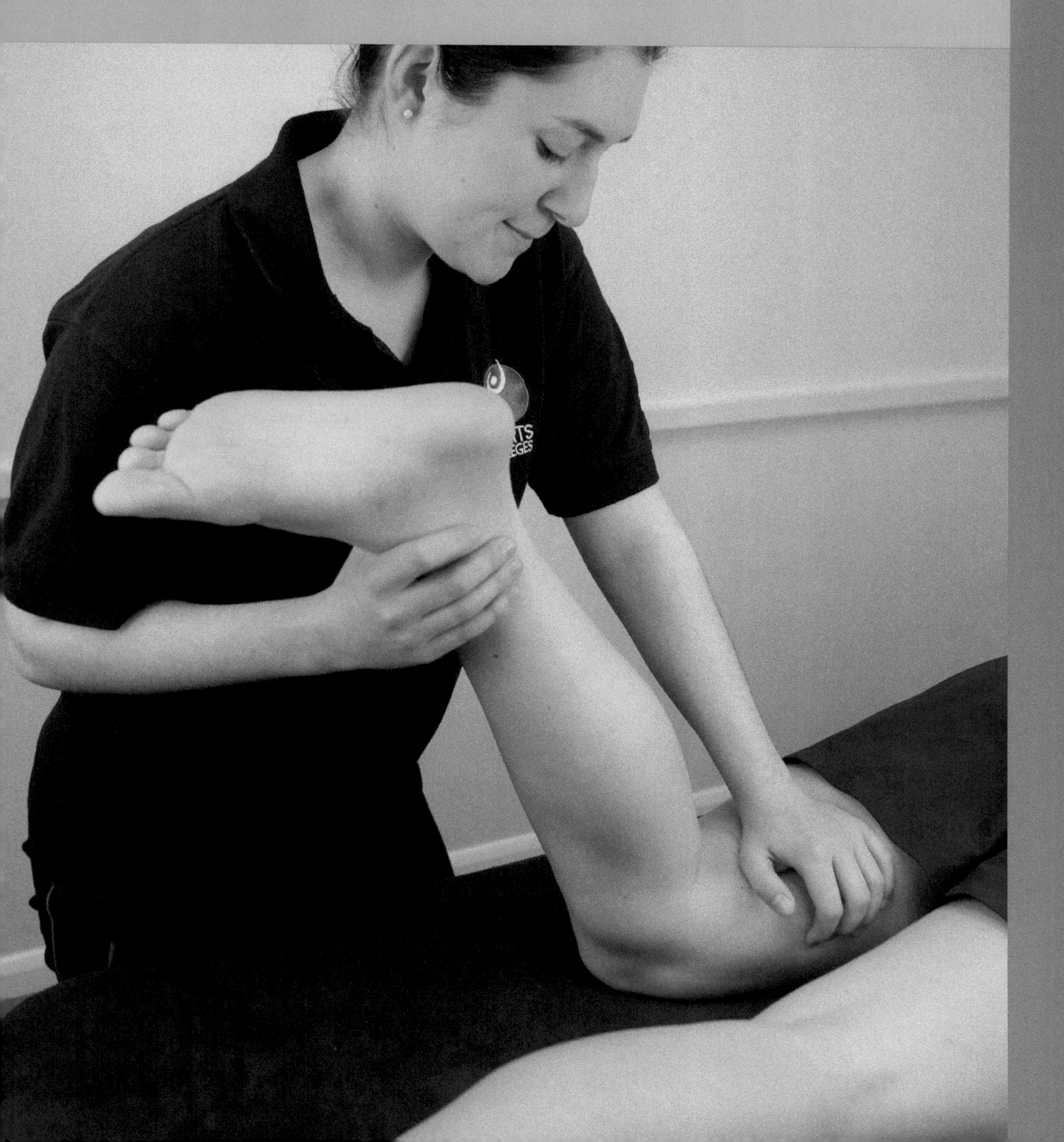

Getting to know your unit

Assessment
You will be assessed by a series of assignments set by your tutor.

Regular training and competition places a lot of physical and psychological demands on an athlete, for example, fatigue, muscle soreness, tight muscles and excess mental stress. One common method to enable athletes to meet these demands is the use of sports massage.

Sports massage is a form of soft tissue therapy and can be used for many reasons to benefit performers. It can be used to prepare for training or competition, recover from the demands of training or competition, or used to aid the healing process from sports injury. Many elite performers including athletes, rugby players, and footballers will receive sports massage treatments on a regular basis. This unit will introduce you to both the theory and practice behind using sports massage.

How you will be assessed

This unit will be assessed by a series of internally assessed tasks set by your tutor. Throughout this unit you will find assessment activities that will help you work towards your assessment. Completing these activities will not mean that you have achieved a particular grade, but you will have carried out useful research or preparation that will be relevant when it comes to your final assignment.

In order for you to achieve the tasks in your assignment, it is important to check that you have met all of the Pass grading criteria. You can do this as you work your way through the assignment.

If you are hoping to gain a Merit or Distinction, you should also make sure that you present the information in your assignment in the style that is required by the relevant assessment criterion. For example, Merit criteria require you to discuss, and carry out practical demonstrations in a confident and effective manner. Distinction criteria require you to justify and evaluate.

The assignment set by your tutor will consist of a number of tasks designed to meet the criteria in the table. This is likely to consist of a mixture of written and practical assignments and include activities such as:

- writing an essay on standards of practice in sports massage, professional bodies, and the role of practitioners
- carrying out consultation and assessment on performers
- creating and justifying sports massage treatment plans for performers.

Assessment criteria

This table shows what you must do in order to achieve a **Pass**, **Merit** or **Distinction** grade, and where you can find activities to help you.

Pass	Merit	Distinction
Learning aim A Understand the sports massage profession		
A.P1 Explain the role of a sports massage practitioner, the relevant standards of practice and professional associations. **Assessment practice 11.1**	**A.M1** Discuss sports massage standards of practice and professional associations using specific examples. **Assessment practice 11.1**	**A.D1** Evaluate the sports massage standards of practice in a variety of sporting environments, and the benefits of working in a multi-disciplinary team. **Assessment practice 11.1**
Learning aim B Undertake client consultation and assessment		
B.P2 Conduct client consultations and assessments on two contrasting sports performers and formulate safe treatment plans for each performer. **Assessment practice 11.2**	**B.M2** Conduct client consultations and assessments on two contrasting sports performers in a confident and effective manner and produce a safe and effective treatment plan for each. **Assessment practice 11.2**	**B.D2** Justify the consultation and assessment procedure adopted, as well as both treatment plans produced for the two contrasting sports performers. **Assessment practice 11.2**
Learning aim C Carry out sports massage on a sports performer		
C.P3 Conduct sports massage treatments appropriately for two contrasting sports performers, ensuring sports massage standards are upheld. **Assessment practice 11.3**	**C.M3** Conduct sports massage treatments in a confident and effective manner for two contrasting sports performers, providing justification for treatments administered. **Assessment practice 11.3**	**CD.D3** Evaluate the physiological, mechanical and psychological responses to the two sports massages performed, justifying the effectiveness, future recommendations and considerations. **Assessment practice 11.3**
Learning aim D Examine the importance of sports massage to the sport and exercise performer		
D.P4 Explain the physiological and mechanical responses to sports massage. **Assessment practice 11.3**	**D.M4** Discuss the physiological, mechanical and psychological responses to each sports massage, with regard to the requirements of the sports performers, using specific examples. **Assessment practice 11.3**	
D.P5 Explain the psychological responses to sports massage. **Assessment practice 11.3**		

Getting started

Sports massage is used regularly in elite sport including by track and field athletes and international rugby union teams. As a treatment sports massage can have many outcomes or effects. Create a mind map of why elite athletes may want to receive regular sports massage treatments.

A Understand the sports massage profession

Being a sports massage practitioner is exciting, rewarding and challenging. The environments sports massage practitioners work in include:

- **clinical environments** – e.g. private health clinics, medical rooms
- **non-clinical environments** – e.g. hotel rooms, athletes' homes, offices
- **event environments** – e.g. before and after mass participation events such as the London Marathon
- **sports club environments** – e.g. in changing rooms, at the side of the pitch, in the pavilion.

Sports massage or soft tissue therapy is a profession in its own right. All sports massage practitioners must be aware of industry standards and industry codes of practice and conduct.

Industry standards of practice

Industry standards of practice are designed to protect the athlete, the practitioner and others from bad practice. Following industry standards of practice ensures each athlete receives high-quality care, and safe and effective treatment. A sports massage practitioner being unaware of or breaking these standards of practice can lead to harm, **malpractice** and potential **litigation**.

Key terms

Malpractice – an instance of negligence or incompetence by the sports massage practitioner.

Litigation – resolving disputes by filing or answering a complaint through the public courts system.

Each professional association (see page 300) has its own standards of practice, but broadly these standards of practice cover:

- complying with health and safety legislation and insurance requirements
- safeguarding children and vulnerable adults
- creating and using a safe environment
- responding appropriately to emergency situations
- professional conduct.

Health and safety legislation

Some sports massage practitioners work self-employed, others for people/organisations, and some may employ a number of other practitioners. Regardless, there is a range of legislation any sport massage practitioner should be aware of to guide their business operations and treatments, shown in Table 11.1.

▶ **Table 11.1:** Summary of key legislation

Legislation	How it applies to sports massage therapists
Health and Safety at Work etc. Act (HASAW) 1974	This primary health and safety legislation covers what employers and employees should do and need to remain safe in workplace.
The Workplace (Health, Safety and Welfare) Regulations 1992	This includes access to adequate toilets, washing facilities, drinking water, protective equipment and first aid equipment. Emergency situations (e.g. fire) should be pre-planned and practised.
Employers' Liability (Compulsory Insurance) Act 1969	This ensures you have a minimum level of insurance cover in case one of your employees seek compensation following illness or injury.
The Health and Safety (First-Aid) Regulations 1981	This means you should have adequate level of first aid training and access to appropriate provision of first aid (e.g. first aid kit, automated external defibrillator (AED), equipment rooms).
Reporting of Injuries, Diseases and Dangerous Occurrences Regulations (RIDDOR) 2013	Any accident or incident needs recording and reporting so that the **Health and Safety Executive (HSE)** can audit you, checking on safety practices and operational procedures.
Management of Health and Safety at Work Regulations 1999	This requires you to carry out a **risk assessment** for each environment you work at (e.g. clinic, tent, pavilion). This should identify **hazards** and the risk of these occurring, and include measures to reduce their harm/severity.
Control of Substances Hazardous to Health Regulations (COSHH) 2002	This covers all substances, fluids or lotions used within your place of work, including the oils/creams you massage with and cleaning fluids. You should know what chemicals are in them, what happens if they are ingested or absorbed into the body, and have a protocol if an incident occurs.
Manual Handling Operations Regulations (MHOR) 1992	Makes sure practitioners are trained to safely and effectively carry, lift or move loads. For sports massage therapists, loads include the couch and the athlete's body parts.
Data Protection Act 1998	You must have a record of your treatments, and this legislation ensures you store all athlete records safely and securely and retain them for at least seven years. Records should be stored in a fire proof, lockable filing cabinet or password encrypted electronic folder. For further information, see www.ico.org.uk.

Key terms

Health and Safety Executive (HSE) – the organisation responsible for proposing and enforcing safety regulations throughout the UK.

Risk assessment – a systematic process of looking at an activity or environment, evaluating the hazards and risk associated with it, and coming up with preventative measures.

Hazard – something with the potential to cause harm. 'Risk' is the likelihood and severity of the harm that could occur as a result of the hazard.

PAUSE POINT How can you assess risk in sports massage environments?

Hint Create a list of potential hazards and risks you may face when carrying out a sports massage treatment.

Extend For each hazard, think of preventative steps you could take to reduce the risk.

Insurance

Every sports massage practitioner should have appropriate **insurance** in case an athlete or employee suffers some form of harm within your place of work and decides to claim for **compensation**. You need to be insured for all of the treatments you might carry out on an athlete.

The two main types of insurance used by sports massage practitioners are:

- **professional indemnity insurance** – protects you or your business against claims made by clients due to bad advice you might give them: loss, damage or injury caused by errors, negligent advice or omissions of important information
- **public liability insurance** – protects you or your business against claims made by clients due to your actions: loss, damage or injury due to your actions or the sport massage treatment.

It is wise to have a combined insurance policy as sports massage practitioners offer both physical services (actions) and professional guidance (advice). In the event of a claim your insurance should pay out for legal expenses and other costs.

Professional malpractice is the breach by a sports massage practitioner of either a standard of care or a standard of conduct, caused either by their advice or actions. Failing to follow the codes of conduct can leave you vulnerable to accusations of improper care/advice which could invalidate your insurance cover.

Safeguarding children and vulnerable adults

Sports practitioners should be aware of child protection legislation, policies and guidance. Child protection refers to anyone under the age of 18 years and vulnerable adults. If you are treating children or vulnerable adults, it is good practice for them to be accompanied by an adult chaperone. While the child can give **assent** for the treatment to be carried out, the adult will give their **consent**. Even though there is an adult present you should still explain your massage treatment in an appropriate way for the child or youth athlete to understand.

Every team or sporting organisation you work with should have a **safeguarding** policy. This policy should outline who is responsible for child welfare, and the process to follow if you suspect a child is suffering any form of abuse or neglect or if they disclose information to you.

Key terms

Assent – an expression of willingness to proceed with a treatment by people who are unable to understand likely risks and benefits (e.g. people under 18 years, vulnerable adults).

Consent – agreement by an adult to proceed with a treatment.

Safeguarding – protecting children and vulnerable adults from harm and maltreatment.

Safety tip

If you are working with a child or vulnerable adult and suspect a form of abuse or neglect, report this to the sports team's child welfare officer for advice or phone the NSPCC on 0808 800 5000.

Environmental issues

A practitioner must strive to make any environment they are working in as appropriate as possible. Key issues to consider in your sports massage environment include:

- Is it comfortable for the athlete and you (air temperature, etc.)?
- Is the environment safe and spacious enough for effective treatment?
- Is your equipment and the athletes' belongings secure?
- Can the athlete's privacy be maintained?
- Is the environment clean and well ventilated, and how will you keep yourself and your equipment clean?
- Is there access to first aid equipment and a phone?

Theory into practice

Imagine you are working at a rugby union club providing post-match sports massage to players in the changing room. What challenges are there in this environment? How would you overcome these?

Equipment issues

All sports massage equipment should be fit for purpose, clean and regularly maintained. As a minimum, sports massage practitioners should have access to the following equipment.

- **A treatment couch**
  - Make sure its fixtures and adjustable settings work correctly.
  - Be aware of its weight limit - working with athletes greater than the weight limit could cause the couch to buckle or collapse.
  - Adjust the height of the couch (if possible) based on your height and the techniques you are performing.
- **Mediums (oil, talc, cream/lotion)** to reduce friction on skin during massage
  - Always perform an allergy test, even if you may have treated the athlete before (different batches of the same product can be contaminated or use different formulas).
  - Choose a massage medium based on your athlete and your intended therapeutic effect - see Table 11.2.

Safety tip

To allergy test an athlete place a little of the massage medium on the skin between index finger and thumb (thenar eminence) and monitor for redness, swelling and changes in sensation.

Table 11.2: Advantages and disadvantages of different massage media

Medium	Advantages	Disadvantages
Oil	• Longer lasting lubrication • Additives can be relaxing or stimulating	• Quite expensive • Can contain nut derivatives • Not practical for people with a lot of body hair
Talc	• Produces greater friction to gain a quick therapeutic effect	• Can be quite messy • Can only be used pre-event
Cream/lotion	• Generally cheaper than oils • Better for people with more body hair as is more viscous • Tend to be more hypo-allergenic	• Can be absorbed quite quickly so apply it little and often

- **A bolster, couch roll and towels** to support the athlete and maintain privacy
- **Cleaning/hygiene materials** to maintain hygiene of the environment and equipment, and prevent infection from direct and indirect contact
  - Wash your hands and clean the couch and surfaces before and after each treatment.
  - Make sure the cleaning materials have got a COSHH assessment.

Emergency situations

Before a treatment takes place, it is vital to identify appropriate or designated exit routes. Make sure your couch does not block your exit route. You should have protocols to follow in emergency situations, such as a fire or bomb threat, a medical emergency or a threat to your personal security (for example, if an athlete becomes aggressive). Make sure you know the protocols for the organisation you are working in.

You should also be first aid trained to provide care in the event of a medical emergency.

Therapists' general conduct

How you look, smell and behave are all important factors in making the athlete feel confident in you as a practitioner and the treatment you will perform. If the athlete does feel confident it is more likely your sports massage treatment will be effective. General conduct of practitioner includes:

- personal hygiene (fresh breath, no body odour, short clean nails)
- appropriate dress (clean plain sports clothes, clean flat bottomed shoes, no jewellery that could hinder the application, e.g. rings, watches, chains)
- appearance (smart, hair tied back, limited make up, tattoos covered up if possible)
- attitude (always ask for consent to touch, non-judgemental, empathetic, interested)
- code of conduct (displaying membership of professional associations and their codes of conduct).

Professional associations

There are several different professional associations associated with sports massage therapy. The role and function of these associations is to provide support and opportunities for their members, while making sure effective standards of practice are applied. To become a member you must be appropriately trained, qualified and insured, commit to regular continual professional development (CPD) and always follow their codes of practice. Benefits of joining a professional association include:

- giving performers some assurances over the standard of care they will receive
- advertising (paid and voluntary) and CPD opportunities - often jobs will specify the need for relevant professional association membership
- discounted sports massage equipment, CPD resources/events and insurance.

The different professional associations include:

- **Sports Massage Association (SMA)** - exclusively for sports massage/soft tissue therapists
- **Society of Sports Therapists (SST)** - for sports therapists using massage alongside other treatments/therapies
- **British Association of Sport Rehabilitators and Trainers (BASRaT)** - for sports rehabilitators and trainers using massage alongside other treatments/therapies
- **Chartered Society of Physiotherapy (CSP)** - for physiotherapists that might use soft tissue skills in more clinical or hospital settings
- **Complementary and Natural Healthcare Council (CNHC)** - a voluntary regulator of many healthcare professionals and therapists
- **Federation of Holistic Therapists (FHT)** - includes a broad range of professionals from sport massage to complementary health and holistic beauty treatments.

Research

Go to the Sports Massage Association (SMA) website (www.thesma.org) and find out about the qualification requirements to join and the member benefits.

Sports massage practitioner role

General roles of a sports massage practitioner are to:

- plan and deliver safe and effective sports massage treatment based on the performer's needs
- prevent injury by improving the physical and psychological condition of performers
- promote recovery from exertion and injury
- enhance athletic performance.

It is often beneficial to work in a **multidisciplinary team** (MDT) or have a network of trusted professionals to refer on to. An MDT is a number of professionals working together and sharing their expertise. These professionals may vary based on the organisation you work in or the individual needs of performers. Examples of professionals that might be part of a multidisciplinary team are shown in Table 11.3.

Table 11.3: Example roles in an MDT

Osteopath	Chiropractor	Sports therapist or physiotherapist
General practitioner	Radiographer	Sports scientist
Sports psychologist	Nutritionist	

Part of being a good practitioner means knowing when to perform a treatment and when to refer on to another appropriate professional. This means that different professionals can use their different treatment skills to support the athlete. A practitioner should always be aware of the limits of their practice so they do not exceed professional boundaries.

There are some situations in which a practitioner should not perform a treatment, for example:

- **if a client is displaying red flag symptoms** – these are severe physiological symptoms that would require referral to hospital or at the very least an emergency GP appointment. Examples of red flag symptoms include:
  - stroke-like symptoms – dizziness, fainting, double vision, slurred speech, struggling to swallow
  - peripheral nerve compression/spinal cord lesion symptoms – loss of function in arms or legs, shooting pain, loss of sensation in arms or legs, loss of bowel and bladder control
  - symptoms of **deep vein thrombosis** – red, hot, shiny, and painful area usually on gastrocnemius
  - symptoms of cancer – unexplained, severe, persistent night pain
- **if a client has acute pathological tissue** – depending on your level of qualification you may or may not be able to treat injuries. Nevertheless, the general rule is not to use sports massage in the bleeding and acute inflammatory stage. Sports massage is a treatment for soft tissues (muscles, tendons, fascia) so if an athlete has issues with other forms of tissue it is better to refer on
- **if the client is a child, youth adult or vulnerable adult without a chaperone or prior consent** – lack of prior consent means you should not perform a sports massage treatment
- **if the client is showing contraindications:**
  - any condition that is severe, acute, contagious, uncontrolled and/or undiagnosed is known as a **global contraindication** and means you should **not** perform a sports massage
  - in comparison, **local contraindications** allow you perform a treatment, avoiding the affected area
  - you can treat **modifying conditions** (such as asthma, epilepsy or pregnancy) but only if you have an understanding of the condition and how sports massage may affect it. If an athlete has co-existing conditions or pathologies, you should be aware of both and how they may interlink before proceeding.

Research

Research the roles and skills of the professionals listed in Table 11.3.

Key terms

Deep vein thrombosis – the formation of a blood clot inside a blood vessel, obstructing the flow of blood through the circulatory system.

Contraindication – a condition or factor that means a sports massage cannot be delivered, or the treatment must be adapted.

Global contraindication – conditions when a sports massage should not be carried out.

Local contraindication – conditions when a sports massage can be carried out but avoiding the area affected.

Modifying condition – conditions when a sports massage can be carried but only with an understanding of the condition and how the treatment should be adapted because of this.

Safety tip

If ever you have any doubt about whether or not to perform a sports massage treatment, it is better to refer on rather than take a risk.

Case study

Sanjay Siransena – sports massage therapist in Premier League football

Sanjay is employed full time in Premier League football as a sports massage therapist, and is a member of the Sports Massage Association (SMA). In the club he works as part of an MDT, including the team doctor, physiotherapists, sports therapists, strength and conditioning coaches, and sports scientists. On occasion the team also uses a podiatrist.

The MDT meets for 30 minutes every morning to discuss the players and allocate the workload for the day. It is important that Sanjay keeps all members of the MDT up to date with his treatments and any player issues.

Sanjay's day-to-day job involves working very closely with the team's physiotherapist and sports therapist. Players are referred to him based on his specialist soft tissue skills. On training days he carries out player assessments on anyone requiring treatment, and also plans, carries out and evaluates his sports massage treatments. On match days he gives players pre-match and post-match sport massage.

Check your knowledge

- What are the interpersonal skills you need to be an effective sport massage practitioner like Sanjay?
- Why is it important for Sanjay to be a member of a professional association?
- Why might meeting every morning before the players arrive be important for the MDT?
- How could Sanjay evaluate his treatments?

PAUSE POINT Why are standards of practice important to sports massage practitioners?

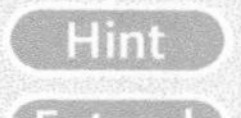

Hint: List the skills/characteristics required to be an effective sports massage practitioner.

Extend: Which of these skills/characteristics are you good at, and which do you need to develop?

Assessment practice 11.1

A.P1 A.M1 A.D1

You are the owner of a popular sports massage clinic. Your need to create a sports massage staff induction booklet, to raise awareness of professional standards in sports massage. The booklet must cover:

- the role of a sports massage practitioner
- the general conduct of a practitioner
- the range of sport massage environments
- application of key standards of professional practice
- key professional associations involved in sports massage
- other professional sports injury practitioners you may work alongside or refer to in a MDT (with the benefit and challenges of this).

Plan

- Do I know what an effective booklet looks like?
- Have I planned out the content of each page?

Do

- Do I know what I am doing and what I want to achieve?
- Do I know where to get further information on professional standards and conduct?

Review

- Can I map where I have met the assessment criteria in the booklet?
- Have I made sure my use of terminology is appropriate?

Undertake client consultation and assessment

The assessment process

The assessment process is the starting point of any treatment and has three parts.

- A **subjective assessment** looks at the athlete's perceptions, feelings and expectations. It is about detailing the athlete's background, the reason for treatment, and the potential cause of any complaints they have.
- An **objective assessment** gathers measurable information and/or observational data.
- An **interpretation stage** is where the sports massage practitioner uses the evidence collected in the subjective and objective assessments to draw up a safe and effective treatment plan.

The information gathered from an assessment must be recorded and stored safely.

Subjective assessment

The subjective assessment allows you to collect information relating to the athlete and the condition they are presenting with. Examples of key subjective information include:

- **Personal details**
  - Name, address, date of birth, contact information
  - Past medical history and medical conditions (screening for contraindications) and any medication being taken
  - Activity and lifestyle details (e.g. frequency, intensity, duration and type of training)
  - Occupation
  - The client's aims, priorities, and expectations from treatment
- **Presenting conditions**
  - What and where is the problem?
  - When did it happen (e.g. is it getting better, worse, or staying the same)?
  - How did it happen?
  - What are the symptoms (e.g. pain, the severity of symptoms)?
  - What makes it worse (aggravating factors)? What makes it better (easing factors)?
  - Do you have consent/assent to proceed with treatment?

Objective assessment

Objective assessment should be used to confirm or disprove your thoughts from the subjective assessment. Using reliable and valid outcome measures can help you quantify function and how effective your treatment has been. Examples of key subjective information include:

- **Observation**
  - Facial expressions may reveal discomfort or pain
  - Removal of clothing may show painful or restricted movements
  - Standing and/or sitting posture (check from front, side and back for symmetry, abnormal curvature of the spine e.g. **flat back**, excessive **kyphosis/lordosis**, **scoliosis**, alignment e.g. anterior/posterior or lateral **pelvic tilt**)
  - Walking and/or running gait (check the whole body moving from the front, side and back)
  - Affected area vs the non-affected area

Key terms

Flat back – a decreased curvature of the lumbar spine.

Kyphosis – an outward curve of the spine associated with the thoracic region.

Lordosis – an inwards curve of the spine associated with cervical and lumbar regions.

Scoliosis – an abnormal sideways curve of the spine.

Pelvic tilt – misalignment of the pelvis. For example, not being level (lateral pelvic tilt) or iliac spine being abnormally forwards or backwards (anterior or posterior pelvic tilt).

- **Active range of movement testing** (use tape measure, goniometer or inclinometer to measure)
  - Compare non-affected with affected side
  - Check for pain, range of movement and quality of movement
- **Palpation**
  - Check for resistance, muscle spasms and tenderness

Link

See *Unit 2: Functional Anatomy* for further information on joint movements and key anatomical structures to palpate.

You can read more about walking and running gait assessment in *Unit 15: Sports Injury and Assessment*.

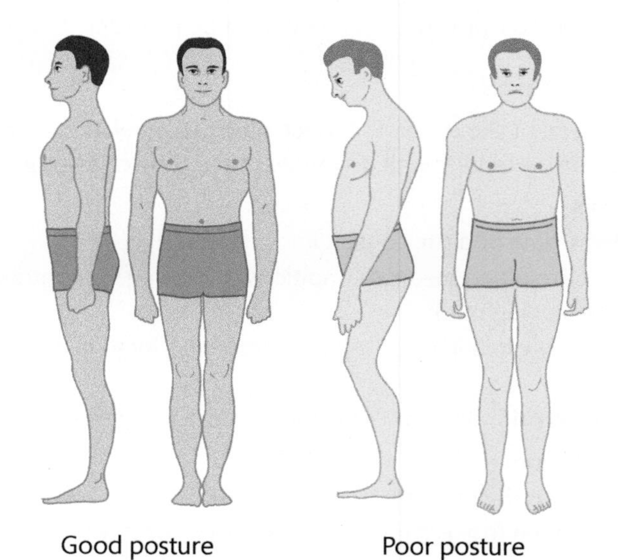

Figure 11.1: Can you identify the key postural differences? How does your posture compare to this?

Theory into practice

List the movements you would look at for the following joints:

- ankle joint
- knee joint
- hip joint
- wrist joint
- elbow joint
- shoulder joint
- neck
- lower back.

Now go and assess these on another person and note down any issues with pain, quality of movement, or restricted range of movement.

Treatment planning

Once you have completed your assessment and interpreted the information you collected, a safe and effective treatment plan can be created. The treatment plan should consider the following information:

- overall aim and intended benefit/effects of the treatment
- type of treatment (e.g. pre-event, inter-event, post-event)
- treatment duration
- muscle priorities
- contraindications (e.g. global, local, modifying - see page 301)
- positioning for the treatment (e.g. prone, supine, side lying, seated)
- massage medium (e.g. oil, talc, cream/lotion)
- massage techniques (e.g. effleurage, petrissage, tapotement, depth of application - see pages 306–307).

Creating a treatment plan that considers many types of information and evidence is called **clinical reasoning**. The treatment plan should be fully explained to the athlete to keep them informed about the treatment process and its benefits and effects. Be realistic when explaining the intended benefits of the treatment so you do not give false expectations and misinformation.

At the level you are studying, the criteria for proceeding with sports massage treatment are that the performer has:

- pain-free (not necessarily discomfort free) movement patterns
- no global contraindications, disease or red flag symptoms
- aches and pains that are not injury-related (pathological)
- areas of scar tissue, tightness or tension
- modifying conditions that can be effectively managed
- expressed that they want to enhance sports performance
- a chaperone present if required.

PAUSE POINT When should you not perform a sport massage?

Hint Using the criteria for massage as a guide, create criteria for when you should not perform a treatment.

Extend If you could not proceed with a treatment where would you refer the athlete on to?

Case study

You are working as a sports therapist within an elite youth sport setting. Maddie, one of the best players in the under-15 teams, comes to you saying her muscles are achy and tight, and asks whether you could give her a sports massage on her legs. She also feels stressed about a big competition coming up. From her medical records you are aware that she has Type I diabetes, an allergy to most nuts, and has eczema on the back of her knees.

Check your knowledge

1. Would Maddie benefit from a sports massage? Why?
2. Would you be able to proceed with Maddie's request for a sports massage?
3. What type of contraindications has Maddie got?
4. How would you need to modify your treatment based on Maddie's details?

Assessment practice 11.2

B.P2 B.M2 B.D2

Contrasting performers may want different types of sports massage, be from contrasting sports and/or have contrasting personal factors.

1 Carry out a subjective and objective assessment on two contrasting performers. Remember to ask about personal details and presenting conditions in the subjective assessment. The objective assessment should include observation, movements and palpation. Record the assessment information, noting down anything of interest.

2 Create a treatment plan for each performer, including:
- the overall treatment aim and intended effect
- the type of sports massage and treatment duration
- key information from the assessments (e.g. contraindications, sport demands)
- key muscles/muscle groups to massage
- what massage medium you will use
- a detailed step-by-step order for how you will massage the performer (e.g. which position, which muscles, which techniques, timings).

3 Now justify your treatment plans to some else and get feedback.

Plan
- Do I understand what is meant by contrasting performers?
- When can I practise carrying out assessments on my classmates?

Do
- Do I know who my two contrasting performers will be and have I checked this with my tutor?
- Do I know what to include in a subjective and objective assessment? Have I created templates for the performer assessments and treatment plans?

Review
- Did I carry out the assessment of the two performers confidently?
- Were my treatment plans complete and was I able to explain these effectively?

Carry out sports massage on a sports performer

Massage application

An effective sports massage practitioner has a broad range of techniques and can apply these to meet the individual needs of athletes. The techniques should be appropriate for the aims of each type of sports massage and their effectiveness monitored throughout the treatment.

Techniques

There are a range of sports massage techniques that can be applied in a treatment plan. You must know the different intended effects of each technique to ensure it is appropriate to use (see Table 11.4). For example, tapotement aims to increase neuromuscular stimulation so would not be appropriate to use when trying to relax the soft tissues.

Theory into practice

Once you have been shown how to perform massage techniques in class, ask someone to take a video on your phone of you performing them. You can use this to help practise your techniques.

Table 11.4: Massage techniques, intended effects, and examples of associated techniques

Technique	Intended effects	Examples of associated techniques
Effleurage Superficial to deep strokes, slides and glides with continuous motion – these can be applied linear or cross fibre	• Introduces touch to the client • Stimulates parasympathetic activity and relaxation • Relaxes the muscles • Spreads the massage medium • Increases circulation of blood and lymph • Stretches tissues • Effective linking strokes • Flushes the area	• Half-moon • Longitudinal glide • Opposing glide • Bilateral glide • Flat hand • Rotary technique • Cam and spindle • Forearm glide • Butterfly technique
Petrissage Lifting, squeezing and twisting the soft tissue under or between the hands	• Increases mobility • Separates tissues • Loosens adhesions • Stretches muscle fibres • Increases circulation of blood and lymph (e.g. venous return)	• Kneading (thumbs, palms and heel of hand, knuckles) • Picking up • Wringing • Skin rolling
Frictions Small focused and controlled movements applied through the thumb or finger tips	• Separates adhesions • Breaks down scar tissue • Realigns scar tissue • Stimulates blood flow • Relieves pain • Reduces muscle spasm	• Circular frictions • Transverse frictions
Tapotement Percussion techniques applied at a fairly rapid rate	• Warms muscle tissue • Increases circulation • Improves muscle tone • Stimulates nerve endings via reflex action	• Cupping • Hacking • Pounding • Beating
Compressions Pressing, squeezing and lifting tissues applied superficial to deep	• Warms muscles • Increases blood flow • Deactivates over-stimulated muscles and muscle spasm • Flushes the area	• Squeezing • Lifting
Vibrations Shaking or rocking the soft tissue	• Relieves tension • Provides relaxation • Stimulates nerve endings • Relieves pain • Loosens connective tissue	• Static vibrations • Running vibrations

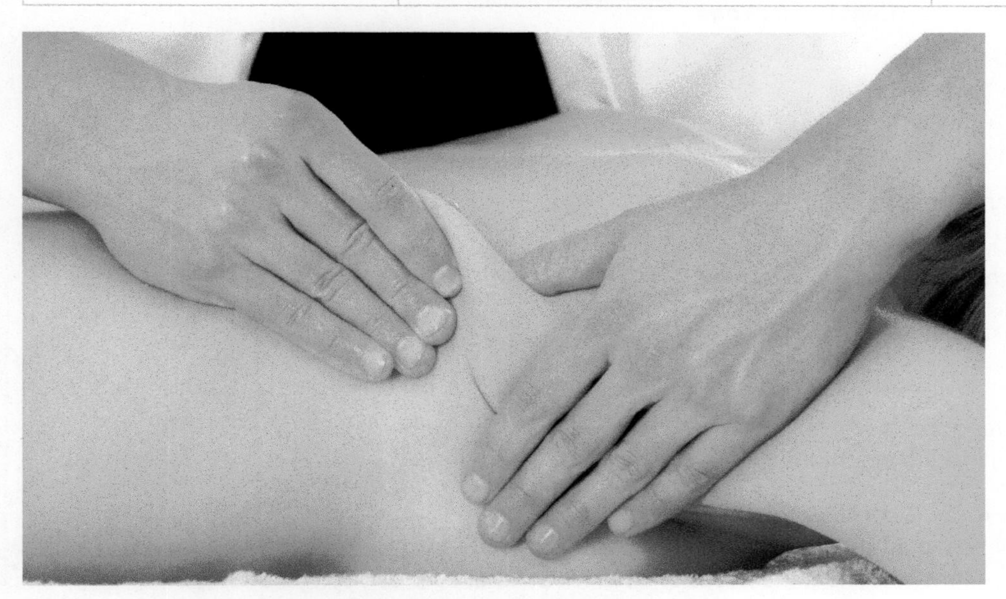

Petrissage is just one of a number of different massage techniques

Types of sports massage

There are different types of sports massage. Each of these differs in terms of overall aim, the techniques that are appropriate, speed and rhythm of application, and duration of treatment.

> **Key terms**
>
> **Neuromuscular stimulation** – the amount and rate of neural input to a muscle or muscles.
>
> **Anxiety** – negative emotional state in which feelings of nervousness, worry and apprehension are associated with activation or arousal of the body.

Pre-event massage

A pre-event massage aims to prepare the athlete physically and mentally for activity. Specifically it aims to:

- warm up and increase local area circulation in specific muscles
- decrease muscle tension and improve mobility
- increase **neuromuscular stimulation** of the soft tissue
- reduce **anxiety** and stimulate a positive mental attitude.

It is generally a short duration treatment delivered within a few hours of performing. Techniques tend to be superficial and stimulating, including superficial effleurage, petrissage, compressions and tapotement. The box below suggests a pre-event massage routine.

A 15 minute pre-event massage routine for a central midfielder in football

Massage the front of the legs with the client lying supine

1. Superficial effleurage with long strokes of the whole leg
2. Effleurage on the thigh – fast, short, vigorous movements
3. Palmar kneading on the thigh, checking depth and pressure to ensure no bruising occurs
4. Wringing of the quadriceps
5. Wringing of the adductors
6. Palmar kneading of the iliotibial band, checking depth and pressure to ensure no bruising occurs
7. Hacking, cupping or shaking of the thigh
8. Thumb kneading around the knee joint
9. Thumb kneading of the tibialis anterior
10. Effleurage lower leg
11. Thumb knead ankle around lateral and medial malleoli
12. Effleurage the whole leg, finish with shaking

Massage the back of the legs with the client lying prone

1. Superficial effleurage the whole leg
2. Short, vigorous effleurage to the hamstrings
3. Palmar kneading of the hamstrings
4. Wringing of the hamstrings
5. Hacking or cupping of the hamstrings
6. Effleurage of the hamstrings
7. Muscle rolling of the hamstrings
8. Effleurage of the calf
9. Wringing of the calf
10. Hacking/cupping of the calf
11. Thumb kneading of Achilles tendon
12. Effleurage to whole leg, finishing with vibrations

When you have read through the routine, consider the following questions.

- Do you think that this routine would be suitable for all sports?
- How could you alter this treatment to meet the needs of different athletes such as younger athletes?

Post-event massage

This type of massage aims to help the athlete recover physically and mentally from activity. The treatment can be carried out any time from the completion of the activity to a few days afterwards. Specifically the treatment aims to:

- help with the removal of waste products
- prevent muscle soreness
- support metabolic recovery and lymph flow
- restore flexibility and mobility
- relax the athlete.

The treatment generally lasts 20–30 minutes. Techniques should be superficial and relaxing. Deeper techniques will irritate sore muscles. Appropriate techniques include superficial effleurage, petrissage and superficial compressions. Passive stretching may also be carried out to help lengthen soft tissues.

A 30 minute post-event massage for the legs and back of a rugby prop

Massage the front of the upper legs with athlete in a supine position

1. Slow superficial effleurage of the thigh
2. Strong linear stroking of the thigh
3. Kneading/ringing of the thigh
4. Linear stroking of the tensor fascia latae
5. Palmar linear stroking of the iliotibial band
6. Effleurage to the adductors with the therapist supporting the knee
7. Wringing of the adductors
8. Gentle thumb stroking around the knee joint line
9. Effleurage to the whole of the quadriceps, finish with vibrations and passive stretching

Massage the back of the legs with the athlete in a prone position

1. Slow superficial effleurage to the whole of the back of the lower leg
2. Effleurage to calf region
3. Kneading of the calf region
4. Wringing of the calf region
5. Finger kneading of the Achilles tendon
6. Effleurage to the hamstrings
7. Linear stroking of the hamstrings
8. Kneading of the hamstrings
9. Wringing of the origin and insertion of the hamstrings
10. Effleurage to the whole of the back of the legs, finish with vibrations and passive stretching

Massage the back with the athlete in a prone position

1. Slow superficial effleurage of the back
2. Effleurage of the paraspinal muscles
3. Kneading of the paraspinal muscles
4. Kneading of the rhomboid region
5. Kneading of the trapezius and both shoulders
6. Thumb and finger kneading of the upper trapezius and cervical region of the neck
7. Wringing lateral regions of the back
8. Knead lateral regions of the back from waist to shoulder
9. Effleurage of the whole back, finish with passive stretching

When you have read through the routine, consider the following questions.

- Do you think that this routine would be suitable for all sports?
- How could you alter this treatment to suit different athletes, e.g. those with less or greater muscle bulk?

A rugby prop might have a very specific post-event massage routine

Injury prevention

Massage can be carried out to reduce the likelihood of soft tissue injury. If an athlete complains about tight muscles and/or through assessment you find limited range of movement, you can use massage techniques to help relax and lengthen the at-risk soft tissues. Appropriate techniques would include deep effleurage, petrissage and deep compressions. **Passive stretching** could be performed to further lengthen the soft tissues.

General maintenance

Many athletes include sports massage as part of their routine. They might not have specific complaints but use massage to maintain the condition of their soft tissues and unwind from training/competing. Without the time constraints of event-based massage, these treatments can last up to an hour. The techniques used would vary based on the athlete's expectations of the treatment.

Key terms

Passive stretching – the sports massage therapist stretching the muscle(s), as opposed to the athlete doing the stretching themselves.

Distal – furthest away from the centre of the body.

Proximal – closest to the centre of the body.

Medial – towards the inside of a body part.

Lateral – towards the outside of a body part.

Considerations for treatment

There are a number of factors to consider both immediately before treatment but also during the treatment itself. You should monitor how the treatment is going regularly by looking for visible cues and asking for feedback (e.g. on the depth and discomfort on a 0–10 scale). There might be times when you need to adapt your treatment based on this feedback.

Your techniques

- **Sequence** – always start with superficial before you go progressively deeper.
- **Direction** – always aim for **distal** to **proximal**, and **medial** to **lateral**.
- **Depth of pressure** – regularly monitor this with the athlete as deep techniques can be painful. You can add depth to a technique by slowing down its application or reinforcing your hands (placing one hand on top of the other). There are areas on the body where deep pressure should not be applied; these are called 'areas of precaution' and include the axilla, popliteal space, femoral triangle, kidneys, and the anterior/posterior triangle of the neck.

Research

What specific structures are located in the axilla, the femoral triangle and the popliteal space? Why would deep pressure in these areas be ill advised?

- **Speed** – slower techniques are generally deeper and promote more relaxation. Faster techniques tend to stimulate the soft tissues.
- **Different muscle groups** – your application of the techniques should reflect the size of the muscle/s. For example, a broad technique such as a forearm glide should not be used on small muscles.
- **Massage medium** – the medium you use should be based on your athlete and the intended effect of your treatment. For quick warming of the tissue less friction is desirable.

Adverse reactions

Always monitor for reactions such as a rash, hair follicle irritation, **erythema** and allergic reaction.

Key term

Erythema – superficial reddening of the skin.

Your body position

- Adopt a wide stance for a greater base of support.
- Keep your shoulders square and maintain a straight back.
- Transfer force with your legs, not just your arms – this will prevent fatigue and overuse injury to the practitioner.
- Keep your arms lengthened with locking.
- Adjust your body position and the height of the couch based on the technique you use – the couch should be roughly level with your wrist joint although the height should change based on your athlete (size, body part working on) and technique (more body weight over the athlete will give greater depth).

The position you want the athlete in

Are their limbs and joints supported? Is it comfortable? Is there good accessibility to the muscle/s?

- **Supine** – athlete laid on their back, face upwards, with a pillow under the head and knee for support.
- **Prone** – athlete laid on their front, face downwards, with a pillow under the hips and ankles for support.
- **Side lying** – athlete laid on their side with alignment of the spine and pillow between flexed legs for support.
- **Seated** – athlete is sat up on a couch or in a seated position with pillows behind their back and under their knees for support.

Presence of contraindications

Be aware when and how a treatment plan should be adapted, and symptoms meaning the treatment should stop and the athlete be referred on.

PAUSE POINT What position can athletes be put in for a sports massage treatment?

Hint Create a list of muscles you could effectively massage with the client lying: i) prone, ii) supine, iii) on their side.

Extend What are the advantages and disadvantages of these positions?

Legalities

You must keep accurate records of all the treatments you give, so that you can monitor your clients' progress. All documentation should be stored in a safe place (such as a locked filing cabinet or a password-protected computer) and you must make sure you follow the requirements of the Data Protection Act 1998.

Before beginning any treatment, you must explain the treatment to the sports performer and ask them to complete an informed consent form. This form will include:

- a description of the treatment
- information about the possible risks and benefits of the treatment
- a section that offers to answer any questions and confirms these have been answered fully
- an explanation that any information collected about the client will remain confidential
- a section for you, your client and any other relevant individual (such as a parent or carer if the sports performer is under 18) to sign and date.

You must also make sure you are fully insured, as described on pages 297–298.

After the treatment

Some form of aftercare advice should be given. This advice aims at maintaining/improving the condition of the athlete until you can next treat them and relates to:

- rest after a lengthy sports massage (not being overly active)
- hydrating the body by drinking fluids
- being aware of possible treatment effects, e.g. soreness, erythema, hair follicle irritation
- home exercises, e.g. regular stretching
- giving an opportunity for the athlete to feed back on the treatment and clarify their understanding.

Case study

The Olympic decathlete

You are working with the Great Britain Olympic decathlon squad. The decathlon requires competitors to complete multiple events in a short period of time. The first day consists of (in order): 100 m, long jump, shot put, high jump and 400 m. The second day's events are 110 m hurdles, discus, pole vault, javelin and 1500 m. Preparing for each event and recovering in time for the next one is very important.

You have been asked to give treatment to one of the decathletes to prepare him for the first event of the competition, and another treatment to recover from the demands of day one. Create a plan for each treatment, considering the following questions.

Check your knowledge

1. What is the aim and intended effect of the treatment?
2. What would be the massage duration?
3. What massage medium would you use?
4. What are the muscles/groups of muscles you need to massage?
5. What techniques would you use to have the desired effect?

Create a step-by-step order of how the treatment would be carried out (including positioning).

Examine the importance of sports massage to the sport and exercise performer

Link

This content links with *Unit 1: Sport and Exercise Physiology* and *Unit 2: Functional Anatomy.*

The major focus of sports massage is to improve the functioning of soft tissues. However, it affects a number of interlinking physiological systems (e.g. musculoskeletal, cardiorespiratory, nervous, lymphatic, endocrine, digestive and urinary).

This means sports massage can have many multiple and different effects on an athlete. Depending on the technique you can get different effects (refer back to Table 11.4 on page 307). Broadly these effects can be categorised as being physical/physiological, mechanical or psychological.

Physical/physiological effects

There are a number of physical/physiological benefits of sports massage, relating to how the athlete's body works (see Figure 11.2). This is largely because sports massage affects the **autonomic nervous system**, responsible for controlling the function of vital organs of the body. The autonomic nervous system is made up of the **sympathetic** and **parasympathetic** nervous systems. The sympathetic system stimulates physiological activity, whereas the parasympathetic system reduces activity.

Most sports massage techniques increase sympathetic activity to some extent, leading to greater local area metabolism and stimulation of blood/lymph flow. However, using slow and superficial techniques will increase parasympathetic activity which will affect **hormone balance** (increasing relaxation hormones - e.g. serotonin, dopamine - and reducing stress hormones - e.g. cortisol), relaxing the athlete and promoting recovery.

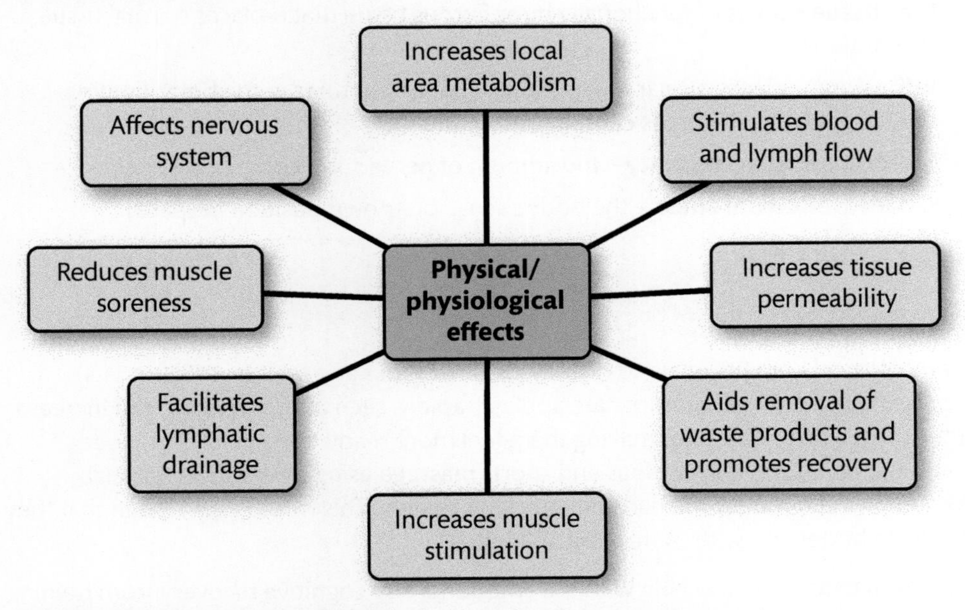

Figure 11.2: Major physical/physiological benefits of sports massage

Mechanical effects

Mechanical benefits relate to how the athlete moves (see Figure 11.3). Often an athlete's overall mobility is restricted by their soft tissues. Sports massage can improve the condition and function of the soft tissue by improving the range of movement around joints and reducing tissue resistance.

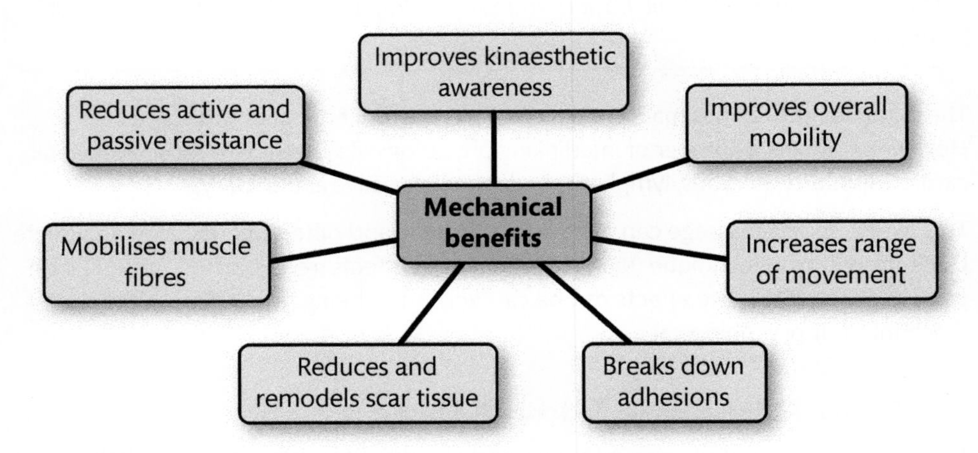

Figure 11.3: Major mechanical benefits of sports massage

It is common for athletes to have **scar tissue** and **adhesions** which can cause pain and limit movement. By loosening adhesion and reducing the impact of scar tissue the athlete will be able to move better. Techniques such as tapotement can mobilise muscle fibres by affecting the nervous system and increasing **motor neuron excitability**. This will improve the muscles ability to contract leading to better power, speed and strength output. The process of being touched and recognising pain, tightness and tension could give an athlete more **kinaesthetic awareness**.

Key terms

Scar tissue - areas of functionally poor fibrous tissue that replaces normal tissue after trauma.

Adhesions - pieces of scar tissue that attach to structures in the body, limiting movement and sometimes causing pain.

Motor neuron excitability - the amount of nerve stimulation of a muscle.

Kinaesthetic awareness - the body's sense of its own position in space.

Psychological effects

Psychological benefits relate to how the athlete thinks and feels (see Figure 11.4). Sports massage techniques that are applied rapidly, such as tapotement, can increase the arousal level of athletes making them feel more ready to perform. However, certain athletes get very anxious and sports massage using slow and superficial techniques can reduce the harmful effects of anxiety. This would again mean that they perform better and with more self-confidence.

Sports massage can also help with the emotional and cognitive recovery from training and competition. Perceptions of discomfort and pain can be reduced by **stimulating receptors** that distract the brain from recognising pain signals.

Research

One way sports massage can reduce pain is through the Gate Control Theory of Pain (Melzack and Wall, 1965). What is this theory? Using only diagrams create a leaflet explaining this theory. According to the theory how might massage reduce perceptions of pain?

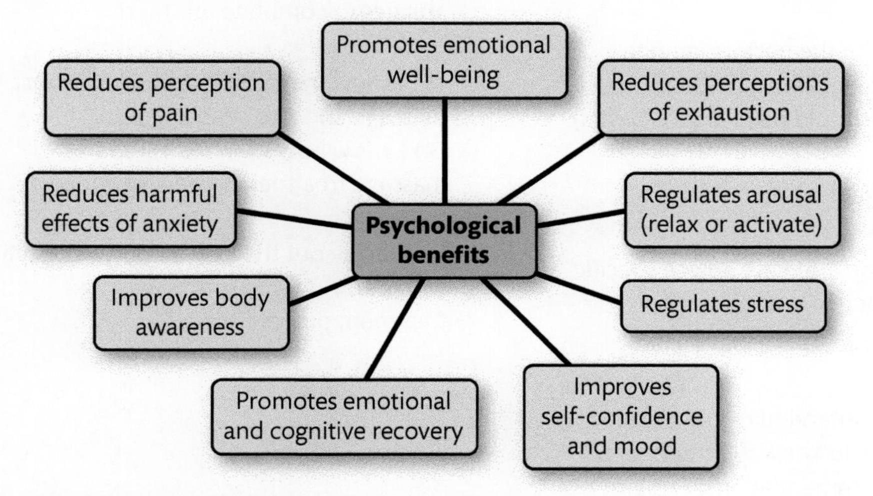

Figure 11.4: Major psychological benefits of sports massage

PAUSE POINT What are the main physical, mechanical and psychological effects of treatment?

Hint What are the problems associated with a limited range of movement? Which techniques could increase range of movement?

Extend What problems are caused by the accumulation of waste products? Which techniques would you use to help remove these?

Case study

The Association of Tennis Professionals (ATP)

The ATP tennis season lasts for 11 months, placing many physical and psychological demands on players. You are a sports massage therapist for an ATP tennis player who is young and relatively new to the tour and seems to be struggling with the demands placed upon him. He is concerned about his fitness compared to other players and has increased his training load as a result. He regularly tells you he feels sore and stiff.

At a Grand Slam, he wins his first round match in five tough sets, but faces his next opponent within 48 hours. As his second round match approaches he seems very nervous and under-prepared. He mentions this is affecting his sleep patterns and he does not want his nerves to ruin his performance.

You are asked if you can provide sports massage treatments to help him prepare for the match and recover more effectively.

Check your knowledge

1. What do you think the physical and psychological demands of the game are?
2. How could a sports massage treatment benefit the player before a match?
3. How could a sports massage treatment benefit the player after a match?

Assessment practice 11.3

C.P3 D.P4 D.P5 C.M3 D.M4 CD.D3

Using the two contrasting performers that you focused on in assessment practice 11.2, carry out the sports massage treatments from your treatment plans, covering the following steps.

1. Prepare the massage area and your performer according to good professional standards.
2. Verbally justify the treatment plan with the performer with the intended effects (physical/physiological, mechanical, psychological) of the treatment (this should be evidence based), and ask for consent.
3. Carry out the planned sports massage treatment while monitoring the performer throughout.
4. Provide, demonstrate and justify some aftercare advice specific to the performer (this should be evidence based).
5. Wipe down the couch, wash your hands and complete any documentation.
6. Complete a written evaluation of the intended responses to the treatment, including how you would know the treatment was effective and provide future recommendations. Explain who else might be involved in the MDT care of the performer (outlining the benefits and challenges of this).

Plan

- When can I practise my sports massage treatments?
- How confident do I feel in my own abilities to complete this task?

Do

- Do I know the different effects of sport massage and can I explain them?
- Do I know how to make my sports massage treatments safe and effective?

Review

- Did I carry out the treatment confidently?
- Did I carry out the sports massage treatment professionally?

Further reading and resources

Books

Benjamin, P.J. and Lamp, S.P. (2004) *Understanding Sports Massage*, Champaign, IL: Human Kinetics.

Holey, E. and Cook, E. (2011) *Evidence-Based Therapeutic Massage – a practical guide for therapists*, 3rd edition, London: Churchill Livingstone.

Findlay, S. (2010) *Sports Massage*, Champaign, IL: Human Kinetics.

Forsdyke, D., Gledhill, A., Mackay, N. and Randerson, K. (2011) *Foundations in Sports Therapy*, London: Heinemann.

Mills, R. and Parker-Bennett, S. (2004) *Sports Massage*, Oxford: Heinemann.

Websites

www.massagenerd.com – Massage Nerd: sports massage technique videos.

www.susanfindlay.co.uk/Massage-Mondays – Susan Findlay: sports massage technique videos.

www.co-kinetic.com – Co-Kinetic: sports massage research news and practitioner commentary.

THINK FUTURE

Cerys Jones

Freelance sports massage practitioner

I am a qualified sports massage therapist and a level three member of the Sports Massage Association (SMA). Most of my work is based out of a small treatment room in my local gym. I get plenty of trade from achy and sore gym goers and my local sports teams. I must be doing quite a good job as business is booming.

Some people think that all I do is get paid to 'rub' but being a sports massage therapist is much more than that. I have important specialist skills and I constantly need to know why I am doing what I am doing. My role involves assessing people, and also planning, delivering, and evaluating sports massage treatments. I treat a wide variety of people and that's the challenge I love about the job I do. You can't treat athletes exactly the same and have to deliver individualised treatments.

I am always aware of my professional standards and limitations of practice. I have had to refer a few people because of certain issues when other health practitioners' expertise complemented what I was doing.

In the future I want to complete my level four and five sports massage qualifications as this will allow me to treat injured tissues, and open more doors for me. Maybe one day I will work at an Olympic Games or another major international tournament.

Focusing your skills

Building a business

It is important to have some basic business skills to be a freelance sports massage therapist. Here are some simple tips to help you.

- Where would you conduct your treatments (e.g. clinic, mobile, non-clinical setting)?
- What would be your start-up costs (e.g. couch, massage medium, couch roll, towels) and other costs (e.g. professional association fees, room rent, insurance)?
- How would you promote your business (e.g. business cards, flyers, adverts, a website)?

Safe and effective practice

It is vital to follow the highest possible professional standards to build your business and keep you and your clients from harm. Here are some basic tips to keep in mind.

- What are your professional limitations (i.e. when should you refer on)?
- Always keep in mind good hygiene practices (e.g. washing hands before and after treatments and cleaning all high-usage surfaces after each treatment).
- Develop an understanding of contraindications and how these affect sports massage.

Getting ready for assessment

José is working towards a BTEC National in Sport and Exercise Science. He was given an assignment for learning aim B with the title 'Creating effective treatment plans'. He had to produce a written report on two contrasting performers, detailing the assessment and consultation of each, and the sports massage treatment plans for each. The written report had to:

- explain why a performer consultation and assessment is important and justify each part of an assessment
- include details of the performer consultations and assessments, a summary of the findings, and tutor observation records of the consultation and assessment
- create and justify safe and appropriate treatment plans for each performer.

José shares his experience below.

How I got started

I decided to check whether my chosen performers were sufficiently contrasting so I asked my tutor as I wanted to get this sorted nice and early. I chose a classmate who plays rugby league wanting a pre-event massage and a classmate who takes part in cross country needing a post-event massage.

I collected all my notes on this learning aim and sorted them into those focusing on consultation/assessment and those on treatment planning. I practised consultations, assessment and drawing up treatment plans on family members as I wanted to be confident and able to carry them out without hesitation or uncertainty. I also made a summary sheet of why a consultation/assessment is important and why we do each part. I went to the library to find books on the benefits of pre- and post-event massage and searched for journals online.

How I brought it all together

For the observation I made sure that I behaved professionally, dressing appropriately and doing all the necessary things like washing my hands. I made sure I had blank copies of the consultation/assessment template with me, asked the performers' consent, and went through the consultation in a logical order.

I decided to put my written report into four sections after an introduction.

- Section one included general information on why a performer consultation/assessment is important, the parts of an assessment (e.g. subjective and objective), and why we conduct each of these parts.
- Sections two and three included the template I completed with the performers, a summary of their important information, their specific treatment plan using the template, and a justification of my plans.
- Section four was the written observation record from my tutor.

Because I used some books and journals to support my work, I produced a bibliography. I got my parents to read over the work to make sure my use of terminology and writing style were OK and to check for any errors.

What I learned from the experience

It was important to make sure my performers were contrasting. Some of my classmates didn't do this and ended up panicking towards the deadline. All the practice assessments on my parents and grandparents must have been useful as the tutor thought I was confident. The extra reading I did in the library to find books and journals to support my treatment plans was important, as well as being a useful transferable skill.

Think about it

- Have you written a plan with timings so you can complete your assignment by the submission date?
- Do you have the recommended resources as well as your class notes to help you to provide evidence and references to support and develop the arguments that you plan to make?
- Is your information written in your own words and referenced clearly where you have used quotations or information from a book, journal or website?

Sociocultural Issues in Sport and Exercise 12

Getting to know your unit

Assessment

You will be assessed by a series of assignments set by your tutor.

Sport is often said to 'mirror society' – some would even say that it not only reflects but actually shapes society. Many people in the modern age have a regular sporting passion, either as spectator, player, coach or official. It is difficult to imagine a society without sport so it is completely appropriate that sport is explored from a sociological standpoint.

To start with, this unit looks at the historical perspective, at how such phenomena as order, fair play and the establishment of rules formed a critical part of the development of sports in Britain and arguably society as a whole.

Having established this background, you will next consider sociological theories that look at the reason, purpose and functions of modern sport. No unit of this sort would be complete without considering modern phenomena such as the impact and changing face of the media and its effect on the perception of sport, commercialisation, professionalisation and the business of sport.

How you will be assessed

This unit will be assessed by a series of internally assessed tasks set by your tutor. Throughout this unit you will find assessment activities that will help you work towards your assessment. Completing these activities will not mean that you have achieved a particular grade, but you will have carried out useful research or preparation that will be relevant when it comes to your final assignment.

In order for you to successfully complete the tasks in your assignment, it is important to check that you have met all of the Pass grading criteria. You can do this as you work your way through the assignment.

If you are hoping to gain a Merit or Distinction, you should also make sure that you present the information in your assignment in the style that is required by the relevant assessment criterion. For example, Merit criteria require you to analyse whereas the Distinction criteria require you to evaluate.

The assignment set by your tutor will consist of a number of tasks designed to meet the criteria shown in the table. This assignment is likely to consist of a mixture of written and practical assignments, for instance, you may be asked to produce:

- a report that justifies the sociological theories used to interpret the role of sport in society - this requires you to apply sociological theory to everyday sporting scenarios outlining how sport can influence behaviour, the political involvement in sport when exploring critical theory, as well as linking the development of sport in the UK in the school systems and beyond
- a report that includes an evaluation of the impact of historical, cultural and social issues on the development of sport and exercise in the UK - making detailed analysis of historical and cultural changes to sport in the UK, and examining the changes that have had an impact on sport and exercise
- a report that evaluates the impact of the media and commercialisation on the development of sport and exercise - you will also need to concentrate your evidence on contemporary phenomena such as the impact of the media and commercialisation on a sport and how sport has become a global product.

Assessment criteria

This table shows what you must do in order to achieve a **Pass**, **Merit** or **Distinction** grade, and where you can find activities to help you.

Pass	Merit	Distinction
Learning aim A Understand the social theories used to study and interpret sport and exercise in society		
A.P1 Explain a sociological theory and its impact on sport and exercise in society. **Assessment practice 12.1**	**A.M1** Analyse the use of sociological theory and its impact on sport and exercise in society. **Assessment practice 12.1**	**A.D1** Justify the use of sociological theory in interpreting the role of sport and exercise in society. **Assessment practice 12.1**
Learning aim B Investigate the historical and cultural changes, and the social and ethical issues that have impacted on sport and exercise development in the UK		
B.P2 Explain how historical and cultural changes in the UK have impacted on sport and exercise. **Assessment practice 12.2**	**B.M2** Analyse how historical and cultural changes in the UK have impacted on sport and exercise. **Assessment practice 12.2**	**B.D2** Evaluate the impact of historical, cultural, social and ethical issues on the development of sport and exercise in the UK. **Assessment practice 12.2**
B.P3 Explain how social and ethical issues in the UK have been addressed by sport and exercise. **Assessment practice 12.2**	**B.M3** Analyse how social and ethical issues in the UK have been addressed by sport and exercise. **Assessment practice 12.2**	
Learning aim C Investigate the relationships between commercialism, the media, and sport and exercise		
C.P4 Explain the role of the media and commercialisation in the development of sport and exercise. **Assessment practice 12.3**	**C.M4** Assess the impact of the media and commercialisation on the development of sport and exercise into a global product. **Assessment practice 12.3**	**C.D3** Evaluate the impact of the media and commercialisation on the development of sport and exercise as a global product. **Assessment practice 12.3**
C.P5 Explain how sport and exercise has become a global product. **Assessment practice 12.3**		

Getting started

Sport continues to play a significant role in UK society. Sport contributes to the overall economy, and some of the country's largest events are sporting. Sport and the history of sport helps define communities across the UK, and also has the potential to help transform deprived areas. Before you start the unit, list the ways in which sport has an impact in your local area, not just the obvious educational ones but also how it may be used to fight crime, engage the apathetic or combat obesity.

A Understand the social theories used to study and interpret sport and exercise in society

Link

This unit has links with *Unit 5: Applied Research Methods in Sport and Exercise Science.*

Sport is a large part of our culture and is important in many people's lives, whether participating or spectating, or both. Over time, different researchers have come up with different **social theories** that attempt to define not only the purpose of sport but also how it contributes to society and its influence on culture.

Key term

Social theories – frameworks developed by social scientists that attempt to interpret evidence to study and understand social events, such as the development and uses of sport and exercise in society.

Functionalist theory

Functionalist theory views each part of society in terms of how it contributes to the stability of society as a whole. In other words, society is diverse but each different part has a function to play in contributing to the stability of the whole society. Society is a complex multi-structured system within which people must find ways to interrelate, with each part depending on all the others.

Sport and exercise contributes to society because it provides an emotional release and a means of integrating new members into society and introducing acceptable behaviour. It can also be a means of movement between classes in society and help to reinforce a society's values.

Functionalist theory states that sport contributes to society by:

- **developing character by teaching social norms and values** – sport can offer a set of rules for polite living or established social norms, and teach respect for authority
- **encouraging a positive work ethic** – sport can give a sense of purpose and stresses the importance (particularly in team sports) of people performing specific functions and being accountable to superiors such as captains or coaches and even spectators
- **encouraging individuals to get together to achieve common values and goals** – sport can teach common values and goals, through competition and achieving personal and team targets
- **helping integration across different social and cultural groups** – sport can introduce other cultures to each other and so help to develop overall community harmony
- **increasing the fitness and overall health of a nation** – Sport England put health at the top of their agenda and believe taking part in sport has major health benefits for the nation.

Discussion

What does a sport have to contain to be called a 'sport'? Many people do not consider darts a sport, but it has a competitive structure and the performers train very hard. Does a sport need to have a physical element? Darts is more physically active than archery and yet more people consider archery to be a sport (with Olympic and Paralympic status) than darts.

In pairs research the following, often confused, terms:

- sport
- physical activity
- exercise
- recreation.

As a group try and agree on definitions for each by first collecting the agreed attributes of each and then forming coherent sentences.

Conflict theory

Conflict theory suggests that people in positions of power - either political, economic or both - use sport for their own gain. The key characteristics of this theory are that sport is used as a form of control:

- **by powerful groups for their own motives** - think about who owns football Premier League clubs. Why might they own these large organisations? It could be an entertaining hobby, but these clubs also make a large profit and can be used as financial tools to demonstrate power and control
- **to entertain and control the masses** - conflict theorists believe that the rich and powerful prefer the majority of people to be playing or watching a sport because it distracts them from considering their circumstances in life, which might lead to resentment

Conflict theory says sport is used to distract the masses from their plight

- **to promote capitalist growth** - the theory argues that **capitalism** cannot be successful unless the ruling classes dominate the working classes and exploit them economically. In this theory sport is a tool for rich athletes and sports clubs, helping them to profit from the loyalty of their fans and spectators
- **to promote national pride** - perhaps the most sinister assumption of conflict theory is the idea that sport is also used as a political pawn to show off national pride and prowess. This can be used by those in power to suggest that they are politically or economically superior to other nations.

Key term

Capitalism - a system of economics based on the private ownership of capital (money and other resources) and production (companies, etc. that make goods and services) and individual profit.

Reflect

Do you feel controlled when playing or watching sport? How much do you pay and who do you pay your money to? Who is making money at your expense?

- Research the cost of taking part or spectating in your favourite activity. Remember to include all costs.
- Next list five sports you could take part in for a low cost or for free.
- Compare how you feel about both experiences and describe your feelings.

Critical theory

Critical theory is based on a few central ideas outlined below.

- Groups are best identified by their shared values and conflicts of interest. For example, a group of young netball players who have formed a team for competitive reasons are far less likely to share values with an older group of women in the same league with very different social motives for playing and forming a team in the first place.
- Social life is an ever changing struggle involving persuasion, **coercion**, compromise and negotiation.
- The passage of time leads to a shift of power in societies and between groups.

According to this theory, sport can be used to bring about change in society.

- **Political involvement in sport** – critical theory states sport should be used to challenge those seeking to exploit or oppress others, and to challenge those in power with a consistent voice. Politicians can use sport to implement social policy (e.g. by promoting participation), can pass laws affecting sports (such as anti-fox-hunting legislation) and even use it as a means of diplomacy to influence international relations.
- **Use of sport as a means to change society** – sport can help heal dysfunctional parts of society, promote health, encourage healthy competition and bring isolated communities together. The range and diversity of sports participation can be a reflection of a society that shares values and promotes social life.
- **Educational messages through sport and exercise** – using sport in education is not a new idea: motor skills development (**physical literacy**) has for a long time been seen to have a clear relationship with **psychosocial** development. Sport can also promote qualities such as honesty, teamwork, fair play and respect for rules and others, e.g. through the work of Kick It Out to tackle racism in football.
- **Critical feminist theories** – **feminist theory** says society is male orientated and sports are mostly based on the values and experiences of men, with sport and sexuality exploited by the media in how they portray masculinity and femininity. Feminists seek to challenge this by directly confronting sports that consistently favour male dominance and try to expose oppressive forms of sexism and homophobia.

Key terms

Coercion – making someone do something through the use of threats or force.

Physical literacy – when a child becomes competent at basic movement skills and other sports skills which allow them to assess sporting situations and make good quality decisions confidently and under control.

Psychosocial – the combination of psychological and social behaviour.

Feminist theory – aims to understand and remove inequality between men and women.

Research

In June 2014 *The Guardian* reported that approximately 40 per cent of UK schools offered cheerleading, but is it a sport or just another example of how a male-dominated sports culture exploits women and girls for its own purposes?

Research how academics view cheerleading and its role in our sporting society. When you have done this you may want to hold a class discussion.

Figurational theory

This theory is defined by those who believe social life is made up of patterns of interdependencies among different individuals and groups. This means that the individuals and groups all depend on one another. Within this, sport reflects both acceptable and non-acceptable behaviour in society.

A rugby scrum has several layers of interdependency, with each row relying on the next

The key ideas of figurational theory are outlined below.

- Aggression and violence in modern sport have reduced and this reflects a reduction of aggression and violence in society as a whole - sports are exciting activities that can relieve boredom and control violence, so sport has a positive use when applied as a crime reduction tool.
- Sport can have a **cathartic** effect on people - many theorists have recognised the positive effects sport or exercise has on individuals. Is it possible sport could cure a range of social ills? Sport can help reduce stress and even be a way of venting anger and hostility in a controlled environment. Releasing stress in this way can help people feel liberated and even refreshed without producing negative social effects.
- Sport has had significant involvement in legal matters - laws have been passed that help protect the rights of participants and spectators from harm (for example, the condition of facilities and stadiums).
- There has been a large growth in sport **spectatorship** since the early 1970s, and a large increase in the money available in sport. This has led to more money in sport, which has had a marked impact both on how sports are conducted and the lives of the athletes.
- Sport can also lead to violence in the real world, such as football hooliganism - examples go back almost as long as the game has existed, particularly between local rival fans, right through to the darkest days of the 1980s and continuing to this day. Sociologists suggest much of this violence is pre-planned and that local or international rivalry plays a large part in people excusing their own violence. Results and sporting action itself often have roles in prompting violence, for example, events such as the award of a red card or penalty.

Key terms

Catharsis - releasing emotions, generally with the purpose of relieving the stress that can build up if these emotions are kept bottled up and not expressed by an individual.

Spectatorship - a spectator is someone who will engage in a sporting activity by observing regularly. A spectator sport is one for which there are more spectators than actually engage with the sport, such as football.

Case study

Spectatorism

Norbert Elias, a German sociologist, suggested that humans are driven to satisfy a need to be involved in re-enactments of our hunter-gatherer past, and that sport is often seen as a good way of doing this. Think about fans at a large sporting event: shouting, singing, swearing, often drinking alcohol, and sometimes shouting abuse at officials.

The media stoke the passion of the crowd at sports events and glamorise the superfan, for example, England cricket's Barmy Army. 'Fan' comes from the word fanatic, meaning someone whose enthusiasm borders on obsession. So what is a 'spectator'?

Check your knowledge

Research home advantage in a sport of your choice. Consider the motivations of spectators and the revenue they generate in the form of admission money. When you have completed your research answer the following questions, feeding your answers into a group discussion.

1. Are all spectators beer-drinking couch potatoes?
2. Should they take part in something rather than live their sporting lives through others?
3. Is being a spectator like an addiction?
4. Do the ruling classes and those in power promote 'spectatorism' because it helps control the behaviour of the masses - in other words is someone watching a football match not likely to injure themselves or be involved in crime, and to be a more reliable worker?

What are the main sociological theories that apply to sport?

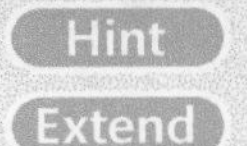

Hint: Name the four main theories and some of their features.

Extend: For one of the theories produce a three sentence summary describing it to someone who knows nothing about the theory, explaining what it is and how it applies to sport.

Assessment practice 12.1

A.P1 A.M1 A.D1

You have been asked to advise a local youth club about what kind of activities they should offer. The club members range in age from 12 to 17 years. The youth club has good resources but the organisers have not really listened to what the young people want: the activities have become stale and boring and the numbers attending have decreased recently.

1 Create a short presentation (no more than five slides) outlining the sports, activities, resources and events that you think could make the club a success again.

2 Look at the four main sociological theories and see how your suggestions support or challenge each theory. Add further slides to your presentation, illustrating how your version of the youth club matches the social theory. For example:
   - you could refer to conflict theory and give examples of how sport has promoted local pride but may have also have weakened it
   - you could refer to political involvement in sport and the critical theory view which implies that sport can be used to bring about change like reducing crime in your area
   - you could apply functionalist theory and explain how sporting events can encourage individuals to get together to meet common values and goals, promoting integration across different groups.

Whichever theory you feel fits best, use examples to explain why you feel this. Then think about why this theory is the most appropriate and justify your thinking with a detailed explanation.

Plan
- What am I learning? Why is this important?
- Are there any areas I think I may struggle with?

Do
- Have I considered the age of the youth club members when planning activities and events?
- Have I considered each of the four main sociological theories?

Review
- Is my outline clear? Will it be useful to the youth club?
- Can I explain my thought processes?

B Investigate the historical and cultural changes, and the social and ethical issues that have impacted on sport and exercise development in the UK

Historical and cultural changes on sport

Before 1750 most people in England and Wales lived in the countryside and life for the majority was brutal, with a lack of law and order. Most people lived and died in the same way their ancestors had since the Norman invasion (1066). Life expectancy was short and living conditions were poor, with little time for sport and leisure activities.

Different classes took part in different activities, such as mob football for peasants and real tennis for the gentry. Other sports, such as archery, were encouraged as they were seen as good preparation for war.

In most communities the drinking house or pub was central to village life and the focus for leisure activities. It would host events like bear and badger baiting, dog fighting and prize fighting. Landlords often provided prizes for these events or the basic equipment for playing other games like billiards, quoits, bowls and skittles.

For centuries the church was an important feature in most people's lives and religious festivals and feast days offered the working classes a day of rest and leisure that could involve gambling and drinking.

'Mob football' is still sometimes played in some parts of the UK on special occasions such as Shrovetide

The effects of urbanisation and industrialisation

The introduction of large machinery on farms led to less demand for workers. At the same time the growth in factories meant a huge expansion in the size of towns and cities, creating new jobs for these workers. Conditions were still tough. The demand for housing in towns meant space was limited, with some families all living in just one room. There were no building restrictions, so very little recreation space was left.

Old village sports were quickly replaced with new activities, although longer factory working hours and lack of available space restricted the amount, and types, of sport played. However, over time public parks and open spaces were commissioned. At first these were mostly built to separate working-class slums from the more respectable parts of the town, but they were gradually opened for all. Football remained a popular working-class game. Factory owners realised money could be made from workers watching football at in-town stadiums.

Research

Many of the largest football teams in the UK have moved away from their original industrial-age football stadiums. Look at the reasons why they have done so. Try to look at the social changes: are the fans all working-class males as they would have been 150 years ago? What impact has been felt in the area of the old stadium and what are the reasons for the move? Discuss your findings with the rest of your class.

Rational recreation and public school games

Certain schools were called public schools because they were not privately owned (owned by an individual) but were controlled by a group of **trustees** who ran them. The riotous games and activities popular at these schools at the beginning of the nineteenth century were vastly different from those they would play a century later.

Boy culture, bullying and brutality (c. 1790–1824)

At the end of the eighteenth century, English society showed a stark contrast between the high culture of **Regency period** fashion and the low culture of blood sports (such as bear baiting, hare coursing and bare-fist fighting). Both contrasts were mirrored in public schools.

Discipline was strict, but schoolmasters had little interest in their students outside the classroom. All recreational activities were organised by the boys themselves. 'Boy culture' was chaotic, reflecting a world of revolution (both in America and France) and war (the Napoleonic Wars between Britain and France lasted almost 20 years).

Games could range from violent football games (with different rules followed by each school) to hoops and marbles. Sports such as cricket (already **codified** by the gentry) were also adopted and played. But the focus of much 'boy culture' was violence and chaos.

Key terms

Trustees – people responsible for managing and promoting an organisation or asset, such as a school.

Regency period – a time of high fashion during the late-eighteenth and early-nineteenth centuries, associated with the Prince Regent (the son of George III who ruled during his father's illness).

Codify – collect together and organise rules and procedures.

Thomas Arnold, religion and social control (1828–1842)

This was a time of widespread social change. Laws were changing (for example, cruelty to animals was banned), and transport and communications were dramatically improving (for example, the growth of railways). Similarly, in public schools there was a gradual move away from 'boy culture' to regulated games.

Dr Thomas Arnold (1795–1842) is regarded as one of the key reformers of the English public school system. He was Headmaster of Rugby School from 1828 until his death in 1842. He was shocked at what he saw as the immorality and sinfulness of the boys and determined to reform them, their attitudes and their school lives.

▸ Public school reformer Thomas Arnold

Arnold used sports as a vehicle for establishing **social control**. Arnold believed the aggression and violence of 'boy culture' could be redirected into sports, as controlled aggression and 'healthy' competition. Arnold's primary aim was to deliver a Christian message - known as **muscular Christianity** - but as a result the status, regularity and organisation of sports was changed hugely.

Key terms

Muscular Christianity - the belief in having a strong soul within a strong body. Arnold believe sport could be played to win but always for 'the glory of God' - not for its own sake or the glory of the players.

Cult - a craze or obsession.

Athleticism - the combination of physical endeavour, or trying hard, with moral integrity - a mix of honour, truthfulness and sportsmanship.

Elementary schools - the first state funded schools which ran from 1870 to 1944, many becoming primary schools after further education reform. They catered for 5–14 year olds.

Arnold introduced the house system which became the focus of boys' personal, social and sporting existence. Games of inter-house cricket and football kept boys out of trouble and the playing field became a central feature of public school life.

The characteristics of public schools shaped the development of team games. Boarding schools meant boys had a great deal of time available for games. The house system gave this sporting time structure. As the schools charged fees, money could be invested in sport facilities. Sport became a way in which schools could compete against each other and trustees took pride in the performance of the boys in sports. These changes in schools reflected changes in society at large.

The cult of athleticism (1842–1914)

The conventional image of late-nineteenth-century English public schools is one of mellow stone buildings and magnificent playing fields, with players wearing house colours and caps. These were all symbols of the **cult** of **athleticism**: the craze for team games and a lack of interest in academic work. Many schools made sports compulsory. With its Empire, Great Britain was the most powerful nation in the world, and this filled its population with confidence and pride. Sporting success became a symbol of the 'manliness' that 'made Britain great'. Sports and athletics became the pride of schoolmasters.

Research

There was a delay in the development of opportunities for upper- and middle-class girls. This was linked to the view of women at the time as having less status in society, as well as being weaker. However, there were some prominent female educationalists who worked hard to change this.

In pairs, select one of the following women and research their career and impact. Prepare a short report for the rest of the group.

- Frances Mary Buss
- Dorothea Beale
- Madame Bergman Österberg

The development of physical education (PE)

Before 1870, education for those not able to afford public schools was the responsibility of the local parish and was very inconsistent. Many children had little or no schooling. While some factory owners invested in education (wanting to profit from a better-educated workforce), these opportunities were few and far between.

The Forster Education Act (1870) created a countrywide system of education, with more schools built. As far as sport was concerned, from 1902 **elementary schools** offered military drill as a response to a lack of fitness of soldiers in the army.

In 1944 the Education Act made secondary schools available for all, with the school leaving age raised to 15. For the first time PE teachers were considered equal to other teachers and specialist training centres opened around the country. In 1988 a new National Curriculum made PE compulsory until the age of 16 and placed a specific focus on physical activity and a healthy lifestyle.

In 2015, the National Curriculum changed again. Attainment measured against levels was removed and new core aims were introduced relating to development of physical competence in a wide range of activities.

Recreation, mass participation and Sport for All

Outside schools and education, the idea of sport as a recreational activity, and an awareness of maintaining a healthy lifestyle, have grown in the UK, The rise is due in part to labour saving appliances such as washing machines, better and cheaper transportation, and more free leisure time. In addition television and the internet have allowed greater access to sports not previously considered or even created and promoted sport and exercise examples of their own. For example, parkour, ultimate Frisbee, slamball and Quidditch have emerged as popular and competitive sports as a result of the influence of the internet.

The idea of **mass participation** is to encourage as many people as possible to take up healthy lifestyles by breaking down traditional barriers which prevent participation in sport. The benefits of sports participation are that it:

- helps to build social networks
- improves educational achievement
- relieves stress and promotes self-esteem, positive behaviour and self-confidence.

The Sports Council of Great Britain (founded in 1972 and now replaced by UK Sport) had the motto 'Sport for All' and aimed to emphasise the value of sport and help make sport accessible to all. This led to a large investment in sporting facilities. Recently, focus has shifted away from the whole population to specific parts of the population such as the over 50s, and women and girls (for example, the *This Girl Can* initiative).

PAUSE POINT How has sport influenced society in the UK?

Hint Produce a timeline starting before industrialisation, up to the present day. Add key dates and changes to society, paying particular attention to the role of public schools in the development of sport in the UK.

Extend Focus on a particular sport that demonstrates how sport reflects society.

Social and ethical issues in the UK

A number of social and ethical issues continue to affect the growth and development of sport in the UK.

Crime

Youth crime and anti-social behaviour are very difficult issues that continue to be controversial. They can be major issues in deprived areas, where the average income is low. The cost of crime is high: a youth club may cost £30,000 a year to run but the average cost (without taking into account prosecution and police action) of just **one** young offender is almost £50,000. Sport can be used:

- as an attractive 'hook' to encourage people to take part in other programmes
- as an engaging alternative to crime
- for behaviour modification, channelling the feelings that lead to crime into positive activities - outdoor and adventurous activities are particularly valuable (e.g. canoeing and climbing) as they have an element of risk which is also one of the attractions of anti-social behaviour
- to promote social inclusion - barriers such as faith or belief systems that exclude others are countered with the use of sport, where people work as part of a team. It can also help build pride in the community
- to help improve self-esteem.

Discrimination

Racism

Racism involves treating people unfairly, or holding biased or unfair views about them, because of their nationality or ethnicity. In sport this can mean people judging others involved in sport based on their racial background.

Unfortunately, incidents of racism in sport are still common, for example, racist comments at football matches directed at non-white or non-UK players. The Professional Footballers' Association has been running a strong campaign for several years called 'Let's Kick Racism Out of Football' (www.kickitout.org) and in 2000 a Racial Equality Charter for Sport was launched (www.sportingequals.org.uk).

Research

American sociologists identified 'stacking' in which non-white athletes occupy only certain sporting positions. The same may be true in British sport. In a recent study, black cricket players were often identified as fast bowlers and hard-hitting batsmen, but not captains or wicket keepers. Historically, black rugby players were rarely forwards, but more likely to be on the wing or a halfback. Why is this? Research this issue and suggest how this could be improved.

Sexism

Gender differences in sport have a long history - sport is traditionally male-dominated (some argue it still is) and women have had to fight to compete in many sports. Participation rates in sport among women remain lower than for men. Men are often still seen as authority figures, and despite an increase in female sports programmes there has been a decline in the number of female sports coaches.

Sexism is still prevalent today - in 2015 the FA was criticised for referring to its successful England women's football team coming back from a World Cup to return to being 'mothers, partners and daughters'. This outdated view of women being defined by their relationship with men continues to be casually used in society.

Minorities can face high levels of stigma from their own communities, as well as the wider population. This is particularly so for the lesbian, gay, bisexual and transgender (LGBT) community, where engagement with sport is not widespread.

Disability

In the UK there are over 10 million disabled people. Historically, access to disabled sport was based on luck and was restricted to very few areas. Now the UK is a world leader in providing disabled sporting opportunities, funding and hosting a variety of national and international events and leading in technology, innovation and research in this field. The UK is perhaps as proud of its Paralympic athletes as their Olympic counterparts and while there is still a vast disparity in finance, sponsorship and media coverage, the gap has shortened significantly.

In recent years the positive portrayal of high profile disability events such as the equal billing of the London Olympic and Paralympic Games, the Invictus Games and a positive portrayal in the popular media has helped destigmatise both familiar and unfamiliar events.

Case study

This Girl Can

This Girl Can is a nationwide campaign, developed by Sport England, which aims to get women involved in sport, regardless of their shape, size and ability. Research reveals a huge difference in the number of men and women playing sport. Millions of women report being afraid to exercise because of fear of being judged. The campaign aims to use images that are the opposite of the idealised and stylised images of female athletes in the media. The campaign clearly captured a mood: 13 million people viewed the flagship *This Girl Can* film online.

The campaign encourages women to beat barriers. Slogans like 'Sweating like a pig, feeling like a fox' and 'I kick balls, deal with it' have been used to prompt a change in attitudes and help boost women's confidence. They have also been criticised by some women for still placing some focus on physical appearance.

Check your knowledge

Watch the *This Girl Can* video online. How does it make you feel? Start a discussion about female participation in sport. Discuss the following statements:

- You cannot make people who do not want to play get out of their chairs.
- Sports should be for everyone.
- More money should be spent on participation at amateur level and less on elite sports like the Olympics.

Case study

English Federation of Disability Sport

Disability Sport England (now the English Federation of Disability Sport) was founded in 1961 by the neuro-surgeon Sir Ludwig Guttmann, who worked at Stoke Mandeville Hospital. The Stoke Mandeville Stadium is built to competition standard and has been the venue for thousands of disabled athletes at world, European and national championships.

The stadium creates opportunities and makes sport accessible to everyone, enables and encourages disabled people to take part in sport for fun and enjoyment, and aims to educate others about the sporting abilities of disabled people.

Check your knowledge

1. What are the facilities and organisations like for disabled people in your area?
2. Should disabled children be segregated or included in mainstream schools? Research the advantages and disadvantages of either before reaching your conclusion.
3. Provide one example of how you could make a sport or exercise session inclusive. Your tutor may be able to provide you with a list of activities to adapt.

Promoting health

The link between health and physical fitness has been long established. There is growing concern in the UK about the fitness of the population, in particular that of children. Obesity for children has reached epidemic levels as they exercise less and spend more time at home on electronic devices and gaming. Sport and exercise are increasingly being promoted as helping to control this situation. As well as the physical benefits, physical activity can also help to reduce feelings of depression and anxiety. All of this has a beneficial impact by reducing the amount of money that has to be spent by the National Health Service.

Link

More information on the benefits of physical activity can be found in *Unit 6: Coaching for Performance and Fitness.*

Employment

Sport is now considered one of the top 15 mainstream activities in the UK economy, above legal services, accounting, telecommunications, advertising and publishing. According to Sport England, sport accounts for 2.3 per cent of the UK workforce. There are a number of different job roles available in the sporting industry in areas like sports science, fitness training and sports therapy, education and the leisure industry.

Participation initiatives

As well as supporting elite athletes and government bodies, National Lottery funding in the UK has provided millions of pounds to fund local programmes that support participation. These initiatives can contribute a great deal to the local community, putting in place programmes to encourage participation and community engagement in the local area.

- **Promoting community cohesion** – the idea of community cohesion was first developed following anti-social behaviour and rioting in the North of England in 2001. Sport is used to help tackle the issues that led to these disturbances, including social exclusion, poor schooling, reduced education opportunities and barriers to cohesion such as different faith or cultural beliefs. The challenge is to provide an environment for people to form new social groups that bring the community together.
- **Providing positive role models** – role models can influence the attitudes and behaviour of young people. Sporting Champions is a Sport England initiative bringing world class athletes and young people together to increase and sustain participation, raise aspirations and discover new opportunities. They use current and retired athletes and are available to support a range of sports programmes at no cost.
- **Community outreach programmes** – these are generally offered by large organisations such as local authorities or universities. For example, Durham University offers a programme including 47 local schools, 100 volunteers and approximately 2000 children. The children have access to the university's sports facilities for a range of sporting activities. This programme has been extended to offer activities for the homeless, substance misuse clients, vulnerable women and young offenders. The aim is to offer alternatives and new opportunities for the people the programmes are trying to help.

- **Local leagues/competitions** – these are the backbone of sport in the UK. Their membership far outweighs the elite level and provides a base or platform for people to try competitive sport and either go on to be an elite athlete or to simply enjoy local sporting competition.

Case study

Tower Hamlets Olympic Summer of Sport

Tower Hamlets in the East End of London has a very ethnically diverse population with a lot of segregation. With the awarding of the 2012 Olympic Games and the nearby Olympic Park, the borough was one of the first and most successful organisations to deliver a community cohesion programme with sport at the core.

A programme of sport sessions inspired by the 2012 Olympic bid was designed to take advantage of the local enthusiasm for the Olympics. It targeted children and families from deprived areas. Sessions were themed around the Olympic and Paralympic sports, encouraging participation by previously under-represented children and young people. The programme also included a number of targeted sports events such as an Asian Sports Festival featuring traditional sports such as Kabbadi, a Disabled Sports Festival, and an Estate-based Sports Programme aimed at reducing anti-social behaviour among young people.

The borough has expanded the programme to offer:

- school holiday sessions for young people including dry rowing, tennis and hockey
- links to cultural activities particularly for young people, specifically dance and movement sessions
- schemes and workshops to promote food education initiatives and health and fitness
- triathlon challenges for all the family and all abilities, and informal social clubs for all ages
- outdoor games to engage the whole family in inter-generational fun and physical activity.

Check your knowledge

1. Think back to learning aim A. Which of the sociological theories do you think most applies here and why?
2. How could this kind of programme be adapted to work in your area? Design a brief that shows which activities could be included and detail who should be involved.

Ethical issues

A number of ethical issues in the UK that are reflected in sport are examined in Table 12.1.

Table 12.1: Ethical issues in sport

Ethical issue	Description
Performer violence	Violence by sports performers is both shocking and anti-social. It also goes against sports codes and takes away from the value of the sport. It may cause injury and also influence the behaviour of children. Performer violence commonly happens as a result of actions in the game, such as decisions, results, crowd provocation or as a response to local rivalries. It can be addressed by rule changes (including tougher punishments), better training for officials for resolving conflicts, and better education for participants, including use of sports psychologists.
Spectator behaviour	Many of the causes of spectator violence are similar to performer violence, and some violence such as football hooliganism is even organised in advance. It is also linked to alcohol or drug consumption. Tighter control of these substances can help to control it. Harsh deterrents (including stadium bans), better stadium facilities, the use of technology to identify offenders and an effort to change the focus of sporting events into a family experience, have had an impact in reducing this, particularly in football.

▶ **Table 12.1:** Ethical issues in sport – *continued*

Ethical issue	Description
Performance-enhancing drugs	Many athletes, not just at elite level, use drugs to enhance their performance and build up strength or body mass. Drug use is unethical, breaks the rules, can have a serious health impact and increases the costs of policing the sport.
Match-fixing	This is where the result of a match is agreed in advance by some or all of the participants. It is often connected to betting, where players and gamblers profit from 'fixing' a result. Games that are deliberately lost are sometimes called 'thrown' games. Greed like this can have a serious impact on respect for the sport.
Spot-fixing	This is fixing a part of a match or game that does not affect the final result of the contest but is usually a smaller part. Cricket has suffered from this, with some bowlers paid large amounts of money to bowl wide or no balls. This is so unlikely bets can be made to defraud bookmakers who place longer than usual odds. This activity is illegal and several high profile cases have resulted in lifetime bans from sports and even imprisonment.
Dispute resolution	Two competitors, clubs or even sports companies can disagree on a sporting matter, such as the transfer of a player, and it is not possible to reach a solution. In these cases the sport's national governing body may step in to help, using the judicial (court) system or an organisation that will settle the dispute. In the UK the Sport Resolutions Panel offers advice, mediation and tribunal services.

Excellence and elitism

Public schools continue to have a large influence on sport, but this has not always been seen as positive. Many successful athletes come from private education. This suggests that there are a lot of talented people outside the private school system who are failing to get the opportunities they need for success, such as access to excellent coaching and training. They are effectively missing out because of where they are born.

Football is the most representative sport with 94 per cent of Premier League players and 97 per cent of elite female football players from state schools. However, 55 per cent of elite rugby players were privately educated. A recent study by school inspectorate Ofsted (based on UK athletes at the 2012 Olympics) found:

- 66 per cent of the athletes attended state schools, 27 per cent attended independent schools, 1 per cent attended both a state and independent school, and 6 per cent attended schools overseas
- all of the Olympians from badminton, taekwondo, boxing, judo and modern pentathlon were state educated, although there were comparatively low numbers of athletes in these sports
- the sports with a higher percentage of independently educated athletes than state educated ones were rowing, equestrianism and tennis. Triathlon and fencing had an equal proportion of athletes coming from state and independent schools.

PAUSE POINT What factors might prevent people from taking part in sport?

Hint Can you identify the groups who have the greatest need of support? For each group, mind map the main barriers to their participation.

Extend Write a brief report on the ethical issues in cricket and the problems of introducing cricket to all parts of the UK. Make suggestions about how they might be overcome.

Assessment practice 12.2

B.P2 B.P3 B.M2 B.M3 B.D2

Produce a detailed report that explores the history, value and issues of a major team sport of your choice in modern society, reflecting both local and national developments. The report should have three sections.

1. Outline the national history of the sport and also how it developed in your local area. For example, which is the oldest club, who supported them, who founded the team and why, and who and how many people watched them? Your work should be clearly and accurately researched, including key points of interest. Explain how the sport has changed over time and consider the impact of these changes, considering the sport's historical and cultural development and how it reflected society in general at the time. For instance, is there any evidence that the sport has been used to address cultural or ethical issues?
2. Look at the ethical issues the sport has come to terms with and the initiatives the sport offers on a national basis. Is there any evidence that the sport has tackled key issues locally, such as crime, unemployment or racism?
3. Critically review the provision and worth of a large local club and reflect on how improvements could be made. Consider the value of the sport locally. What does the local team do in the community? Who does it help? Are there school or similar outreach projects?

Plan

- What sport will I focus on?
- Where will I find out more about the history and development of my chosen sport?

Do

- Am I confident that my information is reliable and up-to-date?
- Have I found local examples to support the information in my report?

Review

- Have I covered all the key information?
- Could I apply the information in my report to other areas of my work?

C Investigate the relationship between commercialisation, the media and sport and exercise

The use of media to promote sport

There are several different forms of media and each raises issues for sport, some positive, others negative. Communication between people and organisations has received a massive boost with the growth in use of the internet and smartphones. However, this new technology has brought many issues with it as it draws young people away from physical activity.

The main types of traditional media are:

- **Television** – this has probably had the largest impact on sport so far, including **commercialisation**, good and bad presenting, reporting and journalism. Digital and satellite television (e.g. BT Sport and Sky Sports) provide sports coverage 24 hours a day from around the globe. Many sports events have changed start times and other aspects to suit television audiences. The money in televised sport is increasing. In the late 1980s a single season of English football cost £3 million to televise. In August 2016 the cost had risen to £5.1 billion. Terrestrial 'free to view' TV, such as the BBC and ITV, now often finds itself unable to afford to show sporting events.

Discussion

Pay-to-view TV such as Sky remains controversial, many suggesting that sports such as cricket and Formula 1 have suffered because they are now rarely seen on terrestrial 'free to view' TV by casual viewers, reducing public awareness. Discuss whether the benefits of money gained from commercial TV deals are sufficient to outweigh the reduction of public exposure.

Key term

Commercialisation – managed or exploited in order to make a profit.

- **National press** – this has a strong influence on public perceptions of sport, with circulations of millions of people. Many national newspapers devote a large portion of their pages to sport, knowing that it is a way to persuade readers to buy their papers. However, negative stories and comments about sporting individuals can damage their careers.

- **Local press** – these are very good at reporting the progress of local teams. Reports and scores can be featured for everything from under-11s football and cricket, to the achievements of individuals in cross-country or swimming. These stories and photos are essential to help sell local newspapers.
- **Sport-related magazines** – these cover health, fitness, exercise, diet and the body. They can provide good guidance and programmes to follow. However, many images of slim, fit people put pressure on others to attain an ideal, and this can lead to dietary and emotional problems.

The internet and social media

The internet has had a huge influence, offering real-time viewing of sport and global coverage, making events more accessible to more people. High-speed fibre optic broadband gives faster access to more information than ever before, and lets people catch up with news and TV coverage. The growing use of smartphones and the growth of free Wi-Fi have also helped this.

Social media gives people the chance to communicate over great distances with many others. This can spread information and gossip about sports stars. On fan sites, people keen to follow a sport or club can sign up and receive news of their favourite team or player. This can give teams and individuals a global presence, for example, the Tottenham Hotspur Singapore fan site. The sites carry advertisements which provide revenue.

Research

The range and function of the social media market is huge. Most marketing and promotional people have recognised this and are using social media apps such as Facebook, Twitter, Instagram, Snapchat and WhatsApp to get their message across.

In small groups or pairs, choose two sports. Research the potential impact that each of these apps has had on your two sports and list their advantages and disadvantages.

Role of the media

The media can inform and educate people, as well as offer entertainment. It can promote or advertise different sports and events, either by simply covering the events or by becoming an 'official partner', as well as offering a space for sporting organisations to place paid-for advertisements. The media can also provide public service announcements around issues such as health and fitness.

Symbiotic relationship between sport and the media

Sport and the media are said to enjoy a **symbiotic** relationship. Symbiosis is a close and often long-term interaction between two different organisms, in this case the media and sport. Essentially, both thrive and grow on the other: the more sport there is, the more coverage in the media there is, and the more demand the media makes for more sport.

Table 12.2: Advantages and disadvantages of the media–sport relationship

Advantages for sport	Disadvantages for sport	Advantages for the media	Disadvantages for the media
Spectators pay more to see the performers and build their knowledge	Match attendance figures might fall	Subscription fees/ increased sales mean larger profit	Some sports fans may not pay for access to their sport
Easier to attract sponsorship	Sports stars lose privacy	Sports are attractive brands and add to company credibility	Online streaming means that many people do not pay to watch
Viewer gets close up action and information can be instant	Changes to event timings, rules and playing season	Can draw in large amounts of money from advertisers	Cost in subscriptions is very high in a competitive market
Improves participation rate and popularity of the sport	The media decide what matters, to some extent	Can sell other products and services, e.g. pay to view	Subscribers can be fickle

In an ideal world all media should be **unbiased** and maintain the highest standards of journalism. But if the media own the product, how objective can they be? Is it really possible that events remain unedited? Have you ever wondered if the media – whether in print, online or on TV – are making more out of a story just to keep you interested in watching or reading? When you hear a quote starting with 'sources close to the star say...', is there actually a source?

Key term

Bias – inclination or prejudice for or against one person or group, especially in a way considered to be unfair.

Discussion

Gather together a range of media, e.g. newspapers and magazines, access to websites and apps and social media. Choose a sports story that is new and trending.

In groups, analyse the story. Who is the intended audience? Is it presented as a matter of fact (reported) story or as a narrative (story-telling)? Is it sensationalist? Discuss each of these styles and why the media chooses them.

When you are reading or watching any coverage, it is important to understand that the media has its own interest in the events it is reporting. The media is a powerful force for shaping people's opinions and perceptions on almost every issue.

PAUSE POINT What influence does the media have on sport?

Hint List the difference types of media reporting on sport. What are the bias issues with each medium?

Extend Imagine you are the owner of a large UK sports team and you want to establish a new 'feel' to the organisation. Which media will you use and how will you spread the message to supports and fans?

The impact of media attention

Media attention can have a range of different impacts on sports, athletes and spectators. Some of the features of media attention, and the impacts they can have, are shown in Table 12.3.

Table 12.3: Media impact on sport

Feature	Potential impact	Example
The popularity of a sport	If presented as an exciting and vibrant alternative to more widely available sports, it can be very successful.	**Cycling** – since the success and media focus of the 2012 Olympics it became in 2014 the third most popular sport in England.
The perceived value of a sport	If the quality of the presentation is of a high standard and there is an emphasis on its value, then results can be noticeable.	**Zumba** – now the UK's largest fitness-class brand after widespread media exposure. The business has grown 800% since 2008 and is now worth almost £318 million.
The amount of coverage of a sport	Less coverage can often have a very poor effect on the popularity of the sport.	**Basketball** – in spite of both GB teams coming very close in key games at the 2012 Olympics, the event was not largely featured in the media. One of the results has been a cut in funding for GB basketball, both for men and women.
The funding available to a sport or activity	Money is without doubt key to continued success, as it controls every aspect of provision.	**School sports** – when school sport money was cut in 2010 it was widely reported in the media. While school sport remains underfunded, awareness of the issue has forced changes to policy that should see reinvestment in the future.
Public education around a sport or activity	Knowledge of a sport as introduced by the media can raise awareness in the public eye.	**Parkour** – this artistic form of urban gymnastics is portrayed as a positive sport for young people and has helped raise awareness and increase participant numbers.
Participation figures	The popularity of most sports is seasonally affected by growth in participation rates, especially when TV coverage is saturated.	**Tennis** – during and immediately after Wimbledon fortnight local tennis court usage is higher than ever, sometimes by as much as a 600% increase.

▶ **Table 12.3:** Media impact on sport - *continued*

Feature	Potential impact	Example
Encouraging trends in sports or activities	Media coverage can have a huge impact on trends in certain sports.	**All sports** - professionals receive social media training as a result of some ill-advised comments made on social media and the reaction these comments provoke.
Spectator perceptions/expectations	This is most clear in sports not previously exposed to the media (and in particular exposed to TV).	**Rugby union** - players used to socialise with fans and played part-time. TV coverage and professionalisation changed this and players now follow a less accessible but more professional approach.
Rule changes	Occasionally the media dictates that sport is made more viewer friendly.	**Squash** - when first televised the ball was too quick for the viewer to pick up. As a result, televised games were played with bigger balls coated with reflective material. Players were unhappy as it changed the nature of the contest.
The timing of events	Season ticket holders who are unavailable except for traditional start times either accept changes or simply give up their season ticket.	**Football** - to suit television coverage, kick off times are often moved to Sundays, Mondays or even early Saturdays instead of the traditional Saturday kick off at 3 p.m.
Sports kits or uniforms	Kit can be used to further the career of the team or individual.	**Golf** - a number of top professionals wear distinctive colours and designs to raise awareness of their sponsor.
Facilities	Raising awareness of the need for specialist facilities can help generate funding.	**Curling** - the only curling facility in southern England is in a converted barn in Kent. The money came largely with the support of local media.
Number/location of organised events	Internet and social media groups have spread the word for a number of different sports events.	**Athletics** - the parkrun organisation offers hundreds of coordinated runs staffed by volunteers every Saturday morning and the number is growing, largely through word of mouth.
Niche sports	The media can turn a low interest sport into a relatively large one.	**Ultimate Fighting Championship® (UFC)** - watched by only those with a particular passion for the sport, this niche sport would probably disappear without the media.

Performers can have a tough time at the top end of a sport influenced by the media.

- They are often subjected to analysis and criticism of every aspect of their performance, with slow-motion replays and expert pundits subjecting them to increased scrutiny.
- Their private lives can become wide open to the public as they become a 'media celebrity' just as much as a sporting performer.
- The media's interest has led to a growth in the number of competitive events available for them to cover, which also affects performers. For example, tennis is a sport in which it is very difficult to identify an off-season: it is possible to enter a tournament every week of the year so it is important for the player to ensure they rest properly in spite of commercial and media pressure to compete.

Spectators have an easier time but must also consider balancing the time to watch sport and how much it costs.

- For the dedicated fan, the prospect of paying for a satellite TV subscription is often an extra cost. If attending in person, they have to pay not just for tickets but also all the extras such as travel, and fixture changes often mean an overnight stay is required or previously bought travel tickets become unusable.
- For performers, extra events mean more pressure to perform. However, spectators often welcome this as it gives them more opportunities to watch their favourite sports and performers.
- The increased cost means that spectators are beginning to measure the quality of the sports performance in terms of value for money, although the money put into sport by the media is also often credited with raising the quality of performances (e.g. by allowing the Premier League to import top quality players from abroad).

For minority groups, the media can play a positive role. Increased exposure of certain sports, such as women's football, has helped to increase participation and promote social equality. Similarly, increased coverage of sports can lead to the promotion of sportspeople as positive role models: media coverage of the 2012 Paralympics in London helped lead to the emergence of performers such as Ellie Simmonds and Jonnie Peacock as figures in the public eye, promoting their sports.

Sport as a commercialised product

Look at pictures or videos of sport today and then compare them to those of 30 years ago and you should be able to notice some major differences in how they are presented. Sport has become a product. Some of the likely side effects of commercialisation are explored below.

- Sports are now large scale, expensive **spectator events** that sometimes last longer than the sport itself, and events like the Olympics reach millions of people in a hungry global market.
- **Admission fees** have also increased for a range of sports in recent years. As there is more demand to attend live events - not just from fans but also tourists and corporate entertainment - many traditional fans complain of being 'priced out' of the market.
- **Concessions** at sports fixtures are the typical extras available to the captive audience once they are at the venue, such as food and drink. These are usually higher in price compared with facilities outside the venue and this is another source of frustration for spectators. At the Rugby World Cup in 2015 fans complained that prices of some food and drink products were 20 per cent higher inside the stadium than in a supermarket. In particular, the sponsor's beer was £1 higher in price in the stadium - and was the only beer being sold.
- Media giants like BT Sport pay huge amounts of money for exclusive **broadcast rights**, such as £897 million for the exclusive rights to show the UEFA club competitions. Companies are invited to bid for the rights to screen major sporting events, such as Formula 1 and the Cricket World Cup. Increasingly viewers want a range of options for watching events, including at times and on devices of their choice, and even to pay for 'bite-size' helpings (to watch only the matches they are interested in) rather than a long subscription.
- The success of sports **merchandising** is fairly recent. Branded shirts and scarves have been available for years but are now a much sought-after product. Think about the range of products and services you can now buy that tie you into a brand like a professional sports club. There is somewhere in the region of 940 officially licensed Manchester United products that range from egg cups to funeral services and from pens to wedding ceremonies.
- **Gambling** companies have invested heavily in sport, and people can bet on a huge range of events in sport - not just the final result but virtually any statistic or incident in a match. Some companies have tried to persuade customers to think of the 'rush' of a successful bet as being the same as the excitement of watching their team win.
- **Fair trade** is a trading partnership based on dialogue, transparency and respect that seeks greater equity in international trade. It contributes to sustainable development by offering better trading conditions to, and securing the rights of, marginalised producers and workers. It allows sports organisations to introduce a moral dimension to the production of commercial goods.

Case study

Bala Sport balls

Bala Sport sell footballs in the UK which are made in Pakistan, where 70 per cent of the world's footballs are made. The difference between Bala Sport and other manufacturers is that they are a cooperative (all of those working for the company have a stake in it) and they ensure that those making the balls get a fair wage and have good working conditions. The money generated as profit is spent on education, healthcare and community projects. It is expected that more companies like this will be established in the coming years as business faces increasing pressure to demonstrate its responsibility to employees.

Check your knowledge

1 What are the advantages of schemes like this for local people, and what effect do you think this will have on football?
2 Many say that fair trade is fine but it means that products and services cost more, so are the advantages worth it?

The performer as a product

Sport is a global industry that generates vast amounts of money. If sport is a business, then the performers can be seen as **commodities**. It is no surprise to hear high level professionals being discussed as having a value or a perceived value to other organisations.

As such in many sports, players are traded or transferred between clubs. In some sports, players have contracts where they can be traded without their consent. In other sports, the players themselves (with their agents) can play a strong role in pushing through a transfer, to earn higher wages elsewhere. Either way, the player is treated more as a commodity or asset than as an individual person.

Performers are now seen as such a critical factor in success that the transfer deadline days in the UK and draft days in the USA have become media events in their own right, attracting large viewing figures and achieving thousands of online hits as people attempt to stay up-to-date regarding the latest moves.

Key term

Commodity – a raw material or asset that can be bought or sold. In sport, the athletes are the 'raw materials' that make the sport happen, and therefore have a financial value to the clubs that 'own' them.

Advertising and endorsement

Players have for a very long time been used to advertise products as product manufacturers attempt to associate themselves with a sporting personality's popularity in order to increase sales. These days, most international sporting events allow either branding or for players to display sponsors – Wimbledon tennis fortnight is the only professional sporting event that does not allow advertising in this way, although kit manufacturers' logos can be shown. Table 12.4 shows some of the advantages and disadvantages of sports performers being able to arrange their own advertising or endorsement deals.

Discussion

Following fairly recent banning of tobacco sponsorship, Formula 1 is now under increasing pressure to drop alcohol manufacturers as sponsors. Objectors argue that allowing alcohol to sponsor motor sport contradicts global legislation on road safety. A recent report demonstrated that the sport's reported 500 million worldwide audience is exposed to the image of an alcohol brand every five seconds. Should alcohol advertising be banned in Formula 1?

▶ Professional sportspeople such as Roger Federer can profit from endorsement deals

▸ **Table 12.4:** Advantages and disadvantages of advertising/endorsements

Advantages	Disadvantages
Young and new stars gain money to train and compete, e.g. kit, travel, accommodation	Young athletes may have sponsorship withdrawn if performances do not improve
Athletes' careers are short and top athletes can make a lot of money through sponsorship	Athletes in less well-known sports may not get the same opportunity
Young people may receive a scholarship to a college or centre of excellence	Athletes may feel exploited by a sponsor
Healthy, positive brand image	Athletes may end up having no choice over equipment

Foreign investment in UK sport

Many sports in the UK have attracted overseas investment as companies and wealthy individuals recognise the prestige and money that can be made from sport. This has had a particularly big impact on football. Owners such as Roman Abramovich at Chelsea and Sheikh Mansour bin Zayed Al Nahyan at Manchester City have completely transformed both clubs from mid-table teams to title winners.

The value of buying UK football clubs can be shown by looking at Manchester United. Purchased for £790 million by the Glazers in 2005, the club is now valued at £2.23 billion. Foreign investors have collectively more than doubled the value of 24 English clubs from £3.765 billion to £5.788 billion. Foreign owners are not just purchasing major clubs: in 2016 the Jordanian Al-Qadi family purchased control of Bristol Rovers, who were in the bottom half of League Two at the time.

Globalisation of sport

Globalisation is the process by which the world is becoming increasingly interconnected as a result of massively increased trade and cultural exchanges between different countries. Globalisation has come about due to:

- transport improvements and greater ease in international travel, such as cheaper air travel
- greater trade between more countries
- better communication around the world, especially due to the growth of the internet.

A key focus of many companies is profit, leading to environmental and social effects. For example, sports clothing made in sweatshops where labour is cheap may not be fair or ethical but it is profitable.

Sports can also use globalisation to build up their global brand and to help market their events and products around the world- read the case study below for more information about how the Premier League does this. Bigger sporting clubs also often set up 'feeder' clubs around the world, both to help increase their profile and so that they can snap up any local talent. This is part of an increasing movement by both participants and spectators around the world.

Globalisation has also helped unify sports around the world as different countries find it easier to work together to set down their sport's rules. For example, in basketball there is a world congress every four years coinciding with the Olympiad and each country's delegation has an equal voice on issues such as how rules can be changed to improve the sport.

Case study

The Premier League as a global product

The largest and most profitable football business is the English Premier League.

- Its broadcasts reach over 160 countries and have a global audience base of over 570 million people.
- It is the first league that could potentially make more money from TV rights sold abroad than at home.

Asia is the most valuable market after the UK for TV rights. It provides about 45 per cent of the £750 million per year total earned by the Premier League for selling TV rights. Thailand pays $106 million a year, Singapore $100 million and Hong Kong and Malaysia around $66 million each.

Check your knowledge

1. How much does the Premier League currently pay to each club?
2. When a club is relegated from the Premier League, to cushion the financial blow they are paid what has become known as a 'parachute payment'. Find out why and how much is currently paid to each relegated club and for how long.

PAUSE POINT What is the global impact of sport and how does this affect the way it is presented?

Hint List the factors that have led to globalisation. Provide examples of each factor using specific sports.

Extend Select a sport that has benefited from globalisation and produce a factsheet that demonstrates how. Suggest what is likely to happen from a global perspective for that sport in the next ten years.

Environmental effects

Sport has a huge impact on the environment around the world. Attending and running major sports events leads to a huge consumption of resources such as fuel. Increased global transportation has contributed to a greater emission of greenhouse gases and to ozone layer depletion, while construction of new stadiums and facilities can have an impact on fragile ecosystems and lead to greater waste generation.

Balancing social issues and globalisation

Acknowledging that their high-profile position gives them the ability to inspire others, many professional sports clubs, particularly in football, involve themselves in community and social issue projects such as anti-crime, anti-racism and poverty-related programmes in other parts of the world. For example, the Premier League's Kicks programme aims to promote social inclusion in the most deprived areas of the country through participation in football.

▶ The Premier League's Kicks project aims to reduce crime

Many sport governing bodies also have strategies that are aimed at improving grass roots participation, particularly schemes that encourage participation by previously under-represented groups or those whose financial hardship might otherwise discourage participation. Schemes such as these are often sponsored in order to reduce their cost.

Sometimes high profile sports stars use their celebrity status to promote the cause of a particular charity or community. For example, in 2014 Lionel Messi called for more resources to combat a little known condition called Chagas disease, transmitted by a biting insect which currently infects 6–8 million people in the Americas.

Ethical sourcing of resources ensures that products such as leather for footballs are responsibly sourced and that employees are given good, safe working conditions and paid a fair wage. It also implies that employers pay due respect to the environment.

Legacies

Organisations such as the International Olympic Committee (IOC) are keen to encourage a lasting legacy when they award the games to a city. This means that the facilities built to host the games are used afterwards to encourage sport and exercise participation, and funding is put in place to support and promote participation at grass-roots level.

Research

A number of new facilities were built in order to host the London 2012 Olympic and Paralympic Games, but Sport England also launched a strategy called Places People Play to fully exploit the growth in popularity in sport aimed particularly at mass participation. Use the internet to find out more about this strategy and Sport England's work.

Regeneration of brownfield sites

One of the ways in which an increase in sports facilities can be funded is for local authorities to require them to be included in 'brownfield' development. Brownfield sites are those that are derelict or disused. Housing developers who build on this land can be required to provide community structures such as schools and shops, but might also be asked to build sport and leisure facilities for the people who move into the new homes or flats.

Assessment practice 12.3

C.P4 C.P5 C.M4 C.D3

Using a range of sports, create a presentation that explains the relationship between those sports and the media, and considers the impact of commercialisation and globalisation on sport. Your work should include examples from a range of sport and exercise activities and consider the impact of the media, commercialisation and globalisation on both sportspeople and spectators.

Make specific reference to the rules of your chosen sports' national governing bodies and explain how collaboration between countries in relation to the rules has allowed these sports to be played globally. In your presentation, you should:

1. discuss the impact of the media on each sport, including the development of new media, case studies about media influence and suggestions for future developments (e.g. you could explain how football kick-off times are now managed by the media for maximum viewing figures)
2. explain how the impact of the media has contributed to the commercialisation of sport, providing local and national examples
3. assess the rules of each sport and explain how international collaboration has brought about rule changes, considering the local and national impact of these changes.

Plan

- What am I being asked to do?
- Do I have any existing knowledge around the task at hand?

Do

- Have I provided examples to support my arguments?
- Have I made sure my information is accurate and up-to-date?

Review

- Does my report provide all the necessary information?
- Do I have a fuller understanding of the impact of the media on sport?

Further reading and resources

Books

Cashmore, E. (2000) *Making Sense of Sports*, 3rd edition, London: Routledge.

Coakley, J. J. (2001) *Sport in Society: Issues and Controversies*, 7th edition, Boston: McGraw-Hill.

Jarvie, G. (ed.) (2009) *Sport, Racism and Ethnicity*, London: The Falmer Press.

Houlihan, B. (2007) *Sport and Society: A Student Introduction*, 2nd edition, London: Sage Publications.

Websites

www.gov.uk/government/organisations/department-for-culture-media-sport – UK Government Department for Culture, Media and Sport: information related to national sports and including research material, strategy and allied blog space.

www.disabilitysport.org.uk – Disability Sport: information on organised sport and recreational opportunities for people with disabilities at both local and international levels.

www.sportengland.org – Sport England: information about Sport England's projects, which aim to increase participation in sport across England.

www.sportscoachuk.org – sports coach UK: organisation focused on recruiting, retaining and developing coaches.

www.sportsdevelopment.org.uk – Sports Development: academic resources for sport development, sport management and sports coaching.

THINK FUTURE

Donna Elton

Higher education student and rugby coach

I'm currently a student at university but have also been working part-time with some local rugby clubs for a few years now. Through my studies at university I have become particularly interested in how sport has been affected by society and even more so about how sport can impact on society.

As a women's and girls' rugby coach I have been made particularly aware of the prejudices, barriers and difficulties in arranging sports provision for women and girls. Rugby is often presented as 'a man's game' which can discourage women from taking part. The media often seem to view women in sport from a particular angle, even down to commenting on how glamorous they look rather than talking about their sporting performances.

As a result I have decided to produce my final large piece of work for the course that I am studying on the role of the media on the trends in female participation and performance, obviously with a rugby focus.

Focusing your skills

Researching and assessing

Sociologists looking at sport often need to do research to determine what the current relationship between the media and sport is. Numeracy skills are essential, and a key task is to work out to what extent any differences between participation levels are due to media influence. For example, if statistics show 19.7 per cent of women participate in 3 × 30 minute sessions of moderate-intensity sport and active recreation a week, compared to 25.8 per cent of men (Women's Sport and Fitness Foundation, WSFF), is that due to the images that the media presents?

Understanding current trends

Sports theorists need to be able to produce a coherent, well-informed piece of work in a logical, dispassionate manner with consideration to both the current situation and potential improvements. Those looking at similar themes as Donna will often cover current trends in sport such as:

- the sexualisation of women in the media
- the continued lack of media coverage for women's sport in general
- the disparity of prize money and payments to women in sport compared with men
- the importance of influencers and the role that they play in encouraging women's sport
- the significance of the male dominance in sports journalism and potentially in the social media.

Getting ready for assessment

Ella and Mabel are working together to prepare their assessments in this unit, although they understand that the work they submit will need to be very much their own. They have been presented with their assessment and have some extra research material, textbooks and access to the internet. They decide to set about the task in this by:

- including information on sport and a brief history of UK sport
- finding a way to link all aspects of the unit with a single thread – in this case a single sport.

Ella and Mabel share their experience below.

How we got started

First we collected all our notes on this topic and put them into a folder. We decided to divide the work into six parts related to history and culture.

Next we researched the histories of netball and rugby (Ella chose to base her report on netball, Mabel on rugby union) to see if there was a link between these sports that would provide sufficient evidence for our work from a variety of online resources. We researched together and compared notes and found that the combined experience was very beneficial, even though we were working on different sports and would have to produce our own reports.

How we brought it all together

When we had completed our research, we put everything into a folder that was divided into six parts, so each part of the unit was covered. Mabel found that when she could not find much information about the media and women's rugby, she was able to leave this part, move on and return later. Ella also found that she was perhaps spending too long focusing on the history of netball, which interested her, at the expense of the other areas of her work.

We produced a presentation, a written report and finally a leaflet making use of all of our research. Mabel had even managed to meet an elite rugby player and talk to her about her experiences, both as a young player and as an international sportsperson. She was able to include these thoughts in her work, using a survey with the player as additional evidence.

What we learned from the experience

We both learned a lot and feel very well-informed about our sports and their value as a result. Working together made us think in a way we hadn't expected; although we disagreed on some things, we found the experience very valuable since there were always at least two opinions on everything!

Planning was most important to both of us. Being able to jump from one part to the next prevented boredom and meant that we both started and restarted our coursework more quickly. Ella also had some very interesting discussions with the other netball players and an umpire, who are interested in hearing more of her ideas.

Think about it

- Plan your work carefully. Think about all the different tasks you need to complete, then add completion dates for them so you can be sure you will finish everything by the deadline.
- Ensure that you choose the right sport to research, that it reflects UK history and culture, and provides sufficient evidence for your assessment.
- Make sure that you check your spelling and grammar in all areas and ask someone else to review your work before you submit it.

13 Nutrition for Sport and Exercise Performance

Getting to know your unit

Assessment
You will be assessed externally through a written task.

This unit explores how nutrition affects sports performance and how to apply nutritional principles to meet sport-specific nutritional requirements. You will focus on the concepts of nutrition and digestion and the components of a balanced diet, exploring the roles of macronutrients and micronutrients and the energy and nutrient demands of different sports. You will also learn how to optimise nutritional strategies.

This unit does not develop the breadth of knowledge and skills of a registered sports dietitian or nutritionist, but you will gain an appreciation of how diet affects sporting performance.

How you will be assessed

This unit will be assessed by a written task set and marked by Pearson. This task will assess your ability to interpret, modify and adapt a nutritional programme for a given scenario. The assessment will take place under supervised conditions.

You will be provided with a case study a set period of time before the supervised assessment date. This case study presents an individual who needs guidance on nutrition in response to the personal and training needs affecting their performance. You should independently research the case study and prepare notes.

As the guidelines for assessment can change, you should refer to the official assessment guidance on the Pearson Qualifications website for the latest definitive guidance.

You must be able to modify a programme for an individual in a way that demonstrates knowledge and understanding of nutrition and fluid intake relevant to requirements. You will need to show an understanding of the individual's health and well-being requirements and apply relevant nutritional principles and strategies, demonstrating the ability to conduct relevant research. You will also need to identify the impact of factors affecting digestion and absorption, and provide guidance and justification for your proposed adaptations to the nutritional programme.

The assessment outcomes for this task are as follows:

- **AO1** Demonstrate knowledge and understanding of nutritional principles, strategies and concepts
- **AO2** Apply knowledge and understanding of nutritional principles, strategies and concepts to sport and exercise performance in context
- **AO3** Analyse and evalute information and data relating to an individual's needs in order to determine modifications and guidance to improve sport and exercise performance
- **AO4** Be able to develop and adapt a nutritional programme in context and with appropriate justification.

Getting started

Take a few minutes to think about the factors that might influence your food intake and choices. If you can think of ten factors, you are doing well, while 20 or more is excellent. Awareness of these factors will help you to formulate realistic and achievable dietary goals and plans when meeting the assessment requirements of this unit.

Principles of nutrition and hydration

It is important to understand the basic principles of nutrition and the effects of nutrients on the body's ability to function during sport and exercise. **Foods** contain varying amounts of nutrients including carbohydrate, protein, fat, vitamins, minerals, fibre and water.

Any activity stimulates your body's need for fuel and fluid. Knowing the nutrients your body requires, along with the different functions of the nutrients, forms the basis for the science of **nutrition**.

The amount of each nutrient you need is referred to as your **nutritional requirement**. This differs depending on your age, sex, levels of activity and state of health. Some nutrients are more essential during different stages of life, such as calcium in childhood and iron during pregnancy.

Key terms

Food – any substance derived from plants or animals containing a combination of carbohydrates, fats, proteins, vitamins, minerals, fibre and water.

Nutrition – the means by which your body takes in energy and nutrients from food to sustain growth and development, and to keep you alive and healthy.

Why is it important to have a balanced and varied diet in order to stay healthy?

Basic nutritional principles

Nutritional measurements and units

Energy is obtained from the foods you eat and is used to support your basal metabolic rate (the minimum amount of energy required to sustain your body's vital functions while you are awake – this is covered in more depth on page 349), and all activity carried out at work and leisure. Energy is measured in **calories** or **joules**. As both these units are very small they are multiplied by 1000 and referred to as **kilocalories** (the UK system) or **kilojoules** (the metric or international system).

Key terms

Calorie (cal) – 1 calorie is the energy required to raise the temperature of 1 gram of water by 1°C.

Joule (J) – 1 joule of energy moves a mass of 1 gram at a velocity of 1 metre per second. Approximately 4.2 joules = 1 calorie.

Kilocalorie (kcal) – 1 kilocalorie is the energy required to raise the temperature of 1 litre of water by 1°C. It is equal to 1000 calories and is used to state the energy value of food. Kilocalories are often simply referred to as calories.

Kilojoule (kJ) – a unit of energy, equivalent to 1000 joules.

Recommended daily allowance (RDA)

Dietary standards have been used in the UK since the Second World War. The first set of standards focused on a **recommended daily allowance (RDA)**, which aimed to prevent nutritional deficiency by recommending an intake target per day for each nutrient. In the late 1980s, the government set up a panel of experts to review the RDAs of nutrients, and new **dietary reference values (DRVs)** were established. The phrase 'dietary reference value' is an umbrella term that can be applied to any of the following measures of nutrient intake values:

- estimated average requirements (EAR)
- safe intake (SI)
- reference intakes: reference nutrient intake (RNI) and lower reference nutrient intake (LRNI).

Estimated average requirements (EAR)

Estimated average requirements (EAR) are the most widely used value in assessing energy requirement. Many individuals require more than the EAR and many require less.

Safe intake (SI)

Safe intake (SI) is a term used to represent an intake that is thought to be adequate for most people's needs but not so high as to cause undesirable effects on health. It is used when there is insufficient scientific information to estimate the different requirements of different segments of the population.

Research

Find out more about DRVs by looking at the Department of Health's *Report on Health and Social Subjects 41: Dietary Reference Values for Food Energy and Nutrients for the United Kingdom*, HMSO, 1991.

Based on your research develop a summary table of reference nutrient intake (RNI) requirements for males and females aged 15–18 years and 19–50 years.

Reference intakes (RIs)

On food labels the term reference intakes (or RIs) has replaced guideline daily amounts (GDAs), but the basic principle is the same. RIs are guidelines based on the approximate amount of energy and nutrients needed daily for a healthy, balanced **diet**. They are not intended as targets, as requirements are different for everyone, but they provide a useful indication of how much energy the average person needs.

Key term

Diet – a person's usual eating habits and food consumption.

Metabolism

Metabolism refers to the chemical processes that occur within the body in order to maintain life. Technically it consists of both **anabolism** (the build-up of substances), and **catabolism** (the breakdown of substances), but the term is typically used to refer to the breakdown of food and its transformation into energy.

Basal metabolic rate (BMR)

Basal metabolic rate (BMR) reflects the energy required to maintain body systems and to control body temperature at rest.

BMR is measured under strict conditions of rest in the morning, after an overnight fast in a temperature controlled environment free from distractions, medications and stress that would increase metabolic activity. Because measures of BMR require the need to sleep overnight in a laboratory, measures of **resting metabolic rate (RMR)** are often used instead, where the subject will have followed the same process but will have slept at home.

These terms are often used interchangeably when referring to energy expenditure, and measures of BMR and RMR usually differ by less than 10 per cent.

Prediction equations can be used to estimate basal metabolic rate. For example, the Harris–Benedict equation takes into account sex, weight, height and age.

Harris–Benedict equation

Males: BMR = 66.5 + (13.75 × weight, kg) + (5.0 × height, cm) – (6.76 × age, years)

Females: BMR = 655.1 + (9.56 × weight, kg) + (1.85 × height, cm) – (4.68 × age, years)

Worked example

An 18-year-old female athlete weighs 55 kg and is 175 cm tall.

655.1 + (9.56 × 55 kg) + (1.85 × 175 cm) – (4.68 × 18 years) = 1420 calories

To predict total daily energy requirements, a **physical activity level (PAL)** needs to be applied. The Harris–Benedict equation recommends the following PAL values to enable calculation of an individual's daily **total energy requirement (TER)**.

Physical activity levels (PALs)

Little to no exercise: TER = BMR × 1.2

Light exercise (1–3 days per week): TER = BMR × 1.375

Moderate exercise (3–5 days per week): TER = BMR × 1.55

Heavy exercise (6–7 days per week): TER = BMR × 1.725

Very heavy exercise (twice per day, extra heavy workouts): TER = BMR × 1.9

Worked example

Using the same example, the female athlete trains 6 days a week, so her TER = 1420 calories × 1.725 = 2449.5 calories

Theory into practice

Based on your current body weight and level of physical activity and training, estimate your total daily energy requirement. Do you think your energy requirements are constant, or do they vary from day to day? What practical considerations does this have for trying to estimate and meet your requirements?

Key term

Lean body mass – body weight minus body fat, primarily composed of muscle, bone and other non-fat tissues.

Energy balance

You achieve 'energy balance' when the amount of energy you take in as food and drink (**energy intake**) equals the amount of energy you expend (**energy expenditure**): you will neither be losing nor gaining weight.

There are four major components of energy expenditure: resting metabolic rate (RMR), dietary thermogenesis (DT), physical activity (PA) and adaptive thermogenesis (AT).

- **Resting metabolic rate (RMR)** can account for 60–75 per cent of total energy output and represents the largest component of total daily energy expenditure. RMR is closely related to **lean body mass** and so is influenced by body composition: muscle tissue is much more active metabolically than fat tissue. Gains in muscle mass will result in increases in RMR. RMR is also influenced by your age, sex and genetic background.
- **Dietary thermogenesis (DT)** refers to the energy expended above RMR for digesting, absorbing, transporting and storing food. It is influenced by calorie intake and the composition of your diet, along with your individual nutritional status. High energy intakes and a regular eating pattern are thought to help maintain higher rates of DT, while skipping meals and restrictive dietary practices lead to a reduction in DT.
- **Physical activity (PA)** represents the most variable component of your total energy expenditure. This is the additional energy expended above RMR and DT, and will contribute more to total daily energy expenditure in active individuals. Exactly how much it contributes varies depending on:
  - how active your general lifestyle is
  - how often, how energetically and for how long you exercise
  - what type of activity it is.
- **Adaptive thermogenesis (AT)** is energy expenditure that occurs as a result of environmental or physiological stresses placed on your body, such as a change in temperature that may require you to respond by shivering, or stress that causes anxiety or fidgeting – both will increase your energy expenditure.

When energy intake exceeds expenditure, this is referred to as **positive energy balance** and weight is gained. If intake is less than requirements, the additional energy required will be drawn from your body's fat reserves and weight will be lost. This is referred to as **negative energy balance**.

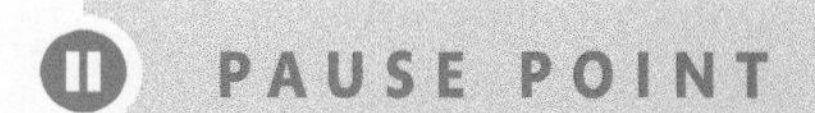

Do some research to find other equations for predicting BMR and TER. Which do you think is the best?

Hint Consider factors related to sex, size and body composition that might affect the ability to predict requirements accurately.

Extend What could you do to control some of the limitations of these equations?

Physical activity

The relative value of fuels for activity differs. Fat and carbohydrate are the main energy fuels for your exercising muscles. Exercising muscles prefer **glucose** as a fuel, particularly as the intensity of the activity being undertaken increases. Protein may be used during prolonged periods of exercise and towards the latter stages of endurance events like the marathon, particularly if fat and carbohydrate as sources of fuel within the working muscles have become limited.

Key term

Glucose – the main type of sugar in the blood; a major source of energy for the body's cells.

When you exercise, your muscles use energy at a rate that is directly proportional to the intensity of your activity and its duration. If this energy is not replaced as it is used up, your muscles will be unable to maintain their rate of work and the intensity of the activity will need to be reduced or stopped.

Calories expended in different activities

At rest, we use energy at a rate of about 1–1.2 calories per minute, which is equivalent to about 1400 to 1700 calories per day, the basal metabolism for the average individual. Any activity will increase the rate of energy expenditure. Walking or jogging requires about 1 kcal per kg of body weight per km covered, but those with a larger body mass burn more energy at the same speed. Distance covered, not speed, will have a greater influence on total energy expenditure.

Worked example

Two men are starting a health and fitness regime: one weighs 70 kg and the other weighs 100 kg.

- Both men start by walking slowly (3 km per hour) for 30 minutes. The man who weighs 70 kg will use up about 105 calories, but the man who weighs 100 kg will use about 150 calories.
- As their fitness improves, the intensity is increased to jogging. They cover 4 km in 30 minutes. The man who weighs 70 kg uses up around 280 calories, but the man who weighs 100 kg uses around 300 calories.

A trained athlete with a body mass of 70 kg who ran 10 km in 30 minutes would use about 700 calories in that time.

Body weight and body mass index

Body weight (or, more precisely, 'body mass') is usually measured in kilograms. Body mass can be classified by using the **body mass index (BMI)**. BMI assumes that there is a healthy weight range for any given height (see Table 13.1). An individual's BMI can be calculated by dividing their weight, in kilograms, by the square of their height, in metres (kg/m^2).

Worked example

An adult who weighs 65 kg and whose height is 1.70 m will have a BMI of 22.5: BMI = 65 kg ÷ (1.70 m^2) = 22.5

Using Table 13.1, they would be classified within the normal weight range.

▶ **Table 13.1:** BMI classifications based on World Health Organization's International Classification of Adult Underweight, Overweight and Obesity

BMI	Classification
Less than 18.50	Underweight
18.50–24.99	Normal weight
25.00–29.99	Overweight/pre-obese
30.00–34.99	Obese class I
35.00–39.99	Obese class II
40.00+	Obese class III

Body composition

Body composition refers to the proportions of lean body mass and body fat that make up total body weight.

- **Lean body mass** includes bone, muscle, water, connective and organ tissues.
- **Body fat** includes both essential and non-essential fat stores.

People actively engaged in fitness regimes are often concerned about their weight, whether for performance or health reasons. Some athletes wish to alter body composition, with exercise generally increasing lean body mass and decreasing body fat.

Changes in body composition can be monitored by a range of methods including skinfold analysis, bioelectrical impedance analysis and hydrodensitometry (underwater weighing). All these methods are best used for measuring changes in body composition over time, rather than for judging a single measurement in isolation. To minimise potential errors when measuring changes in body composition over time, always use the same method; ensure the subject is assessed by the same person, and take repeat measurements at the same time of day.

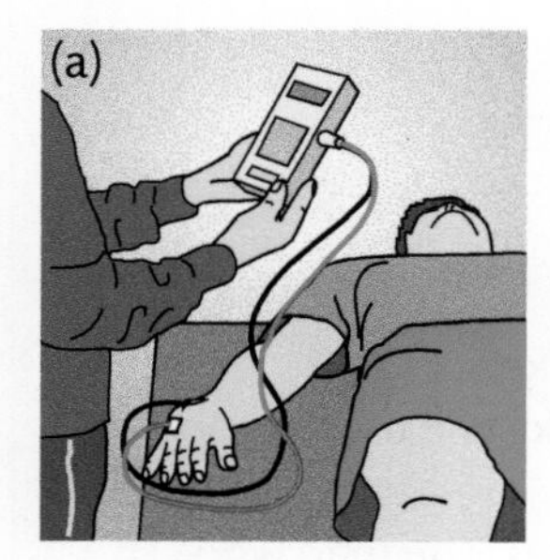

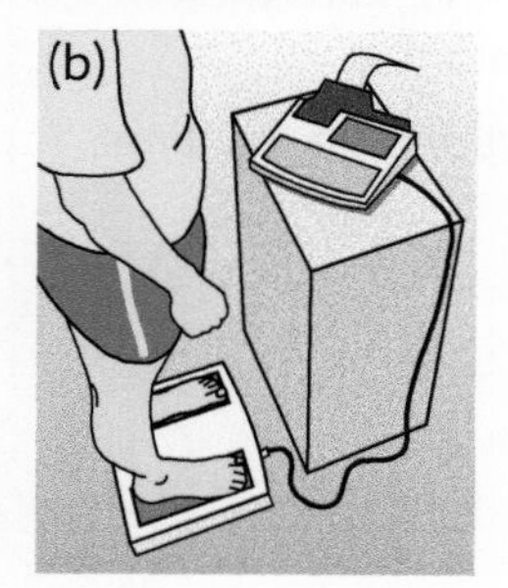

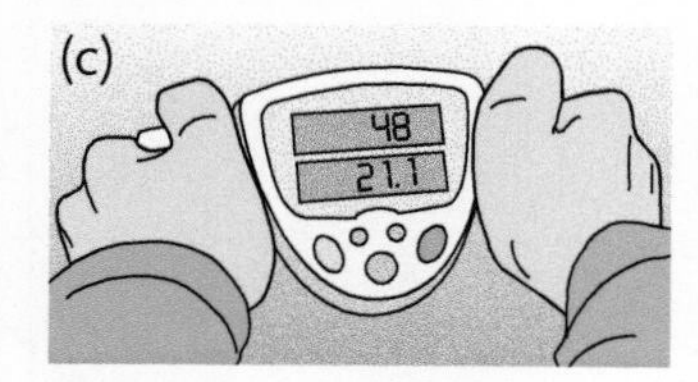

▶ **Figure 13.1:** Bioelectrical impedance machines: (a) using electrodes, (b) foot-to-foot and (c) hand-to-hand

Bioelectrical impedance analysis (BIA)

Bioelectrical impedance analysis (BIA) is a standard technique for assessing body composition, particularly in the health and fitness sector. BIA machines (Figure 13.1) provide a quick, easy and non-invasive method of estimating percentage body fat. Some equipment uses electrodes attached to the hands and feet, other equipment requires the subject to stand on specially designed scales or to grip handles.

BIA machines measure resistance to the flow of an electrical current through the body, using the fact that different body tissues restrict (or impede) the flow of the current to different extents. Tissues that contain a large amount of water, such as lean tissue, provide a lower impedance than tissues such as bone and fat.

When using BIA techniques a number of assumptions are made, and equations applied, to obtain a body fat percentage figure. One potential drawback is that impedance measurements are related to the water content of tissues, so subjects must be fully hydrated and must abstain from exercise and substances that exert a diuretic effect - such as alcohol or caffeine - for at least 24 hours before the test. Invalid results may also be obtained for women immediately before or during menstruation, when the body's water content may be higher than normal.

Link

You can read more about measuring body composition in *Unit 4: Field- and Laboratory-based Fitness Testing*.

Research

Search online for 'body composition assessment'. Evaluate the range of assessment products available in terms of affordability, ease of application and suitability for use with athletes. Be sure to consider skinfold assessment, air displacement plethysmography and dual-energy X-ray absorptiometry.

Macronutrients

Nutrients in food are categorised according to the relative amounts required by your body. Carbohydrate, fat and protein are termed **macronutrients**, as they are required in relatively large amounts on a daily basis. These nutrients are also the energy-providing nutrients of your diet.

Key term

Macronutrient – a nutrient required by your body in daily amounts greater than a few grams, e.g. carbohydrate, fat and protein.

Carbohydrates

Carbohydrates form your body's most readily available source of energy and can be accessed rapidly. One gram of carbohydrate provides approximately 4 kcal or 17 kJ of energy. Carbohydrate foods are divided into two basic types: simple and complex.

Simple carhohydrates

Simple carbohydrates are essentially sugars. They are formed from single and double sugar units and are easily digested and absorbed to provide a quick energy source.

The simplest carbohydrate unit is the **monosaccharide**, the most common of which is glucose. 'Saccharide' means sugar and 'mono' means one, so a monosaccharide is a single sugar unit. Glucose is used to produce adenosine triphosphate (ATP), the compound required for muscle contraction. Other monosaccharides include fructose, also called fruit sugar because it is found in fruits and vegetables, and galactose, found in milk.

Monosaccharides mostly occur combined in carbohydrates. Two monosaccharides together form a **disaccharide** or double sugar. The most common disaccharide is sucrose or table sugar. Others include lactose (found in milk) and maltose (found in cereals).

Complex carbohydrates

Longer chains of simple sugar units are called **polysaccharides** or complex carbohydrates. These allow large quantities of glucose to be stored as starch in the cells of plants or as glycogen in the muscles and liver of animals. All carbohydrate consumed ends up as glucose to provide energy.

Complex carbohydrates are an important source of energy since they are broken down slowly in your body to release energy over longer periods. They should form the largest percentage of your total carbohydrate intake. Unrefined sources such as wholemeal bread, wholegrain rice and pasta are preferable as they also contain a higher nutritional value by way of micronutrients and fibre.

▶ **Table 13.2:** Sources of simple and complex carbohydrates in the diet

Simple	Complex
Sugar, syrup, jam, honey, marmalade, sugary fizzy drinks, boiled sweets, fudge, fruit juice, sports drinks, energy gels	Bread, bagels, crispbread, crackers, rice, pasta, polenta,noodles, couscous, potatoes, breakfast cereals, pulses, root vegetables

Recommended daily intake (RDA)

To support health and performance, it is recommended that around 50–60 per cent of your total daily calorie intake is derived from carbohydrates. Greater intakes may be required by athletes in regular intense training. For example, a marathon runner or a triathlete may need to get 65–70 per cent of their total daily energy from carbohydrates.

However, the average sedentary individual will require around 50 per cent of their total daily calorie intake to be supplied by carbohydrates, of which the majority should be from starchy complex sources. This would equate to around 250 grams per day for females and 300 grams per day for males. Table 13.3 estimates the carbohydrate requirements based on activity levels.

Table 13.3: Carbohydrate requirements based on daily activity levels

Level of daily activity	Carbohydrate per kilogram of body weight (g)
Sedentary	3–4
Less than 1 hour	4–5
1 hour	5–6
1–2 hours	6–7
2–3 hours	7–8
More than 3 hours	8–10

Whether eating for health or performance, the best approach to achieving an adequate carbohydrate intake is to eat at regular intervals and ensure all meals and snacks are centred around starchy carbohydrate foods, such as wholegrain breads, rice, pasta and potatoes. Athletes with high carbohydrate requirements may need to eat more frequent meals and snacks or consume more simple carbohydrates to achieve their requirements.

Glycaemic index (GI)

The glycaemic index (GI) is a rating that describes how quickly a food containing carbohydrate increases blood glucose after eating. Foods are ranked on a scale of 0–100, with glucose having a score of 100.

- Foods that have a **high GI** are broken down quickly in the body and cause a rapid rise in blood glucose. High GI foods, such as grapes, rice cakes and jelly beans may be useful in promoting optimal recovery after exercise as they will stimulate insulin release and a replenishment of muscle glycogen stores.
- Those with a **low GI** are broken down more slowly and cause a more gradual increase in blood glucose. It is thought that low GI foods help to control appetite and keep you feeling fuller for longer, which can be useful when trying to reduce body mass. They also promote better blood glucose control and more stable energy levels.

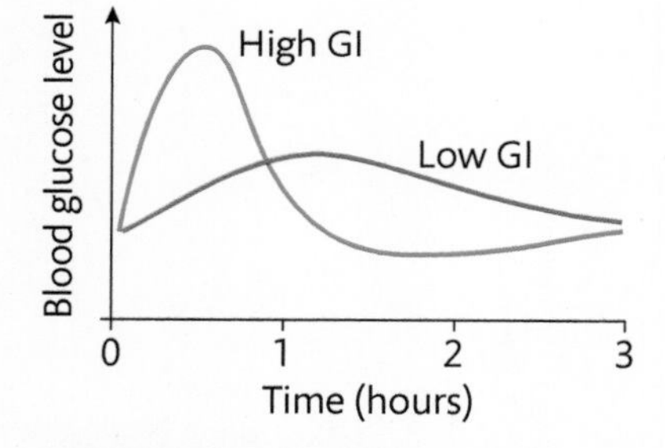

Figure 13.2: Blood glucose response to high and low GI foods

The GI of a food is determined by its composition in terms of its macronutrient and fibre content and how it is processed and cooked. Fat, fibre and protein content lower the GI of a food.

Research

Draw up a list of the common carbohydrate-rich foods you consume in your day-to-day diet. Carry out an internet search using the term 'glycaemic index' and use your research to categorise your food choices as high, moderate or low GI.

Theory into practice

Based on your current body weight and level of physical activity, estimate your carbohydrate requirements in grams per day. Do you think your requirements are constant, or do they vary from day to day? What practical strategies could you implement to ensure you achieve your carbohydrate requirements?

Fats

Fat is an essential nutrient. **Triglycerides** form the basic component of fats. Each triglyceride consists of a glycerol molecule with three fatty acids attached. When triglycerides are digested and absorbed by your body they break down into **glycerol** and **fatty acids**. Fats are obtained from animal and vegetable sources.

Fatty acids contain chains of carbon atoms to which hydrogen atoms attach. If all the carbons are associated with two hydrogens, the fat is **saturated**, but if one or more of the carbons is without hydrogen then the fat is **unsaturated**. Unsaturated fatty acids can be of two kinds: **monounsaturated** and **polyunsaturated**.

All fats in your diet are a mixture of these three fatty acid types. Fats that contain mostly saturated fatty acids are generally solid at room temperature, like butter, and are usually found in meat, eggs and dairy foods. The two exceptions are palm and coconut oil, which are plant sources. Fats composed mainly of unsaturated fatty acids are usually liquid at room temperature, like olive or sunflower oils.

Most dietary experts recommend cutting back on fat intake. This is sound advice for athletes as it allows them to consume a greater proportion of energy intake from carbohydrates to maintain glycogen stores, to support training and competition.

The primary function of fats is to provide a concentrated source of energy, forming your body's largest potential energy store. Even the leanest of individuals will have large amounts of energy stored as fat. Fat is more than twice as energy-dense as other macronutrients, yielding 9 kcal or 37 kJ per gram.

Fat protects and cushions your vital organs, provides structural material for cells and acts as an insulator to help maintain body temperature. Animal fats are a source of the fat-soluble vitamins A, D, E and K. Fat also adds flavour and texture to foods, which can lead to over-consumption.

Some sources of the different types of fat are shown in Table 13.4. It is generally recommended that we reduce our total fat intake and intake of foods which are high in saturated fat from non-dairy sources.

▶ **Table 13.4:** Sources and types of fat in the diet

Saturated	Monounsaturated	Polyunsaturated
Full-fat dairy products, butter, hard margarine, lard, dripping, suet, fatty meat, meat pies, pâté, cream, cakes, biscuits, chocolate, coconut, coconut oil	Olive oil, olive oil spreads, rapeseed oil, corn oil, peanuts, peanut butter, peanut oil	Soft margarine, low-fat spreads labelled high in polyunsaturated fats, sunflower oil, safflower oil, soya oil, oily fish, nuts

Transunsatured fats or trans fatty acids are unsaturated fatty acids produced by the partial hydrogenation of vegetable oils. They are found in hardened vegetable oils, most margarines, commercial baked foods and most fried foods. An excess of these fats in the diet is thought to raise cholesterol levels.

Recommended daily intake

It is recommended that fat intake represents 30–35 per cent of total calorie intake: around 70 grams per day for females and 90 grams per day for males. Of this, only 6–10 per cent should be from saturated fats. Athletes involved in regular intense activity may need to further reduce their overall fat intake as a percentage to around 25–30 per cent of total energy consumed to achieve adequate carbohydrate intakes. However, in absolute terms this may equate to the same proportion of intake as that of the sedentary individual, as athletes will be eating more calories to meet their increased energy requirements.

Discussion

Government guidelines recommend 70 grams of fat per day for the average female and 90 grams per day for the average male. What nutritional strategies can be put in place to ensure recommended intakes are not exceeded?

Proteins

Proteins are essential to maintaining optimal health and physical performance. The smallest units of proteins are **amino acids**. You do not need to know the names and functions of the 20 individual amino acids, but the body needs all of them to be present simultaneously for protein synthesis to occur, to sustain optimal growth and functioning. Different protein foods contain different numbers and combinations of amino acids. The eight that your body is unable to make are called **essential amino acids (EAAs)** – they are a necessary part of your diet. The remaining amino acids are called **non-essential**, meaning your body is able to synthesise them if all the essential ones are present.

The chief role of protein in your body is to build and repair tissue. Protein may also be used as a secondary source of energy when carbohydrate and fat are limited, such as towards the end of prolonged endurance events or during severe energy restriction that may accompany dieting.

Proteins, like carbohydrates, have an energy value of approximately 4 kcal or 17 kJ per gram. Unlike carbohydrate and fat, excess protein cannot be stored in your body. If your protein intake exceeds requirements to support growth and repair, excess is used to provide energy immediately or converted to fat or carbohydrate and stored.

Protein foods are classified into two groups (see Table 13.5). The value of foods for meeting your body's protein needs is determined by their composition of amino acids.

- **High biological value** or **complete proteins** contain all of the EAAs. These are mainly of animal origin like eggs, meat, fish, milk and other dairy products, but also soya.
- **Low biological value** or **incomplete proteins** lack one or more of the EAAs. These come from plant sources such as cereals, bread, rice, pasta, pulses, nuts and seeds. Vegetarians and vegans must ensure that they eat a variety of these in careful combinations to ensure adequate intake of all EAAs; for example, beans and wheat complement each other well.

In the context of sports performance, does the typical UK diet contain adequate amounts of protein?

Table 13.5: Sources and types of protein foods in the diet

Complete/high biological value proteins	Incomplete/low biological value proteins
Meat, poultry, offal, fish, eggs, milk, cheese, yoghurt, soya	Cereals, bread, rice, pasta, noodles, pulses, peas, beans, lentils, nuts, seeds

Recommended daily intake

Active individuals have higher protein requirements in order to promote tissue growth and repair following training and competition. Overall, protein intake should represent between 12 and 15 per cent of your total daily energy intake.

The misguided belief that additional protein will automatically help to build muscle has been perpetuated since the times of the ancient Greeks. Regular exercise does increase protein needs, but most people already eat enough protein. Athletes are likely to be eating more to meet increased calorie requirements, and therefore should already be eating enough to meet any theoretical increase in requirements.

▶ **Table 13.6:** Daily protein requirements based on type of activity. Note nutrition experts do not generally recommend intake beyond 2 g per kg of body weight

Type of activity	Protein per kilogram of body weight (g)
Mainly sedentary	0.75–1.0
Mainly endurance	1.2–1.4
Mainly strength	1.2–1.7

Theory into practice

Based on your current body weight and level of physical activity, estimate your protein requirements in grams per day. Do you think you meet your protein requirements? Are there any factors related to your exercise or training regime that influence your protein requirements?

PAUSE POINT Reflect on your current ability to meet your targets for energy, carbohydrate and protein. Are there any barriers to you achieving these on a day-to-day basis?

Hint Consider whether any of the factors identified in this unit affect your ability to meet your daily targets.

Extend Identify any common themes that might be affecting the success of achieving your targets.

Micronutrients

Vitamins and minerals are referred to as micronutrients as they are required in much smaller amounts – some in minute quantities. Despite your relatively small requirements for these nutrients, many play a critical role in regulating chemical reactions in your body.

Vitamins

Vitamins are vital, non-caloric nutrients required in very small amounts. They perform specific metabolic functions and prevent particular deficiency diseases. Vitamins play essential roles in regulating many metabolic processes in your body, particularly those that release energy. They also support growth and the functions of the immune and nervous systems, and some are involved in producing hormones.

Most vitamins required to maintain health cannot be produced by your body and must be supplied by your diet. The exceptions are vitamin D, which your body is able to synthesise by the action of sunlight on the skin, and vitamin K, which can be produced by the bacteria of the large intestine.

Vitamins are obtained from a variety of plant and animal sources (see Table 13.7) and are broadly grouped depending on whether they are fat- or water-soluble.

- **Fat-soluble vitamins** are vitamins A, D, E and K. They have a number of common features. As the term suggests, they are found in the fatty or oily parts of foods. Once digested they are absorbed and transported in the lymph and ultimately reach the blood. As a result of their insolubility in water, they are not excreted in the urine and can accumulate in the liver and **adipose tissue**.
- **Water-soluble vitamins** consist of the B vitamins and vitamin C. Many of the B vitamins serve similar functions, facilitating the use of energy within your body. Excesses are excreted via the urine, so your body has only limited stores, necessitating regular intakes. It should be noted that many of these vitamins are destroyed by food processing and preparation.

Key term

Adipose tissue – loose connective tissue composed of adipocytes, specialised cells for the storage of fat. Its main role is to store energy in the form of fat, but it also cushions and insulates the body.

Different vitamins have specific functions and are required in different amounts. Individual requirements are determined by age, sex, state of health and levels of physical activity. The UK Department of Health has set dietary reference values (DRVs) for all nutrients for different groups of healthy people, and the reference nutrient intake (RNI) value should meet the needs of 97 per cent of the population (see Table 13.7). A balanced and varied diet with an adequate energy content should supply sufficient intake of all vitamins.

It is important to note that large amounts of some vitamins can be harmful to health. This is particularly true for the fat-soluble vitamins, as they can be stored in your body. The only situation in which large doses of any vitamin may be beneficial is when the body has a severe deficiency of a particular vitamin or is unable to absorb or metabolise vitamins efficiently, in which case supplementation may be medically advised.

Table 13.7: Vitamins – their sources, functions and deficiencies

Micronutrient and adult daily requirements (RNI)		**Good dietary sources**	**Functions**	**Deficiency**
A Retinol or beta carotene	Males 700 μg Females 600 μg Pregnancy +100 μg Lactation +350 μg	Retinol: liver, oily fish, eggs Beta-carotene: carrots, red peppers, tomatoes and green vegetables	Visual processes, connective tissue, immune response	Night blindness
B_1 Thiamine	0.4 mg/1000 kcal	Whole grains, meat, pulses, nuts, milk and yeast extract	Metabolism of fat, carbohydrate and alcohol	Neurological problems
B_2 Riboflavin	Males 1.3 mg Females 1.0 mg Pregnancy +0.3 mg Lactation +0.5 mg	Liver, dairy produce, meat, fortified cereal, eggs and yeast extract	Carbohydrate metabolism, vision, skin health and nervous system function	Poor growth
B_3 Niacin	6.6 mg/1000 kcal Lactation +2.3 mg	Meat, dairy produce and eggs	Carbohydrate and fat metabolism	Dermatitis, diarrhoea and confusion
B_6 Pyridoxine	15 μg	Meat, whole grains, pulses, nuts and fortified cereals	Protein metabolism and red blood cell formation	Deficiency is rare
B_{12} Cyanocobalamin	1.5 μg Lactation +0.5 μg	Meat, dairy produce, eggs, fortified cereals and yeast extract	Red blood cell formation and central nervous system function	Pernicious anaemia and neurological problems
Folic acid	200 μg Pregnancy +100 μg	Pulses, green leafy vegetables, wholegrain and fortified cereals	Regulates growth of cells, including red blood cells	Anaemia and diarrhoea
C Ascorbic acid	40 mg Pregnancy +10 mg Lactation +30 mg Smokers 80 mg	Green leafy vegetables, citrus and soft fruit, potatoes	Connective tissue formation, iron absorption and wound healing	Scurvy, bleeding gums, poor wound healing, weakness and fatigue
D Calciferols	No RNI set for adults	Dairy produce, oily fish, eggs and liver	Bone mineralisation and immune system function	Rickets in children, osteomalacia in adults
E Tocopherols	Males 8 mg Females 6 mg	Vegetable oils, nuts and seeds	Protects cells from free radical damage	Impaired coordination
K	No RNI set	Green leafy vegetables, vegetable oils, eggs, meat and dairy produce	Clotting of blood	Poor blood clotting

Minerals

Minerals are non-caloric nutrients that are essential to life, and like vitamins they are required in small or trace amounts. All minerals are essential to health and form important components of your body such as bone, connective tissue, enzymes and hormones. Some play essential roles in nerve function and muscle contraction; others regulate fluid balance in your body.

Levels of minerals are closely controlled by absorption and excretion to prevent excessive build-up. Some minerals compete with each other for absorption, especially iron, zinc and copper.

▶ **Table 13.8:** Main minerals – their sources, functions and deficiencies

Micronutrient and adult daily requirements (RNI)		Good dietary sources	Functions	Deficiency
Sodium	1.6 g	Salt, cheese, meat, fish, tinned vegetables, salted nuts and savoury snacks	Neuromuscular transmission, fluid and acid-base balance	Hyponatremia (low sodium concentration in the blood)
Potassium	3.5 g	Meat, dairy produce, vegetables, cereals, nuts, fruit and fruit juices	Neuromuscular transmission, fluid and acid-base balance	Hypokalemia (low potassium concentration in the blood)
Calcium	Males 700 mg Females 700 mg Lactation +550 mg	Dairy produce, white bread, tinned fish with bones and pulses	Bone and tooth structure Nerve conduction and blood clotting	Stunted growth in children, osteoporosis in adults
Iron	Males 8.7 mg Female 14.8 mg Females aged 50+ 8.7 mg	Red meat and offal, eggs, dark green vegetables, breakfast cereals, pulses and dried fruit	Haemoglobin and myoglobin formation and a component of some enzymes	Anaemia and fatigue

Salt

Salt, or sodium chloride, is necessary to maintain fluid balance and to help muscle contraction and nerve transmission. Small amounts are required daily but most people exceed the required levels. Too much salt can raise blood pressure and increase the risk of heart disease. Adults should consume no more than 6 grams of salt per day.

Research

Investigate the signs and symptoms of hypokalemia and hyponatremia. Which groups of people are likely to suffer from these conditions?

PAUSE POINT

How can you ensure that you achieve good dietary intakes of vitamins and minerals to avoid potential deficiencies?

Hint It might be helpful to review the 'Getting started' activity at the start of this unit.

Extend Undertaking your own research, can you identify any dangers of over-consumption of the vitamins and minerals listed in Tables 13.7 and 13.8?

Fibre

Fibre is a complex carbohydrate. It is the indigestible portion of food derived from plants. **Non-starch polysaccharide** (NSP) is the scientific term for dietary fibre. NSP forms the main component of plant cell walls, which is the principal component of dietary fibre. It resists digestion by the stomach and small intestine, providing bulk which aids the transit of food through your digestive system.

Key term

Non-starch polysaccharide – the scientific term for dietary fibre.

Fibre is obtained from wholegrain cereals, nuts, pulses, fruits and vegetables. It is thought to help in both preventing and treating certain diseases including cancer of the colon, diabetes, heart disease and irritable bowel syndrome. A high-fibre intake plus a high-fluid intake also helps to keep your bowel functioning efficiently. Adequate amounts may also play a role in weight control by helping to achieve the feeling of fullness.

There are two types of fibre: soluble and insoluble.

- **Soluble fibre** can be found in oats, rye, barley, peas, beans, lentils, fruits and vegetables. This is important in the control of blood glucose and cholesterol.
- **Insoluble fibre** is found in wholewheat bread, rice and pasta, wholegrain breakfast cereals, fruits and vegetables. It is thought to be important in the prevention of bowel disorders.

Adult daily requirements for fibre are 18 grams per day.

Athletes with high carbohydrate requirements will need to manage fibre intake because consuming large quantities of fibre-rich carbohydrate food can make the diet bulky and filling, with the potential to limit overall food and energy intake. It may also be necessary for some athletes to remove high fibre foods from their pre-competition meal if they suffer from gastrointestinal discomfort during competition.

Fluid intake

Water is one of the most important nutrients. You cannot survive more than a few days without it. Losses may be as high as a litre per hour during endurance-type exercise, even higher in hot or humid conditions.

During exercise, fluid requirements increase according to the type, duration and intensity of the exercise and the environmental conditions under which it is taking place. Understanding the relationship between hydration and sports performance is vital for achieving optimal performance in training and competition.

Maintaining hydration levels

Key term

Thermoregulation – the ability to keep the body's temperature constant, even if the surrounding temperature is different.

Water is the main transport mechanism in your body, carrying nutrients, waste products and internal secretions. It also plays a vital role in **thermoregulation**, and aids the passage of food through your digestive system.

Water makes up around 50–60 per cent of your total body weight. Actual amounts vary depending on age, sex and body composition. Muscle has a higher water content than fat tissue, so leaner individuals have a higher water content than fatter individuals of the same body mass.

To maintain water balance, a sedentary individual requires 2–2.5 litres of fluid per day. Around 10 per cent of your daily fluid requirements come from metabolic processes that release water within your body. The rest comes from your diet.

Water is lost from your body through a number of routes including urine, faeces, evaporation from the skin and expired breath. If water loss is high, your body becomes **dehydrated**. Fluid losses for athletes during training and competition are linked to the body's need to maintain temperature within very narrow limits. During exercise, body temperature rises and extra heat is lost through sweating. If fluid lost in sweat is not replaced, there is a risk of dehydration and performance may suffer.

Normal fluid requirements are in the region of 30–35 ml per kilogram of body weight per day, or 1 ml per calorie of energy requirement. Thirst is a poor indicator of dehydration, so drinking to just stay ahead of the sensation of thirst is recommended to ensure adequate fluid status.

Theory into practice

Using the equations 30–35 ml per kilogram of body weight per day, or 1 ml per calorie of energy requirement, calculate your daily fluid requirements. Do you think your fluid requirements are similar from day to day? What factors do you think might affect them?

Types of fluid

Water is considered adequate and suitable for most exercise, but some sports drinks may be useful if exercising at higher intensities for longer durations. Most sports drinks provide three nutrients: carbohydrates to replace energy, water to replace fluid and **electrolytes** to replace minerals lost in sweat. The carbohydrate is usually glucose, fructose, sucrose or maltodextrin – all saccharides that are quickly absorbed. Sports drinks often contain a range of minerals and vitamins, but most include the electrolytes sodium and potassium. The different types of sports drink are outlined in Table 13.9.

Key term

Electrolytes – salts in the blood, for example, potassium and sodium.

▶ **Table 13.9:** Types of sports drink

Type of fluid	Function
Isotonic	• Contain the same concentration of glucose to water as blood: 4–8 per cent or up to 8 grams per 100 ml of water • Usually contain sodium, making them more quickly absorbed into the bloodstream • Useful when exercise has been prolonged or during warmer weather • Can also be used before exercise
Hypertonic	• Contain over 8 per cent of carbohydrate and are absorbed more slowly • Provide a source of carbohydrate replenishment, but are not ideal for optimal rehydration and may need to be consumed with other fluids • Best used in the recovery stage after exercise
Hypotonic	• Have a lower concentration of carbohydrates and are more diluted than isotonic or hypertonic drinks • Contain less than 4 per cent carbohydrate (4 g per 100 ml of water); generally easily absorbed and well tolerated • Although water is adequate for non-endurance training or when sweat losses are small, these drinks may encourage fluid replacement through enhanced taste

Carbonated drinks

Carbonated drinks can contribute towards achieving overall daily fluid intake, but it might not be best to consume them during or after exercise. The gas bubbles in carbonated drink expand the stomach, leading to the sensation of fullness resulting in the athlete consuming less fluid than required to achieve effective rehydration.

Research

Investigate a range of commercial sports drinks and evaluate their potential use before, during and after exercise. What are the advantages and disadvantages of a high carbohydrate content in a sports drink?

Dehydration

Dehydration can reduce strength, power and aerobic capacity. Severe dehydration can cause heatstroke and may be fatal. A loss as small as 2 per cent of body mass can be enough to begin to affect your ability to perform muscular work. For a 75 kg male this would be equivalent to a fluid loss of only 1.5 litres from the body.

It is therefore important to minimise the risks of dehydration, and to note that thirst is a poor indicator of your body's hydration status. Warning signs for dehydration include:

- lack of energy and early fatigue during exercise
- feeling hot
- clammy or flushed skin
- not needing to go to the toilet
- nausea
- headache, disorientation and/or shortness of breath – signs of advanced dehydration.

Hypernatremia

Hypernatremia is associated with dehydration. It is a common electrolyte problem and is defined as a rise in serum sodium concentration above 145 mmol/L. It is generally caused by impaired thirst and/or restricted access to water.

Speed of rehydration

Fluid replacement can be accelerated by drinking still, cool drinks of reasonable volume. They should not be too concentrated, and they must be palatable to drink.

The more intense the activity, the more the absorption of fluid is slowed. Starting exercise well-hydrated and keeping a larger volume of fluid in the gut also facilitate rehydration, as does the inclusion of sodium in fluids.

Hyperhydration

Hyperhydration, also called **water intoxication**, usually occurs because the athlete is drinking too much water to try to avoid dehydration. Water intoxication can lead to **hyponatremia** (low sodium concentration in the blood), a potentially fatal disturbance in brain function that results when the normal balance of electrolytes in the body is pushed outside safe limits. Normal serum sodium levels are 135–145 mmol/L.

Theory into practice

Devise your ideal sports drink and a five point plan to ensure adequate hydration. What practical strategies could be employed to monitor hydration status before, during and after exercise?

Exercise-associated hyponatremia is common in marathon runners, particularly slower runners who have plenty of time to take fluid on board during the event. Severe hyponatremia can result in seizures, coma and death. The warning signs for hyponatremia are similar to those for dehydration and include:

- nausea and vomiting
- headaches
- confusion
- lethargy
- restlessness and irritability
- muscle weakness and cramps.

B Factors affecting digestion and absorption of nutrients and fluids

Before your body can make use of the energy and nutrients in food, the food has to be broken down to release them through the process of digestion.

Basic principles of digestion

The digestive system takes the food and fluid that you consume, extracts nutrients from it, and then jettisons any waste products. The functions are summarised in Table 13.10. The process is as follows.

1. Digestion starts in the mouth (the **buccal cavity**). Your teeth and jaws crush and grind food to mix it with saliva, which contains the enzyme amylase that begins the breakdown of starch.
2. After swallowing, food enters the **oesophagus**, the tube that connects your mouth to your stomach. The food bolus (a small round mass) is squeezed along the oesophagus by the process of **peristalsis** (a series of wave-like muscle contractions that push along the food). It takes around 3–6 seconds for food to travel from your mouth to your stomach.
3. Your stomach acts as a large mixing bowl, churning the food into a liquid called **chyme**. Lining your stomach are cells that produce and release gastric juices containing **enzymes** and hydrochloric acid which help break down the food and kill any bacteria present in it. Food normally remains in your stomach for 1–4 hours, but fluid may pass through much more rapidly.

Key term

Enzymes – proteins that start or accelerate the digestive process.

4 From your stomach the chyme passes to your **duodenum** and then to your **small intestine**, a tube about 6 metres long. As the chyme enters your small intestine, it is mixed with more digestive juices, this time from the **pancreas**. Pancreatic juice contains **bile** made by the **liver** as well as **enzymes** to further assist the breakdown of carbohydrate, protein and fat. Bile is also alkaline (having a pH greater than 7) to neutralise the acid from the stomach. (Your **gall bladder** stores and concentrates bile until it is required for digestion, then it is released into your digestive tract to emulsify fats and neutralise the acids in partly digested food.)
5 Peristalsis continues to move the chyme through your digestive system to your **large intestine** (another long tube) and eventually the **rectum** and **anal canal**.

Key term

Bile – a greenish-brown fluid secreted by the liver and stored in the gall bladder that aids digestion.

Table 13.10: Functions of the digestive system

Function	Description
Breakdown of food	Digestion is a multi-stage process following the ingestion of raw materials (food). It involves mechanical and chemical elements in the process that leads to enzymes in the gut breaking down the larger chemical compounds in food into smaller compounds absorbed by your body.
Absorption of nutrients and fluid	The movement of digested food from your stomach and small intestine into your body tissues and blood. Absorption happens in the villi lining the small intestine. Each villus has a network of capillaries to quickly absorb nutrients. Amino acids (from proteins) and glucose (from carbohydrates) enter your bloodstream directly. Fatty acids and glycerol (from fats) are taken up by your lymphatic system.
Excretion of waste products	The removal of potentially poisonous end-products from metabolism, normally in urine and faeces. The main organs of excretion are the kidneys, through which urine is eliminated, and the large intestine, through which solid or semi-solid waste is expelled.

Absorption of nutrients and fluid

It is as the chyme moves through your small intestine that vitamins, minerals, amino acids, fatty acids and sugars are absorbed by your intestinal wall. Lining the wall of your small intestine are finger-like projections known as villi, which increase the surface area available for absorption. By the time the chyme reaches your large intestine, it is less fluid and has been reduced to mainly indigestible matter.

Your large intestine does not produce any digestive enzymes but continues to absorb water. Bacteria in your large intestine produce vitamin K. The residue (faeces) left behind is eliminated (excreted) from your body through your anus.

The digestive system is shown in Figure 13.3.

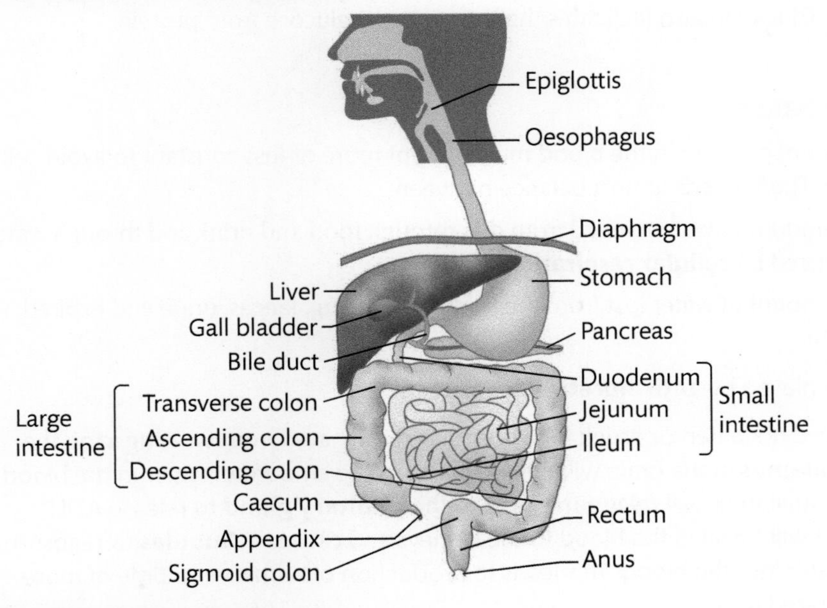

Figure 13.3: The digestive system

Timing of digestion and absorption

Gastrointestinal blood flow increases after meals, an experience known as **postprandial hyperemia**. The extent and the duration of hyperemia appears to depend on the composition of the meal. In general, fat and protein-rich meals are more powerful than carbohydrate-rich meals in stimulating hyperemia.

Digestion and absorption time varies for individuals. For healthy adults it is usually between 24–72 hours depending on what has been consumed. In general, after you have eaten it takes between 6–8 hours for food to pass through your stomach and small intestine.

Carbohydrates spend the least amount of time in the stomach and are digested quickest. Protein takes a bit longer, while fat takes the longest to fully digest. The precise time depends upon the food that you ate and the complexity of its structure. Digestion and absorption are slowed by a high fibre content.

Hormonal control of blood sugar and water balance

Blood sugar (glucose) levels

Key term

Secretion – the process of a substance being released from the interior of a cell to its exterior.

The body requires blood sugar to be kept within narrow limits (3.5–5.5 mmol/L). The hormones **insulin** and **glucagon** are responsible for this. Both are **secreted** by cells called the Islets of Langerhans within the pancreas. These regulate the use and storage of **glucose** by cells.

After eating a meal containing carbohydrate, starch and larger sugar units are broken down to glucose, absorbed in the small intestine and enter the bloodstream. This triggers a rise in blood glucose. The pancreas monitors blood glucose, and once it rises above normal levels it releases insulin into the bloodstream. Insulin causes glucose to move from the blood into the cells where it is used for energy, stored in the liver or muscle cells as glycogen, or converted and stored as fat.

When blood glucose drops below normal levels, between meals and during exercise, the pancreas secretes glucagon. The effect of glucagon release is to make the liver release glucose stored in its cells into the bloodstream to increase circulating blood glucose. Glucagon also facilitates the liver to make glucose from protein.

Water balance

The amount of water in the blood must be kept more or less constant to avoid cell damage. There needs to be a balance between:

- the amount of water gained from diet through food and drink and through water produced by **cellular respiration**
- the amount of water lost from the body in sweating, faeces, urine and expired breath.

This is achieved by **anti-diuretic hormone (ADH)**.

If you have not eaten or drunk for a while, or if you have been sweating a lot, the **hypothalamus** in the brain will detect a drop in the amount of water in the blood. The hypothalamus will relay a message to the **pituitary gland** to release ADH. The ADH will travel in the blood to the kidneys and cause the **tubules** to reabsorb more water into the blood. This leads to production of a smaller volume of more concentrated urine.

In other situations, the level of water in the blood may go up, for example, when it is cooler and the body is not losing as much water through sweat or because excess fluid has been consumed. Here the hypothalamus detects the change and sends a message to the pituitary gland slowing or stopping the release of ADH. Without ADH the kidneys will not save as much water and large volumes of dilute urine are produced until the level of water in the blood falls to normal levels.

Control of glycogen synthesis

Glycogen is a crucial source of glucose for fuelling activity. Around 80 per cent of glycogen is stored in your muscles while the rest is stored in your liver, with a small amount of circulating blood glucose. Excess carbohydrate which is not required to replenish glycogen stores is converted to fat and stored in your body's adipose tissue.

Carbohydrate can only be stored as glycogen in limited amounts - approximately 375–475 grams in the average adult, equivalent to approximately 1500–2000 kcal.

Day-to-day stores of glycogen are influenced by your dietary carbohydrate intake and levels of physical activity or training. Regular exercise can encourage your muscles to adapt to store more glycogen. This is an important training adaptation for elite athletes, particularly in endurance-type sports.

PAUSE POINT How can cool downs help athletes to improve their performance and avoid injury?

Hint Intensity and duration of exercise influence the rate and amount of glycogen usage. Are there particular days in the week when you are more at risk of not recovering adequately?

Extend Can you develop a five point plan to ensure you maintain adequate muscle glycogen levels to support optimal adaptation and recovery from training?

C Nutritional intake for health and well-being

Performance in and recovery from exercise are enhanced by optimal nutrition. For most sports, carbohydrate requirements are likely to contribute 55–65 per cent of total energy intake and protein 12–15 per cent, with the remainder coming from fat. Vitamin and mineral supplementation will not improve the performance of athletes whose diet is already adequate and varied.

To plan a diet for a sports activity, you need to consider the physiological demands of the activity, the phase of training and the individual's needs. These will help you to plan a **balanced diet** across the food groups.

Balanced diet for health and well-being

Foods are popularly classed as 'good' or 'bad' and 'healthy' or 'unhealthy', with **healthy eating** often viewed as a hardship or a chore. However, it is better to look at the overall balance of foods eaten as either healthy or unhealthy (see Figure 13.4).

Key terms

Balanced diet - a diet that provides the correct amounts of nutrients without excess or deficiency.

Healthy eating - the pursuit of a balanced diet to support health and reduce the risks of chronic disease. Healthy eating principles should form the solid foundations on which athletes can build more specific nutritional strategies to support training and competition.

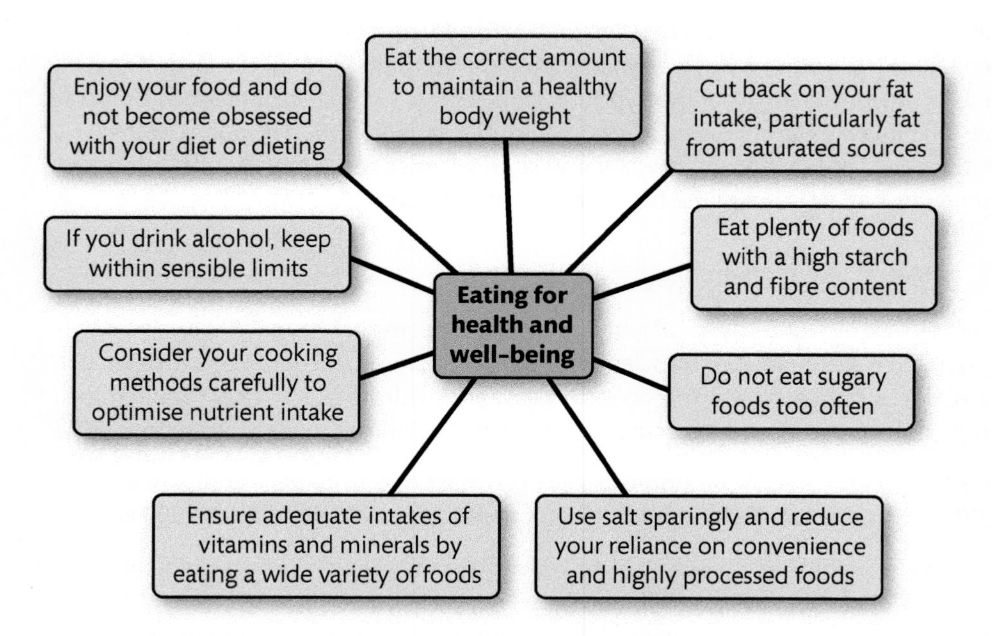

▶ **Figure 13.4:** A simple guide to eating for health and well-being

The Eatwell Guide

The Eatwell Guide is produced by the UK government and represents the proportions of the main food groups that form a healthy, balanced diet (see Figure 13.5). It applies to most people in the UK, except children under the age of five.

People with special dietary requirements or medical conditions should speak to a registered dietician about how to adapt the Eatwell Guide to meet their individual needs.

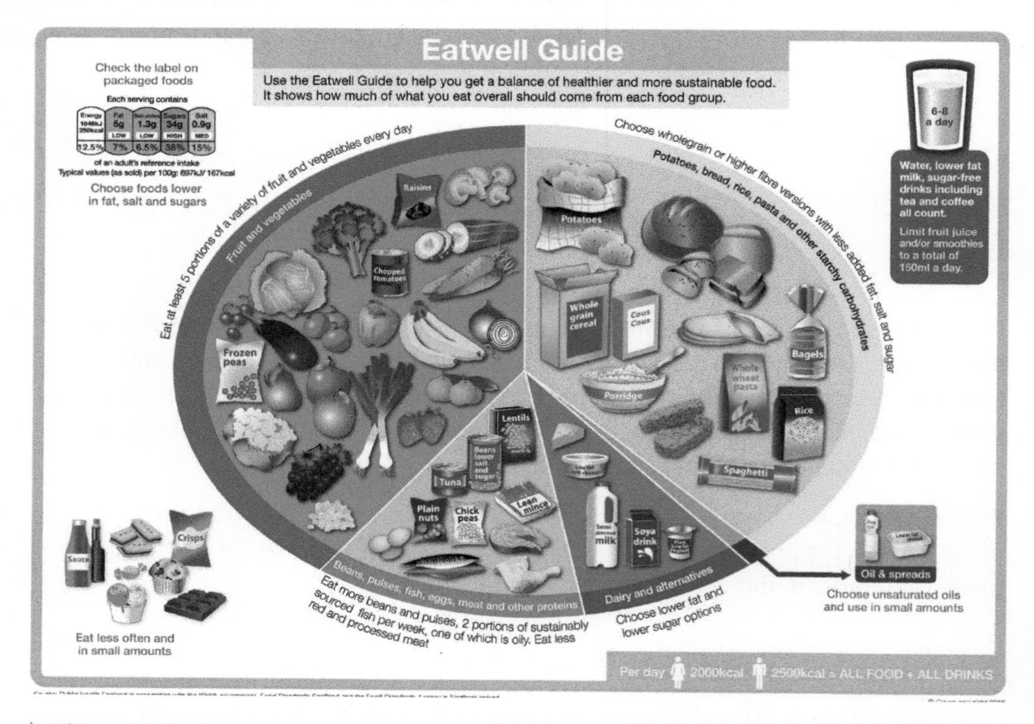

▶ **Figure 13.5:** The Eatwell Guide (Source: Public Health England in association with the Welsh government, Food Standards Scotland and the Food Standards Agency in Northern Ireland. © Crown Copyright). Do you try to limit your intake of foods with a high fat or sugar content?

Table 13.11: Recommended daily amounts and nutrients supplied by each of the main food groups (Adapted from The Eatwell Guide © Crown copyright 2016. Re-used under the terms of the Open Government Licence v.3.0)

Food	How much	Tips
Fruit and vegetables		
All fruits and vegetables including fresh, frozen, canned, dried and juiced varieties; potatoes do not count as they are considered a starchy carbohydrate food	Aim for at least 5 portions of a variety of fruit and vegetables every day A portion of dried fruit is 30 g and only counts as one of your 5-a-day A portion of fruit juice or smoothie is 150 ml and only counts as one of your 5-a-day	Try to eat as many different types of fruit and vegetables as possible Avoid adding sauces or dressings that are high in fat, salt or sugar Limit fruit juice and smoothies to a combined total of 150 ml per day
Starchy carbohydrates		
Bread (soda bread, rye bread, pitta, flour tortilla, baguettes, chappatis, bagels), rice, potatoes, breakfast cereals, oats, pasta, noodles, maize, cornmeal, couscous, bulgar wheat, polenta, millet, spelt, wheat, pearl barley, yams and plantains	Eat plenty of starchy carbohydrates including potatoes, bread, rice and pasta Choose wholegrain varieties, or keep the skins on potatoes, for more fibre, vitamins and minerals	Base your meals around starchy carbohydrates Choose products that are lowest in fat, salt and sugar Avoid adding too much fat or sauces
Dairy and dairy alternatives		
Milk, cheese, yoghurt, fromage frais, quark, cream cheese, and non-dairy alternatives to these foods	Eat some dairy or dairy alternatives each day Choose lower fat options when possible	Try swapping to 1% fat milk as opposed to whole or semi-skimmed milk Try buying reduced fat cheese
Proteins		
Meat, poultry and game, white fish, oily fish, shellfish, nuts, eggs, beans and other pulses, vegetarian meat alternatives	Eat some protein every day Eat at least two portions of fish each week, one of which is oily Limit processed meats	Try not to add extra oil when cooking or serving these foods Choose lean cuts of meat
Oils and spreads		
Unsaturated oils including vegetable oil, rapeseed oil, olive oil and sunflower oil, soft spreads made from these oils	Use sparingly and less often as they are often high in fat	Choose lower fat spreads where possible Choose oils high in unsaturated fat and low in saturated fat
Foods to eat less often and in small amounts		
Cakes, biscuits, chocolate, sweets, puddings, pastries, ice cream, jam, honey, crisps, sauces, butter, cream, mayonnaise	These foods are not required as part of a healthy, balanced diet. If included, they should be consumed infrequently and in small amounts	Use lower fat spread instead of butter Swap cakes and biscuits for a slice of malt loaf or a teacake with low fat spread

Food preparation and nutritional composition

Some nutrient loss is a consequence of almost all food preparation processes. Exposure to heat, light or oxygen will alter the nutrients in food. The effect of food preparation on nutrients will vary depending on the characteristics of the food and the processes followed. Cooking methods that involve water, such as boiling, often reduce micronutrients as they get washed out, a process known as leaching. Steaming and microwaving will help to preserve micronutrient content. Processing, including preparation, can make food healthier, safer, tastier and extend its shelf-life.

To optimise nutrient availability, choose good quality foods, preferably natural or lightly processed as these are likely to have a higher nutritional value. Boiled, grilled and baked items are likely to be lower in fat than fried and roasted items. Cured foods, particularly cured meat or fish, will have undergone a range of different preservation and flavouring processes involving the addition of a combination of salt, sugar and either nitrate or nitrite. The curing processes may also involve smoking.

Research

Juicing and raw foods are now a popular means of trying to increase the nutrient content of the diet for the health conscious. Investigate the potential advantages and disadvantages of these two methods of food preparation.

Benefits of a balanced diet

Scientific research suggests that the benefits of a healthy balanced diet include increased energy and vitality, improved immune system function, maintenance of healthy body weight and reduced risk of chronic disease.

Deficiencies, excesses and imbalances in dietary intakes all produce potentially negative impacts on health which can lead to a range of dietary-related disorders. Disorders of deficiency include **osteoporosis** (lack of calcium) and **anaemia** (lack of iron), while disorders of excess include **obesity** (excess calories) and **coronary heart disease** (excess fat). Imbalances of dietary intake may occur during periods of high nutritional demand such as growth or pregnancy, or when physical or psychological difficulties impact on meeting adequate nutritional intake such as during old age.

The obesity epidemic is growing at a steady rate. Obesity increases the risk of various diseases, in particular, **cardiovascular disease** and **Type 2 diabetes mellitus**. Both are considered lifestyle diseases which can be prevented and managed by diet and activity.

Cancer

The role of diet in heart disease or diabetes is fairly clear, but it is not as clear-cut for cancer. Many foods and nutrients have been studied for cancer prevention, but finding specific links between a food or macronutrient and cancer is difficult. Foods contain an array of components, macronutrients, micronutrients and non-nutrients that may contribute to cancer prevention. But we also eat and drink a variety of foods, creating interactions between them that are challenging to study, and in some cases the way food is prepared can be an influencing factor.

However, there is some strong evidence for the role of fruits and vegetables. These are thought to protect against several cancers, including those of the mouth, pharynx, larynx, oesophagus, stomach, lung, pancreas and prostate. However, the extent of the protection and how it works requires further research.

Fibre also appears to have a protective role in some cancers. Fibre adds bulk to your stools and moves food more quickly through your digestive system. Protein is often studied as a risk factor for cancer. Most of these studies suggest that people who eat more red meat have a higher risk of developing colorectal cancer than those who eat less red meat, but avoiding processed meats appears to be even more important. Alcohol is also thought to increase the risk of several cancers.

Case study

Diet diary

Keep a record of everything you consume for at least 3 days, including one weekend day. Be as accurate and honest as possible, and do not modify your usual intake, otherwise you will not be evaluating your typical diet. Carry your record with you at all times and:

- list the type and quantity of food/drink consumed
- estimate the portion size using standard household measures, such as slices of bread, millilitres of fluid, or give the weight if known from packaging
- say when and where the food or drink was consumed – this will help you to assess external factors that affect your dietary intake
- state the methods of food preparation or cooking
- note any activity or exercise you took part in, including its duration and intensity.

Check your knowledge

1. Compare your record to the Eatwell Guide. Write a short report on your findings.
2. Is there room for improvement in your diet?
3. Does your diet meet the demands of your participation in sport and exercise?

Eating disorders

The phrase 'eating disorders' covers a wide spectrum of harmful eating behaviours used in an attempt to lose weight or achieve a lean appearance, including those listed in Table 13.12. People with an eating disorder often display a gross disruption of eating behaviour in which they deliberately and dangerously manipulate diet and body weight. Ritualistic eating is often combined with purging behaviours such as self-induced vomiting, laxative abuse and/or excessive exercise.

Anorexia nervosa and bulimia nervosa are psychiatric disorders because they are accompanied by other emotional disturbances. They are more common in women than men, and there is a higher incidence in those who participate in sport.

Table 13.12: Eating disorder descriptions

Eating disorder	Description
Anorexia nervosa	• Usually occurs in teenage years, but can start at any age. • A dangerous condition that can lead to serious ill health or even death. • Symptoms include fear of fatness, excessive worry about weight, under-eating, excessive weight loss, inability to stop losing weight even when below a healthy weight, excessive exercise, abuse of laxatives or other weight-loss tablets, and an irregular or ceased menstrual cycle.
Bulimia nervosa	• May start in the mid-teens, but not usually present until the mid-20s, as most sufferers are likely to be of normal weight making the condition easier to hide. • Symptoms include worrying more and more about weight, binge eating, feeling guilty about weight and eating patterns while staying within a normal weight range, use and abuse of laxatives, self-induced vomiting and an irregular menstrual cycle.
Binge eating disorder	• Condition where the sufferer feels compelled to regularly over-eat. • Tends to develop in young adults, but often does not present until sufferers are in their 30s/40s. • Involves binge eating followed by dieting, but not vomiting. • Sufferers consume large quantities of food over short time periods, even when not hungry. • A distressing condition, but not as harmful as bulimia. • Sufferers are more likely to become overweight and suffer health complications from being overweight. • Men are equally as likely as women to suffer from this eating disorder.

PAUSE POINT Evidence suggests participants in appearance-orientated sports, where performance is evaluated by judges, may be more prone to eating disorders. Why do you think this might be?

Hint Research high-profile elite athletes who have suffered eating disorders.

Extend How could some of these concerns around weight control be avoided?

D Nutritional strategies for sports performance

Nutritional strategies

Athletes should pay careful attention to foods that can enhance, not hinder, their preparation for, participation in and recovery from training and competition. Most athletes obtain all the energy and nutrients they need by eating when they are hungry and choosing a balanced and varied diet.

Every sport requires sound nutritional strategies to support successful performance, but with different considerations to be taken into account. For example, with the intermittent nature of team sports, intensity of performance can alter at any time.

These changes are irregular and can be random, and may draw significantly on the body's glycogen stores. Performance may be impaired towards the end of a match if glycogen stores are running low. In contrast, weight-loss methods and restrictive dietary practices are often used by athletes in weight category and aesthetic sports, with potential dangers to both health and performance.

Reflect

When developing nutritional strategies to support sport and exercise there should be no conflict between eating for health and eating for performance. For a sport of your choice, reflect on what matters to the athlete and how sound nutritional principles and practice could help to maintain health and improve performance.

Carbohydrate loading

The aim of carbohydrate loading is to increase the muscles' capacity to store glycogen above their normal level. This may be useful to athletes competing in endurance events that last longer than 90 minutes, such as marathon running, triathlon and endurance swimming. When your muscle cells run out of glycogen, fatigue sets in. High pre-race glycogen stores help to delay fatigue and improve performance during the latter stages of a race.

The amount of glycogen available for storage in the muscles is related to the amount of carbohydrate consumed and the level and intensity of activity undertaken. For most sports, a diet consisting of between 5-10 grams of carbohydrate per kilogram of body weight will maintain liver and muscle glycogen stores.

Guidelines for carbohydrate loading suggest that athletes maintain their normal carbohydrate intake for the first three days, but increase it in the last three days before competition (see Table 13.13). This technique offers elevated muscle glycogen levels, with the possibility to increase stores by as much as 20–40 per cent.

Carbohydrate loading will not increase your endurance unless you are a highly conditioned athlete: additional carbohydrate will not result in extra muscle glycogen stores unless the enzymes within the muscles are primed by regular hard training. Instead, the extra carbohydrate is likely to be stored as fat.

Table 13.13: A guide to carbohydrate loading

Days before race	Training	Diet
7	Intense 90 mins	Usual 50–60% carbohydrate diet
6 & 5	Moderate 40 mins	Usual 50–60% carbohydrate diet
4	Moderate 30 mins	Usual 50–60% carbohydrate diet
3	Moderate 20 mins	70% carbohydrate diet
2	Light 20 mins	70% carbohydrate diet
1	Rest	70% carbohydrate diet
Race day		Well-tested pre-race meal

Theory into practice

Devise a suitable carbohydrate loading strategy for a runner undertaking their first marathon. Be sure to include practical meal and snack suggestions.

Increased protein intake

Many athletes believe they need to eat large amounts of protein to build muscle and increase strength, but this is often not necessary. Some of these foods are high in animal fats, considered bad for long-term health. They may also leave no appetite for carbohydrate foods to provide sufficient energy stores to support training. In most cases, eating a normal, varied diet and meeting energy (calorie) requirements should provide enough protein.

When active individuals do require more protein per kilogram of body weight in order to promote tissue growth and repair, the International Olympic Committee recommends an intake of 1.2–1.6 grams per kilogram of body weight per day. The lower end of this range should cover the requirements of most endurance athletes, with the upper end meeting the needs of those engaging in more strength and power activities.

Weight loss

For some sports, low body weight may be crucial, sometimes below an athlete's natural weight. These include weight-category sports, such as boxing, weight lifting, rowing and some martial arts, and weight-controlled sports such as distance running, gymnastics, figure skating and diving. These sports present challenges in maintaining a nutritionally adequate diet while reducing or maintaining weight. Inappropriate weight-loss practices include:

- fasting or skipping meals
- laxative abuse
- bingeing and purging
- intentional dehydration via sweatsuits or saunas.

Most athletes who talk about achieving weight loss usually mean fat loss, as losses in muscle mass may result in unfavourable changes in their power-to-weight ratio. A sensible goal is to reduce body fat by about 0.5–1.0 kg per week (a loss of 3500–7000 calories). It is preferable to make these calorie savings by reducing the intake of dietary fat while maintaining carbohydrate and protein intakes. Some athletes on restricted energy budgets may require the guidance of a registered sports nutritionist to achieve weight loss targets while maintaining a healthy diet.

Theory into practice

Produce a short leaflet for athletes in a weight-controlled or category sport that focuses on maintaining health and performance while attempting weight loss.

Weight gain

Weight can be gained by increasing the amount of fat or the amount of lean body mass. Both will register as increases in weight on the scales, but the results will be very different for body composition. Gains in fat weight are relatively easy to achieve, but gains in lean body mass can only be achieved by adapting to a progressive strength training programme, supported by an adequate diet.

When athletes talk about weight gain, they usually mean muscle gain. Strength training provides the stimulus for muscles to grow, while adequate nutrition allows them to grow at an optimal rate. Rates of weight/muscle gain depend on genetics and body type.

To gain strength and size, it is necessary to achieve a slightly positive energy balance – approximately an extra 500 calories per day – and a protein intake of about 1.4–1.7 grams per kilogram of body mass. A high-protein diet, or supplementing with amino acids (common practice for many athletes wishing to gain muscle bulk and size) will not automatically lead to great increases in muscle size or strength. Achieving an adequate energy intake is more important.

In a very few instances the athlete may wish to gain fat weight, such as in contact sports where additional body fat may provide extra protection.

Case study

Building up

Will is 24 years old and works as a security operative at a local nightclub. He has been training regularly for the last two years by attending the gym six times a week and is considering becoming a competitive body builder. He consumes large quantities of high biological value protein foods at regular intervals throughout the day at mealtimes and for snacks, along with 500 mls of a whey protein supplement each day.

Since starting training Will has made some improvements in his bulk and strength, but a significant amount of the weight gain appears to be round his midriff, and he often complains of tiredness and low energy levels. He would like to achieve greater gains in strength and more overall gains in muscle bulk.

Check your knowledge

1. What nutritional advice would you give Will to help him achieve his goals?
2. Is there any additional information on his diet and exercise habits that would be helpful to know in order to formulate appropriate advice?

Application of nutritional strategies for different sports events

The sections on weight loss and weight gain have hinted that different activities require different dietary plans or strategies to optimise performance.

Endurance events

Endurance activities significantly challenge an athlete's energy and fluid stores. The longer and more intense the aerobic training or competition, the more depleted these stores become.

Endurance athletes should aim to maximise glycogen stores. Increasing carbohydrate intake during the two or three days before competition is a useful strategy. Carbohydrate supplements (energy drinks, bars or gels) may be a useful dietary addition.

Endurance athletes should start exercise fully hydrated. The longer the duration of the activity, the more important it is to consume fluids during it. Sports drinks can provide carbohydrate as well as replacing fluids.

Strength and power events

In strength, power and sprint sports, nutritional strategies support the development of lean body mass (muscle) as well as meeting energy demands. Although carbohydrate requirements are not as great as for endurance events, they are still important. Combining carbohydrate with protein post-exercise promotes an **anabolic** environment and increases protein synthesis that helps promote muscle development. However, excessive protein intake should be avoided.

Key term

Anabolism – the constructive metabolism of the body – the building of tissue.

▶ Sprinters may find it helpful to take on both carbohydrates and protein after exercise

Sports requiring strength and endurance

Many sports require high levels of both strength and endurance. For example, high levels of muscular strength and endurance are required for rugby as well as weight-category sports such as judo. Nutritional demands will be dictated by the nature of the individual sport and participant requirements, but key nutrients in all cases are carbohydrate and fluid.

Weight-category or weight-controlled events

Leanness or a specific weight may be considered important for optimal performance, placing greater emphasis on what the athlete eats. It is important to remember that the fewer calories consumed, the fewer nutrients consumed. Calcium and iron intakes are reported to be particularly low in studies investigating the diet of female participants in these sports.

Healthy eating and Eatwell Guide principles apply to the planning of dietary intakes for these sports, but greater emphasis may be placed on a low-fat diet. However, this should not be at the expense of essential nutrients such as carbohydrate, protein, vitamins and minerals. Adequate fluid intake and hydration are also essential to maintain concentration for the technical demands of these sports.

Case study

Macronutrient energy distribution

Maxwell has recently taken up the triathlon. His usual diet consists of a macronutrient energy distribution of 40 per cent carbohydrate, 40 per cent fat and 20 per cent protein. He is about to enter his first major competition.

Check your knowledge

1. What effect could this macronutrient distribution have on his performance?
2. What practical advice could you offer to improve his diet?
3. What could Maxwell do in his preparation for the competition to help to delay fatigue?

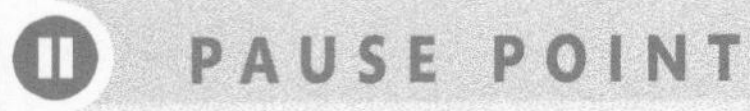

What factors are likely to impact the nutritional requirements of team sports?

Hint Consider the physiological demands of team sports and the energy systems involved.

Extend Using a team sport of your choice, develop nutrition guidelines you would apply to meet the nutritional needs of players during in-season training and competition.

Supplements to support nutritional strategies

Discussion

The sports world is flooded with pills, powders, bars and drinks that promise to provide a competitive edge within the rules. Should you invest in these products or in sports science support, such as nutritional advice, sports psychology and training techniques?

Athletes are always looking for something to give them a competitive advantage. The financial cost of dietary manipulation and nutritional supplementation is often high. Misinformation often supports questionable practices, some of which can be harmful. The supplement market is worth millions but the manufacture, processing, labelling and marketing of these products is poorly regulated with variable quality control. The products available all make convincing claims including better recovery, increased strength and size, loss of body fat and enhanced immune function.

Supplements can essentially be broken down into two main categories.

1 **Nutrient or dietary supplements** help the athlete meet their overall nutritional needs, by providing a practical alternative to food or by helping to meet higher than average requirements for nutrients, particularly carbohydrate and protein.
2 **Nutritional ergogenic aids** generally aim to enhance performance through effects on energy, body composition and alertness.

Key term

Ergogenic aids – ergogenic refers to the application of a nutritional, physical, mechanical, psychological or pharmacological procedure or aid to improve physical work capacity or athletic performance. Ergogenic aids are assumed to enhance performance above and beyond what would normally be expected, for example caffeine and creatine.

Nutrient or dietary supplements

Nutrient supplements include:

- sports drinks, gels and bars
- liquid meal and protein supplements
- carbohydrate loaders and powders
- multivitamin and mineral supplements.

Some athletes find these products help them to meet their nutritional goals during particularly demanding periods of training and competition. For example, sports drinks are a convenient way to meet the high energy demands of training or competition.

Athletes must know how and when to use them to get maximum benefit towards supporting nutrition goals. If used in the correct way (time and amount), supplements can assist athletes to train and compete at their best. However, poor regulation of the supplement industry means marketing hype often overstates unproven benefits.

Supplements should be safe, effective and legal. Poor practice can lead to problems. Athletes must balance the potential benefits against risks, particularly of anti-doping rule violations: a significant number of supplements on the market contain doping agents that will cause an athlete to fail a drugs test.

Supplements will not compensate for consistently poor food choices, but may provide a short-term solution for a nutrient deficiency until a dietary solution can be implemented, particularly if the athlete is travelling and living away from home.

Athletes often follow hearsay about supplement use, and can take them in larger doses than is sensible. Supplement use requires assessment and advice by a registered sports nutritionist and/or medical practitioner. Supplements should not be used by young athletes (those under 18 years of age), unless medically indicated and monitored.

Discussion

Athletes need a training diet that can be adapted to situations such as injury or specific competition requirements. Discuss how nutrient supplements can help athletes meet macronutrient intake goals for training and competition.

Common supplements

Caffeine

The most common source of caffeine in our diet is coffee, but cola drinks, energy drinks, and specialised sports foods and supplements also contribute.

Caffeine was removed from the World Anti-Doping Agency (WADA) prohibited list in 2004. This change was made despite the acknowledgment that caffeine enhances performance even in small doses (similar to everyday consumption); however, monitoring caffeine use via urinary caffeine concentrations was not reliable.

On consumption, caffeine is rapidly absorbed and transported to body tissues and organs. Its effects can vary between individuals with both positive and negative influences, including:

- the mobilisation of fat from adipose tissue and muscle cells
- changes in muscle contractility
- alterations to the central nervous system influencing perception of effort or fatigue
- stimulation of adrenaline
- effects on the heart, such as increased blood pressure and heart rate.

Recent research suggests that caffeine's major effect is to reduce the actual or perceived fatigue which occurs with prolonged activity. It enhances alertness and increases the time that an individual can sustain their optimal output or pace.

Athletes wanting to use caffeine to enhance performance should develop supplementation strategies that use the lowest effective dose. The effects of acute intake follow a U-shaped curve: although low to moderate doses produce positive effects and a sense of well-being, the effects of higher doses can include:

- increases in heart rate
- impairments or alterations of fine motor control and skilled performance
- anxiety or over-arousal.

Theory into practice

You have been approached by the strength and conditioning coach of a local rugby club. The club is concerned about the increased use of caffeine-rich energy drinks and supplements by players. Consider how you might develop a caffeine-use strategy for implementation by the club.

Creatine

Creatine is a naturally-occurring compound found in the brain and skeletal muscle due to dietary intake and endogenous synthesis from amino acids. Muscle creatine content varies between individuals, mostly likely due to age, gender and fibre type. Vegetarians not consuming a dietary source of creatine are reliant on the body's synthesis of creatine and have lower muscle creatine concentrations than meat-eaters.

Creatine supplements can be used in different ways, including acute loading (taking a high dose of creatine over a short period of time, usually 5 to 7 days) or chronic use (taking a low dose every day for a longer period of time, e.g. 28 days). They may help:

- athletes undertaking resistance training to build lean body mass
- during sprint training sessions where athletes are required to repeat short explosive maximal efforts with brief recovery intervals
- in sports with intermittent work patterns, such as basketball, soccer and tennis.

Research

Investigate the range of creatine supplements available on the market and different protocols for use. What advice would you give a 17-year-old basketball player considering creatine supplementation?

There appears to be considerable variability in response to creatine supplementation but it is advised that supplementation is limited to experienced and well-developed athletes. Those with the lowest initial levels, such as vegetarians, may show the highest response, while those with resting creatine content near the muscle threshold may show no or little enhancement. Creatine uptake into the muscle may be boosted by simultaneous intake of a carbohydrate-rich meal or snack.

The long-term consequences of creatine use are still considered to be unknown. There have been few reports of adverse outcomes over its 25-year history of use, but there are anecdotal accounts of an increased risk of muscle cramps, strains and tears, and weight gain of up to 1 kg is often associated with supplementation. Some users also experience gastrointestinal discomfort or an increase in headaches.

Energy gels

Energy gels provide an easy-to-consume and quickly digestible source of carbohydrate - around 20–25 grams per pouch. They have a greater carbohydrate concentration than sports drinks. Individual products vary in flavour, consistency, type and amounts of carbohydrate and the addition of other ingredients such as electrolytes and caffeine. Good oral hygiene should be practised around their use, such as routine tooth brushing and regular dental checks.

Energy gels should be consumed with water or other dilute fluids. This fluid intake will reduce the overall carbohydrate concentration, reducing the risk of gastrointestinal disturbance and helping to meet the general hydration needs of the activity.

Energy gels can help tour cyclists such as Geraint Thomas

These products are a costly alternative to common food and fluid options and are best used for specific conditions for which they are appropriate, rather than as an everyday snack. They are particularly useful as a compact source of fuel for endurance athletes during exercise lasting more than 90 minutes, such as cycling, triathlon and marathon running. To assess tolerance, athletes should practise using gels during training sessions if they intend to use them in competition.

Protein shakes and powders

Protein supplements can be classified according to their nutrient profile as providing:

- protein only
- a combination of protein and carbohydrate
- a supplement containing additional ergogenic ingredients such as creatine, specific amino acids, proposed fat burners or vitamins and minerals.

The decision to use any protein supplement should be based on a range of issues relevant to the individual athlete, particularly their training load and goals, daily energy requirements, usual diet, post-exercise appetite and budget. Before considering supplementation, atheletes should consult a registered sports nutritionist to establish if protein supplementation is necessary.

Protein shakes and powders are typically based on whey, casein and soy protein. Whey protein is rapidly digested and rich in branch chain amino acids, particularly leucine. Soy protein is also rapidly digestible and often used in mixed protein supplements and protein bars. In contrast, casein clots in the acidic environment of the stomach, resulting in slower digestion.

The timing of protein intake may be a more important factor than the total amount consumed. Each time protein is consumed a small spike in muscle synthesis occurs, with 20–25 grams of high biological value protein producing the maximal response. Eating quantities in excess of this offers no added benefit to muscle protein synthesis. Spreading protein consumption across the day and including it in meals and snacks will produce multiple spikes in muscle protein synthesis. In addition, eating protein in the hour following exercise can help to prolong the protein synthesis response, promoting muscle gains and minimising muscle breakdown.

Theory into practice

Draw up a list of meals and snacks providing 20–25 grams of high biological value protein that would provide athletes with enough protein throughout the day to support muscle protein synthesis.

Beetroot juice

Beetroot juice is a relatively new nutritional supplement. Beetroot is rich in nitrate. Following ingestion, nitrate is converted to nitrite and stored and circulated in the blood. In conditions of low oxygen availability, such as during exercise, nitrite can be converted into nitric oxide, known to play a number of roles in vascular and metabolic control.

From a health perspective, dietary nitrate supplementation increases plasma nitrite concentration and reduces resting blood pressure. From an exercise perspective, nitrate supplementation reduces the oxygen cost of submaximal exercise and can, in some situations, enhance exercise tolerance and performance. It also appears to represent a promising new approach for enhancing physiological responses to exercise, such as muscle efficiency and oxygenation.

The precise conditions in which nitrate may be ergogenic have yet to be fully established. The effectiveness of nitrate use might depend on factors such as:

- age and overall diet, health and fitness status
- the nature, intensity and duration of the exercise
- the dose and duration of the nitrate supplementation.

It appears that inactive and recreationally active individuals show greater performance improvements than elite athletes. Potential side effects include mild gut discomfort in some athletes and pink coloured urine and stools, both of which are harmless.

Diuretics

Diuretics increase urine production and, because some athletes use them to flush out residue from steroids, they are banned by WADA. They are also used to shed water as a temporary weight loss measure in sports with weight categories such as boxing and mixed martial arts. Naturally-occurring diuretics include alcohol and caffeine. These substances would not be recommended for use within safe and effective nutritional strategies.

Vitamin and mineral supplements

Vitamin and mineral deficiencies will impair health and performance. However, there is no evidence that supplementing with these nutrients will enhance performance except where a pre-existing deficiency exists. Those at risk of deficiency include athletes who regularly restrict energy intake or lack sufficient variety in their diet.

Supplementation may be justified where known food intolerances exist which limit the types of food that can be eaten. It can also be justified when there is a prolonged and unavoidable reduction in energy intake or nutrient density of dietary intake; this might be because of an extended period of travel or a sustained period of energy restriction to support weight loss or maintenance.

Vitamin and mineral supplements are often seen as a substitute for poor intakes of fruits and vegetables. However, these supplements do not contain the array of phytochemicals found in fruits and vegetables that promote health benefits. Also, it has been shown that, in respect of the adaptive response to exercise training, large doses of antioxidant vitamin supplements (vitamins A, C and E) may be counterproductive because they disturb the balance of the body's antioxidant system.

Branch chain amino acids

Branch chain amino acids (BCAAs) have been widely used within body building but in recent years have become increasingly popular among the general athletic population. The BCAAs leucine, isoleucine and valine are essential amino acids that cannot be synthesised by the body and must be obtained from dietary sources. BCAAs have the unique characteristic that they can be metabolised in skeletal muscle, while other essential amino acids are metabolised via the liver.

It is suggested that they benefit performance in a number of ways including as a stimulant for muscle protein synthesis, by:

- preventing muscle protein breakdown
- reducing markers of exercise-induced muscle damage.

There is also a suggestion that BCAAs may impede the transport of tryptophan to the brain, reducing the synthesis of serotonin thereby lessening perception of fatigue.

Athletes with weight management concerns who are on tight energy budgets may benefit from supplementation with BCAAs. Research investigating the effects of supplementation has used a wide range of dosing strategies, but to get maximal benefits for muscle protein synthesis and recovery, a dose of BCAAs that provides around 2–3 grams of leucine is advised. However, BCAA supplementation should always be considered on an individual basis and guidance should be sought from a registered sports nutritionist.

Points to consider with supplement use

When evaluating the safety and efficacy of supplements of any kind, consider the following questions.

- Is it a banned substance?
- What are the perceived benefits?
- What does the weight of scientific evidence suggest?
- Is the research from a genuine, independent source?
- Does the research apply to the targeted sport?
- Are there any contraindications for use?
- Are there any side effects?

As the term suggests, even supplements that are proven to have performance benefits should be just that: supplements, not replacements for a sensible, well-planned, balanced and varied diet. Indiscriminate use of supplements is unwise.

Before deciding to use any supplement it is worth undertaking a cost-benefit analysis in terms of the potential performance benefits weighed against the costs, not only financial but also potential adverse effects on health and performance and the likelihood of contamination with banned or other undesirable substances. (Animal excrement and glass are just two undesirable elements that have been found in supplements due to unscrupulous production processes.)

The World Anti-Doping Code holds the athlete entirely responsible for any prohibited substance found in their system. Athletes are strongly advised to be cautious and vigilant about the use of any supplement and to optimise diet, lifestyle and training before turning to supplements.

Generally products manufactured within the food and pharmaceutical industries are safer because standards are more rigorous. You should have reasonable confidence in vitamin and mineral supplements produced by a pharmaceutical company and sports drinks and bars produced by a reputable food manufacturer.

It is wise to seek evidence-based reasons for using a supplement that can be supported by a substantial amount of independent scientific evidence. The evidence ought to be very compelling to outweigh any potential risks.

Research

Visit the WADA website and find out about the World Anti-Doping Code and its education programmes on the dangers and consequences of doping. Why should athletes be cautioned against the indiscriminate use of dietary supplements? What is the prohibited list and why is it important for athletes to be aware of this? How regularly is this list updated?

Nutritional intake during different phases of training and event

When developing sound eating habits and nutritional strategies to support training and competition, you should consider the overall issues shown in Table 13.14.

Table 13.14: Issues to consider when developing sound eating habits and nutritional strategies

The types of food eaten to support training and competition	The timing of meals and snacks around training and competition
Ensuring a balanced diet is achieved in respect of all nutrients	The problems of travelling to training and competition venues
Encouraging an adequate calcium and iron intake, particularly for females	Promoting long-term health and reducing the risk of chronic disease
Maintaining a sufficient fluid intake	Minimising the risk of injury and illness

The nutritional requirements for different sports and individuals will vary according to:

- the type of sport and training methods undertaken
- the intensity, duration and frequency of training or competition
- the training status and fitness level of the individual.

The Eatwell Guide principles should still be used to plan meals (see page 366). They should form the foundation on which to develop more specific performance nutrition strategies (see Figure 13.6).

Athletes should eat sufficient carbohydrate and **start refuelling** as soon as possible after training, when muscle's capacity to refuel is at its greatest. This may not coincide with traditional mealtimes. Eating may need to be fitted in around the training process, with smaller, more frequent meals and snacks being necessary. Snacks and fluids should be carried in the kit bag at all times.

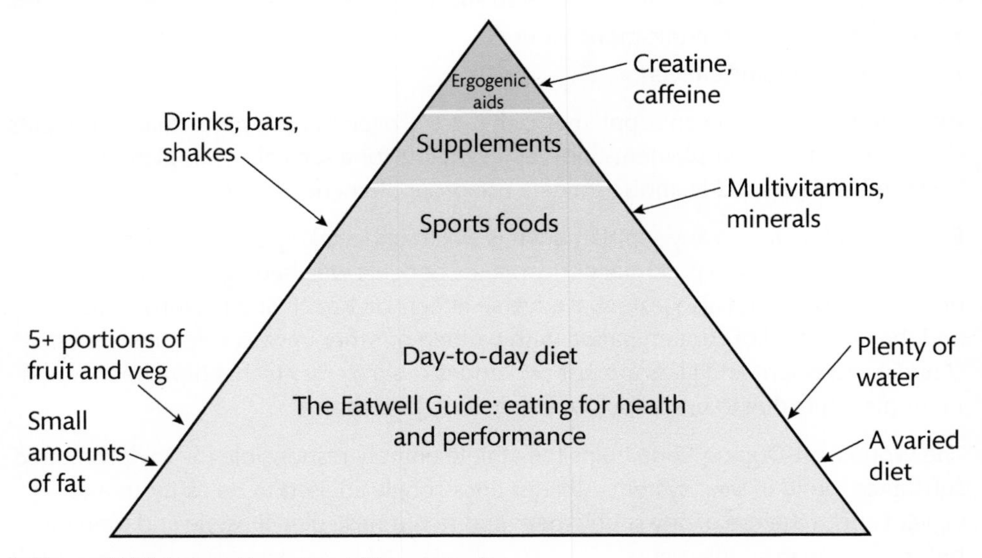

Figure 13.6: Value of sports nutrition strategies

A **high fluid intake** should be encouraged - see Table 13.15. In many sports, drinking alcohol after a match is traditional, especially at non-elite levels, but it is important to rehydrate with other fluids before drinking alcohol. Where an injury has been sustained, alcohol consumption may delay recovery and should be avoided for at least 48 hours.

Table 13.15: Fluid replacement strategies for exercise

Before	During	After
300–500 ml 10–15 minutes before activity	150–200 ml every 15–20 minutes	Based on body mass lost; replace losses 150%

Timing of food intake

Pre-event

Competition is not a time to experiment with new foods, so pre-event meals should be made of familiar foods and provide adequate fluids. A pre-competition meal should aim to top up muscle and liver glycogen stores, so it should be rich in carbohydrate but low in fat and fibre and should contain a moderate amount of protein.

Larger meals take longer to digest and nervousness can result in delayed digestion. Solid foods can usually be consumed with comfort up to two hours before an event, but liquid meals or carbohydrate drinks can be consumed up to 30–60 minutes before. Athletes in events lasting longer than 90 minutes should, where possible, taper training in the week leading up to the event, include a rest day, and consume more carbohydrate and fluid than normal.

Athletes should begin the event fully hydrated and drink plenty of water both during and after activity. Training should be used to practise fluid-replacement strategies. Drinking 300–500 ml of fluid 10–15 minutes before exercise is recommended.

During event

During training and competition, fluid loss is a major consideration. During intense training or competition, isotonic sports drinks may be consumed. This may be beneficial especially if training or competition lasts longer than 60 minutes. Drinking 150–200 ml every 15–20 minutes during exercise is recommended.

During endurance or ultra-endurance events lasting longer than four hours, solid foods may be required. In these instances, energy bars or gels might be useful as a more concentrated source of carbohydrate.

Theory into practice

Regular sports performers should be encouraged to practise their fluid and fuelling regimes in training to ensure that they do not run into any unexpected problems during competition, such as gastrointestinal distress. What practical advice can you give an athlete about this?

Case study

Nutrition and competition

Jon is 16 years old and is competing in a national squash tournament next weekend. He has improved his performance significantly this season and really wants to do well at this event. His goal is to gain selection for an international competition in Asia. He has noticed in previous tournaments that as he progresses through the rounds he becomes more fatigued and struggles to make shots.

Check your knowledge

1. Suggest a suitable pre-competition meal plan for Jon and give him some advice on suitable snacks and supplements he could use to keep himself fuelled and hydrated during the tournament.
2. Suggest ways in which you might monitor or evaluate Jon's nutritional preparation for the competition and the impact of your advice on his performance.
3. Are there any additional factors to consider if Jon achieves his goal?

Post-event

Good nutrition can make its greatest contribution in aiding recovery after training or an event. It is important to refuel as soon as possible after each workout or competition. The longer refuelling is delayed, the longer it will take to fully refuel. Athletes may find it easier to have small, frequent meals and snacks at regular intervals to help to maximise glycogen synthesis.

To refuel efficiently, a high carbohydrate diet is required. Post-exercise, carbohydrates that are easy to eat and digest are preferred. Athletes are advised to consume a high-carbohydrate (at least 50 grams) low-fat snack as soon as possible after training or competition, preferably within the first half-hour, when the muscles' capacity to refuel is greatest. They should eat their next meal, which should be rich in carbohydrate, within two hours.

After exercise, rehydration should start immediately. Drinks containing carbohydrates will also help with energy and glycogen replacement. These may be particularly useful if the activity has been intense and led to a suppression of appetite and a reluctance to eat solid foods.

Weight and urine-colour checks are a useful and simple way of monitoring fluid status during and after training and competition.

- A weight reduction of 1 kg is equivalent to 1 litre of fluid loss.
- Frequent trips to the toilet to pass plentiful quantities of pale-coloured urine are an indicator of good hydration, whereas scant quantities of dark-coloured urine indicate poor hydration.

These simple checks before and after exercise can be useful in determining fluid requirements post-training or during competition. As a guide, after-exercise fluid losses, based on mass loss, should be replaced 1.5 times within the first two hours of recovery.

Reflect

Consider what you have learned about pre-event, during event and post-event nutrition. How might the same principles be applied over a season of competition: pre-season, mid-season and post-season?

Assessment practice

Alex is a triathlete who is looking to make better food choices to optimise training and recovery. Her profile is shown below.

Age	20
Sex	Female
Height	1.75 m
Weight	59 kg
Body fat measured by bioimpedence analysis	21%
Activity levels	Intense

Alex has been competing since the age of 14 and is currently ranked in the top five nationally in her age group. She is a university student living at home with her parents and siblings.

- Her meals are prepared mainly by herself or her mother.
- She has no current medical history but had a bout of illness three months ago where she lost 3 kgs in weight.
- She would like to increase her variety and quality of food choices and reduce her cravings for sweet foods.
- She has no food allergies or intolerances.

Alex has an important race coming up in six weeks time and is aware that the course is going to be particularly challenging and wants to make her race day preparation as good as it can be. The food record below represents what she typically eats.

Typical food record		
Day 1 (Friday)	8.45 a.m.	1 medium bowl of porridge with 180 ml skimmed milk
	9.30 a.m.	• 1 standard tub fat-free yoghurt • 500 ml blackcurrant squash
	11.45 a.m.	• 500 ml water
	12.00 p.m.	• Beef and mustard sandwich: 1 medium wholemeal bread roll, 2 slices of beef, thin spread of mustard • 1 small packet salt and vinegar crisps • 1 apple and 1 orange • 250 ml blackcurrant squash
	5.00 p.m.	• 1 small roast chicken breast • 1 tbsp each of roasted courgette, carrots, parsnips, onion • Large serving basmati rice • 500 ml blackcurrant squash
	6.00 p.m.	330 ml can of ordinary lemonade
	8.30 p.m.	• Small bowl of leftover rice and roasted vegetables • 500 ml blackcurrant squash
	9.30 p.m.	• 1 medium bowl of honey nut cornflakes with 200 ml skimmed milk • 2 fun size chocolate bars
	Extra fluids	Approx. 1.5 l isotonic sports drink during training

Day 2 (Saturday)	8.45 a.m.	• 1 medium bowl of porridge made with 180 ml skimmed milk • 250 ml fresh orange juice • 1 standard tub fat-free yoghurt
	11.30 a.m.	500 ml electrolyte drink
	12.00 p.m.	• Beef and mustard sandwich: 1 medium wholemeal bread roll, 2 slices of beef, thin spread of mustard • 1 small pot rice pudding • 1 pear and 1 apple • 250 ml blackcurrant squash
	3.00 p.m.	• 1 small bowl multi-grain cereal with 160 ml skimmed milk • 1 × 150 g bag of jelly sweets
	6.30 p.m.	• Beef stir fry: 150 g beef, half a small jar of black bean sauce, 75 g pre-sliced stir fry vegetables • 2 scoops of mango sorbet • 500 ml blackcurrant squash
	8.30 p.m.	1 standard tub fat-free yoghurt
	Extra fluids	500 ml water during strength and conditioning session
Day 3 (Sunday)	8.30 a.m.	• 1 medium bowl of porridge made with 180 ml skimmed milk • 1 medium banana • A handful of jelly sweets
	12.00 p.m.	• 3 medium slices of toast with 1 tsp jam and 40 g cheddar cheese • 1 pear and 1 apple • 250 ml blackcurrant squash
	3.00 p.m.	330 ml can of lemonade
	6.00 p.m.	• Large supermarket salad bowl: pasta, rice, sweetcorn, beetroot, cherry tomatoes • 2 scoops of mango sorbet
	8.00 p.m.	2 fun size chocolate bars
	9.30 p.m.	• 1 medium bowl of multi-grain cereal with 200 ml skimmed milk • 250 ml blackcurrant squash
	Extra fluids	Approx. 1.5 l isotonic sports drink during training

1. Interpret Alex's current nutritional intake in relation to health and well-being. Is there any additional information that might help you to make suggestions to improve Alex's nutritional strategies?
2. Modify Alex's current nutritional strategies for the requirements of training and competing in triathlon.
3. What is your recommeded guidance for Alex based on her phase of training?
4. What guidance and nutritional strategies would you recommend for Alex's race day preparation?

Plan

- Do I understand that I am being asked to interpret an athlete's current nutritional intake and develop nutrition strategies based on their current phase of training to optimise health and performance?
- Do I need to undertake further research before I get going?

Do

- How am I going to present the information? How can I ensure this is clear and logical?
- How can I make sure I justify my proposed modifications and recommendations?

Review

- Have I proposed nutritional recommendations that are specific to the individual and their sporting event?
- Have I considered the impact of factors affecting digestion and absorption on my proposed modifications and recommendations?

Getting ready for assessment

This section has been written to help you do your best when you take the assessment test. Read through it carefully and ask your tutor if there is anything you are still not sure about.

Sample answers

For your set task you will be provided with some background information on a client which requires you to interpret current nutritional intake, demands of the athlete's sport and phase of training and recommend strategies to optimise health and performance.

Look at the sample scenarios which follow and our tips on how to answer them well.

Example 1

Billy is a junior national squad cross country athlete. He is a student and prefers to follow a vegetarian diet. Recently he has been feeling increasingly fatigued after finishing his training sessions and wonders if this is linked to his eating habits.

From chatting with Billy you establish he has a very irregular meal pattern with frequent long gaps between his meals. He knows he should try to manage his hydration better but often forgets to think about his fluid needs around his training programme. He is concerned as he has a big race coming up in five days' time where he would like to achieve selection for an international race in Berlin the following weekend.

Based on what you know about Billy, recommend nutritional guidance based on his phase of training and upcoming event.

Answer: There are three likely nutritional causes for Billy's increased fatigue: (1) inadequate carbohydrate intake and poor refuelling strategies following training, (2) dehydration as a result of a poor fluid intake or (3) iron deficiency as a result of being vegetarian. The iron deficiency is the least likely and can only be medically determined and so it would be more appropriate to concentrate on his carbohydrate and fluid intakes.

Billy's most important concern is his upcoming race. Billy should try to eat regular carbohydrate-rich meals and snacks throughout the day. He can use the Eatwell Guide principles to plan his meals. He should aim to eat sufficient carbohydrate and start refuelling as soon as possible after training, when his muscle capacity to refuel is at its greatest. A sample day's meal plan might include:

Before considering recommendations and modifications, try to interpret the impact of current dietary habits to show you understand their implications for health and performance. This shows you have considered the athlete's profile carefully.

- *breakfast: a bowl of porridge made with semi-skimmed milk topped with some dried or fresh fruit with a slice of toast and jam and a small glass of fruit juice*
- *lunch: a jacket potato with baked beans, a yoghurt and an apple*
- *evening: bean and pasta bake with a green salad and a rice pudding pot*
- *bedtime: a bowl of cereal with semi-skimmed milk.*

He should ensure that he does not leave long gaps between his meals. To help with this, Billy should develop a kit bag snack pack of durable snack items (such as cereal bars, dried fruit, milkshakes and Jaffa cakes) to carry around with him, so he can start to refuel as soon as possible after training. Billy should also make sure he carries fluids at all times, or at least a water bottle that he can fill up when necessary. He should try to just stay ahead of thirst, as thirst is a sign that he is already dehydrated. He can also monitor his urine colour and volume as a sign of his daily hydration status. The following guide to fluid management before, during and after exercise might help him to manage his hydration status.

Before	*During*	*After*
300–500 ml 10–15 minutes before activity	*150–200 ml every 15–20 minutes*	*Based on body mass lost; replace losses 150%*

On race day, Billy should ensure that his pre-race meal contains fluid to support hydration and is low in fat and fibre to facilitate gastric emptying and prevent gastrointestinal distress. It should also be high in carbohydrate to maximise control of blood glucose and moderate in protein content so it does not take too long to digest but helps him feel satiated. Most importantly, it should be made up of familiar foods he tolerates well. He should carbohydrate-load the night before with a pasta- or rice-based meal and make sure he is well hydrated before going to bed.

This answer does recommend nutritional guidance based on his phase of training and upcoming event. To achieve a higher mark it would have been useful to have considered the role of sports foods and supplements in helping Billy to meet his needs.

Example 2

Rhianna is a journalist; she weighs 52 kg and is 1.60 m tall. She trains 3–4 times a week with varying methods including circuits, runs, track and plyometrics sessions. She is training for her first 10 km run and aiming to improve her running, overall fitness and strength.
Rhianna's diet and activity record is detailed below:

Day 1:

- Breakfast: two slices of white toast with butter
- Lunch: jacket potato with cheese and beans
- Mid-afternoon snack: banana
- Evening circuit session
- Dinner: pasta with tuna and pasta sauce, medium size portion
- Drinks: four teas with semi-skimmed milk, litre of water, large glass of orange juice

Day 2:
- Breakfast: raisin Danish
- Mid-morning: 3-mile run on the treadmill
- Lunch: salmon and cream cheese sandwich, apple
- Dinner: jacket potato, salad, tuna burger
- Drinks: one cappuccino, three teas with semi-skimmed milk, litre of water, large glass of orange juice

Day 3:
- Breakfast: small bowl of frosted flakes, semi-skimmed milk, one slice of toast with butter and marmalade
- Lunch: toasted ciabatta with mozzarella, sun-dried tomato and pesto
- Mid-afternoon snack: flapjack
- Evening track session (15 × 60-metre sprints)
- Dinner: baked beans on two slices of white toast
- Drinks: three teas with semi-skimmed milk, litre of water, large glass of orange juice

Interpret Rhianna's current nutritional intake in relation to health and well-being. Then suggest modifications in relation to her sport-specific demands.

Answer: Looking at Rhianna's current intake she tries to follow a high carbohydrate diet with most of her meals based around carbohydrate-rich foods, such as bread, cereals, potatoes and pasta, but she could swap the raisin Danish for a bowl of cereal. In this way, she will have less fat and include a better source of vitamins and minerals, particularly calcium, with the addition of milk. Calcium intakes could be enhanced with the inclusion of nutritious desserts such as yoghurt or rice pudding, which would also provide useful carbohydrate. The glass of orange juice each day will be helping Rhianna to meet her vitamin C requirements, but overall she should aim to include a greater variety of fruits and vegetables in her diet. She has a reasonably high fluid intake and does try to include a litre of water each day. Higher intakes may be required to cover her training sessions. An increased frequency and duration of training will result in greater fluid requirements, so to minimise the effects of fluid losses while training she should always aim to start sessions fully hydrated and drink during and after.

To ensure that her energy stores are maintained it is best to increase the percentage of her daily calories consumed from carbohydrate to around 60 per cent and drop fat to 25 per cent. She should aim for a carbohydrate intake equivalent to 5–6 g for every kilogram of body weight providing around 250–300 g per day. A protein intake in the region of 1.2–1.4 g per kilogram of body weight should be adequate to meet her requirements giving 59–69 g per day, with a fat intake of no more than 70 g per day. To achieve her carbohydrate requirements she should aim to base all her meals around starchy carbohydrate foods, with at least two good quality protein portions around 75–100 g and at least three servings from the dairy food group each day.

While higher intakes are likely to be required to cover her training, it would be helpful in interpreting Rhianna's current intake to calculate actual requirements using one of the equations provided and then give more prescriptive advice on what to drink and how much, and when.

The answer does suggest modifications to Rhianna's diet in relation to the demands of her sport but for a higher mark it could go into more detail about her current nutritional intake for health and well-being and provide detail on factors affecting digestion and absorption of nutrients

Sports Injury and Assessment 15

Getting to know your unit

Assessment

You will be assessed by a series of assignments set by your tutor.

For anyone involved in any aspect of sport science, experiencing or witnessing an injury is common. Depending on your role within the sporting environment, an appreciation and understanding of sports injuries and their symptoms is essential in order to ensure appropriate treatment is administered.

Injury prevention is important to reduce the risk of injury and can be achieved by understanding the mechanism of injury, the role of biomechanics and effective preventative measures.

For sport participants who are suffering an injury, effective treatment may result in a quicker return to their chosen activity or onto rehabilitation.

How you will be assessed

This unit will be assessed by a series of internally assessed tasks set by your tutor. Throughout this unit you will find assessment practice activities that will help you work towards your assessment. Completing these activities will not mean that you have achieved a particular grade, but you will have carried out useful research or preparation that will be relevant when it comes to your final assignment.

In order for you to successfully complete the tasks in your assignment, it is important to check that you have met all of the Pass grading criteria. You can do this as you work your way through the assignment.

If you are hoping to gain a Merit or Distinction, you should also make sure that you present the information in your assignment in the style that is required by the relevant assessment criterion. For example, Merit criteria require you to assess and apply, and Distinction criteria require you to evaluate and justify.

The assignment set by your teacher/tutor will consist of a number of tasks designed to meet the criteria in the table. This is likely to consist of written assignments but may also include activities such as:

- giving a presentation about the various risk factors of sports injury and preventative measures
- creating a rehabilitation programme
- applying sports injury treatments under observation.

Assessment criteria

This table shows what you must do in order to achieve a **Pass**, **Merit** or **Distinction** grade, and where you can find activities to help you.

Pass	Merit	Distinction
Learning aim A Understand acute and overuse injuries, their associated signs and symptoms and mechanism of injury		
A.P1 Discuss acute and overuse injuries, including signs and symptoms. **Assessment practice 15.1**	**A.M1** Assess acute and overuse injuries, including signs, symptoms and examples of mechanisms of injury. **Assessment practice 15.1**	**AB.D1** Evaluate injury mechanisms and the associated physiological and psychological responses to injury and rehabilitation, using specific examples. **Assessment practice 15.1** **Assessment practice 15.2**
Learning aim B Examine the physiological and psychological responses to injury and rehabilitation		
B.P2 Explain how the body responds physiologically and the mind psychologically to sports injuries. **Assessment practice 15.2**	**B.M2** Assess the physiological and psychological response to sports injuries, with regard to stages of injury including rehabilitation, using specific examples. **Assessment practice 15.2**	
Learning aim C Investigate aetiology of sports injuries and their associated prevention strategies		
C.P3 Explain how extrinsic and intrinsic risk factors including gait analysis contribute to sports injuries and identify how they can be prevented, using specific examples. **Assessment practice 15.3**	**C.M3** Assess gait analysis and injury, considering preventative measures for intrinsic and extrinsic risk factors, using specific examples. **Assessment practice 15.3**	**C.D2** Evaluate the sequence of prevention model, justifying the different stages, using specific examples. **Assessment practice 15.3**
Learning aim  Explore common treatment and rehabilitation methods		
D.P4 Apply appropriate protocols when performing a range of treatment methods for four contrasting scenarios. **Assessment practice 15.4**	**D.M4** Apply appropriate protocols in a confident and effective manner when performing a range of common treatment methods for four contrasting scenarios. **Assessment practice 15.4**	**D.D3** Justify the rehabilitation programme design, including consideration of factors that may affect rehabilitation, future recommendations and considerations. **Assessment practice 15.4**
D.P5 Design an appropriate rehabilitation programme for a specific sports injury, identifying factors that may affect rehabilitation. **Assessment practice 15.4**	**D.M5** Design a detailed, safe and appropriate rehabilitation programme for a specific sports injury, including adaptations and alterations. **Assessment practice 15.4**	

Getting started

Taking part in sport and exercise is really good for your health but, by taking part, you also increase your risk of sports injury. When we sustain a sports injury it affects us physically and psychologically. Think about a high-profile sports performer who has been injured. Who was injured? What do you think were the physical signs they were injured? How do you think the injury would affect them psychologically?

A Understand acute and overuse injuries, their associated signs and symptoms and mechanism of injury

For sports injury practitioners to effectively manage injuries it is important to know what a sports injury is and the different types of injury that their athletes might sustain.

Link

This unit has particularly strong links with *Unit 1: Sport and Exercise Physiology*, *Unit 2: Functional Anatomy* and *Unit 7: Biomechanics in Sport and Exercise Science*.

What is a sports injury?

A sports injury is often defined as any physical complaint that occurred during a scheduled training session or performance. Usually the injury will require some form of medical attention and require the athlete to have a period of time when they cannot take part in training and competition.

It is often the time lost due to being unable to train or compete that is used to determine the **severity** of the injury.

Research

What does the term 'injury incidence' mean? Why is this a better phrase than 'injury rate'? In pairs or small groups research these two terms and report back to the rest of the group.

Types of sports injury

There are two main types of sports injury. These are determined by the mechanism of injury, or the way it is caused, and how quickly the symptoms show themselves.

- **Acute injuries** tend to occur because of sudden high force to the tissue, e.g. contact with another player or a direct blow, and the symptoms occur quickly. Most of the dramatic injuries we see on television are acute injuries.
- **Overuse injuries** tend to occur because of repeated force to the tissues, e.g. repeated movements with little recovery, and the symptoms occur gradually. These are far less dramatic than acute injuries but can have the same severity.

Acute injuries

Acute injuries tend to occur due to sudden force being exerted on the tissues. These are the injuries that most of us have seen when an athlete requires medical attention in sport. Sports that involve frequent contact, collisions, and high-intensity changes of direction have high rates of acute injuries, for example, rugby, football, and basketball. Acute injuries can affect bone, joints, muscle, bursa, and connective tissue. In fact, some acute injuries can involve more than one tissue type. For example, high grade ankle sprains involving lateral ligaments can also cause a fracture to the fibula.

Usual signs and symptoms of acute injuries include:

- swelling
- pain
- bleeding (internal or external)
- loss of function
- redness
- heat
- increased joint laxity (or looseness).

Table 15.1 shows the major types of acute injury by tissue type.

Table 15.1: Common acute injuries

Tissue type	Acute injury types	Brief description
Bone	Fractures including: • transverse fracture • oblique fracture • spiral fracture • comminuted fracture	A crack or full break in bone/s. The shape of the break describes the type of fracture
Cartilage	Osteochondral tear	An injury or small fracture of cartilage surface of bone
	Meniscal tear	Injury to the fibrous cartilage between joint surfaces
Joint	Dislocation	Complete separation of joint surfaces
	Subluxation	Partial separation of joint surfaces
Ligament	Sprain (grades 1–3)	Tearing of ligament fibres
Muscle	Strain (grades 1–3)	Tearing of muscle fibres
	Haematoma (intra and intermuscular)	Localised bleeding within muscles (intra) or between muscles (inter) – see Figure 15.1
	Cramps	Painful involuntary muscle contractions
	Acute compartment syndrome	Increased pressure due to swelling within a body compartment e.g. the compartment of the lower leg
	Delayed onset muscle soreness	Microtrauma to muscles as a result of overloading the muscle
Tendon	Tear (partial to complete)	Injury where tendon fibres are damaged
Bursa	Traumatic bursitis	Inflammation of a bursa caused by a collision or fall
Skin	Abrasions, lacerations and puncture wounds	Open wounds caused by scraping, cutting, or piercing the skin
	Contusions	A direct blow causing muscle damage and bleeding below the skin surface

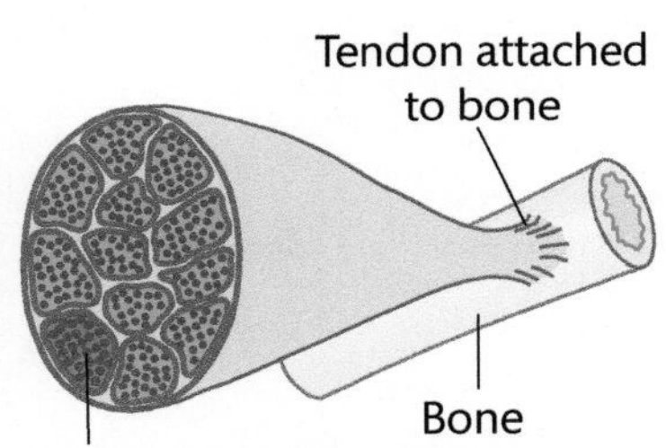

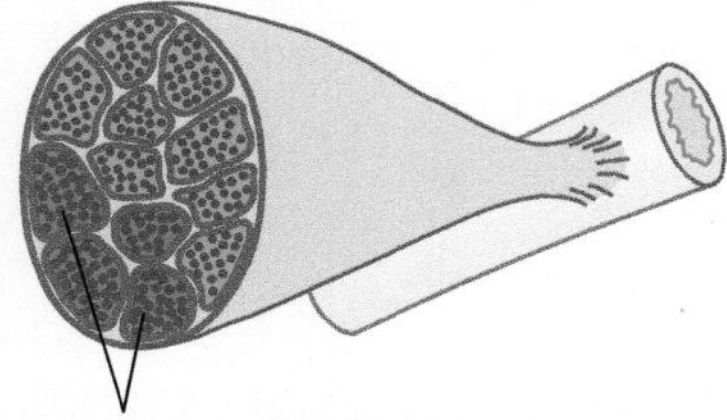

Figure 15.1: Intramuscular and intermuscular haematoma

Types of fracture

A fracture is a partial or complete break in bone, and is a common hard tissue injury. The way the injury takes place (its mechanism) causes the bone to break differently. Most fractures are due to direct impact such as a fall, or direct blow. The site of the injury and how it occurs results in different types of fracture.

There are four common fracture types based on the shape of the break:

- **transverse fracture** – a break that is perpendicular (at right angles) to the length of the bone
- **oblique fracture** – similar to the transverse fracture, but the break occurs diagonally across the bone and can result in sharp ends where the break is
- **spiral fracture** – the break is in a spiralling pattern along the bone
- **comminuted fracture** – a break with multiple fragments of bone.

Grades of strain and sprain

The severity of strains and sprains is commonly graded from 1 (mild) to 3 (severe). Important symptoms include pain, swelling, and laxity (looseness) of joints. Loss of function often refers to muscle strength and the range of motion at the joints.

Research

Use the internet to find out more about the different grades of strain and sprain.

Overuse injuries

Overuse injuries tend to occur from repetitive frequent forces through the tissues with little in the way of time for recovery. Just as with acute injuries, overuse injuries can affect a number of tissue types. Table 15.2 highlights common overuse injuries and what each one is.

Table 15.2: Common overuse injuries

Tissue type	Overuse injury types	Brief description
Bone	Stress fracture	A micro-fracture in bone Inflammation of bone-muscle attachment site
	Osteitis	Inflammation of bone–muscle attachment site
	Apophysitis	Inflammation of growth plate
Cartilage	Chondropathy	Degeneration of cartilage
Joint	Synovitis	Inflammation of synovial membrane
	Osteoarthritis	Painful and stiff joints usually caused by injury or general 'wear and tear'. It is a degenerative condition (it gets worse over time)
Ligament	Inflammation	Pain and swelling caused by repetitive loading
Muscle	Chronic compartment syndrome	Long-term increased pressure in a body compartment due to repetitive exercise
	Muscle focal thickening	Chronic change to muscle causing reduced range of motion
Tendon	Tendinopathy including: • tendinitis • tendinosis • paratenonitis • tenosynovitis	Painful conditions of the tendon
Bursa	Bursitis	Swelling of a bursa
Skin	Blister	A pocket of fluid caused by repetitive friction
	Callus	Chronic change to skin from repetitive friction making it hard and thickened

Overuse injuries typically occur:

- in sports that have monotonous training regimes such as swimming and distance running
- in sports that have repetitive similar movement patterns such as cricket or tennis
- in sports where a rapid increase in training/competition load occurs.

Youth athletes may be particularly susceptible to overuse injuries during periods of growth. Whereas acute injuries have quite clear signs and symptoms, the symptoms of overuse injuries tend to be less obvious. This means they can be challenging to diagnose and manage.

Research

Tendinopathy is an umbrella term for a number of tendon-based injuries. Research and define the following terms:

- tendinitis
- tendinosis
- paratenonitis
- tenosynovitis.

PAUSE POINT Which types of injury are most common in different sports?

Hint Identify sports where the rate of (a) acute and (b) overuse injuries is high.

Extend Discuss what about your chosen sports makes it more or less likely for athletes to suffer acute and overuse injuries?

Osgood-Schlatter disease

Osgood-Schlatter disease is an example of an **apophysitis injury** that is common in youth athletes. An apophysitis injury affects where a tendon attaches to a bony growth plate. In Osgood-Schlatter disease it is where the patellar tendon attaches to the tibial tuberosity.

Overuse of the quadriceps muscles causes repeated strain on the tendon attachment causing irritation, pain, redness and swelling. In some cases, a bony bump may develop below the knee. This bump is permanent but becomes painless as the tibia matures.

Mechanism of sport injuries

When we take part in sport and exercise, our body, and specifically the different types of tissue, have to effectively respond to a number of different **forces** (both internal and external). The forces that affect the body during sport and exercise are generated from gravity, the surface (ground reaction force), from opponents and from external objects such as balls and equipment. The types of forces that are regularly applied to the body during sport and exercise are compressive, tension, and shear.

- **Compressive forces** push and compact tissues together (e.g. stress fracture).
- **Tension forces** pull tissues apart (e.g. muscle strain).
- **Shear forces** involve twisting of tissues (e.g. anterior cruciate ligament sprain).

All tissues in the body, including bone, muscle, ligament, and tendon, react predictably to these forces and have an **elastic response**. This is known as **tissue deformation**.

A sports injury results from a transfer of force at a rate or in an amount that exceeds the tissue's ability to respond. For example, if a direct force is applied to a bone that exceeds the bone's elastic response, the skeletal tissue will fail, and a fracture will occur.

All of this means that biomechanical principles are important in understanding the mechanism of sports injury (how injuries are caused). When referring to the biomechanics of an athlete or movement, you can look at their kinematics and/or kinetics.

- **Kinematics** is a description of movement without referring to the forces involved.
- **Kinetics** is an assessment of movement specifically referring to the forces influencing it.

PAUSE POINT Think of an injury you have had or that you have seen on television. How was this injury caused?

Hint What tissues were involved in this injury? Which forces caused these tissues to become injured?

Extend Explain in a diagram how these tissues went from being non-injured to injured using your knowledge of loading and elastic response of tissues.

Kinematics and sports injury

Describing the kinematics of sports injury requires understanding of the following key factors:

- **timing of movement** – duration of the load that causes the sports injury
- **body position or location** – often the position of the body or specific joints will determine what injury occurs. For example, whether the knee is in a flexed or extended position when injured will cause different types of injury. The location of the impact will also determine the severity of injury; load applied to tissues with smaller surface areas causes greater stress than to tissues with greater surface area
- **displacement** – the difference between the initial and final position of the body or tissues, e.g. with a complete fracture or dislocation injury
- **velocity** – the rate the body or tissues are displaced can determine the severity of acute injuries
- **acceleration** – the rate of change of velocity of an object, e.g. increased acceleration, will increase impact of collision between two players.

Kinetics and sports injury

When looking at the kinetics of sports injury, several factors that relate to force will determine the type and severity of the injury. These factors include:

- how much force is applied to the tissues (large or small)
- where the force is applied (which tissues and the specific area of the body)
- the direction of the force (from the front, back, side, top or bottom)
- the time period the force is applied for (over time or suddenly)
- how regularly the force is applied (sustained or intermittent)
- whether the force is constant or varies (does the force stay at the same level?)
- how quickly the force is applied (fast to slow impact)
- how much tissue deformation there has been because of the force.

Theory into practice

Using your knowledge of kinetics and sports injury, compare the kinetic factors involved in:

- a lateral ankle sprain
- medial tibial stress syndrome (shin splints)
- patellar tendinopathy
- a hamstring strain.

Types of forces involved in injury

Different types of force can act on the body and cause a sports injury, including:

- **gravity** – the constant force exerted by the pull of the earth. This has a compressive effect on the body
- **ground reaction forces** – the equal and opposing force that is exerted by the ground on the body. For example, there is greater ground reaction force exerted on hard ground than soft ground

- **impact of objects** – the impact of objects such as opponents, balls and sticks all stress the tissues
- **compression forces** – through participating in sport and exercise we regularly compress our long bones in the lower extremity and weight-bearing joints
- **ligament forces** – ligaments resist forces on joints and offer stability. Too much laxity (looseness) in the ligaments means joints are less stable
- **musculotendinous forces** – the muscles generate force and the tendon transfers this to bone. In eccentric movements this can be too much, causing an injury.

Table 15.3: Newton's three laws of motion applied to sports injury

Law	Description	Application
Newton's first law	A body will remain at rest (or in uniform motion) unless acted upon by an external force	**A hard frontal tackle in rugby league.** Before the tackle, the player with the ball will be sprinting at a specific speed. When the player is tackled, the force of the tackling player will cause the first player to slow down rapidly or stop. For a short time, the player's head will keep going at the original speed (obeying Newton's first law). The player's neck will resist this motion, causing rapid extension into hyperextension. This flexion–hyperextension pattern is typical of a cervical whiplash injury.
Newton's second law	A force acting on a body will produce an acceleration that is proportional to that force: force = mass × acceleration	**A weightlifter attempting to dead lift 250 kg.** The body structures involved in weight lifting (e.g. quadriceps, knee joint) must provide enough force to move the weight upwards and resist the load that is placed upon them by the weight. If they cannot, they will be more susceptible to injury (e.g. muscle strain, ligament strain or cartilage tear).
Newton's third law	For every action, there is an equal and opposite reaction	**Ultra-endurance athlete training for competition.** An ultra-endurance athlete will run on roads for long periods of time. As each foot strikes the ground, the ground exerts an equal and opposite force on the foot; this force acts through the lower extremities. Depending on the size, duration, frequency and rate of the force applied (as well as other factors, such as footwear) this could cause overuse injuries such as stress fractures.

Mass, inertia, torque and sports injury

It is important that sports injury practitioners consider the effect of **mass**, **inertia** and **torque** on the tissues and how these can contribute to injury. An example of this is in the following case study.

Key terms

Mass – the overall amount of matter in an object.

Inertia – the resistance to changes in motion.

Torque – the twisting motion created from rotational forces.

Case study

Megan Rapinoe suffers a severe knee injury for the third time

In December 2015 Megan Rapinoe of the US World Cup winning football team tore her right anterior cruciate ligament (ACL) during training.

ACL injuries are more common in sports that require frequent and fast changes of direction with the foot often remaining in a fixed position. When this happens there is some resistance from the tissues to this movement while at the same time the body parts are twisting. This can lead to large amounts of torque force going through the joint/s. When this twisting force increases beyond the tissue's ability to respond an ACL injury will occur.

- Which joint would have large amounts of torque going through it?
- What is the role of the ACL?
- Which tissues might provide resistance when the knee is rotating?
- How might a poor playing surface increase the risk of injury?

Assessment practice 15.1

A.P1 A.M1 AB.D1

You are working as a freelance sports therapist for your local sports club. You have been asked to write a blog on the sports club's social media site about common sports injuries. The blog should be short and to the point, containing images of each injury. In the blog they would like you to:

- identify the three most common acute injuries, and three most common overuse injuries in the sport
- evaluate the usual signs and symptoms of these injuries
- evaluate the expected severity of each injury
- evaluate the specific force or combination of forces that causes each injury.

The blog can be based on a sport of your choice.

Plan

- What does a blog look like?
- How confident do I feel in my own abilities to complete this task? Are there any areas I think I may struggle with?

Do

- Am I accessing all the support offered to me?
- Do I know where I can find out more about sports injuries and mechanisms of injury?
- Can I identify when I have gone wrong and adjust my thinking/approach to get myself back on course?

Review

- Can I explain what the task was and how I approached the task?
- Can I explain how I would approach the hard elements differently next time (i.e. what I would do differently)?
- Can I say where and how I met the task's criteria?

B Examine the physiological and psychological responses to injury and rehabilitation

When an athlete suffers a sports injury it affects them both physiologically and psychologically. These responses to injury can be mild or more severe. Often physiological and psychological healing do not happen at the same time or at the same rate. Understanding these different responses to sports injury will help plan effective rehabilitation programmes that mean athletes return to sport when they are physically and mentally ready.

Physiological responses to sports injury

As soon as an injury takes place the body responds in a number of ways. There are three phases of responses. The length of time at each stage depends on a number of factors and may be different for different athletes. These stages start as soon as the injury happens and usually continue well after the athlete has returned to sport.

Phase 1: The inflammatory phase

The inflammatory phase is an essential part of tissue repair. This phase happens quickly following injury (0–3 days), peaks after 24–72 hours, and can last for a few weeks. It is the protective phase involving vascular and cellular changes where chemicals are released that cause pain, swelling, **vasoconstriction** and then quickly **vasodilation** of blood vessels, allowing cell debris to be removed. The rest of the healing process will not occur normally if there is not an inflammatory phase.

Key terms

Vasoconstriction – a reduction in the diameter of blood vessels.

Vasodilation – an increase in the diameter of blood vessels.

Discussion

Why does vasoconstriction of our blood vessels occur during the inflammatory phase, and then why does vasodilation occur?

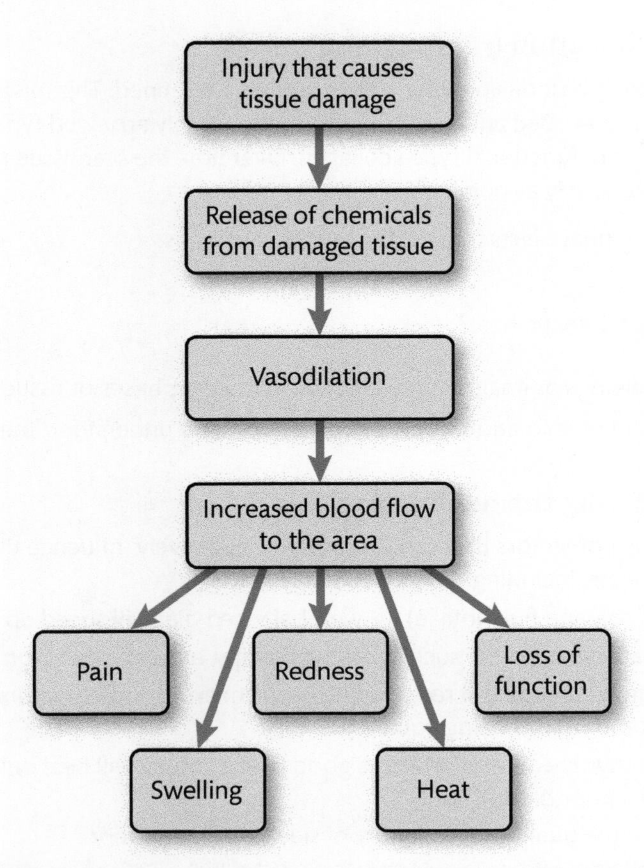

▶ **Figure 15.2:** Signs and symptoms of inflammation. Why does the body react to injury in this way?

Signs and symptoms

The inflammatory phase has five major signs. Knowing these signs and regularly checking them on an injured athlete helps us understand how severe the injury is and how the healing process is progressing. The five signs are:

- **pain** – due to increased pressure and chemical irritation of sensory pain receptors (**nociceptors**)
- **swelling** – happens due to bleeding and chemicals causing the area to swell
- **redness** – caused by increased blood flow to the area by vasodilation
- **heat** – caused by increased chemical activity in the injured area and an increased flow of blood
- **loss of function** – due to the swelling and pain caused by the injury. Loss of function can be partial, e.g. limping, some loss of strength or complete, e.g. cannot bear weight or move the body part at all.

Key terms

Nociceptors – pain sensing receptors.

Collagen – a protein-based building material used in the repair of tissues. Collagen also provides strength and cushioning for body parts.

Phase 2: Proliferation (tissue formation) phase

The **proliferation** (tissue formation) phase is important for generating repair material and has two main events. Firstly, around the injury site there is a development of new capillaries to promote healing. This is called **angiogenesis**. Secondly, cells (**fibroblasts**) start to lay down a supportive network to stabilise the injury site. This is called **fibroblastic repair**.

At this phase the supportive network develops into **scar tissue** and is much weaker than normal uninjured tissue and its fibres are laid down in a random order. The scar tissue at this phase is made up from a fibre called type III **collagen**.

The tissue formation phase can last from 24 hours to 6 months (peaking in 2–3 weeks).

Phase 3: Maturation (remodelling) phase

In the maturation (remodelling) phase the scar tissue is refined. This means that fibres are constantly reabsorbed and repaired, and the randomly arranged type III collagen is replaced with more functional type I collagen. Over time the scar tissue resembles non-injured tissue as closely as possible.

The remodelling phase lasts from 7 days up to 12 months.

PAUSE POINT How does injured tissue heal?

Hint Using only drawings or images (no words) describe the phases of tissue healing.

Extend Explain your drawing to another person and see if they understood the process.

Factors affecting the healing process

There are a range of factors that can positively or negatively influence the duration of the healing process, including:

- **nutrition** (food and fluid intake) - a well-balanced diet will speed up recovery
- **type of treatments used** - such as electrotherapy, exercise therapy, manual therapy
- **age** - a younger athlete will recover quicker from an equivalent injury than an older athlete, all other things being equal
- **tissue type involved** - tissues with a good blood supply will heal quicker than tissues with a poor blood supply
- **sleep** - both the quality and quantity of sleep affect recovery
- **psychology** - the athlete's psychological state will also affect recovery; the following section of the unit looks at this in more detail.

Research

Research how bone heals and draw a flow diagram of this. What are the similarities and difference with soft tissue healing?

Psychological responses to sports injury

Link

This content links to *Unit 3: Applied Sport and Exercise Psychology.*

As well as physiological responses of the body to injury there are also psychological responses. Psychological responses influence physical response and vice versa. Psychological responses change a lot through an athlete's rehabilitation and vary between individuals based on personal and situational factors.

- Personal factors include pain tolerance, mental toughness, resilience, gender, age, and injury history.
- Situational factors include level of competition, relationship with the coach, the medical team, social support network, and team environment.

Psychological responses to injury can be categorised as **emotional** (relating to feelings), **cognitive** (relating to thoughts) and **behaviours** (relating to how we act) - examples are given in Table 15.4. These responses can be beneficial or detrimental to successful rehabilitation. For example, a high level of self-confidence is an important psychological factor in returning to sport after injury. Alternatively, anxiety or fear over re-injury is detrimental when returning to sport.

Table 15.4: Why might an injured athlete feel anxious?

Emotional response (feelings)	Cognitive responses (thoughts)	Behavioural responses (actions)
• Anxiety/fear • Anger • Frustration • Helplessness • Depression	• Changes in self-esteem • Changes in self-confidence • Altered identity • Loss of control • Over-motivation	• Adherence to rehabilitation • Avoidance coping • Malingering • Removal from team setting • Altered diet and alcohol intake

Psychology and injury risk

An athlete's psychological make-up can make them more or less prone to getting a sports injury. Williams and Andersen (1998) created the **Stress and Injury Model** to explore this (see Figure 15.3). An athlete's personality, history of stressors, and coping resources all affect how likely they are to get injured.

- Personality factors include trait anxiety, risk taking, hardiness, optimism, and perfectionism.
- History of stressors consists of sport-related and non-sport-related hassles, and previous injury history.
- Coping resources are related to the athletes 'tools' to deal with high levels of stress such as sleep, stress management skills, and their social support network.

When an athlete appraises a sporting situation as stressful these psychological factors combine to influence the athlete's **stress response**. The stress response leads to changes that are both physiological (e.g. increased muscle tone and spasm) and psychological/attentional (e.g. loss of concentration, poor decision making, narrowed attentional focus). It is thought that these changes affect whether the athlete gets injured or not. Sports psychology can be used to reduce the effect of the stress response and help reduce the chance of potentially harmful changes happening.

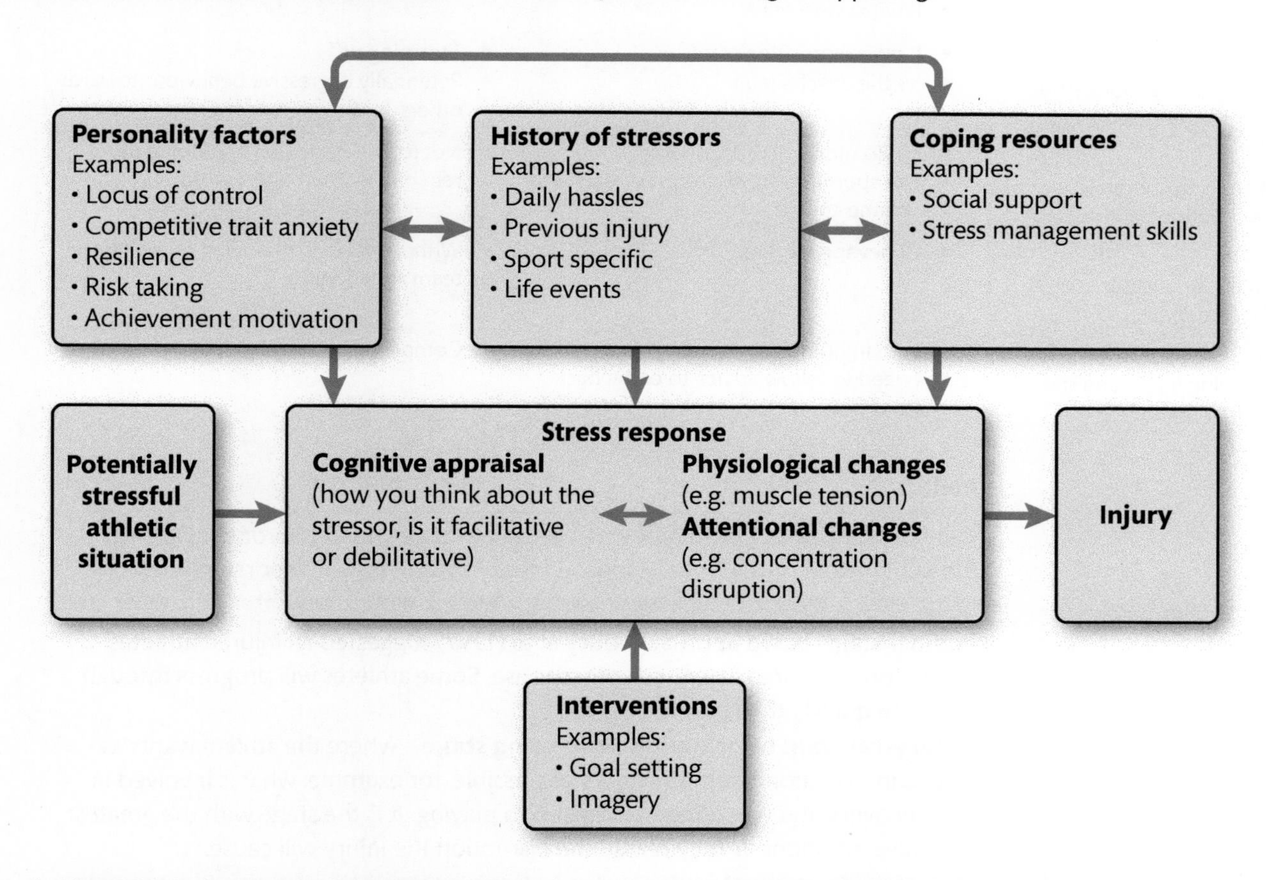

Figure 15.3: The Stress and Injury Model. Which psychological factors might give you an increased risk of injury?

Discussion

Discuss with a group of your classmates examples of injury-prone athletes. What psychological factors might have increased their risk of injury?

Psychology and injury rehabilitation

There are two main approaches to understanding the psychology of injury rehabilitation. These are stage-based and cognitive appraisal approaches.

Stage-based approaches

Of the stage-based approaches the most popular is the Kübler-Ross (1969) **Grief Response Model**. This was originally created to describe a patient's experience of terminal illness but has been applied to sports injury. The model suggests the athlete progresses through five stages of reaction to injury in a predictable pattern. These stages are shown in Table 15.5.

The time spent at each stage varies according to the athlete's psychological factors and the support that they have access to. An athlete that progresses through the stages more quickly will psychologically recover from the injury experience in a shorter period of time.

Table 15.5: How grief responses affect rehabilitation

Grief response stage	Associated thoughts	Associated behaviours
Denial Not acknowledging injury and carrying on regardless	• I'm not injured • I can carry on • It won't stop me	• Continue to participate despite loss of function and pain
Anger High levels of frustration about getting injured and being reliant on others	• It's the opposition's fault • It's the coach's fault	• 'Storming off' • Potentially aggressive behaviour towards others
Bargaining Trying to negotiate with someone that has control over the situation	• If I do more, I'll recover faster • The sports therapist doesn't understand, I'm fine coach!	• Not following advice (e.g. doing more rehab work than one should)
Depression Low mood from not being able to participate with team mates	• I'll never get better	• Withdrawal (e.g. removing oneself from team situations)
Acceptance Finally acknowledging injury and the importance of rehabilitation	• I am injured • I need to follow advice to come back from this	• Compliance with rehab plan

Reflect

Can you think of any problems when applying stage-based approaches such as the Kübler-Ross (1969) Grief Response Model to athletes with sports injuries?

In another stage-based approach, Udry *et al* (1997) suggested all injured athletes progress through three categories of response. Some athletes will progress through these more quickly than others.

1 **Injury-relevant information processing stage** – where the athlete wants as much information about the injury as possible, for example, what is involved in the recovery and when they can return to playing. It is the stage with the greatest negative emotions as they realise the disruption the injury will cause.
2 **Emotional upheaval and reactive behaviour stage** – where the athlete has intense emotions such as being agitated, irritable, and physically tired. An athlete might feel isolated from the team while being very anxious.
3 **Positive outlook and coping stage** – where the athlete starts to accept that they are injured and adapts to the injury. They feel like they can cope with the injury demands and develop a positive outlook as they feel a sense progress is being made.

Cognitive appraisal model approaches

Cognitive appraisal approaches are more supported by research than stage-based models. These approaches include the Cognitive Appraisal Model (Brewer, 1994) and the Integrated Model of Response to Sport Injury (Wiese-bjornstal *et al*, 1998).

In the **Cognitive Appraisal Model** the athlete's thought processes about their injury are affected by personal and situational factors, for example, age, injury history, gender, team environment, stage in career and social support network (see Figure 15.4). This is in addition to the standard responses outlined earlier in Table 15.4. These factors make the athlete appraise their injury in a certain way, which determines their emotional and behavioural response. For example, an athlete might feel their rehabilitation progress is not quick enough, causing frustration and anxiety. This may cause non-adherence to the exercises the practitioner has given.

The **Integrated Model of Response to Sport Injury** is the most widely accepted model and combines pre-injury and post-injury factors. In this model cognitive appraisal, behavioural responses and emotional responses influence each other in a cyclical manner. It is this cycle of responses that ultimately determines rehabilitation outcomes. Rehabilitation outcomes can be physical or psychosocial. The cycle is dynamic and should be seen as a three-dimensional spiral. If the responses are favourable the spiral will lead to positive rehabilitation outcomes. In comparison, if responses are unfavourable the spiral leads to negative rehabilitation outcomes.

There are intermediate **recovery outcomes** and sports injury recovery outcomes. Intermediate outcomes include improvement in strength, adherence, less pain, greater range of motion and perceptions of recovery. Sports injury recovery outcomes include functional performance, quality of life, treatment satisfaction, and readiness to return to sport.

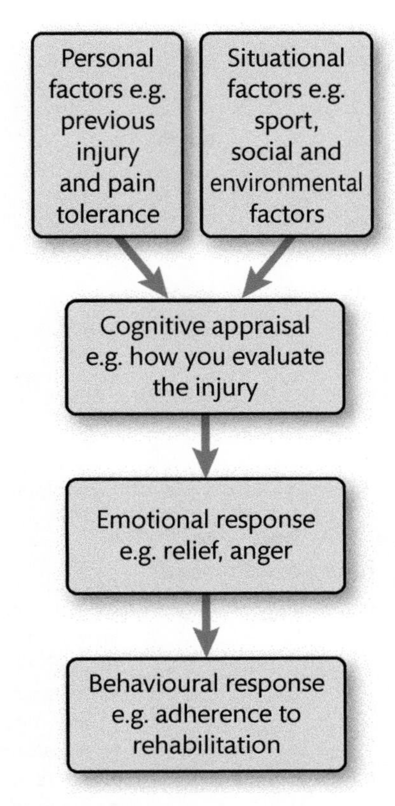

Figure 15.4: Cognitive Appraisal Model. What are your own personal and situational factors affecting cognitive appraisal?

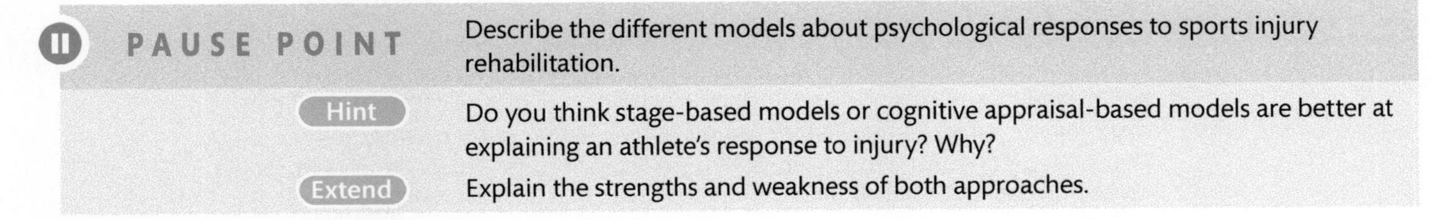

Psychological factors associated with sport injury rehabilitation adherence

Properly following a rehabilitation plan is an essential factor in determining whether an athlete will be successful or unsuccessful in their recovery. It is an important intermediate rehabilitation outcome. For example, an athlete who does not follow the exercises set by a practitioner following an ankle sprain may end up with a long-term reduced range of motion.

Getting athletes to **adhere** to rehabilitation advice is challenging so identifying the psychological factors affecting rehabilitation and using techniques aimed at improving adherence is important.

Psychosocial factors affecting rehabilitation adherence

Rehabilitation takes place in a social environment. Whether an athlete adheres to a rehabilitation plan is affected by a range of psychosocial factors, shown in Table 15.6. These factors can be classified as being personal or situational.

Research

Use the internet to find a diagram illustrating the Integrated Model of Response to Sport Injury. Try to produce your own version of this diagram.

Key term

Adhere – to continue performing a behaviour (e.g. completing rehabilitation plans).

Table 15.6: Psychosocial factors related to injury rehabilitation adherence

Personal factors	Situational factors
• Pain tolerance • Mental toughness • Self-motivation • Independence • Goal orientation	• Belief in the sports injury practitioner process and treatments • Comfortable environment • Convenient appointments and facilities • Quality of social support

Psychological techniques to enhance adherence

Identifying and modifying the factors that affect rehabilitation adherence is vital to the rehabilitation plan's success. Some of the techniques that can lead to greater rehabilitation adherence are goal setting, social support, patient education, imagery, positive self-talk and motivational interviewing - see Table 15.7.

Table 15.7: Examples of psychological techniques to improve adherence

Technique to improve adherence	Description of technique	Purpose in rehabilitation
Goal setting	Creating, implementing and evaluating short-, medium- and long-term goals (performance, process, outcome related) through rehabilitation. Goals should be: • S - shared • M - measurable • A - attainable • R - realistic • T - time orientated • S - self-determined	• Increase motivation to adhere to the rehabilitation plan • Manage expectations • Helps break down longer rehabilitation periods • Faster recovery • Enable the athlete to view injury as a positive developmental experience
Social support	The support network available to an injured athlete in order to meet their demands. Providers of social support include family, friends, team mates, sports injury practitioners, coaches, social media	• Reduce injury-related stress • Increase confidence • Share experiences • Reduce feelings of isolation
Patient education	Getting the athlete to understand what the injury is, what the purpose of each treatment is, and the process in which injury will get better, e.g. use of leaflets, internet, plenary tasks	• Manage expectations • Improve adherence • Greater sense of control
Imagery	Getting the athlete to use polysensoral (involving all senses) mental images to enhance their injury experience. Types of imagery used in rehabilitation are: • healing imagery • pain imagery • performance imagery • motivation imagery • relaxation imagery	• Aid the healing process • Reduce negative emotions • Improve motivation • Help regain skills • Manage pain • Increase confidence
Positive self-talk	Using positive statements throughout rehabilitation at challenging times, e.g. when the injury is painful, or when there might be frustration at progress of rehabilitation	• Change negative thoughts • Reduce injury stress • Improve adherence • Helps retain focus
Motivational interviewing	A counselling-based technique where the athlete is supported in exploring the pros and cons of taking part in rehabilitation	• Improve adherence • Greater sense of control • Helps generate rehabilitation goals

Types of coping resources

Coping resources are the athlete's own ways of dealing with the stressors placed upon them. As there are different stressors from the time of an injury occurring to returning to sport, an athlete must have a range of coping resources. Not being able to deal with the stressors of rehabilitation by having insufficient coping resources will result in negative outcomes.

The three main types of coping resources used by an athlete are:

- **avoidance coping** – where the athlete does not acknowledge there is a problem and carries on, or removes themselves from stressful situations and does something else instead
- **emotion-focused coping** – where the athlete uses strategies to help regulate the emotional upheaval of injury, e.g. use of social support, imagery, using stress management skills
- **problem-focused coping** – where the athlete uses strategies to address injury problems, e.g. gathering information, seeking out practitioners who can help.

Stress management skills such as imagery, progressive muscle relaxation, and positive self-talk are emotion-focused coping strategies that athletes should develop to allow them to deal with the stressors of rehabilitation. These may lead to a more successful rehabilitation and prevent future injury. Some of the benefits of stress management skills include:

- reduced anxiety
- increased confidence
- pain management
- increased adherence.

Reflect

Avoidance coping is often thought to be negative.
Can you think of an example when avoidance coping might be beneficial for an athlete?

PAUSE POINT Why is getting injured a stressful experience for all athletes no matter what gender, ability level or sport?

Hint Describe the possible stressors during the early stages of rehabilitation.

Extend Describe the possible stressors when the athlete nears returning to sport. Are they the same?

Psychological factors and return to sport

Returning to sport after an injury is a really stressful time for athletes. When an athlete returns to sport they have to deal with many physical, social and performance stressors (also referred to as concerns or anxieties).

- **Physical stressors** – these include the risk of re-injury, being unfit compared with others and not having match fitness.
- **Social stressors** – these include feeling isolated, increased pressure from the coach, players and crowd.
- **Performance stressors** – not being at the same level as prior to injury, falling behind the rest, losing their place in the team if they are underperforming.

Case study

Jack Butland (England goalkeeper)

In March 2016, promising young goalkeeper Jack Butland suffered a fractured ankle in an international friendly game against Germany. With the regular first-choice goalkeeper being absent, Butland was taking his big chance to step up and impress the team management. This injury ruled Jack out of the remainder of the season for his club and meant he missed a major international tournament playing for his country.

Check your knowledge

1. Based on Jack's personal and situational factors, what do you think his psychological responses to being injured might have been?
2. What techniques could you use to help a player with these responses?
3. What psychological issue might Butland face when he returns to competition?

Assessment practice 15.2

B.P2 B.M2 AB.D1

You are on work experience with a sports injury practitioner. You have been asked by your placement provider to complete a project aimed at educating youth athletes about what to expect if they get injured. To achieve this you are to produce a poster that clearly:

- places stages of tissue healing into a simple flow chart using key terms
- explains the signs of inflammation and why they occur
- explains the psychological responses they should expect throughout rehabilitation
- evaluates factors that can help the healing process.

Plan

- What does an effective poster look like?
- Are there any areas I think I may need extra support with?

Do

- Do I know what I am doing, what I want to achieve, and how to communicate the information?
- Do I know where to find supportive material, e.g. books, websites, on physiological and psychological responses to injury?

Review

- Can I explain which elements were the hardest to complete?
- Can I map where on the poster the assessment criteria have been met?

C Investigate aetiology of sports injuries and their associated prevention strategies

To repeat an old phrase, it is better to prevent injuries than to cure them (or rehabilitate). Before you can effectively prevent injuries, you must understand the factors that might cause an injury to occur. Once you have understood these factors and how they interlink, robust preventive measures can be put in place to reduce injury risk.

Aetiology of sports injury

The word 'aetiology' broadly means the science of causation - here, it is the study of factors that cause a sports injury to occur. Sports injury can be caused by a variety of factors which fall into two categories - **intrinsic** and **extrinsic**. Identifying the risk factors could dramatically reduce the chances of an athlete suffering an injury.

Key terms

Intrinsic factors - factors within the body that increase the risk of injury.

Extrinsic factors - factors outside the body that increase the risk of injury.

Intrinsic risk factors

These risk factors originate within the athletes body and predispose them to either an increased or decreased chance of getting injured during sport or exercise. The main intrinsic risk factors are described here.

- **Muscular factors** - for instance, muscle imbalances leading to differences between dominant and non-dominant limbs, or between agonist and antagonist muscle groups. A common example is a poor quadriceps to hamstring strength/power ratio. A weaker muscle is more prone to fatigue and injury. The body may have to compensate due to muscular weakness. Muscle weakness and leg length discrepancies also fall into this category.
- **Lack of flexibility** - competitive sport often requires athletes to execute movement patterns right at the end of their range of motion, e.g. stretching to catch a ball in cricket or lunging to make a tackle in football. If there is generalised muscle tightness, focal areas of muscle thickening due to repetitive loading, or restricted range of motion this can increase the risk of injury. This can affect muscles, tendons, and joints. For example, over-tight hamstrings may tear during rapid acceleration or deceleration or over-tight quadriceps may irritate the patellar tendon causing tendinopathy symptoms.

- **Individual variables** – unique characteristics of the athlete contributing to injury. Injury patterns are different based on an athlete's age, growth/development, and gender. For example, younger athletes are more at risk of apophysitis injury and older athletes of strains. The period of **peak height velocity** (PHV) in youth athletes is a time where injury risk is high. Females are more at risk of anterior cruciate ligament (ACL) sprains. One of the biggest risk factors is previous injury history, for example, a history of lateral ankle sprain, ACL sprain, or hamstring strains increase your risk of further injury. Body size and composition are also risk factors with underweight (low body fat %) or overweight athletes having an increased risk. Unfit athletes will fatigue quickly and have an increasing risk of injury compared with an appropriately conditioned athlete.

Research

Create a Twitter status (140 characters) summarising why females may be more at risk of ACL injury than males. Compare your answer with your classmates'.

- **Postural defects** – abnormal curvature of the spine is a potential risk that can become degenerative and restrict sporting potential. Examples of such malalignment of the vertebrae include **scoliosis**, **flat back**, excessive **kyphosis** and excessive **lordosis**. These problems can occur both independently and together (to a certain degree). Overuse and insufficient recovery following exercise and excessive strain on a body part can also exacerbate injuries and worsen existing postural defects. As we get older our intervertebral discs become thinner which can also increase the risk of injury.

Key terms

Peak height velocity (PHV) – the period when growth rate is at is fastest or the 'growth spurt'.

Flat back – a decreased curvature of the lumbar spine; insufficient curvature in the spine to distribute forces.

- **Malalignment** – asymmetry or malalignment within the athlete can lead to excessive forces going through the body as the athlete compensates. For example, an uneven running technique due to one leg being longer than the other (leg length discrepancy) or knees collapsing inwards on landing (genu valgum) due to a broad pelvis (wide quadriceps or Q angle). Common malalignment examples include: pes planus, pes cavus, rearfoot varus, tibia vara, genu varum, genu varus, patella alta, tibial torsion, and femoral neck anteversion.

Research

Research and define the following specialist terms:

- pes planus and pes cavus
- rearfoot varus
- tibia vara
- genu varum and genu varus
- patella alta
- tibial torsion
- femoral neck anteversion.

- **Psychological factors** – an athlete's psychological make-up can make them at risk of injury. This includes their personality, stressors (sporting and non-sporting), and coping resources. Having high life stress, little social support, high trait anxiety, and overusing avoidance coping resources are linked with increased injury risk.

Extrinsic risk factors

These risk factors originate outside the athlete's body and mean they have either an increased or decreased chance of getting injured. Together with intrinsic factors they determine how susceptible to injury the athlete is. The main extrinsic factors are described here.

- **Training errors** – excessive training load (volume, intensity) often with little or no recovery are common factors in athletes suffering injury and fatigue. Any sudden increase or changes to training load (volume, intensity, type) are also important risk factors. Training frequently involves repetitive movements, sometimes with resistance or weights so doing these movements with poor technique can increase the risk of injury. Competing too often (e.g. twice per week or more) can also increase the risk of getting injured.
- **Coaching and social factors** – the types and number of injuries their team suffers tends to follow a coach from club to club. This means your coach is an injury risk factor. The coaching style, style of play, communication, expectations, adherence to rules and professional body guidelines may all influence whether athletes get injured. The attitude and culture of the team/sport may also be an injury risk. For example, a play to hurt the opposition mentality.
- **Incorrect technique** – an athlete who moves well is less at risk of injury and vice versa. Sports skills are made up of fundamental movement patterns, and if these are poor the risk of injury can be increased when then athlete is fatigued or has to do these with intensity. For example, the defending position in football is the same as a semi-squat. If a player cannot perform a semi-squat correctly they are at risk every time they get into the defending position. Poor manual handling and lifting techniques can increase risk of injury in sports where this occurs, such as in a line-out in rugby union.
- **Clothing and footwear** – not wearing the correct equipment for your sport will create major extrinsic risk factors. Examples include wearing the wrong footwear for the activity or playing surface, damaged or too much or too little protective equipment, or the wrong protective equipment for the sport.
- **Safety hazards** – it is important for coaches, support staff and players to be aware of hazards and risks associated with the activities being undertaken. Various health and safety considerations must be applied to all activities both before and during participation. For example, risk assessment, medical emergency action plans, and health screening (sometimes including electrocardiogram screening) should all be implemented.
- **Environmental factors** – the weather conditions can affect the likelihood of an injury. For example, rain may make the playing surface slippery, which will increase the chance of injury. The playing surface itself also has an impact (i.e. whether it is hard or soft, natural or artificial).
- **Misuse of equipment** – the misuse and abuse of equipment causes risks to sports players, as it is specifically designed to do a particular job. Tampering with or modifying equipment will make it less useful and often dangerous.
- **Inadequate nutrition and hydration** – if an athlete has too little energy due to an inappropriate pre-match meal, they will become fatigued more quickly and their risk of injury will increase. A regular energy deficit for an athlete may increase the risk of injury and other health issues. Taking part in sport when dehydrated is also linked to early fatigue and can cause heat-related illness. Poor nutrition after training and competing will delay recovery and over time become an injury risk factor as tissues fail to repair.

Theory into practice

To reduce the impact of sports injuries it is important that practitioners help prevent them from occurring. Many practitioners may have a role to play in injury preventions. Using the information on extrinsic risk factors create a list of 'do's and 'don't's for rugby union players to follow with the aim of reducing injuries.

PAUSE POINT Explain the process of how sports injuries occur.

Hint What do you think your own unique predisposing/intrinsic risk factors are?

Extend What are the extrinsic risk factors in your sport?

Gait analysis

An abnormal **gait** is usually a risk factor or can be caused as a result of injury. Conducting an observation of gait, or a 'gait analysis', may help identify some of the causes of non-contact injuries and allow us to see how well the body moves as a whole. The easiest way to do this is to observe an athlete from the front, side, and back while looking at the key phases of walking and running.

Key term

Gait – a person's manner of walking or running.

Walking gait

A walking gait is made up of a **stance phase** and a **swing phase** (see Figure 15.5). The stance phase starts and ends with a period where both feet are in direct contact with the floor and weight is transferred from one leg to the other. This is known as the **double support phase**, a sub-part of the stance phase. The stance phase begins with initial contact with the floor, progresses through mid-stance where the foot goes from being flat to the heel raising up, and ends with propulsion off the big toe into the swing phase of the cycle.

In walking, for the duration of the gait cycle each foot is in the **stance phase** for 60 per cent of the time and in the **swing phase** 40 per cent of the time.

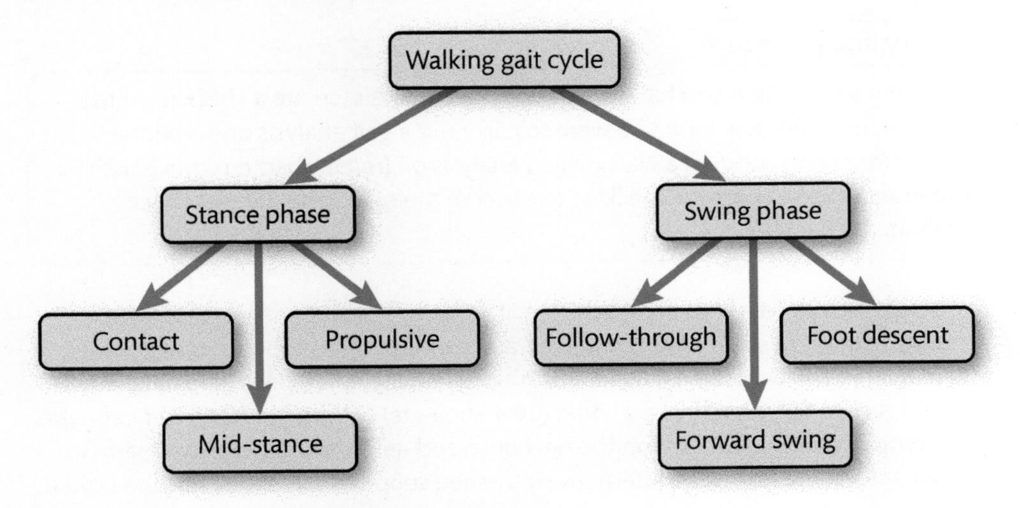

Figure 15.5: Key elements of the walking gait cycle

Running gait

The mechanics of running are similar to walking as they both share a stance phase and a swing phase, but in the gait cycle of running there is no double support phase. Instead running has a **flight phase**, where neither foot is in contact with the ground. As speed increases so does the flight phase and the forces through the body.

Factors to look out for when you observe an athlete's running gait are:

- the duration of the gait cycle – is the timing of the gait cycle the same on both sides?
- the motion of the sections of the body during the phases, for example, the foot, ankle, knee, hips and spine
- the position of the body during the gait cycle – is it leant forward, upright or leaning to the side?
- how speed and fatigue affect the gait cycle – does technique change under greater intensity or when fatigued?
- whether there are major differences in gait from different footwear, e.g. barefoot, trainers, day-to-day shoes.

Gait and structural abnormalities

Key terms

Pronation – when the foot rolls inwards during walking or running.

Supination – when the foot rolls outwards during walking or running.

When observing an athlete's walking or running gait it is common to find factors that are slightly abnormal. Pronation and supination are important and subtle movements of the feet during a normal gait. For example, we tend to progress from **pronation** to **supination** to pronation during a normal gait cycle.

Excessive or inappropriate pronation (forefoot valgus) and supination (forefoot varus) can lead to injury. Typically athletes with a high arch (pes cavus) over-supinate while those with flat foot or collapsed arch (pes planus) over-pronate. It is also fairly common to see a lateral (sideways) pelvic tilt when an athlete transfers weight from one leg to the other. This could be because of a leg length discrepancy or weak muscles stabilising the hip. You can identify other abnormalities during gait analysis by asking the following questions.

- Does the calcaneus, or heel bone, roll inwards of outwards (rearfoot valgus or varus)?
- Is there parallel motion at the legs? If not are their knees knocked or legs bowed?
- Are they scuffing their feet? (a sign of poor dorsiflexion)?
- Is there is an equal arm swing?
- Is there good postural control during the gait cycle?

Theory into practice

From the information you have read about gait analysis, create a checklist of the things you would look for if you were to carry out a gait analysis on someone. Find someone to conduct a walking gait analysis on (remember to remove their shoes and socks). Use your checklist to observe their gait, and give feedback to them.

If you notice an athlete with gait problems, it is worth advising them on footwear or referring them to see a **podiatrist**, who assesses and treats biomechanical issues with feet. There is modified footwear available especially for athletes who have a high arch and run on the outside of their feet (over-supinate) or with flat feet (over-pronate). These modifications are based on the heel drop and amount of supportive foam on the mid-sole of the footwear. Alternatively in-shoe supports (orthoses) may be used to add extra arch support, cradle the calcaneus to prevent excessive movement, and to give better individualised fit.

Gait and lower limb injuries

We do around 5000–10,000 gait cycles per day and even more, with high forces produced, if we take part in sport or exercise. It is easy to see then that having gait or structural abnormalities can lead to injury. Common injuries associated with a gait issues include:

- overuse injuries – plantar fasciitis, Achilles tendinopathy, patellar tendinopathy, medial shin pain (medial tibial stress syndrome – shin splints), stress fractures, patellofemoral pain syndrome, iliotibial band friction syndrome, calcaneal bursitis, blisters
- acute injuries – hamstring strain, bruising, acute lower back pain, lateral ankle sprains.

Research

Research the common running injuries listed above. With a classmate, create an information sheet which:

- defines these injuries
- explains how they are caused
- describes the common signs and symptoms of each injury.

Preventative measures

One of the most important roles of a sports injury practitioner is to prevent injuries and thus the physical, mental, social and financial harm that goes with them. **Primary prevention** is preventing injuries occurring in individual or team sports. **Secondary prevention** is working with an injured athlete and working out how to reduce further injury or re-injury. Any approach to preventing injuries should be well informed, logical and use a framework.

Principles of injury prevention

There are two major sports injury prevention frameworks by van Mechelen *et al* (1992) and van Tiggelen *et al* (2008). The four-step model of injury prevention (see Figure 15.6) suggests a cycle of stages going from establishing the injury problem to ultimately evaluating if the preventive measure has been effective on the number and type of injuries.

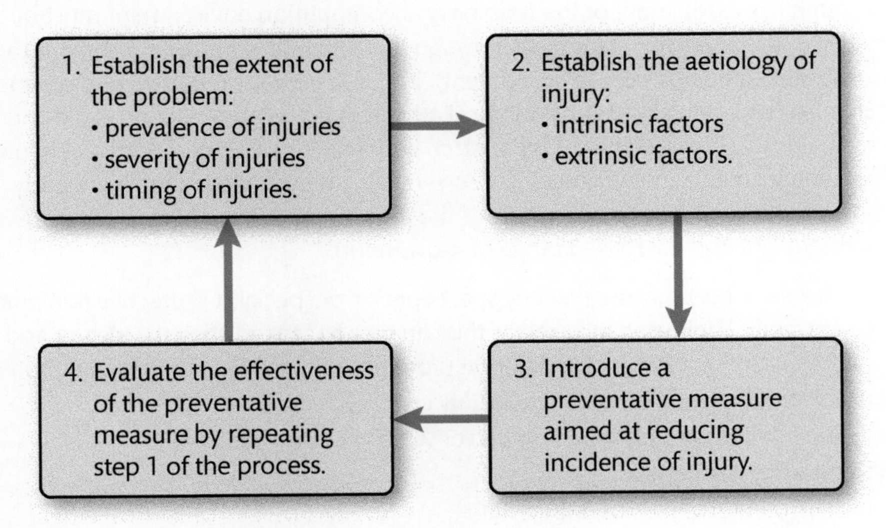

Figure 15.6: The four-step model of injury prevention (van Mechelen *et al*, 1992)

Research

Van Tiggelen *et al* (2008) suggested a slightly different approach to injury prevention. Find out about their model and identify the key differences between their work and van Mechelen *et al*'s ideas.

- **Efficiency** – what are the time and resourcing demands?
- **Compliance** – are athletes likely to adhere to it?

Theory into practice

For a sport of your choice explain how you would go through van Mechelen *et al*'s four steps of injury prevention. Why is the van Tiggelen *et al* (2008) approach to prevention beneficial for sports injury practitioners?

Many preventative measures vary based on the demands of the sport, the level of competition, resources available, and contact time with athletes. But many individuals are responsible for injury prevention including the coach, players, sports injury practitioners, referees, sports scientists and conditioning coaches – it should be a real team effort. Some general preventative measures are covered in this section.

The role of the coach

The coach has a huge role to play in preventing injuries. A coach should have up-to-date qualifications and knowledge of the sport and their athletes. This includes monitoring of loading (physical and cognitive), and each athlete's strengths and weaknesses. They should be able to adapt their coaching style, communication style, and expectations based on the athlete's ability, age, fitness, gender, and motivation. For example, they should not coach children as if they are mini adults, and should stress the dangers of early specialisation in sport.

The coach also has a role in reinforcing health and safety, making sure athletes wear protective equipment, surveying the playing surface and ensuring equipment is safe to use.

Equipment and environment

A thorough risk assessment of the training and competition environment must be carried out. It is also important to go through this procedure for the equipment that is used (for example, protective equipment). In many sports, protective equipment has changed dramatically as technological advances in the materials available and biomechanical analysis techniques (research and analysis of movement) have allowed improvements in quality. Advances have been in both protection of specific body parts, and limiting the negative impact of the protection on playing performance (such as excess weight and decreased range of movement).

Sports players need to ensure that any sport-specific or specialist protective equipment is used correctly. If it is used incorrectly, this can be a hazard, putting the wearer and other athletes at risk. When using different types of protective equipment, you should:

- ensure that the equipment is thoroughly checked before use
- use the equipment only for the sport for which it is designed
- use only the correct size
- not make modifications to equipment
- be aware that protective equipment does not make you invincible
- use the equipment for both practice and competition.

Environmental conditions should also be considered to help reduce injury risk. For example, a training session held on grass might reduce the risk compared with holding the same training session on a hard or artificial surface. And if weather conditions change, perhaps with rain making a surface slippery, then the session could be moved so that it is held indoors.

Performer preparation

Properly preparing the athlete to take part in training and competition will also reduce their risk of injury. An effective warm-up should prepare the athlete to work at game pace. A good warm-up should follow the RAMP acronym:

- R - **raise** the blood flow, breathing rate and heart rate
- A - **activate** key muscle groups using dynamic stretches
- M - **mobilise** the major joints
- P - **potentiate** muscles to improve effectiveness through jumping and landing, sprinting, cutting movements.

An athlete who has been sat or stood still for a period of time (e.g. being a substitute) should be encouraged to re-warm up. All athletes should also take part in a cool-down after training or competition.

Measures to improve flexibility should be done on most days. These measures only work if they are done on a regular basis. This could include stretching, foam rolling, or having a regular sports massage.

Theory into practice

For your sport create a warm-up routine that could reduce the risk of injury. Carry this out and gain feedback from coaches and athletes. Did they enjoy it? Would they do it again? What would you change?

Appropriate training

Athletes should be appropriately trained to meet the demands of the sport and have sufficient recovery after training and competition. This means carefully following a **periodised** training without rapid increases in the frequency, duration, intensity or type of training.

Training methods should be as specific to the demands of the sport as possible. Preventative exercises usually try to develop core stability for greater postural control, **proprioception** and balance, muscle strength, e.g. eccentric hamstring strength, and good landing control.

Key terms

Periodised - based on a structured cycle. A periodised training programme will increase performance and reduce injuries and boredom.

Proprioception - the ability to sense where the body is in space.

Correction of biomechanical abnormalities

Each player should be screened to identify any potential abnormalities that could lead to injury. For example, screening athletes for adequate range of motion at major joints (too little or too much), limb length discrepancy (e.g. leg length), posture and gait analysis, and assessing the quality of fundamental movement patterns will highlight any issues that might need to be addressed. This may then lead to the athlete needing one-to-one strength and conditioning support, engaging in a programme of suitable core stability training or stretching, or referring to a podiatrist to correct these faults.

Other measures

Taping and bracing certain 'at risk' joints or muscles (e.g. using athletic tape or kinesiology taping) may prevent injuries through correcting biomechanical issues by providing stability to joints or addressing muscle weakness and tightness.

Ensuring an athlete's diet contains plenty of energy facilitates adequate recovery, and making sure they are fully hydrated will help prevent injury and illness.

Psychological skills training (PST) such as imagery, progressive muscle relaxation and self-talk, will also reduce the physical and mental impact of stressors and reduce injury risk.

Sleep (both its quality and quantity) is an important part of recovery and following good sleeping practices that improve sleep patterns may reduce injuries (e.g. no mobile phones in the bedroom, avoiding big meals before bed).

PAUSE POINT Imagine you are working for a sports team. Create a fact sheet for staff and players of the team, outlining injury prevention strategies appropriate for the sport.

Hint For a sport or exercise you are personally involved in, list the ways in which you try to prevent injury from occurring.

Extend List strategies you do not currently use that could be of future use.

Assessment practice 15.3

C.P3 C.M3 C.D2

The manager of the team you are working with has read that the most successful teams suffer fewer injuries compared with others. He has asked you to produce an information sheet that outlines your plan for injury prevention for the upcoming season. You have decided to use the four-step model of injury prevention (van Mechelen *et al*, 1992) framework to help structure your decisions. On the information sheet you need to explain each step using examples.

- Step 1 – assess the extent of the problem and explain how you have done this.
- Step 2 – assess the common intrinsic and extrinsic risk factors in the sport, and how they interact.
- Step 3 – suggest three specific preventive measures you would introduce and explain how they would work.
- Step 4 – explain how you would evaluate the preventive measures.

You may choose which sport to base this activity on.

Plan

- What information do I need to put on my sheet?
- Which sport am I basing this on?
- How confident do I feel in my own ability to complete this task?

Do

- Do I know the four steps of the model and can I apply them to my sport?
- Do I know where to find an evidence base to support my information?

Review

- Can I explain how I would improve the content on the information sheet next time?
- Can I identify the assessment criteria I have achieved on my work?

D Explore common treatment and rehabilitation methods

Rehabilitation is the process of restoring sport function following an injury. It starts as soon as the injury occurs and finishes after the athlete has successfully returned to sport. Understanding the basics of early trauma management (first aid) and selecting effective methods to improve the athletes' function (a rehabilitation plan) is important for a successful rehabilitation.

Treatment methods and the need for medical referral

To make sure that injuries can be dealt with effectively each sports team should have a medical **emergency action plan** (EAP). This is a detailed breakdown of what should happen if an athlete is injured during sport. It should cover minor injuries (e.g. muscle strains) and more severe injuries/conditions (spinal injury or cardiac arrest).

The first aid care of an injured athlete is usually a real team effort involving many people (e.g. coaches, sports injury practitioners, club doctors, parents, etc.) so everyone needs to understand the EAP to provide the best care possible.
The EAP should answer these basic questions.

- Who are the qualified practitioners at the venue?
- How can injured athletes be safely removed from the field of play?
- What medical equipment is available and where is it kept (e.g. defibrillator, stretcher)?
- Who calls for the ambulance if an athlete needs transferring into hospital care?
- Where is the nearest hospital with an accident and emergency department and head trauma unit?
- Where is the ambulance access?

Theory into practice

For a sports team you are involved with create your own medical EAP.

Principles of first aid

First aid is the immediate treatment given to an injured person. All sports governing bodies require their coaches to have a recognised first aid qualification. The severity of sporting injuries can vary, from minor cuts and bruises to life-threatening problems. Some knowledge of first aid can potentially save an athlete's life, and can also help with minor problems to speed the recovery process and limit potential complications. In the application of first aid you should, in order of importance:

- P – **protect** yourself, the athlete and others
- P – **preserve** life
- P – **prevent** deterioration
- P – **promote** recovery.

With potentially serious accidents, a specific primary survey should be carried out.

Safety tip

Completing this unit does not qualify you as a first-aider. If you do witness a serious accident, the most qualified and experienced individual should be the one who carries out the first aid procedures. Do not crowd the injured person, but assist in any way that the first-aider asks.

Primary survey

This is a dynamic process to address the life-threatening injuries before moving to minor less life-threatening issues. It is of paramount importance that it is carried out first and repeated to monitor the athlete.

- **Danger** – check the area for potential danger to yourself. Another casualty will worsen the problem. Also remove any potentially hazardous objects from around the casualty.
- **Response** – check if there is any response from the injured person. If not, call for help immediately. Do not leave the injured person.
- **Airway** – gently tip the head backwards to open the airways and check if there are any foreign objects in the person's mouth, blocking the airway.
- **Breathing** – check to see if the person is breathing 'normally' (for up to 10 seconds). If not, send someone for an ambulance (dial 999 or 112) and to get the automated external defibrillator (AED).
- **Circulation** – can you confirm the presence of a pulse (for up to 10 seconds), and the strength/rate of this (beats per minute)?

- **Disability** – have they got a head or spinal injury? Determine consciousness status. Is there any seizure activity, for example, involuntary jerking movements of arms and legs?
- **Environment/exposure/extrication** – do they need moving? Keep them warm, wait for the emergency services.

Reassess continually.

Secondary survey

A secondary survey should be carried out if an unconscious person is breathing normally and if life-threatening conditions have been identified and dealt with. This is done to check all areas of the body for damage. The process should be carried out quickly and in a systematic way.

- **Bleeding** – check the area, and check the patient head-to-toe for blood.
- **Head and neck** – check for bruising and/or deformity. Gently feel the back of the neck for damage.
- **Shoulders and chest** – compare the shoulders; feel for fractures in the collarbones and ribs.
- **Abdomen and pelvis** – feel around the abdomen for abnormalities and to see if the person feels any pain.
- **Legs and arms** – check legs, then arms, for fracture and any other clues.
- **Pockets** – check the person's pockets to make sure there are no items that could injure them when you roll them into the recovery position. Be very cautious of sharp objects (for example, needles). If possible, have a witness if you remove anything from their pockets.
- **Recovery** – make sure you do not cause further damage to the person when placing them in the recovery position. If a neck injury is suspected, as long as their airway is maintained do not move them and instead stabilise the head either side with your hands.

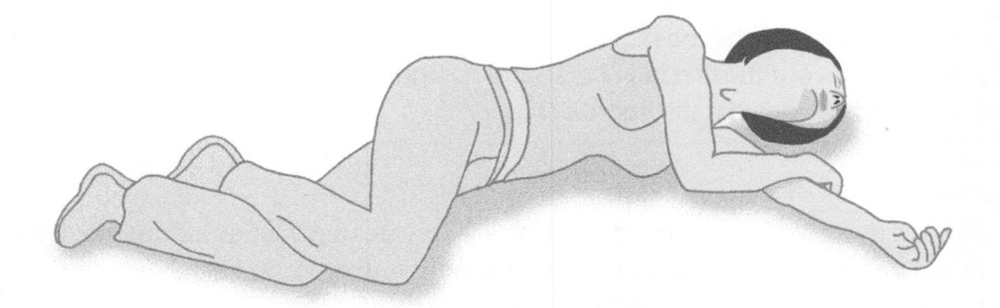

Figure 15.7: The recovery position in which the athlete is turned onto their side with the airway opened and supported

Safety tips

- Be aware of jewellery or sports equipment (e.g. GPS monitors) to make sure they are not worsening the problem – remove it in such cases. Also look for medic alerts (such as diabetes bracelets/necklaces).
- Make a mental and/or written note of anything you have observed during the primary and secondary surveys. This information should be passed on to the emergency services to help with treating the patient.

The recovery position is a way of positioning an unconscious casualty, minimising the risk of their airway becoming compromised. Two potential dangers that are to be avoided are:

- the tongue relaxing and blocking the airway
- the patient vomiting and the vomit blocking the airway.

First aid treatment

Cardiopulmonary resuscitation (CPR)

CPR should be performed when a person is not breathing and shows no signs of circulation. This process keeps the vital organs alive until help arrives. An oxygen supply to the brain is essential to sustain life, via inhaled air and the movement of blood in the body. If a person is not breathing and their heart is not beating, this will need to be done for them.

CPR involves breathing for the casualty and performing chest compressions at a ratio of 30 compressions to 2 breathes for adults and children. Early access to an **Automated External Defibrillator** (AED) is vital to the success of this process with CPR being carried out to buy time until the AED can be used.

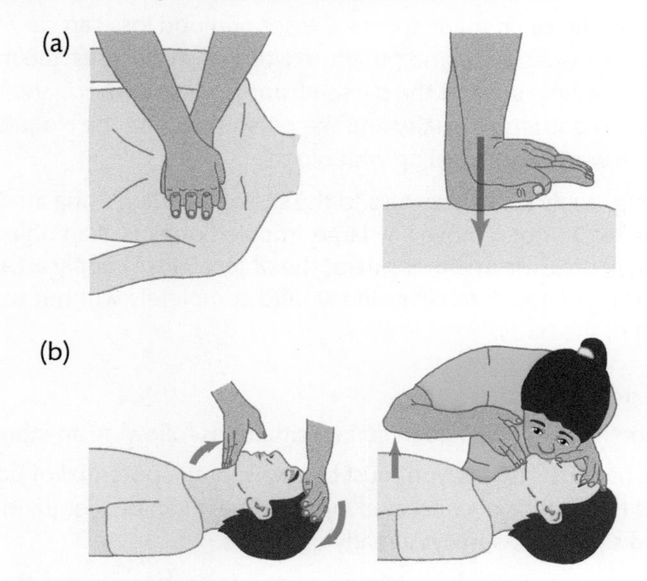

Figure 15.8: The CPR process. What is the ratio of compressions to breaths?

Shock

Shock is caused by a drop in blood pressure or blood volume. Shock can be a secondary reaction to many serious injuries (for example, injury with major blood loss). There are three classifications:

- **cardiogenic shock** – the most common type, caused by the heart not pumping effectively
- **hypovolaemic shock** – caused by a loss in bodily fluids resulting in low blood volume (can be common for traumatic major sports injuries)
- **anaphylactic shock** – caused by a severe allergic reaction.

The signs and symptoms of shock include:

- increased pulse rate (can become weaker as the condition worsens)
- pale and clammy skin, sweating as shock worsens (lips can become blue)
- fast, shallow breathing
- nausea or vomiting

- dizziness and/or feelings of weakness
- with severe shock, deep breathing can develop, with confusion, anxiety and possibly aggression
- casualties can become unconscious.

To treat shock:

- address the cause of shock (for example, immobilise a fracture)
- lay the person down and, if possible, raise the legs (keeping the flow of blood to the vital organs)
- keep the person warm and loosen any tight clothing.

Safety tip

With all cases of shock, the emergency services should be contacted immediately. The casualty should be monitored continuously (for breathing, pulse and response).

Fortunately, the majority of sports injuries are not serious enough to require CPR or treatment for shock. However, the correct treatment of injuries is critical to ensure that the healing process can occur without complications. If in any doubt, seek a professional opinion.

Blood-loss treatment

Loss of blood is common in many sports. Causes of blood loss can vary from minor scratches to serious lacerations and puncture wounds. In all cases, the main priorities are to stop the bleeding, prevent the person from going into shock and reduce the risk of infection, to both the casualty and the person treating the wound. Disposable gloves should be worn when dealing with blood.

To treat bleeding, apply direct pressure to the site of bleeding using an appropriate bandage or gauze. Do not remove any large, impaled objects: if an object is embedded in a person, apply pressure at either side of the object. Firmly apply an absorbent, sterile dressing large enough to cover the wound completely without restricting blood flow to the rest of the body.

Further considerations

Special attention needs to be paid in certain situations following an injury.

- For an unconscious casualty you must be aware of the potential of both head injuries and the chance of concealed injuries. These can be identified through the primary and secondary surveys already discussed.
- If fractures are a possibility it is essential to minimise the movement of the injury.
- Where the risk of infection is high, this must be minimised, often through appropriate covering of the injury. For example, any open wound should be washed and sterilised to prevent infection.

With any of these injuries, it is important to summon qualified assistance and the emergency services.

Whether an accident takes place in the workplace or during sporting competition, it is essential to complete an accident report form if treatment is required. This process is a legal requirement for insurance purposes.

Safety tip

If you are in any doubt about a condition or injury it is better to be cautious and refer.

PAUSE POINT A player collapses unconscious, without any contact, in a match at which you are providing medical support. What could be wrong?

Hint How would you act in this situation?

Extend List the actions you would take to deal with this situation.

Pitch side assessment of sports injuries

If an incident occurs during a sporting event – assuming the injury is not life-threatening and the athlete is fully conscious – assess the athlete to find out what is wrong with them, how it happened, how it affects their function, and whether they could continue or not. This assessment can follow the SALTAPS process.

- **S** – get the athlete to **stop**. Did you see how the injury was caused and mechanism of injury?
- **A** – **ask** questions about the injury, where it hurts, pain severity, how they thought it happened.
- **L** – **look** for specific signs such as redness, swelling or foreign objects.
- **T** – **touch**/palpate the area for heat and tenderness.
- **A** – ask the athlete to perform **active movements** of the body part to check pain and range of motion.
- **P** – gently move the body part with **passive movements** to check how it feels, pain, and range of motion.
- **S** – test the **strength** of the body part by providing light resistance. Can they stand on it? Can they walk, run, jump and sprint? Can they return to playing safely?

In the treatment of all sports-related injuries, the most appropriate individuals to give treatment are the most experienced. The aim of the SALTAPS process is to make an accurate assessment of the type, severity and location of an injury. This can be difficult for some sports injuries – even the most experienced practitioners can find an initial on-site diagnosis difficult.

Safety tip

It is important to stop the SALTAPS process immediately if it indicates that an injury might be serious.

Treatment of sports injuries

After most common sports injuries are suffered, the immediate treatment should follow the acronym of PRICED. This means that even at this early stage of injury the healing process can be enhanced. The guidelines are there to manage the inflammatory response, **not** to remove it completely.

- **P**rotect – the person and injured part of the body to minimise the risk of further injury.
- **R**est – allows healing and prevent any further damage.
- **I**ce – stops the injured area from swelling and reduces the pain.
- **C**ompression – acts as support and also prevents swelling.
- **E**levation – reduces blood flow to the area, reducing swelling with the aid of gravity.
- **D**iagnosis – needs to be done by a qualified sports injury professional or through a scan.

Other immediate care treatments

There are a range of other treatments that can help manage the symptoms in the early stages of injury. These treatments can be categorised into cryotherapy (cold treatments), thermotherapy (heat treatments), stability treatments, and electrotherapy (electric-based treatments). Some examples include:

- **cryotherapy** – use of bagged ice, ice packs, ice sprays, frozen peas, ice bandage, cryo-compression equipment
- **thermotherapy** – heat packs, radiant heat lamps, heat creams/gels, heat pads, paraffin wax, spa baths
- **stability treatments** – athletic tape, kinesiotape, bracing, joint supports, slings, crutches, splints, bandaging
- **electrotherapy** – ultrasound, shockwave, transcutaneous electrical nerve stimulation (TENS).

Theory into practice

Recently the PRICED acronym has been adapted to POLICE to reflect the importance of exercise in rehabilitation.

- What does the POLICE acronym stand for?
- How does it differ from the PRICED acronym?
- Create a tweet (max. 140 characters) about why optimal loading is important in sports injury rehabilitation.

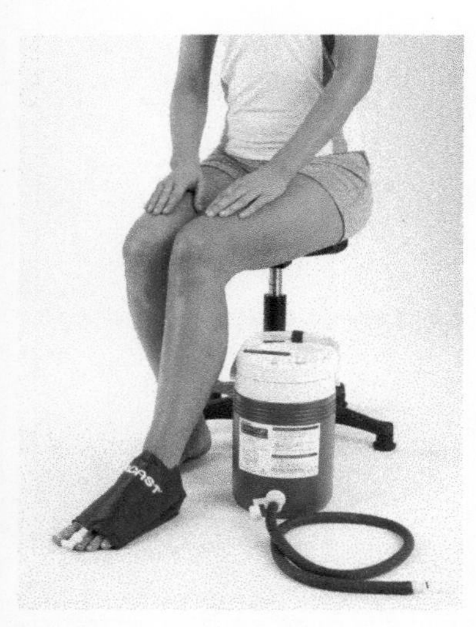

▶ Example of a cryo-compression device. What are the advantages and disadvantages of this treatment?

Some practitioners may combine a number of these treatments as opposed to using them on their own, for example, with hot and cold treatments including contrast bathing. This is alternating heat with cold treatments to quickly take the blood vessels from vasodilation to vasoconstriction in order to remove swelling and cell debris, lessen pain, and improve range of motion.

The **Lewis hunting response** is important to understand when applying cryotherapy to athletes. Applying ice causes narrowing of the blood vessels in the injured area (vasoconstriction). After a number of minutes (approximately 10–15 minutes) blood vessels start to re-open (vasodilation) to prevent tissues dying from a lack of oxygen. This can mean icing an injured area for too long can increase bleeding and swelling, albeit less than if ice was not applied.

Safety tip

You must be qualified to use treatments and know what conditions might mean a treatment is not appropriate for the athlete to have. Some of the treatments, if used at the wrong time, may slow down tissue healing. For example, using thermotherapy in the very early stages of healing may increase or re-start bleeding.

Medical referral

Depending on the nature of the injury it may be necessary to refer an individual to a specialist. Such individuals could include:

- general practitioner or club doctor
- St John Ambulance or other qualified in first aid
- local accident and emergency departments (e.g. to access radiology department)
- local minor injuries clinic
- sports therapist or physiotherapist
- soft tissue therapist or sport massage therapist
- specialist consultant and/or surgeon
- podiatrist, osteopath or chiropractor.

You can also phone 111 (the NHS non-emergency medical helpline) to gain medical advice on non-life-threatening issues.

Research

It is important that the transfer of care to the emergency services is effective. This usually follows the ATMIST acronym. What does each letter stand for?

Principles of rehabilitation

General aims

The overall aim of rehabilitation is to restore physical and psychological functioning to the level seen prior to injury, or even better. Any treatment or rehabilitation plan should be based on accurate diagnosis by a qualified practitioner.

Each treatment that you may use has its own particular reason to use it (indications) or why you might not use it or adapt its use (**contraindications**). The overall programme should be well rationalised with a clear specific aim based on which stage the athlete is at, their progress, and how the injury occurred. For example, if the injury was caused by over-stretching tight hamstrings, the programme should seek to lengthen the hamstring group on both sides to prevent further re-injury.

Key term

Contraindication – a condition that means a certain treatment cannot be carried out or has to be adapted in some form.

Discussion

Discuss with a group of your classmates how the body responds to a period of time without training. Create a mind map about the impact this has on rehabilitation.

There are five stages of rehabilitation, shown in Table 15.8.

Table 15.8: Aims of each stages of rehabilitation with examples of treatments

Stage of rehabilitation	Aims of each stage	Suggested treatment
Acute stage	Manage the inflammatory process and reduce pain	Ice, compression, elevation, cryo-compression, TENS
Sub-acute stage	Try to encourage full range of motion, and encourage optimal loading and weight bearing	Massage, stretching, crutch walking (double to single), ice, heat, exercising non-injured limbs
Early rehabilitation stage	Start to fully weight bear, start to restore strength and activate muscles, proprioception and neuromuscular control	Passive mobilisations, strength exercise (isometric at first), muscle activation treatments, e.g. EMS, closed chain exercise, CV exercises, walking/jogging in straight lines, balance exercise
Late rehabilitation stage	Develop muscle power, endurance, multidirectional movement	Introduce isotonic or isokinetic exercise and add greater load, more intense CV exercise
Functional rehabilitation stage	Introduce sports-specific function mirroring the demands of competition, e.g. intensity, frequency of sports-specific movements	High-intensity, multidirectional and unpredictable movements, e.g. diagonal cutting, landing and sprinting, combining many movements in drills

Key principles

Rehabilitation is hard work for an athlete so it is important to use key principles to guide you and them. Any good rehabilitation plan is well explained, contains goals, provides a precise prescription, and makes the most of the available resources.
An effective rehabilitation programme should also use the acronym ATCISIT:

- **A**ggravation – avoid aggravation of the injury and monitor signs of aggravation
- **T**iming – start as soon as possible as too much rest can slow down healing
- **C**ompliance – encourage the athlete to actually do the plan as you have prescribed
- **I**ndividualisation – based on the athlete's own demands and individual needs
- **S**pecific sequencing – the plan should follow a sequence of events in line with the stage of healing
- **I**ntensity - this should challenge the athlete but not aggravate the injury
- **T**otal patient – trying to recognise the athlete holistically, **not** just physically, and optimise trainability.

For rehabilitation to be successful, tissues need to be appropriately loaded (exercised) for them to adapt positively to this loading. This should be based on the tissues that were injured and should be monitored regularly. The **Specific Adaption to Imposed Demands** (SAID) principle means you need to think about:

- what type of loading you are doing
- how heavy the load should be
- how long the load should be applied for
- how frequently the load should be applied.

If the loading is too little the athlete may not progress as quickly as expected. Alternatively, if the athlete is overloaded they may break down and suffer setbacks in their rehabilitation. The loading from the rehabilitation plan should be relatively pain free while performing it and also after the session.

Progression of rehabilitation exercises

An effective rehabilitation plan should use physical and psychological criteria to progress between stages, **not** be purely based on time. A sports injury practitioner can progress rehabilitation load by adapting the following key training variables:

- **type of activity** – exercises that do not directly stress the injured area vs those that do
- **duration of the activity** – time spent performing the exercise
- **frequency of the activity and rest** – how many times per day or week will they do this, and what to do on rest days
- **intensity of the activity** – how hard to exercise is based on perceived exertion, resistance, time to completion
- **complexity of the activity** – performing simple, unidirectional exercises vs high speed, multidirectional and multi-joint exercise.

A pathway to eventual return to sporting action can then be followed, as shown in Figure 15.9.

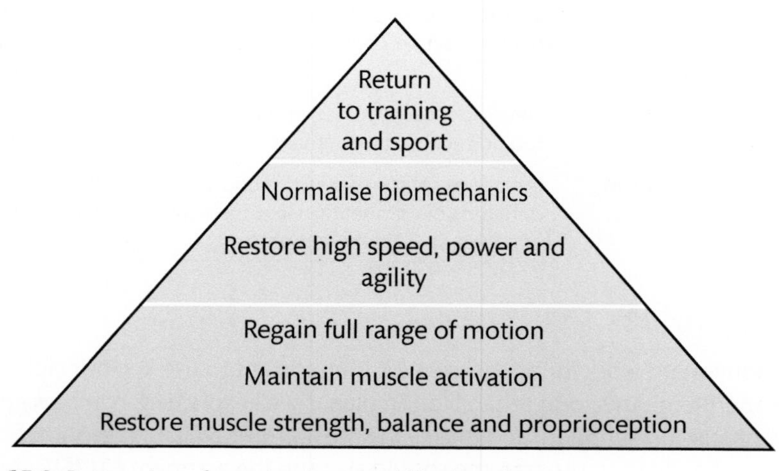

Figure 15.9: Progression of exercises in a rehabilitation plan

Case study

David Silva sprains his ankle playing for Spain

David Silva suffered a lateral ankle sprain playing for Spain vs Luxembourg in October 2015. This is a common injury that is often suffered by footballers. Lateral ankle sprains have also affected athletes from other sports, such as Sachin Tendulkar, Rafael Nadal, and LeBron James. Poor rehabilitation of this injury can lead to long-term losses in function and re-injury. The injury affects the three lateral ligaments of the ankle and in more severe cases cause an avulsion fracture.

Check your knowledge

1. What is the likely mechanism of injury for David Silva's ankle sprain?
2. Name the lateral ligaments that could be sprained.
3. Create a flow diagram of how you progress an athlete from walking with two crutches to finally being able to sprint in different directions, jump and land.

Monitoring the rehabilitation programme

How the athlete is responding to the rehabilitation programme must be monitored regularly based on subjective and objective feedback/measures. Key factors to be monitored include:

- perceived exertion and how they are feeling
- any pain and discomfort during and after exercise

- biomechanical or technical faults
- range of motion
- swelling
- heat and redness
- their progress in performing exercises and functional activities
- number of sets, repetitions, contractions until fatigue, technique worsens or pain is caused
- any concerns or issues the athlete has, e.g. expectations placed upon them, compliance.

Any adverse reactions should prompt the plan to be re-evaluated and modified.

All rehabilitation documents and information should be recorded as they form a legally binding document. The plan should include the precise prescription of what you planned to do and also any changes that were made during the rehabilitation based on how the athlete responds to your intended exercises. Things to consider when documenting a rehabilitation programme include:

- background information about the client (for example, medical issues, injury history, specific requirements of rehabilitation)
- the activities undertaken
- the levels achieved and development of the client
- problems or issues arising from the session
- complications (for example, allergies or illness) that affect the quality of the client's progress during the session
- important legal documents and forms such as parental consent for younger sports players
- dates for review/functional testing (aims, objectives, etc.)
- accurate and up-to-date information that may change during the duration of the treatment
- specific objectives including appropriate and measurable timescales and review dates.

PAUSE POINT Explain how and why rehabilitation plans must be progressive.

Hint Create a rehabilitation plan for rotator cuff strain in the sub-acute stage of rehabilitation. Try to be as specific as possible.

Extend How would you know the athlete was ready to progress? What type of factors would you progress?

Methods of exercise-based rehabilitation

When an athlete sustains an injury it has an immediate effect on their fitness levels. Specifically, the athlete's range of motion, flexibility, muscle condition, neural control over their muscles, and ability to perform skills with good technique are all deconditioned. Therefore, knowing a range of effective methods that can address reduced fitness levels is important when working with injured athletes. An effective practitioner will make the exercises engaging, and have a flexible approach with **progression and regression exercises**. Progression exercises will further challenge the athlete, and regression exercises will be less challenging if you find your exercises are overly difficult for them.

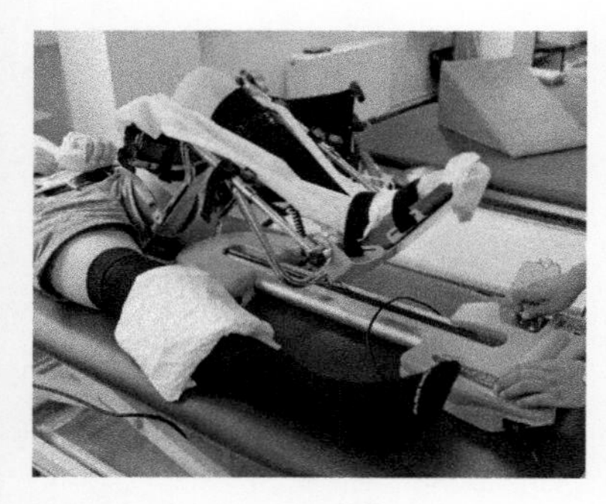

▶ CPM machines can be used to put a joint through continual and controlled movement

Methods to improve joint range of motion

Joint **range of motion** refers to amount of movement permitted at the joint. This is very specific to each joint and the athlete's make-up. It is limited by joint-based and soft tissue structures. The early restoration of range of motion is extremely important in rehabilitation. Methods to restore range of motion include:

- **continual passive motion (CPM)** – this is using a specially designed machine to put the joint through continual and controlled movement. It is mostly used on athletes that have suffered severe knee injuries requiring surgery
- **passive mobilisation techniques** – these are joint-specific techniques where the practitioner will perform different grades (1–4) of joint mobilisation repeatedly to improve pain-free range of motion and joint nutrition
- **passive exercises** – passive exercises allow for a joint to be moved through the available range of motion without any effort required by the athlete. These exercises can be performed by the practitioner or by the athlete using their non-affected limb to support the movement
- **active exercises** – these involve the athlete moving the joint through its available range of motion by themselves. For example, repeatedly flexing and extending the knee joint within the constraints of pain and swelling
- **active assisted exercises** – this is where the athlete performs the range of movement exercise themselves involving the injured joint and then uses the non-injured limb to support the movement, allowing the athlete to move further. For example, if the right knee is injured the athlete might use the left leg to support active flexion and extension.

Methods to improve musculotendinous flexibility

Musculotendinous flexibility refers to the ability of the soft tissue to lengthen, which influences joint range of motion. Muscles and tendons work together so stretching has an effect on both. The beneficial effects of stretching do not last very long. Therefore, to improve flexibility stretching should be carried out repeatedly and regularly, e.g. every day.

There are three main types of stretching techniques and all should be done with a feeling of tightness but not pain. The athlete should breathe normally with all stretching techniques and not hold their breath. Flexibility is gained by altering biomechanical and neurological properties of the tissues.

- **Active stretching** – this involves the athlete stretching their muscles to their active bind point (the point of resistance or tightness) and holding it statically there for a period of time (minimum of 30 seconds). The stretch is then taken off the bind point. The process is repeated a minimum of three times. The bind point should be further along each time.
- **Passive stretching** – this involves a practitioner stretching the athlete's muscles for them. Often the amount of flexibility gains with passive stretching can be greater than active stretching. The process is that the practitioner finds the passive bind point of the muscle, holds it for 45–60 seconds, releases, and then repeats up to five times.
- **Proprioceptive Neuromuscular Facilitation (PNF) stretching** – there a number of types of PNF stretching techniques. These techniques try to improve flexibility by reducing the neural input to the muscle and therefore flexibility can be gained. The most commonly used PNF technique is contract-relax.
  1. The practitioner finds the target muscle's passive bind point and holds for 15 seconds.
  2. In this position the athlete performs an isometric contraction of the target muscle at 25–75 per cent of their maximum. The contraction is held for 10 seconds.

3 The target muscle is taken off the bind point for 3 seconds.
4 The target muscle is then put back on a stretch to a new further bind point.
5 The process can be repeated up to four times.

Ideas for effective stretching

- Include stretching after a gentle warm-up or a soft tissue massage.
- Combine with thermotherapy-based treatments.
- Always ensure correct technique.
- Cryotherapy prior to stretching might reduce pain and spasm.
- Stretching must be pain free, not discomfort free.
- To progress stretching, think about the type of stretching and its duration, frequency and intensity.

PAUSE POINT What are the different stretching-based techniques used in rehabilitation?

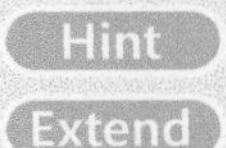

Hint Why do stretching-based exercises need to be carried out on a regular basis?

Extend What are the strengths and weaknesses of each of the stretching techniques?

Methods to improve muscle conditioning

There are three main components to muscle conditioning:

- **muscle strength** – ability to exert force on an object
- **muscle power** – the rate at which a muscle can exert force
- **muscle endurance** – ability to contract repeatedly without excess fatigue.

It is important to restore all components to near pre-injury levels before the athlete returns to full training and sport. When performing muscle conditioning work, the technique must be good to avoid **secondary injury** or causing re-injury.

The key to effective muscle conditioning is with the loading, both resistance and repetitions. Having pre-injury baseline scores is a good way to check the progress of the rehabilitation programme. In the absence of these scores using an injured vs non-injured comparison from testing can be useful.

Link

You can read more about fitness testing in *Unit 4: Field- and Laboratory-based Fitness Testing*.

Muscle strength

Muscle strength is gained by the athlete performing exercises with high weight/low repetitions. The type of muscular contraction the athlete has to perform progresses throughout rehabilitation.

- In the early stages of rehabilitation the athlete should perform **isometric** contractions to maintain muscle strength as these do not involve moving the joint through a full range.
- As rehabilitation progresses, **isokinetic** contractions which are slow and controlled can be used.
- Finally **isotonic** contractions, involving a **concentric** and **eccentric** phase which mirror the demands of sport much more, should be used.

Key terms

Secondary injury – an injury to another part of the body as a result of the initial injury, e.g. through compensating technique.

Isometric – the muscle contracts without a change in length.

Isokinetic – the muscle contracts with constant speed and resistance.

Isotonic – the muscle contracts with a lifting and lowering phase.

Concentric – the muscle contracts and shortens.

Eccentric – the muscle contracts and lengthens.

Using whole body strengthening exercises is often safer and more functional than overly isolating vulnerable tissues too soon in rehabilitation. It is really important that the athlete is both concentrically and eccentrically strong upon return to training and sport.

Muscle power

Muscle power is gained by increasing the speed of contraction or using exercises with rapid transition between an eccentric and concentric contractions. For example, with repeated squat jumps the landing phase is the eccentric contraction and the upwards jump phase is the concentric contraction.

These exercises clearly should be avoided in the early stages of rehabilitation because of high loading of the tissues. Power-based exercises could include:

- fast speed isotonic or isokinetic movements
- increased speed of functional exercises, e.g. calf raises, squats
- **plyometric** exercises, e.g. hopping, bounding, counter movement jumps.

Muscle endurance

Muscle endurance is developed by performing low to moderate weight/high repetition exercises (e.g. body weight squats, lunge walking) or sustained high-intensity, low resistance exercise (e.g. cycling with high resistance intervals, performing exercise in a swimming pool using buoyancy aids). Incorporating many rehabilitation exercises into a circuit training session for the athlete is another good way to improve muscle endurance. With sustained muscle endurance exercises, remember to monitor how fatigue affects technique and pain.

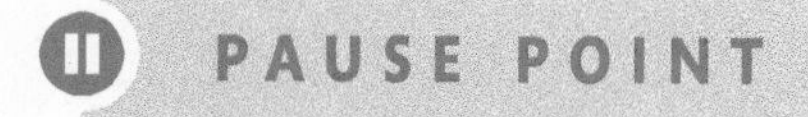

How can we plan safe and effective muscle conditioning exercises for hamstring injuries?

Hint Give five examples of specific muscle conditioning exercises for an athlete with a strained hamstring.

Extend Explain why muscle conditioning exercise must be carried out with the correct technique.

Methods to improve neuromuscular control

Neuromuscular control refers to the ability of nerves to sense and then affect the muscles in order to stabilise joints and maintain balance. It also plays an important role in further injury prevention. This can be developed by the athlete taking part in balance, coordination and proprioception-based exercises. These exercises enhance joint stability through interplay between sensory **mechanoreceptors** (detecting joint and body position) and the central nervous system (CNS).

Key terms

Plyometric – an explosive contraction with rapid transition between eccentric and concentric phases.

Mechanoreceptors – movement sensing nerves.

Exercises such as single leg stands, tandem stands, and jumping and landing exercises can all improve neuromuscular control. You can progress the different surfaces you use through rehabilitation (e.g. trampoline to sprung flooring to harder surfaces), and use equipment such as a wobble board, BOSU, and Swiss balls to challenge the body's ability to maintain stability.

Methods to improve skill acquisition and functionality

Once the athlete has regained their muscle conditioning, range of motion, and neuromuscular control, sport-specific skills and functional exercise should be incorporated into the rehabilitation plan. These can then be progressed until the athlete returns to full training and sport. The exercises should involve combining all other types of exercise but in a realistic environment based on specific sport demands, mimicking the movements and skills that form the basis of their sport. The sooner sports equipment (e.g. rackets and balls) are introduced, the quicker sports skills and confidence executing these skills will be restored.

For example, progression of functional exercise for a footballer who has suffered a severe lower limb injury may follow the pattern of:

- walking with a gradual increase in intensity and distance (without and with the ball)
- jogging with a gradual increase in intensity and distance (without and with the ball)
- running with a gradual increase in intensity and distance, e.g. 20m–30m–40m (without and with the ball)
- linear sprinting with a gradual increase in intensity and distance (without and with the ball)
- curvilinear sprinting, e.g. figures of eight
- agility and change of direction drills, e.g. narrow (45 degrees) and wide cutting (90 degrees).

As the athlete nears return to training and sport, the rehabilitation plan needs to mirror the demands of that sport. Factors to consider include intensity, movement patterns, surface, work/rest ratios, duration, and distance covered.

PAUSE POINT How can we make rehabilitation sport specific to help athletes prepare to return to sport after injury?

Hint Create three sport-specific drills (for a sport of your choice) that an athlete might complete in the late stages of their rehabilitation.

Extend Justify your drills in terms of intensity, distance, movement patterns, surface, and work/rest ratio.

Return to sport decisions

An athlete should return to training and sport when they are both physically and psychologically ready to do so. Criteria should be in place to help practitioners make this decision. These criteria could include:

- full pain-free range of motion and flexibility
- no persistent swelling
- muscle conditioning comparable to the non-affected body part
- fitness levels the same as baseline pre-injury measures or better
- the athlete being psychologically ready (low anxiety, good confidence)
- the coach satisfied with training form
- sport-specific skills having been regained.

Assessment practice 15.4

D.P4 D.P5 D.M4 D.M5 D.D3

Sports injury management aims to provide immediate sports trauma care and safe and appropriate rehabilitation plans. You are working as head sports therapist for a rugby union team. You want to conduct a professional development event for your medical team on the treatment and rehabilitation of sports injury.

Part one

Sports trauma care needs to be pre-planned and follow a logical process. Produce flow diagrams about how you would manage the scenarios below:

- a dislocated shoulder
- an unconscious athlete
- a bleeding athlete with potential shock
- sprained lateral ligaments (grade 2) of the ankle.

The flow diagrams should be clear and identify the process you would follow and who you would refer on to.

Now explain your diagrams to a classmate and get feedback. Could they follow the processes?

Now role play each scenario with classmates. Did you manage the four injuries safely and confidently?

Part two

For an athlete with a grade 2 sprain of their lateral ankle ligaments, design a progressive rehabilitation plan for each of the five stages of rehabilitation to ensure that they return to training and sport physically and psychologically ready. Be as specific as possible. The rehabilitation plans should be supported with an evidence base. Create some criteria that you could use to determine their ability to return to training and sport. How could re-injury to the ankle to prevented?

Plan

- What are the two parts to this task?
- Do I need time to practise providing sports trauma care?
- How confident do I feel in my own abilities to complete this task? Do I need support?

Do

- Will the flow diagrams help me to approach the task logically and effectively?
- Do I know what safe and confident delivery of sports trauma care is?
- Do I know where to find an evidence base to support my rehabilitation plan for an ankle sprain?
- Do I know how to make my rehabilitation plan progressive and specific?

Review

- Do I know that my rehabilitation plan was factually correct, and used correct terminology?
- Have I reflected on my role playing of the four scenarios and can I explain how I would approach this differently next time?

Further reading and resources

Books and journal articles

Brukner, P. and Khan, K. (2012) *Clinical Sports Medicine*, Sydney, Australia: McGraw Hill.

Forsdyke, D. (2014) Risk, response, and recovery: the psychology of sports injury, *sportEX Medicine* 59: 10–15.

Forsdyke D. (2014) It's all in the mind: psychosocial interventions to improve recovery, *sportEX Medicine* 60: 8–13.

Forsdyke, D., Gledhill, A., Mackay, N. and Randerson, K. (2011) *Foundations in Sports Therapy*, London: Heinemann.

Websites

www.physioroom.com – Physio Room: information, advice and guidance about sports injuries and treatment.

http://bjsm.bmj.com/site/podcasts – British Journal of Sports Medicine: podcasts from the British Journal of Sports Medicine.

www.electrotherapy.org – Electrotherapy on the web: information and educational resources about electrotherapy.

www.resus.org.uk/information-for-the-public – Resuscitation Council (UK): information and resources from the Resuscitation Council (UK).

THINK FUTURE

Frances Mulherne

Freelance Sport Therapist

I've been working as a sports therapist for the past two years since graduating with a BSc in Sports Therapy. I first become interested in sports injuries because I have had a few injuries myself and my BTEC Diploma had some injury-related units which I loved. My degree was great as I learned about the science behind sports injury prevention, treatment, and rehabilitation.

One of the biggest lessons I learned was that sports injury affects athletes not only physically but also psychologically. I try to incorporate this into my practice on a daily basis so I'm returning athletes back into sport when they are both physically and psychologically ready. My degree course also showed me that interpersonal skills are really important when working with injured athletes.

I have set up my own clinic in a local gym and also work providing sports therapy support for the under 14s of our local professional football club. My clinic work is really rewarding but I really enjoy working on the side of the pitch using my sports trauma skills when running on. I went on an FA first aid course recently and they were stressing the importance of having a medical emergency action plan. I have just designed one for the academy training and competition venues.

Focusing your skills

Interpersonal skills

When working with injured athletes having effective interpersonal skills is very important.

- What might happen if you do not have effective interpersonal skills?
- With whom do you think you need to show effective interpersonal skills during sports injury rehabilitation?
- What specific interpersonal skills do you think are important? Which of these skills do you need to develop?
- Talk to athletes about their experience of injury and the skills they would want of a sports injury practitioner. Do the same with a coach of a team about the skills they would want from a sport injury practitioner. How do they compare?

Medical emergency action plan (EAP)

A medical emergency action plan is an important document to help ensure the best care of athletes should an injury event occur.

- Which individuals do you think are involved in an EAP?
- How would you communicate the EAP?
- Why is it important to practise an EAP?
- What things should be included on an EAP?
- Why is it important to have an EAP for home fixtures and away fixtures?
- Create a list of medical-related details you would need to manage injuries effectively at an away fixture.

Getting ready for assessment

Mo is working towards a BTEC National in Sport and Exercise Sciences. He was given an assignment for learning aim C with the title 'Prevention is better than cure'. He had to design a poster on how to prevent sports injury in a specific sport which had to outline the four-step sequence of injury prevention:

- Stage one – research the common injuries in your chosen sport
- Stage two – identify the aetiology and mechanism of these injuries
- Stage three – suggest three preventive measures and explain how they might work
- Stage four – describe how the impact of these preventive measures could be measured.

Mo shares his experience below.

How I got started

First I collected all my notes on this topic and put them into a folder. I decided on my sport pretty early on and began to research on the internet and in books the information I needed on injury rate, injury types, and injury causes. I made sure I used a few sources to find this information to make sure the information on the poster was reliable. My tutor said this was a very wise thing to do.

I chose a sport that I am interested in because I knew this would make me more motivated and committed to doing a good job on the work. I created a plan of action so I could spend the week before the deadline just checking things over and so I wasn't rushing to get it finished.

How I brought it all together

I thought about how I was going to present the poster and what an effective poster looks like. I even asked my mum and dad what they thought. I decided to use a variety of colours and pictures to make people want to read the poster. I planned the poster on an A4 sheet of paper before starting. I created an eye-catching title to the poster, then:

- used an image of the four-step sequence as a template to put my information into – this meant my tutor could easily see how I had applied theory
- got feedback from my mum and dad about what the information read like and how the poster looked
- made sure I put the references from the internet, books, and the journals I used on the back of the poster.

What I learned from the experience

The key things I learned from this experience are that researching on the internet is really good but it is important to cross check the reliability of information as different sites said different things. I found this quite confusing to start with so I asked my tutor what he thought. He said sometimes books and journals are more reliable. It took me a long time but I found and included some information from a journal article about how effective the FIFA 11+ warm-up is. My tutor highlighted this in my feedback.

Chatting to my classmates about my progress and sharing ideas was really good as they reassured me mine was of good quality.

Despite me trying to make my poster look effective it has too much small writing on it meaning people might not want to look at it. In the future I will think about the amount and size of my information.

Think about it

- Have you written a plan with timings so you can complete your assignment by the submission date?
- Do you have notes on injury risk factors, and the theories of how injuries can be prevented?
- Is your information written in your own words and referenced clearly where you have used quotations or information from a book, journal or website?

Glossary

A

Accuracy – how close your measurement is to the 'gold standard'.

Adhere – to continue performing a behaviour (e.g. completing rehabilitation plans).

Adhesions – pieces of scar tissue that attach to structures in the body, limiting movement and sometimes causing pain.

Adipose tissue – loose connective tissue composed of adipocytes, specialised cells for the storage of fat. Its main role is to store energy in the form of fat, but it also cushions and insulates the body.

Aerobic respiration – the process of producing energy using oxygen where energy is released from glucose.

Aesthetics – the way a person moves and how the movement looks.

Aggression – intentional behaviour (physical or verbal) with a goal of harming (physically or psychologically) another being.

Alveolar ventilation – tidal volume minus dead space (air that remains in trachea, bronchi, etc.).

Anabolism – the constructive metabolism of the body – the building of tissue.

Anaerobic activity – activity where your body uses energy without oxygen; that is, activity that results in muscle cells using anaerobic respiration.

Anaerobic respiration – the process of breaking down glucose without oxygen to produce energy.

Anatomy – study of the structure of the body such as the skeletal, muscular or cardiovascular systems.

Anecdotal evidence – evidence that is drawn mainly from people's experiences rather than formal research.

Antenatal – during pregnancy from conception to birth.

Anticipatory rise – a minor increase in breathing rate prior to exercise.

Anxiety – negative emotional state in which feelings of nervousness, worry and apprehension are associated with activation or arousal of the body.

Arterial blood – bright red in colour due to high concentrations of oxygen.

Articulation – where two or more bones meet.

Assent – an expression of willingness to proceed with a treatment by people who are unable to understand likely risks and benefits (e.g. people under 18 years, vulnerable adults).

Athleticism – the combination of physical endeavour, or trying hard, with moral integrity – a mix of honour, truthfulness and sportsmanship.

Auditory – you concentrate on the different sounds that you associate with a sporting movement.

Axis – a centre line through any body or object. The body or object to either side of the line should be symmetrical (a mirror image).

B

Balanced diet – a diet that provides the correct amounts of nutrients without excess or deficiency.

Base of support – the area of surface below an object or person (e.g. base of support is increased when the feet are hip width apart in comparison to touching at the ankles).

Behavioural – moment-to-moment changes in behaviour when anxious.

Benchmark – a reference mark against which you can assess the performers' current performance and fitness.

Bias – inclination or prejudice for or against one person or group, especially in a way considered to be unfair; in research, misrepresenting facts about a study, e.g. selectively reporting results or structuring the design in such a way that it will always support your hypothesis.

Bilateral – movement that occurs on both sides of the body in unison.

Bile – a greenish-brown fluid secreted by the liver and stored in the gall bladder that aids digestion.

Blood pH – measure of acidity or alkalinity of a solution.

Bone remodelling – the ongoing replacement of old bone tissue with new bone tissue as well as the redistribution of bone tissue to areas where stress forces are greatest.

C

Calcium – a mineral essential for bone growth and found in a wide range of foods including milk, cheese, yoghurt, nuts, broccoli and beans.

Calorie (cal) – 1 calorie is the energy required to raise the temperature of 1 gram of water by 1°C.

Capitalism – a system of economics based on the private ownership of capital (money and other resources) and production (companies, etc. that make goods and services) and individual profit.

Cardiac cycle – the sequence of events (systole – during which cardiac muscle contracts – and diastole – during which cardiac muscle relaxes) that take place during a single heartbeat.

Cardiac muscle – muscle tissue found only in the heart.

Cartilage – a strong and flexible tissue that is commonly found in joints of the body. It is smooth in texture and acts to reduce friction at joints and stop bones from grinding together.

Catabolic – breaks down tissue, such as muscle, making the tissue weaker.

Catabolised – the breaking down of molecules into smaller units or components.

Catharsis – releasing emotions, generally with the purpose of relieving the stress that can build up if these emotions are kept bottled up and not expressed by an individual.

Cellular adaptations – changes within the cell structure (for example, an increase in mitochondrial size).

Central nervous system – the brain and spinal cord responsible for transferring electrical impulses.

Closed questions – questions that are worded to provoke a single-word response, such as 'yes' or 'no'.

Codify – collect together and organise rules and procedures.

Coercion – making someone do something through the use of threats or force.

Cognitive – the degree to which you worry or have negative thoughts.

Cognitive anxiety – the thought component of anxiety that most people refer to as 'worrying about something'.

Cold feedback – feedback provided after the sports coaching session. This allows the coach to reflect on the performance of the performers in more detail, and then provide detailed feedback.

Collagen – a protein-based building material used in the repair of tissues. Collagen also provides strength and cushioning for body parts.

Commercialisation – managed or exploited in order to make a profit.

Commodity – a raw material or asset that can be bought or sold. In sport, the athletes are the 'raw materials' that make the sport happen, and therefore have a financial value to the clubs that 'own' them.

Competence – having knowledge, skills and experience within a given area and recognising your limitations associated with this.

Concave – having an outline or surface that curves inwards.

Concentric – the muscle contracts and shortens.

Consent – agreement by an adult to proceed with a treatment.

Continuum – a continuous, gradual sequence from one extreme to another but along which there are no clearly marked distinctions.

Contraindication – a physical or mental condition or factor that increases the risk involved when someone is engaged in an activity; a condition or factor that means a sports massage or other treatment cannot be delivered, or must be adapted.

Control group – a group of participants who undergo the control condition (e.g. receiving no treatment or 'sham treatment', where they think they are being treated but they are not).

Convex – curving outwards.

Core – the muscles of the trunk and pelvis that stabilise the spine and pelvis.

Core stability – the ability of the muscles deep within the abdomen which connect to the spine, pelvis and shoulders to maintain good posture – the foundation for all movements.

Cortisol – a hormone that is released in high levels during stressful situations.

Cue words – single words that are a form of self-talk and used to trigger a desired response by an athlete. Common cue words include 'believe', 'relax', 'focus' and 'strong'.

Cult – a craze or obsession.

Curvilinear motion – motion that occurs along a curved line or path.

D

Deep vein thrombosis – the formation of a blood clot inside a blood vessel, obstructing the flow of blood through the circulatory system.

Degree of freedom – used as a correction factor for bias and to limit the effects of outliers, based on the number of participants you have.

Dehydration – depletion of fluids that can impede thermoregulation and cause a rise in core body temperature.

Deoxygenated blood – blood without oxygen (containing carbon dioxide).

Diastolic pressure – pressure exerted in the arteries when the heart relaxes and fills with blood.

Diet – a person's usual eating habits and food consumption.

Diffusion – the process by which a substance such as oxygen passes through a cell membrane either to get into the cell or to get out of the cell. Substances move by diffusion from an area where they are more concentrated to an area where they are less concentrated.

Diplomacy – the art of dealing with people in a sensitive and tactful way.

Disclosure and Barring Service (DBS) – an organisation that helps employers make safer recruitment decisions and prevents unsuitable people from working with vulnerable groups, including children.

Distal – furthest away from the centre of the body.

Duty of care – a legal obligation imposed on an individual, requiring that they adhere to a standard of reasonable care while performing any acts that could possibly harm others.

E

Eccentric – the muscle contracts and lengthens.

Efficacy – the ability to produce a desired or intended result.

Electrolytes – salts in the blood, for example, potassium and sodium.

Electron transport chain – a series of biomechanical reactions during which free energy contained within hydrogen (derived from the Krebs cycle) is released.

Elementary schools – the first state funded schools which ran from 1870 to 1944, many becoming primary schools after further education reform. They catered for 5–14 year olds.

Empathy – understanding another person's condition from their perspective.

Enzymes – proteins that start or accelerate the digestive process.

Equality – treating everyone equally.

Ergogenic aids – ergogenic refers to the application of a nutritional, physical, mechanical, psychological or pharmacological procedure or aid to improve physical work capacity or athletic performance. Ergogenic aids are assumed to enhance performance above and beyond what would normally be expected, for example caffeine and creatine.

Erythema – superficial reddening of the skin.

Ethics committee – a panel that looks at your research proposal and says whether it is safe and ethical. It will confirm whether you can start work on your project.

Evidence-based practice (EBP) – making sure that evidence uncovered in research is included in your everyday work practices for the benefit of clients.

Extraneous variable – a variable outside the scope of the study that could adversely affect the results, reducing the validity and reliability of findings.

Extrinsic factors – factors outside the body that increase the risk of injury.

F

Feminist theory – aims to understand and remove inequality between men and women.

Field test – a physical test carried out in similar conditions to those in a competitive situation.

Fight or flight response – a physiological response that occurs in the body in an attempt to cope with a threat that is posed.

Flat back – a decreased curvature of the lumbar spine; insufficient curvature in the spine to distribute forces.

Flexibility – the range of movement around a joint or group of joints.

Food – any substance derived from plants or animals containing a combination of carbohydrates, fats, proteins, vitamins, minerals, fibre and water.

Freezing – hyper-elevated muscle tension that reduces movement quality or prevents an athlete from moving.

G

Gait – a person's manner of walking or running.

Generalise – the extent to which research results are applicable to other settings.

Girth – the measurement around the middle of a limb or muscle area.

Global contraindication – conditions when a sports massage should not be carried out.

Glucose – the main type of sugar in the blood; a major source of energy for the body's cells.

H

Haemoglobin – oxygen transporting component of red blood cells.

Hazard – something with the potential to cause harm. 'Risk' is the likelihood and severity of the harm that could occur as a result of the hazard.

Health and Safety Executive (HSE) – the organisation responsible for proposing and enforcing safety regulations throughout the UK.

Healthy eating – the pursuit of a balanced diet to support health and reduce the risks of chronic disease. Healthy eating principles should form the solid foundations on which athletes can build more specific nutritional strategies to support training and competition.

Homeostatic response – the body's attempts to maintain a condition of balance within its internal environment, such as its temperature, even when faced with external changes or challenges.

Hot feedback – feedback provided to sports performers by coaches, as soon as the coaching session has finished or during the session when a skill, technique or tactic has been applied.

Hyper-extension – a movement of a joint beyond its normal limits, normally beyond 180°.

Hyper-flexion – the flexion of a joint beyond its normal limits or range.

Hypothesis – the predicted, testable relationship between two or more variables (e.g. imagery training will improve basketball free throw performance).

I

Inequality – social disparity, e.g. inequality between the pay of men and women in sport.

Inertia – the resistance to changes in motion.

Insertion – the end of the muscle that moves. The insertion usually crosses over a joint to allow movement when the muscle shortens.

Instructional self-talk – a task-specific form of self-talk that involves the athlete giving instructions to themselves about different aspects of performance (e.g. technical or tactical elements).

Interval size – the range of values that each group will cover.

Intervertebral discs – fibrocartilaginous cushions that act as the spine's shock-absorbing system which prevent injury to the vertebrae and brain.

Intrinsic factors – factors within the body that increase the risk of injury.

Isokinetic – the muscle contracts with constant speed and resistance.

Isometric – the muscle contracts without a change in length.

Isotonic – the muscle contracts with a lifting and lowering phase.

J

Joule (J) – 1 joule of energy moves a mass of 1 gram at a velocity of 1 metre per second. Approximately 4.2 joules = 1 calorie.

K

Kilocalorie (kcal) – 1 kilocalorie is the energy required to raise the temperature of 1 litre of water by 1°C. It is equal to 1000 calories and is used to state the energy value of food. Kilocalories are often simply referred to as calories.

Kilojoule (kJ) – a unit of energy, equivalent to 1000 joules.

Kinaesthetic – you concentrate on the feel of the movement.

Kinaesthetic awareness – the body's sense of its own position in space.

Kinetic – relating to or resulting from motion.

Kyphosis – an outward curve of the spine associated with the thoracic region.

L

Lactate – product of lactic acid which occurs in blood.

Lateral – towards the outside of a body part.

Lean body mass – body weight minus body fat primarily composed of muscle, bone and other non-fat tissues.

Ligaments – short bands of tough and fibrous flexible tissue that hold bones together.

Litigation – resolving disputes by filing or answering a complaint through the public courts system.

Local contraindication – conditions when a sports massage can be carried out but avoiding the area affected.

Lordosis – an inwards curve of the spine associated with cervical and lumbar regions.

M

Macronutrient – a nutrient required by your body in daily amounts greater than a few grams, e.g. carbohydrate, fat and protein.

Magnitude – a term used in science to describe the size of something.

Malpractice – an instance of negligence or incompetence by the sports massage practitioner.

Mass – the overall amount of matter in an object.

Maximal exercise – level of training intensity when an athlete approaches their maximal heart rate and performs exercise to an increasingly anaerobic level.

Maximal strength – the maximum force that a muscle or group of muscles can exert in a single contraction (e.g. the maximum weight that you can lift once).

Mechanoreceptors – movement sensing nerves.

Medial – towards the inside of a body part.

Medulla oblongata – located in the middle of your brain, it is responsible for involuntary functions such as breathing, heart rate and sneezing.

Meta theory – a theory that is made up of several smaller theories to provide an understanding of a topic.

Minute ventilation – also known as minute volume = tidal volume × frequency of breaths per minute.

Mitochondria – the organelles within cells in the body where aerobic respiration takes place. Pyruvate oxidation and the Krebs cycle take place in the matrix (fluid) of the mitochondria, while the electron transport chain takes place in the inner membrane itself.

Modifying condition – conditions when a sports massage can be carried but only with an understanding of the condition and how the treatment should be adapted because of this.

Motor neuron excitability – the amount of nerve stimulation of a muscle.

Motor unit – a motor neuron and all the associated fibres it affects. Motor units work together to coordinate contractions of a single skeletal muscle.

Muscular Christianity – the belief in having a strong soul within a strong body. Arnold believe sport could be played to win but always for 'the glory of God' – not for its own sake or the glory of the players.

Muscular endurance (also known as strength endurance) – the ability to exert a sub-maximal force for a number of repetitions over a sustained period of time.

N

Neuromuscular stimulation – the amount and rate of neural input to a muscle or muscles.

Neurotransmitters – chemicals used to carry signals or information between neurons and cells.

Nociceptors – pain sensing receptors.

Non-starch polysaccharide – the scientific term for dietary fibre.

Notational analysis – a coach keeps a record of the number of successes or failures in a particular situation.

Null hypotheses – a prediction that there will be no relationship/no significant difference between two or more variables or groups.

Nutrition – the means by which your body takes in energy and nutrients from food to sustain growth and development, and to keep you alive and healthy.

O

Objective - how a sports coach is going to meet their aim.

Objective analysis - based on measured, statistical performance data.

One-tailed test - a test that assumes one group will be better than the other, or at least no worse than the other. For example, girls will be better than boys.

Origin - the fixed end of the muscle that remains stationary.

Osteoblasts - specialised bone cells that build new bone tissue.

Osteoclasts - large nucleated cells that destroy bone cells, reabsorb calcium and play a major role in bone remodelling.

Osteoporosis - a medical condition that weakens bones due to a loss of stored calcium. This makes bones fragile, brittle and more likely to break.

Overload - stretching the body systems beyond their normal functional level - essential for gaining training benefits.

Oxygenated blood - blood containing oxygen.

P

Partial pressure - pressure applied by a single gas in a mixture of gases.

Passive stretching - the sports massage therapist stretching the muscle(s), as opposed to the athlete doing the stretching themselves.

Pathogen - a bacterium, virus or other microorganism that can cause disease.

Peak height velocity (PHV) - the period when growth rate is at is fastest or the 'growth spurt'.

Pelvic tilt - misalignment of the pelvis. For example, not being level (lateral pelvic tilt) or iliac spine being abnormally forwards or backwards (anterior or posterior pelvic tilt).

Performance profiling - giving objective feedback to performers who are trying to achieve a positive change in performance.

Periodised - based on a structured cycle. A periodised training programme will increase performance and reduce injuries and boredom.

Physical literacy - when a child becomes competent at basic movement skills and other sports skills which allow them to assess sporting situations and make good quality decisions confidently and under control.

Physiology - study of the way that the body responds to exercise and training.

Plyometric - an explosive contraction with rapid transition between eccentric and concentric phases.

Post-natal - the period after the baby has been born.

Precision - how fine or small a difference a measuring device can detect.

Prehypertension - means someone does not have high blood pressure now but they are likely to develop it in future.

Prejudice - intolerance or a dislike for people based on race, religion, sexual orientation, gender, age or disability.

Probe questions - questions used to further explore a topic when it appears as part of an interview. Examples of probe questions include elaboration, clarification and continuation probes.

Pronation - when the foot rolls inwards during walking or running.

Proprioception - the ability to sense where the body is in space.

Proprioceptors - sensory receptors found in muscle tissue, tendons and joints which tell the brain about the physical state and position of a muscle or joint.

Protocol - a step-by-step process for conducting a specific test that can be followed every time it is carried out to ensure accurate and consistent results.

Proximal - closest to the centre of the body.

Psychosocial - the combination of psychological and social behaviour.

Q

Qualitative - research that collects non-numerical data and is concerned with understanding opinions, beliefs and emotions.

Quantitative - research that collects numerical data and uses statistical analysis to answer questions.

R

Rationale - the reason for completing a project.

Rectilinear motion - motion along a straight line or path.

Referral - when you recognise that you are not competent to work with a particular person or conduct research in a particular area based on your skill set, contacting another professional who is competent so that they can conduct that work.

Regency period - a time of high fashion during the late-eighteenth and early-nineteenth centuries, associated with the Prince Regent (the son of George III who ruled during his father's illness).

Reliability - the consistency or repeatability of a measure.

Risk assessment - a systematic process of looking at an activity or environment, evaluating the hazards and risk associated with it, and coming up with preventative measures.

Risk averse - somebody who does not want to take risks.

Rule for inclusion - a statement used to define which data is included in a category.

S

Safeguarding - protecting children and vulnerable adults from harm and maltreatment.

Sarcoplasmic reticulum - regulates the calcium ion concentration in the muscle cells.

Scalar quantity - a physical quantity that has only size.

Scar tissue - areas of functionally poor fibrous tissue that replaces normal tissue after trauma.

Scoliosis - an abnormal sideways curve of the spine.

Secondary injury - an injury to another part of the body as a result of the initial injury, e.g. through compensating technique.

Secretion - the process of a substance being released from the interior of a cell to its exterior.

Social support - the presence of a support network that can help an athlete cope with stress through the exchange of resources between one person and another.

Social theories - frameworks developed by social scientists that attempt to interpret evidence to study and understand social events, such as the development and uses of sport and exercise in society.

Soft tissue - the tissue that connects, supports and surrounds structures such as joints or organs. It includes tendons, ligaments, skin, fat and muscles.

Somatic - the perception of changes in physiological activation.

Spectatorship - a spectator is someone who will engage in a sporting activity by observing regularly. A spectator sport is one for which there are more spectators than actually engage with the sport, such as football.

Stroke volume - volume of blood pumped out of the heart's left ventricle per beat.

Subjective - based on or influenced by personal feelings, beliefs or opinions.

Subjective analysis - based on observational judgements, personal interpretations and opinions.

Supination - when the foot rolls outwards during walking or running.

Systolic pressure - pressure exerted in the arteries when the heart contracts.

T

Table of critical values - a table of values to which you compare your results of statistical testing to find out if they are significant at a given level.

Technique - a series of basic movements that combine to result in a recognised sporting or exercise movement.

Tendon - strong fibrous tissue that attaches muscle to a bone.

Testing variables - factors outside the testing protocol design that may change or influence testing data, for example, a high temperature could affect a participant's ability to perform in a test.

Thermoregulation - the ability to keep the body's temperature constant, even if the surrounding temperature is different.

Torque - the twisting motion created from rotational forces.

Treatment group - a group of participants who undergo the treatment condition in an investigation.

Trustees - people responsible for managing and promoting an organisation or asset, such as a school.

Two-tailed test - a test that assumes there will be a difference between both groups, but does not say which will be better. For example, there will be a difference between girls and boys.

U

Unilateral - movement on one side of the body or when each limb is working independently.

V

Validity (in data collection) - whether you are measuring what you intended to measure.

Validity (in data analysis) - the soundness of interpretations of results.

Vasoconstriction - a reduction in the diameter of blood vessels.

Vasodilation - an increase in the diameter of blood vessels.

Vector quantity - a physical quantity that has both size and direction.

Venous blood - darker red than arterial blood due to high concentrations of carbon dioxide.

Viscosity - how thick a fluid is, affecting its resistance to flow.

Visual - you concentrate on the different things that you can see during the movement. This can be an internal perspective (from your own viewpoint) or an external perspective (as if watching yourself on a video).

Index

D

E

I

J

K

L

M

T

U

V

W

Z